Zen Graffiti

Azuki

BUDDHIST PUBLISHING GROUP

Buddhist Publishing Group
Sharpham North
Ashprington
Totnes
Devon
TQ9 7UT
England

ISBN 0-946672-24-5

A catalogue record for this book is
available from the British Library

Printed and bound in Great Britain
by Billings & Sons Limited, Worcester

Zen Graffiti

TRYING TO PUT THE TRUTH
INTO CONCISE TERMS,
THE BRUSH CRIES FOR DIRECTION,
BUT THE UNIVERSE
KEEPS ITS SECRET.

JUST A THOUGHT
WILL TURN AN
INSIGHT INTO A CONCEPT.

IF YOU WHANT THE TRUTH
GIVE UP THE LIE.

BLACK DAYS ALONG THE WAY —
DON'T DESPAIR!
STAND UP IN PRAISE OF YOUR MISERY.

*LOOK, ALL YOU
ASPIRING BUDDHAS!
SAKYAMUNI IS STILL
HOLDING UP THE FLOWER.*

HERESY AND DOGMA
ARE OF THE SAME NATURE.

I BELIEVE IT'S TRUE,
BUT I WISH I KNEW.

BELIEFS AND OPINIONS
CAN ANSWER THE QUESTIONS,
BUT ONLY TRUTH CAN SOLVE
THE MYSTERY.

WE ARE THE
IGNORANCE WHICH
BLOCKS OUT REALITY.

WHAT PLACE
DO DREAMS HAVE
WITHIN THE DREAM?

I JUST OPEN MY MOUTH,
AND SAMSARA POPS OUT.

WITHOUT 'ME',
MARA WOULD BE NOTHING.

MAN ASPIRES TO BE BUDDHA —
POOR OLD BUDDHA.

THE VOID AND ME ARE ONE;
THE TROUBLE IS —
THAT'S ONE TOO MANY.

THE FLOWER AND THE THORN
ARE ON THE SAME STEM.

I THINK I HAVE A MIND,

I THINK I HAVE A BODY,

I THINK I THINK,

I THINK I SEE,

I THINK I TASTE,

I THINK I HEAR,

I THINK I TOUCH,

I THINK TOO MUCH!

THE MANTRA 'BUDDHA'
IS A THUNDERBOLT
FROM THE VOID,
WHICH CLEARS AWAY
ALL DEFILEMENT.

SEE THE PURE LAND TODAY:
NAMU-AMIDA-BUTSU

CAN YOU HEAR THE DHARMA
ABOVE THE DIN OF THE WORDS?

IF WE THINK WE HEAR,
WE NO LONGER LISTEN.

IF WE THINK WE SEE,
WE NO LONGER LOOK.

IF WE THINK WE KNOW,
WE NO LONGER SEARCH.

HERE I AM
MEDITATING
AGAIN.

MEDITATE ON TRUTH —
NOT FOR IT.

HOW LONG HAVE YOU BEEN
LOOKING FOR A GURU?

WHAT WILL YOUR EXCUSE BE
WHEN YOU FIND ONE?

THE DHARMA'S FREE,
BUT EVEN SAKYAMUNI
COULDN'T GIVE IT AWAY.

LOOK HERE, ALL YOU WOMEN,
YOU'RE NOT ALLOWED
TO BE MONKS,
SO YOU'D BETTER MAKE
UP YOUR MINDS TO BE
BUDDHAS INSTEAD.

ALL DAY AND NIGHT
I HUNGER FOR TRUTH,
BUT IN THE MORNING
I HUNGER FOR BREAKFAST.

DON'T WORRY ABOUT
THE WORLD,
IT CAN CRUMBLE ON ITS OWN.

NO MATTER HOW HARD
WE TRY—
THE WORLD WILL
NEVER BE PERFECT

JUST SEE THE FREEDOM
IN IMPERMANENCE.

SAMSARA IS STUFFED
WITH BODHISATTVAS.

HOW CAN ONE TALK
OF SAVING ALL BEINGS
WITH THE SAME MOUTH
THAT EATS THEIR FLESH?

I AM HAUNTED BY THE
GHOST OF TOMORROW.

HOW MANY NOWS IN THE HOUR?

WHAT WOULD THE TIME BE IF
ALL THE CLOCKS WERE STOPPED?

IF IT WERE ONLY A MATTER
OF TIME,
WE WOULD ALL HAVE BEEN
BUDDHAS LONG AGO.

SAY WHEN THIS MOMENT
STARTED —
SAY WHEN IT ENDS.

TO REALIZE THE DEATHLESS,
SEE — ALL LIFE IS IMPERMANENT.

TO REALIZE THE WISHLESS,
SEE — ALL LIFE IS DUKKHA.

TO REALIZE THE VOID,
SEE — ALL LIFE IS NOT SELF.

WE ARE ALL CONTEMPORARIES
OF BEGINNINGLESS TIME,
YET WE RUN IN FEAR OF DEATH.

COMMENTATORS TALK
OF THE GREAT AWAKENING,
BUT THE MOON SHINES
EVERY NIGHT.

I WANT TO BE FREE,
BUT MY CHAINS ARE BROKEN!

STILLNESS TO SHAKE
THE UNIVERSE;
SHUDDERS OF ASTONISHMENT —
THE DEATHLESS WAS
NEVER LOST.

DON'T FALL INTO THE ERROR
OF THINKING THIS IS SAMSARA.

DEFILEMENT IS INSTANTANEOUS.

THERE ARE NO HOLY PLACES,
ONLY MOMENTS OF HOLINESS;

NO GURUS, ONLY
MOMENTS OF UNDERSTANDING;

NO BODHISATTVAS, ONLY
MOMENTS OF COMPASSION;

NO ENLIGHTENMENT, ONLY
MOMENTS OF WISDOM;

NO MOMENTS, ONLY
AWARENESS;

NO AWARENESS, ONLY
BUDDHA.

SIDDHARTHA GAUTAMA —
BORN A LONG TIME AGO,
DIED A LONG TIME AGO.

BUDDHA — NEVER BORN,
NEVER DIED.

THERE ARE MANY PATHS
TO TRUTH —
DON'T DIE CHOOSING.

WHEN SELFISHNESS
REALLY HURTS,
THEN THE PATH IS EASY.

IGNORANCE IS THE LONELINESS
OF ISOLATION,
THE PAIN OF DISCONTENT,
THE MISERY OF BEING OTHER.

MISERY IS THE PAIN
OF NOT REALIZING
OUR TRUE NATURE.

WHEN WE ACT FOOLISHLY,
MEDITATION IS IMPOSSIBLE.
WHEN WE ACT WISELY,
MEDITATION IS INEVITABLE.

THERE'S NO DIFFERENCE
BETWEEN HONESTY AND
MEDITATION.

PLEASANT SIGHTS
CATCH THE EYE;
AWARENESS FREES THE HEART.

THIS IS NOT ME;
THIS IS NOT MINE;
THIS IS NOT MYSELF —
THREE LINES TO SET THE
UNIVERSE FREE.

DELUSION IS KARMIC.
WHAT ARE YOU DOING NOW
THAT KEEPS YOU IN IGNORANCE?

DEFILEMENT IS INSTANTANEOUS.
WHAT ARE YOU DOING NOW
THAT KEEPS YOU IN IGNORANCE?

ENLIGHTENMENT IS EASY;
IT'S KEEPING FREE FROM
DEFILEMENT THAT'S
THE HARD BIT.

BUDDHAHOOD IS HIDDEN
BY GREED AND HATRED.

EATING MEAT KILLS!

THE DEATHLESS IS
A WAY OF LIFE.

REBIRTH IS A MATTER OF FACT;
THE DEATHLESS IS
BEFORE OUR EYES.

REINCARNATION IS A NICE IDEA
UNTIL WE SEE THE LIE
OF BIRTH AND DEATH.

SO WHAT HAPPENS
WHEN WE DIE THEN?

THIS HAPPENS WHEN WE DIE!

TIME IS JUST A COLLECTION
OF THOUGHTS.

THIS MOMENT IS
THE ONLY TIME WE HAVE
TO REALIZE BUDDHA.

THEORIZING'S OKAY,
BUT WOULDN'T YOU RATHER BE A BUDDHA?

ENLIGHTENMENT IS SPONTANEOUS.
WHAT ARE YOU DOING NOW
THAT KEEPS YOU IN IGNORANCE?

'I AM' —
THE CAUSE OF ALL MISERY.

WE SAY, 'MY MIND,' 'MY BODY,'
'MY SELF,' 'MY EGO,'
'MY BUDDHA-NATURE.'
IN THE MIDST OF ALL THIS
LOOSE TALK — LISTEN!
BUDDHA NEVER SAYS A WORD.

THE IDEA OF A SELF
IS IGNORANCE PERSONIFIED.

'I AM' — JUST SIX SENSES
FUNCTIONING IN THE VOID.

WHAT IS A BEING?
JUST DISTANT MEMORIES
OF THE PAST
AND FOGGY PREDICTIONS
OF THE FUTURE.

JUST BECAUSE THERE'S NO-SELF
DOESN'T MEAN
THERE'S NO BUDDHA.

IMAGINED NO-SELF IS A CONCEPT;
THE REALITY OF NO-SELF
IS BUDDHAHOOD.

IF YOU THINK
BUDDHA'S A
PERSON,

YOU'LL NEVER
KNOW BUDDHA.

THINKING IS JUST A COMMENT
ON FACT.

THINKING IS LIKE LIVING
IN ANOTHER WORLD.

WHEN YOU HEAR THAT ALL
BEINGS ARE BUDDHA,
DON'T FALL INTO THE ERROR
OF THINKING THERE'S MORE
THAN ONE BUDDHA.

OUR MINDS AND SAKYAMUNI'S
ARE INSEPARABLE!
ONLY THE THOUGHTS
ARE DIFFERENT.

WATCHING ALL THE COMING
AND GOING,
THE STILLNESS IS MAGNIFICENT.

NIRVANA ONLY EXISTS
IN THE MINDS OF THOSE
SUFFERING IN SAMSARA.

NIRVANA NEITHER COMES
NOR GOES.
WHAT'S ALL THIS TALK
ABOUT REJECTING IT?

TRUTH IS SILENT;
IT'S VIEWS AND OPINIONS
THAT MAKE ALL THE NOISE.

ATTACHMENT TO VIEWS IS THE
CAUSE OF ALL SUFFERING —
DON'T LET BIGOTRY AND
SECTARIANISM DEFILE
YOUR BUDDHA-NATURE.

I'M A PURE LAND BUDDHIST;
I'M A THERAVADIN BUDDHIST;
I'M A TIBETAN BUDDHIST;
I'M A ZEN BUDDHIST;
IN THE MIDST OF ALL THIS
EGOTISM AND ATTACHMENT —
LISTEN!
BUDDHA NEVER SAYS A WORD.

ALL SCHOOLS OF BUDDHISM
ARE HINAYANA.
DON'T CONFUSE TRADITION
WITH THE BUDDHA'S TEACHING!

HAVE YOU EVER HEARD
OF A SECTARIAN BUDDHA?

HAVING TRAVELLED THROUGH

INDIA,
TIBET,
CHINA,
JAPAN,
THAILAND. . .
ON REACHING HOME —
THERE'S THE BUDDHA.

THERE'S NO GURU ANYWHERE
IN THE WORLD
WHO CAN MATCH THE WISDOM
OF YOUR OWN MIND.

THE DHARMA WAS HERE
EVEN BEFORE SAKYAMUNI
MOVED HIS LIPS.

WHO WOULD HAVE THOUGHT —
THE BODHI TREE GROWS
HERE?

ONE PLACE IS MUCH LIKE
ANOTHER,
EXCEPT THERE ARE NO
OTHER PLACES.

HOMELESSNESS
HAS NOTHING
TO DO WITH
WHERE WE LIVE.

BEFORE YOU GO OFF IN SEARCH
OF ENLIGHTENMENT,
SEE THE BUDDHA OF
YOUR OWN MIND!

THOSE WHO SEE INTO
THEIR TRUE NATURE,
ARE INSTANTANEOUSLY
INITIATED INTO ALL
THE MYSTIC TEACHINGS.

SUDDEN ENLIGHTENMENT
IS SO FAST
THAT ALL BEINGS ARE BUDDHA
FROM THE VERY BEGINNING.

TRANSCENDING TIME
AND SPACE —
HERE WE ARE!

WHEN WORKING
LET THE BODY DANCE.

TRY NOT TO LIVE AS IF TIME
WERE A REALITY
WHICH CAN STEAL AWAY
YOUR LIFE.

TIME IS MARA'S REALM,
NOT BUDDHA'S.

YESTERDAY, TODAY, NOW —
JUST DIFFERENT WAYS OF
DESCRIBING THE MOMENT.

THIS MOMENT IS AN
ALL-TIME EXPERIENCE,
NOT JUST A FLEETING EVENT.

LIFE IS SHORT,
YET THE MOMENT
TRANSCENDS ETERNITY.

BUDDHA-NATURE IS JUST
TOO GOOD TO THINK ABOUT.

A BIRD GLIDES ACROSS THE SKY —
HOW CLEAR THE MIND IS!

JUST REST IN THE VOID
AND SEE WHAT HAPPENS.

DON'T WORRY. THE VOID
LOOKS AFTER ITS OWN.

EVERY TIME I
PUT A FOOT WRONG,
THE UNIVERSE SCREAMS.

THOUGHTS, GOOD OR BAD,
ARE JUST ECHOES IN THE VOID.

IF THE DHARMA WERE
AN EGO TRIP,
WE'D ALL HAVE BEEN
BUDDHAS LONG AGO.

WHY IS BODHIDHARMA
ALWAYS SMILING?

BUDDHA-NATURE IS
THE SELF BECOME SELFLESS.

THERE'S NOTHING WORSE
THAN BEING TRAPPED BY
ONE'S OWN WORDS.

GLOSSARY

BODHISATTVA: One who inclines towards enlightenment; one who vows to liberate all beings from samsara.

BODHI TREE: The tree under which the Buddha attained enlightenment; a symbol of enlightenment.

BUDDHA: One who is awakened; Siddhartha Gautama became awakened to truth and was thenceforth known as the Buddha.

BUDDHA-NATURE: The essence of what one really is; one's true nature.

DEATHLESS: That which is not born and does not die; a synonym for nirvana.

DHARMA: The teaching of the Buddha; that which supports reality.

DUKKHA: The pain of ignorance; the misery of samsara; that which defiles reality.

ENLIGHTENMENT: The realization of truth; seeing things as they are; awakening to reality.

GURU: Teacher.

HINAYANA: The smaller or lesser vehicle; a derisory term sometimes used by Buddhists of the northern schools to refer to Buddhists of the southern schools.

KARMA: Action and reaction; cause and effect.

MARA: Delusion; defilement; the personification of evil.

NIRVANA: Beyond eternity and annihilation; beyond description and conception; the very basis and foundation of what we are and of all that is.

SAKYAMUNI: Sage of the Sakya clan; another name for the Buddha.

SAMSARA: The round of birth and death; the realms of appearances; the world of suffering.

VOID: The experience of non-self; experience beyond defilement; truth devoid of delusion.

OTHER BPG PUBLICATIONS

AN INTRODUCTION TO BUDDHISM
Ed. Diana St Ruth
A comprehensive account of Buddhism and its
teachings.
0-946672-22-9

TEACHINGS OF A BUDDHIST MONK
Ajahn Sumedho
Foreword by Jack Kornfield
An instructive and, at times, humorous book
drawn from a collection of talks by the abbot
of Amaravati Buddhist Centre.
0-946672-23-7

THE ZEN TEACHING OF INSTANTANEOUS
AWAKENING
Hui Hai
Trans. John Blofeld
An eighth-century T'ang Dynasty Zen Text.
0-946672-03-2

FINGERS AND MOONS
Trevor Leggett
A collection of humorous and instructive Zen
stories and incidents.
0-946672-07-5

BUDDHISM NOW

A Buddhist journal — interviews, practical advice on living a Buddhist way of life, translations, stories, verse, letters, news, book reviews etc. Six issues a year. (Send £1 or $2 for a sample issue.)

Coming lat

Women who became mo~~~~~~les
describ

Coming late to motherhood
Twenty women tell their stories

edited by

Joan Michelson & Sue Gee

THORSONS PUBLISHERS LIMITED
Wellingborough, Northamptonshire

First published August 1984
Second Impression October 1984

British Library Cataloguing in Publication Data

Coming late to motherhood.
   1. Pregnancy in middle age—Psychological aspects
I. Michelson, Joan   II. Gee, Sue
306.8'743'0922   RG556.5

ISBN 0-7225-0893-X

Printed and bound in Great Britain by
Whitstable Litho Ltd., Whitstable, Kent

Dedication

To Jamie and Jessie

Acknowledgements

We would like to express our appreciation to the editorial staff of *Woman, Spare Rib* and *New Society* for printing our request for contributions on their letters page.

For offering time, advice and support, we'd like to thank Marek Mayer, Geoffrey Adkins, Wendy Bastable and Juliet Crum; for typing, Elaine Dwight and Rosemary Sproule; and for coping with childcare, Pauline Eperson.

Contents

Foreword

Long ago and down centuries of time, women's control of their fertility was limited to abstinence, herbal medicine, folk ritual and, if all else failed, abortion. When the fight for contraception was begun in this country and formalized into the crusading work of the Family Planning Association, various slogans were chosen to simplify and popularize their message. One of these has always been my favourite. I wore it on a sash at the last demonstration against John Corrie's proposed Abortion (Amendment) Bill and it could almost be another title for this book. It is 'Every Child A Wanted Child'.

For this is a book about women who were brought up to take up the freedoms that were available; to delay starting a family while they worked, travelled, studied and built relationships. Many of them went through considerable spiritual search. They grew up and realized themselves, changed their goals, changed them again – and realized nothing else would do. They wanted to be mothers.

Nowadays we take the provision of contraception very much for granted. We talk far more about its application to the young than its value to the adult. It can be argued that the conscious denial of children in a relationship is selfish. But if both people are agreed upon it, this must be the exercise of one of the more positive aspects of selfishness. This way there are far fewer innocent victims than in families where the social pressure demands proof of manhood or womanhood, or the aggrandizement of grandchildren.

Over and over again in this book you will read of a woman surprised at the depth of her own feelings of how much she wanted a child, of how moved she was by her first sight of her child, or with what power did the realization of her own capacity to be a mother come upon her.

It is said that the delusion of reliable contraception (the way in which most of the mothers in this book 'came late to motherhood') is that the years slide by almost too easily until, suddenly, it is almost 'too late'. And there are complications with older bodies – more medical history to take into consideration, more risks for the child, but from this book it would seem that outsiders had more trouble with the older bodies than we, the owners of them. Because I, too, waited to have my baby, partly because of circumstance and partly because of choice. Having a child is a bit like running a race with yourself. It's not winning that matters so much as offering your 'personal best'. And one criticism that could never be levelled at the mothers of this book is that they didn't think about it. They thought about it exhaustively.

All the children in this book were sought. Their parents fought and argued, cried bitter tears, took tests, subjected themselves and their mates to all sorts of soul searching and physical examinations. They had, and took, the choice. They wanted children. In this book, *every* child is a wanted child.

ANNA RAEBURN

Introduction

An increasing number of women are postponing childbearing until they are well into their thirties. Twenty-five years ago, the Council of the International Federation of Obstetricians and Gynaecologists adopted the age of thirty-five as the cut-off point for defining the *elderly primigravida* or first-time mother. The term is used to bring to a doctor's attention the higher level of risk faced by pregnant women above that age. But do the possible medical risks justify the myths, misgivings and anxieties which have gathered themselves around late motherhood?

During the first week of February, 1981, the *Guardian's* Women's Page ran a series of autobiographical accounts about First Babies. A guiding question was: what is the best age to give birth? The third and final piece was by Linda Blandford who, at thirty-eight, had recently given birth to twins. Writing from America, she described her experience:

> They do not stop to talk in the park, these ageing women come so late to motherhood. They, who once proceeded in brittle and unknowing order, are now embarrassed by their inner untidiness. They leak emotions, staining all social exchanges with them. Instead they pass behind their pushchairs and prams bartering their telltale signs. Greying hair for sagging stomach, last year's coat for this year's wrinkles. In their beginning, they imply, looking down at muffled babies, is my end.

We both knew people whose experience of late motherhood differed significantly from this account, as indeed did Joan's (her daughter was born in 1979); and we decided to collect as many accounts as we could to set the picture right.

So, in the first place, the aims of our book were simple. Let's hear from other women. Let each tell her own story. It was to be a way of learning some truths, in order to dispel or support some of the general notions which surround the idea of women becoming mothers for the first time in their thirties. It was to become personally relevant to Sue as well since she too delayed childbearing and, during the time we worked on the book, gave birth to a son, Jamie (born in June 1983).

People in their thirties tend to have worked out their life styles. They have developed routines and attitudes which are based on things other than mothering: jobs, relationships, career-goals, a social life, cultural activities, etc. So the effects of starting a family can be far more disruptive for them than for people in their twenties. At the same time, the experience may well be more intense and all-consuming, for the woman has lived for that much longer with the possibility, and perhaps the hope, of eventually having a child.

While there have always been first-time older mothers in Britain, it is only since the Second World War that there has been a noticeable increase. In part, this has been made possible by the availability of reliable contraception and safe abortion on a scale unknown to previous generations. Along with this, the post-war woman has had a greater opportunity to continue her education to a high level, to choose a career, and, consequently, to find herself fulfilled enough in her public and professional role to hesitate before giving it all up for motherhood. Also her economic dependence on a working male partner has lessened, if not disappeared altogether, and she may opt for a lifestyle different in form from that of the nuclear family. By now the single-parent family is part of our society and, just as the stigma against illegitimacy is fading, so is that against the woman who chooses to bring up a child on her own, or as a member of a lesbian couple, or in a communal household.

Yet images of motherhood continue to restrict themselves to the young. Linda Blandford's sagging, grey-haired, watery-eyed pram-pushers hardly figure as media resources. Therefore, the older new mother has to face certain special problems. While these include physical risks, they go beyond them into the complex arena of emotional and personal adjustments to a role that isn't quite catered for in our society.

Women delay child-bearing for all sorts of reasons: medical, practical, emotional, and career-related. During the interim, the woman matures, learning how to pace herself emotionally, mentally and physically. And yet, no matter how sophisticated she becomes, as she approaches the later years of potential motherhood, she may find herself repeating like a heroine in a real-life melodrama: Do I really want to be a mother? How will I cope? Where will I find the energy? What if I can't conceive? What if I can't carry to term? What if my child is handicapped? Will I suffer post-natal depression? Will I live long enough to see my child through school? What if it's the end of the 'me' I know? How will I survive if I don't have a minute alone ever again?

By putting together an anthology of accounts, we hoped we could go some way towards showing how some women have found answers to these questions. To do this we hoped to represent as wide a range as possible of ages, economic circumstances, family situations, sexual orientations, and ethnic groups. And thus we hoped to gather an assembly of voices which could help the reader (male or female, older mother or not) to learn from, or share the experience of, other women. Disparate as they are, from a wide variety of backgrounds and perspectives, the stories amplify one another. In this way they contribute towards a composite picture in which the decision to become a mother can be seen as an essential life change. While the nature of this change is peculiar to women, and coming late to it accentuates its effect, the fact that it is major and permanent gives it universal relevance.

As we started to collect accounts, we looked for similar publications. At that time there were no British books on the subject. Since then, Sheldon Press has published Sheila Kitzinger's

Birth Over Thirty (although this is not exclusively about first babies). And Penny Cleminson, a Manchester woman who has been collecting accounts of other people's experiences wrote to tell us of her work in progress: 'I was 35 and I started to realize (a) how much of a shock it was to become a full-time mother after working for fourteen years and (b) how many other women are also having their babies late.' At Sisterwrite, a women's bookshop in London, a number of American guidebooks are available, including *Pregnancy After 35*, *The Over-35 Reaction to Pregnancy* and *It's Not Too Late for a Baby: For Women and Men Over 35*. But these, of course, deal with the American experience. The most relevant casebooks we came across were *Why Children* (The Women's Press, 1980), a collection of autobiographical accounts; *From Here to Maternity*, by Ann Oakley (Penguin, 1981), a collection of tape-recorded interviews; *Rocking the Cradle: Lesbian Mothers* by Gillian Hanscombe and Jackie Forster (Sheba, 1982), which uses interviews to show the different ways in which the growing number of lesbian mothers conceive and bring up their children in contemporary Britain; and *The Mother's Book*, co-edited by Ronnie Friedland and Carol Kort (1981), another American collection. Informative as they are, none of these focuses specifically on late motherhood.

We began by collecting accounts through personal contacts. We then wrote to the letters pages of several magazines, including *Spare Rib, New Society* and *Woman*, who were kind enough to print our notice. These brought in nearly two hundred accounts, primarily through the notice which appeared in *Woman*. When completing the final manuscript, we gathered another seven accounts by our first method, as, by then, we had particular circumstances in mind which we felt should be represented.

From the beginning, it was our intention to produce a case book – not a manual, not a tract, not a social history (although, on a small scale, a social history is what this collection represents). Of the two hundred accounts we received, only a small percentage came from women who had given birth during the first half of the century, or who were working class. None came from members of the upper class or from ethnic minorities. There were women of Jewish, Protestant and Catholic upbringing. Of the final selection, at least eighty per cent were born in the nineteen forties. We might have anticipated this since the number of women in higher education has increased significantly during the last quarter of the century. Perhaps inevitably, the question of timing in parenthood and the trend towards older first-time mothers is most acutely relevant to this generation.

Each woman has her own unique 'voice' and so we have left contributions as written, believing that the language used contributes to an understanding of the person whose story is being told. As editors, we provided directives, sending out first a 'prompt sheet' or set of guidelines, which is reproduced in the Appendix. We went back to the contributors whose accounts we finally chose, asking questions which had occurred to us on reading the submitted draft, making comments on strengths and weaknesses, and requesting any information we felt was missing. In some cases we also had the contributor talk through her story – on the telephone and, occasionally, in person – before writing it down. In this way the accounts remain the writers', yet contribute towards the kind of book we hoped to shape.

As we worked on the project, reading our way through the two hundred submissions, we discovered they had a compelling quality – even as aspects of one were repeated in another. Birth stories are intrinsically dramatic. Because of this, and because life changes are best grasped when seen in a recognizable context, we opted for a small number of complete stories, rather than a topically arranged sequence of short extracts. One general rule was that the book should include both stories with which the readers could easily identify, and stories which, like fiction, expand horizons. In addition to a lively telling, we looked for a reflective element, the capacity to analyse and evaluate how the experience of late motherhood was integrated into the woman's life.

The book contains twenty accounts which we have read and re-read without losing our enthusiasm for them. Here is an ex-nun married to an ex-priest. Here is an adventurer who has travelled to the Karakorum Mountains of the Western Himalayas with her six-year-old daughter: they cover hundreds of miles, the child on horseback while the mother walks beside her. Here is another mother working as a data manager, surface photographer and diver on a submarine geological expedition off the north coast of Australia. The only woman on board, she breastfeeds her daughter in the cramped hold. Another is single from the beginning. Two are lesbians; one of them was involved with the father of her child; the other chose to conceive by self-insemination from a donor. There is a woman who lives with the death of her child. Another, unable to conceive, has adopted. Another is the mother of a Down's Syndrome child. There is a writer, a lecturer, a retired social worker, an architect. There are some who have returned to work, others who have left their jobs after many years in their professions, still others who have primarily stayed at home.

Many of the names which appear are pseudonyms because, in telling their stories fully, our contributors frequently saw a need to protect those close to them. In one case a contributor has been unable to include the story of her conception because she wants to protect the father's wife and other children. Others have worried particularly about their mothers, lest they read in the published account a criticism which seems unnecessarily harsh. Each story emphasizes a different aspect, giving a different shading to the tale. Almost without fail mothers mention exhaustion and, in many of the accounts, there is criticism both of the way they are treated by the hospital service and the way in which they found themselves shut in while the fathers of their children could continue to come and go. And yet almost everyone ends with a positive note, as if they have come through to arrive at the right place. Only one concludes that she made a mistake in having children. But even she, now the mother of adults, has arrived at some kind of contentment. For, with the children gone, she feels more calm and relaxed than she has for years and closer to her husband than she has been since the children were born. This doesn't mean these women have had an easy time of it, rather that they have come to clear resolutions and, almost without exception, found their lives enriched.

The women retain their separate voices, yet can be heard as a chorus:

- 'No one who has not been pregnant and had a house and lively toddler to look after at the same time can know the devastating effects of total exhaustion.'

- 'The effect of parenthood is such that, if I were to wake to wonder what happened to my last decade, I would be interrupted before thinking it through.'

- 'The birth had left me feeling a failure. My unhappiness seemed to convey itself to the baby who was fretful . . . I missed my job more than I anticipated and I felt lonely and inadequate.'

- 'I look the same but inside I have completely changed. I have lost my peace of mind. I brood all day over what the minder might or might not be doing . . . Being worldly wise, I see dangers everywhere, not only for my child but for complete strangers and I worry for them. I am turning into a neurotic worrier.'

- 'If being pregnant in Britain is to be one of the most cossetted and cared-for members of society, being a mother at home is to be one of the most neglected.'

- 'Having rejected the housewife-and-mother role at twenty, I was understandably nervous about what it would be like to come to it at thirty-four.'

- 'I had established an identity based on an awareness of my own capabilities. I was not prepared to give all this up in the name of motherhood.'

- 'One of the most ridiculous fantasies was that, after having had a career and always being busy, there would be a wonderful period when I could sit at home and read cookery books.'

- 'A bonus for me that came out of having a baby late in life was, having made a break in my secretarial career, I felt I could pursue something I had always wanted to do: and once my daughter started school I was able to take up full-time study.

- 'Our society seems more interested in the birth process than in life after delivery for parents or baby.'

The women in this volume testify to their lives before and after delivery, illuminating both.

PART ONE

Changing Careers

Marianne Konrad

'After a few weeks, friends were ringing to ask: "Do you feel trapped in the house?" . . . "Are you depressed?" . . . "Is it awful?" I felt more lighthearted than I had done for years, perhaps ever.'

As I begin to write, Timmy lies kicking and cooing under a mobile improvised from Christmas decorations and shiny ribbons, strung across the doorway. Outside, I can hear my neighbour, an old German Jewish refugee, brushing the leaves from her path and chiding her great tomcat. Yesterday evening was an exhausted blur of tears over the nightly battle to put one small person to bed. But now the autumn sun is shining, the wind is rustling the lime trees at the end of our little garden, and I feel as I have felt almost every day since the birth: peaceful and excited. I turn to look at my energetic infant and think: four months ago, there was nothing occupying that particular square of carpet, and I never really believed there would be. And now, this . . .

I grew up knowing that 'one day' I wanted to have children. Indeed, I was convinced that this was what I would do best. One of two children, my brother away at school, I longed for a big family, and had visions of a large rambling house in the English countryside, filled with happy chaos as four children and their pets were let safely loose. As I played with my dolls, and pestered my mother to have another baby (she had had a hysterectomy) I dimly imagined that my own family would be born in my late twenties. That was as far into adulthood as I could project myself. Now, at thirty-six, I have just had my first baby and, far from living in my rambling farmhouse, am squeezed into a small London flat with Timmy's father, whose parents were Polish refugees. It has taken a long time to begin to fulfil a dream.

Although I always longed for children, I also had a deep fear of childbirth. My mother, herself in her late thirties when I was born, had a long and difficult labour, and hearing about it left me convinced I could never endure such an experience. Quite simply, I could not imagine I would live through it. And in the late sixties and early seventies, the press seemed to be full of hospital horror-stories – induced births done for the convenience of the staff; women left alone in labour. My already strong fear increased. I seem to need to be in control of situations – one reason why I have almost no fear of driving anywhere, but can hardly ever fly, or use the underground – and I hated the thought of being unable to cope with pain while nurses turned their backs.

But it probably wasn't only these fears which made me put off having children for so long. By the time I was in my early twenties, and my life was far from stable, I had pushed forward the idea of happiness into the thirties. I saw those years as filled with light and happiness, the years in which, I felt certain, I would find balance and security. In the meantime, I was emerging from a painful adolescence which saw me on the verge of a breakdown at seventeen, taking an overdose of tranquillizers the night before an exam and having what seemed to be – but wasn't – an epileptic fit. My early childhood, spent in the country, including two years on a farm, has left me with very happy memories. My late teens were filled with a black, confused depression. It took many years to recover from them, from a loss of religious faith and a sexual identity in turmoil.

I spent those years teetering through a succession of courses, jobs and affairs of the heart. I lived in a student hostel in Brixton and paced the streets trying to quell mounting anxiety and unhappiness. I fell in love with a music student (female) and a dance student (male) and, while neither of these relationships involved so much as a kiss, I lost my virginity to a Scottish poet I did not love at all. I moved to share a flat with friends and we all fell in and out of love and despair for the next two years. It was the late sixties, and nothing was forbidden – except babies. Some of us were on the pill then, but I have never wanted to be. However safe it may be, however much surer the protection, it feels like too great an interference in a fundamental body process. I used the cap, and lived with the days of dread each month brought. The idea of having a baby at that time was simply out of court: we talked about careers and lovers, not children.

The course completed, with mediocre results, I moved to live in a tiny attic overlooking Hampstead Heath. I wrote bad poetry and fell for a good poet who was soon writing about someone else. In 1971 I answered an advertisement in *Time Out* and moved into a large, two-storey flat with six strangers. The next three years were spent working for a publisher, and having an affair with one of the strangers, a gifted writer. On the whole, it was a happy time, filled with friendship and a great many laughs, as well as the inevitable irritations of communal living. At the end of that time, however, the writer went off to do a belated degree in the north. On a warm September afternoon, just before he went, we made love, and I left out my cap, deciding to try to get pregnant. I succeeded.

It was a foolish and utterly selfish act. My friend did not want a baby – on the few occasions we had discussed it, he had made that quite clear. But I was thrilled to be pregnant and considered bringing up the child alone. I was dissuaded after some weeks, partly by Tom, another member of the household and a close friend of us both. He pointed out all the practical difficulties, and said that if I ever met someone else he might not be willing to take on another man's child. (At the time, that argument weighed quite heavily. It might be different now.) In the end, it was more the fear of my parents' reaction – they would have been shocked and very distressed – which made me decide to have an abortion.

Although at the time I seemed to emerge fairly unscathed, I do now bitterly regret having created a life only to destroy it. In bed one night a few weeks after Timmy was born, I wept for that little creature, wondering if 'she' was all right somewhere. There remains a part of me which has not fully faced up to what I did then.

And so the dream of motherhood was as far away as ever. For the next four years I continued on my zig-zag path. I left my job and, like the writer, began a belated degree. I was lucky enough to get a second grant and this time I was studying because I really wanted to rather than from lack of direction. I worked hard and did very well. After the abortion, I began going out with the brother of the friend who had advised me to have it. Charles was 'straight' – a complete contrast to the unemployed writer. He was studying law, he was clever and shy and attractive and kind. He loved me. He wanted, he said, to give me a baby. We had seen each other only three or four times before I knew that I was going to marry him. I also knew, deep in a place I dared admit to no one, hardly even to myself, that I was not in love with him.

We moved into a dark basement flat and lived together for two years. In many ways we were extremely close, and I frequently persuaded myself that it didn't matter if something was missing. Plenty of people, after all, had marriages based on companionship, and they probably worked as well, if not better, than most. Plans for a wedding went ahead, to the great relief of both our families. Almost two hundred invitations were sent out, the dress was bought, the church booked, the cake made and the presents piling up. Six weeks before the day, I found myself kissing the man who became Timmy's father, and being told what a pity it was that I was getting married. I had to recognize that I was dizzily, deliciously in love, and somehow to tell myself that it didn't matter. Tadeusz was five years younger than me; he was about to leave London to do a post-graduate degree in Manchester; he had long hair; he seemed everything my parents would reject. We kissed goodbye. A week before the wedding he rang: 'Be happy, Marianne.' And I married my dear, kind companion.

If I had never seen Tadeusz again, perhaps the marriage would have lasted. Perhaps. Charles wanted children, and we talked about buying a house somewhere. By now I'd finished my degree and had begun another course, part-time. I was working in publishing again, also part-time, so spent many afternoons driving around looking at houses on my own. I used to see Tadeusz in all of them, his dark head bent over his books, our child playing in the garden, and I would drive off weeping. The future seemed to close in, as dark and oppressive as death. The idea of having a child receded further and further: how could I bring a new life into a world which in my state of mind I could see only as black, chaotic and meaningless?

A year later, Tadeusz and I met for lunch. A few weeks later we stole away to spend a weekend with friends who lived in the country. But on the Monday he went back to Manchester, and I went back to marriage. By now I was twenty-nine and, despite my love for him, perhaps more unhappy through our separation than I had ever been. I could think of little except death, was unable to work properly, or sleep. Tadeusz and I had long phone conversations which resolved nothing. He would not be responsible for the break-up of my marriage, insisting that I must leave only if I wanted to anyway, without taking him into account. I would not leave except to go to him. By now Charles knew what was going on and was suffering as well, but determined to save the marriage. After a year, he agreed we could separate for a week and, by now, to his relief and mine, he was seeing someone else. Tadeusz was back in London; we went to stay in my shabby old communal flat, by now largely repopulated, and had a blissful reunion. There was no question of my returning to Charles after that. We parted amicably and he has since remarried and is much happier with his new wife.

At the end of the first month Tadeusz and I spent together, I wept when my period came, even though we had been using contraception. For the first time I knew what it was to be deeply in love with someone with whom I longed to have children. I was now thirty-one. The thirties, to which I had looked forward for so long, had yielded the love of my life. But at a time when many people are settled, have some financial security and have already started their families, I was living in one room with a man five years younger who had no job, no money and who, although he looked forward to having children eventually, was far from ready to have any yet. It took four years for us to find new jobs and to save enough to buy a flat. Even then, I know Tadeusz felt pushed into starting a family. In addition to my age, there was another factor. In my early thirties I had developed cervical dysplasia, a pre-cancerous cell condition. It is manageable with treatment, and has not caused me alarm, but one method is a cone biopsy, which in a small number of women can compromise fertility. I was anxious to get pregnant before the condition developed to a point where I *had* to have a biopsy. Tadeusz agreed. However small the risk, it was there.

It took six months to conceive. As I had not been on the pill, my body had no adjustments to make, and I hoped to become pregnant straight away. Each month as my period became due I spent half my time rushing to the loo to check whether it had or had not arrived. The fourth month I was nine days late, and we both felt certain I had conceived. When my period came on the tenth day I felt a mixture of disappointment and anger, and began to realize a little how people must feel who long to have children but are infertile. Two months later, I was a week overdue. On the morning of the eighth day I woke with tender breasts, no period and the certainty that this was it. I went to work wearing an enormous red sweater and sat in a meeting hugging my secret and thinking: soon, I'll actually need to wear this baggy old thing.

By day fifteen I was on two weeks' leave. I took a specimen to the local chemist; the hours spent waiting for the result of the test were restless and anxious. When I went back I was told it was negative. I glared at the unfortunate woman. 'It *can't* be.' 'I'm so sorry...' I rushed out, got in the car and burst into tears. I was still certain I was pregnant but began to force myself to face the fact that I could be mistaken. On the nineteenth day I had two more tests done, one at the chemist and one through my GP at the local hospital. The latter would not be through for a few days, and we were going on holiday the next day. Somehow I hoped that the delay in getting the result would mean it would show positive. But when I rang my GP from Yorkshire I was told it was negative. So had the second test at the chemist been. By now, however, I was quite certain they were wrong.

And, having wanted to have a baby for so long, I was suddenly filled with misery. Crying helplessly, I told Tadeusz I was sure I'd be a bad mother, that my children would be bored and unhappy, that they would grow up to hate me . . . He was loving and reassuring, and I did manage to feel better after each bout of tears, and to realize that I was probably being affected by hormonal changes. Back in London, I went straight to my GP on the way to work. This time he gave me an internal. Yes, I was pregnant. He was clearly bored to death with pregnant women, but I refused to be taken aback by his weary: 'Where do you want to have this baby?' and rushed out of the surgery to tell Tadeusz. It was a beautiful autumn morning, and although we both tried suddenly to play down this momentous confirmation, we were too happy and excited.

One night two months later, after we had made love, I felt something pour out. I went to the bathroom and passed two large clots of blood. I put on a sanitary pad, and in icy calm, still bleeding, went to ring for an ambulance. It was almost midnight. I lay on the living-room floor as Tadeusz dressed to come with me, and thought: of course this would have to happen. Why did I ever think that I could have a child?

In the casualty department cubicle a large teddy bear was sitting on the high narrow bed with a blood-pressure strap on his arm and an oxygen mask on his nose. He was removed, and I was examined by a young woman doctor who did her best to reassure me that bleeding in early pregnancy is not uncommon and does *not* always lead to miscarriage. I was to remain in bed, in hospital, and would have a scan. For some reason I can't now recall (but to do with administration, not health) I wasn't able to have one for two days, so I had plenty of time to hope that the baby had *not* been one of the clots I'd passed, and plenty of time to imagine that it might have been. I continued to feel strangely calm. On the day of the scan, as instructed, I drank over a litre of water (so that it is clear on the screen which is bladder and which uterus) and, bursting at the seams, was taken down in a chair.

'Well, you're still pregnant,' said the woman doctor, and I let out a sigh of relief like a whale spray. She showed me the tiny, flickering life on the screen. 'A very mobile foetus.' My eyes filled with tears. Back in the ward I lay glowing, proud of my determined little infant, yet hardly able to believe that the next time I'd be in a hospital bed I'd have a baby in a crib beside me. I was told to rest, and not make love for a couple of months, just in case. Both of us were far too shaken by what had happened to dare to do so anyway.

We now seemed on course, and I began to make plans about what to do about my work. The financial security offered for the first few months of the baby's life by my taking maternity leave was very tempting. But I could not imagine how I would go back to my demanding job and do justice to it or to the baby after so short a time. Nor could I bring myself to take leave knowing I was unlikely to want to return; it didn't seem fair on my department, particularly as the company's current climate was against covering for women on maternity leave, even though it was agreed with the union that they should. I therefore took a gamble and gave in my notice. With a few occasions of panic, but mostly certain that I had done the right thing, I spent the five months until I left building up and re-establishing publishing contacts in order to go freelance as a reader and editor. I also hoped to develop my own writing, having by now had some work published and feeling far more confident and eloquent. I felt very fit, full of optimism and energy.

But there was a shadow over all this. Two months before I conceived, my father had gone into hospital for a second heart operation. He had been settled in for two hours and we were all just about to go home. Tadeusz, my brother and I saw my mother settled into the room where she would stay until the operation was over, and thought we'd just pop back to say goodbye to him. We returned to the ward to see screens round his bed, and nurses swiftly wheeling oxygen equipment towards it. The Sister quickly told us that he was 'rather unwell' and asked us to wait. He had had a cardiac arrest. If this had happened six hours earlier, he would have died peacefully at home. As it was, he was 'rescued' and taken into intensive care. He spent the next six months dying. On Christmas Day I told him he was to be a grandfather, and his face lit up with excitement before he fell once again into his drugged, sleepy state. He finally died in the dark small hours one night in February.

Still a child at heart, he would have been a wonderful grandfather. His illness and eventual pitiful death dominated the first five months of my pregnancy, which was spent going almost every evening to see him and my mother – who stayed with him in hospital, thanks to their kindness, to the very end. I do not think I would have been able to bear it, or give whatever I did manage to give, if I hadn't the prospect of a baby to balance this awful, long-drawn-out ending of a life. Fortunate indeed that I was physically fit during the pregnancy, I was emotionally rushing between the two great extremes, and grew to feel more strongly than ever how deeply we are all locked in this inevitable continuum. When Timmy was born, he looked like his Polish family. Now, I see my father's smile in his, and it is hard sometimes not to believe that something of his spirit has passed into his little grandson.

We began going to NCT classes in April. Here I was acutely aware of the difference it makes to come late to motherhood. There were six couples. All of us were in our mid-thirties and all middle-class and professional. By the last class, six weeks from the date when most of us were due, and when any of us could have gone into labour at any time, not one had packed her bag ready to go to hospital. All of us were still working, all planning to continue to work as soon as possible after the birth. The dominant feeling seemed to be: 'How can I fit a baby into my career?' I found the other class members strongly prejudiced against hospitals; after seeing all the love and care lavished on my father, I found it difficult to listen calmly to people's vision of them as institutions which, as far as pregnancy was concerned, existed solely in order to force a high-tech birth onto a helpless woman.

But the classes were very good, and prepared us well for the actual stages of labour. Tadeusz had always been apprehensive about attending the birth – and hid under the bedclothes when I woke him to tell him I'd been having contractions. When it came to it, he was as relaxed and helpful as if he'd been looking after women in labour all his life. The fear of childbirth, with which I'd lived for so long, was destroyed. Far from being hostile or uncaring, far from treating me as one more woman in labour on the production line, the hospital staff made me feel special, and I was beautifully looked after. The labour lasted twenty-one hours. Short of a Caesarian Section, I did have almost every single technological intervention: my waters were broken; a foetal monitor was put on the baby's head; I had a shot of Pethidine; an epidural with two top-ups — which enabled me to be calmly sitting up and talking for so much of the time; I was on a drip; catheterized; delivered by forceps because of the position of the baby's head, and had an episiotomy and many stitches. And yet, at the end, I felt only as if we had all been helped to make sure that a healthy baby came into the world without him or his mother suffering too greatly, and that he was received with love. Within thirty-six hours, Tadeusz and I were saying, 'Let's have another one soon.'

Timmy was born at two in the morning on our fifth anniversary. He was given to me at once, and as I clasped his sticky little body close to my neck I felt a mixture of love, compassion and numb disbelief. He was taken from me and washed, and then Tadeusz held him while I was also washed, in great sweeping strokes, by a large West Indian nurse. I began to feel depressed and exhausted. By the time we were all wheeled back to the ward I could feel nothing for Timmy at all: I wanted only to be left alone to sleep. I was. Three hours later, I was woken to suckle him, then slept again. At eight I woke and saw a tiny face with eyes wide open facing me from a transparent plastic crib. He was shivering. I stretched out my hand and stroked him. He quivered, then the beetle-black eyes closed, and he fell asleep. And I fell in love.

My mother, so recently widowed, made the journey to London that day and was trembling with exhaustion and emotion as she sat beside the bed and produced two miniature bottles of champagne, which had been sent to my father in hospital to wish him well. With Tadeusz, we toasted the baby he would never see.

Out of hospital it was the middle of a June heatwave. I felt for much of the time as though I had stepped through a door into an enchanted garden. Life seemed full of promise and excitement, and by day twelve, as I got out of the bath, I said aloud, 'I've completely recovered from the birth.' After a few weeks, friends were ringing to ask: 'Do you feel trapped in the house?' . . . 'Are you depressed?' . . . 'Is it awful?' I felt more lighthearted than I had done for years, perhaps ever. It was difficult to settle into a work routine, but Timmy slept for at least one good solid patch every day (and only woke twice in the night, including dawn) and I forced myself to go to my desk as soon as he dropped off.

Somehow, I've done a great deal of work since then, but it is getting more difficult. He's much more wakeful at sixteen weeks, and perhaps in only two out of seven days will he have a sustained nap where I can really get down to anything. Working in bursts of forty-five minutes or an hour is draining, and I am obviously going to have to plan the next few months carefully, and find some affordable help. The situation is not helped by the fact that Tadeusz's job is extremely demanding, and he is home late – say nine or ten – many evenings, and often works at weekends. Although he grows to love Timmy more and more deeply, he is still unable – and unwilling – to do anything except play with him in short sessions, or occasionally try to sing him to sleep. He does not change or dress him, or give him his bath, and obviously cannot feed him since Timmy is still exclusively breastfed.

My day goes something like this. Dawn feed; back to bed or, if Timmy is wide awake, have tea, feed the cat and watch breakfast TV; get up properly, clear up, do the washing; entertain baby; plan supper; shop; feed him; work while he sleeps; answer the phone; feed him; entertain; work while he sleeps; entertain and feed him; cook supper, bath, feed, rock him to sleep; talk to people on the phone; eat, watch the news; collapse. Obviously, in all this, something has had to go, and my social life has slowed right down. At present I feel on a bit of treadmill. Sometimes I can hear myself saying over and over to a mythical Someone: 'If I give you a hundred pounds, will you let me work without interruption all day?'

But, despite the difficulties, I am glad I made the decision not to go back to my job. Life is still flexible enough for me to have time off when I really need it, and the day, though broken and sometimes frustrating, is entirely Timmy's and mine, to have cuddles, songs or tears whenever we feel like it, without feeling guilty. In a busy office, I didn't have shrieks and yells when I got something wrong, but nor did I have the most beautiful smile in the world when I got it right.

It's clear that, far from suffering from post-natal depression, I'm experiencing post-natal elation. Perhaps working so hard all this time has been a good thing, taking the edge off a too-exclusive preoccupation with Timmy's every whimper. Sometimes I look at him asleep and feel completely unrelated to him: the loving custodian of a little boy, not a mother. I think this is a good thing, and means I will be able to allow him enough freedom and independence as he grows up. When I think of his future I feel determined to try to make sure that whatever went wrong for me between a free and happy childhood and a miserable adolescence and early adulthood, does not go wrong for him.

This afternoon I spent over an hour trying to get to my typewriter to finish writing this. In the end I had to give up: he was wide awake, raring to go, and fretful without attention. A radio programme on opera suddenly came on; I turned up the sound and the flat was filled with drama and music. I grabbed Timmy from his chair, we spun dancing round and round the room, and he flung back his head and laughed.

I feel very fortunate that in coming late to motherhood I have not been too late for happiness.

Jane Bennett

'Most important, I do not resent the children for having
prevented me from achieving certain ambitions, for I had
had time to do most of the things I wanted to before they
were born.'

I grew up disliking children. I was an only child with parents who
had strict views on who might be a suitable companion for their
daughter. At the occasional get-together with relations, I watched
my boisterous young cousins with mixed feelings of envy and fear.
Very shy and ill-at-ease in company, I retreated into silence. I
never thought of myself as a child and preferred the company of
adults, though much disliking it if they talked down to me. I
escaped into music and books and lived in a romantic fantasy
world where I was always the heroine, performing deeds of
incredible courage. My teenage sexual fantasies, such as they
were, were of the Sleeping Beauty variety, where the hero, after
considerable difficulties, reached my virginal bed and made love
to me in a blaze of ecstasy. The fantasy always ended there as I
could not envisage a repeat performance.

Though my parents' marriage was a reasonably happy one, my
father's constant serious illnesses imposed a considerable strain. I
adored my father who, being tall, fair, handsome and a war hero,
was the prototype for my fantasy lover. My mother I feared and
disliked, for her anxiety over my charming but vague father

provoked her into a possessive bullying that I deeply but guiltily resented. Her views on any kind of sexual licence were rigid and her sense of propriety highly developed. When she had no choice but to explain menstruation, she stood in front of me like the Statue of Liberty, sternly holding up a sanitary towel by the loop and warning me that under no circumstances could the subject be mentioned in the company of men, including my father. I was given no reason as to why I would start bleeding, nor any practical guidance, and I remember my first periods as being times of mess, smell and acute embarrassment. When, during my first term at boarding school at the age of eleven, I was taught the facts of life, I was shocked to learn of the man's involvement in baby-making. Moreover, the sex act seemed so bizarre I was convinced it must take place in hospital with a nurse in attendance. When I thought of my own father, I felt betrayed and disgusted.

With this background it is not surprising that by the time I married at twenty-two I was, to put it mildly, emotionally confused. I could not see the real reason for my deep-seated unhappiness so I had decided that it was because I was a woman. It was all so unfair, I kept complaining to my long-suffering husband: men did not have to put up with periods or childbirth, they could choose a career they liked, while women had saddled on them the soul-destroying tedium of domestic responsibilities. The thought of having children appalled me but the decision to have a career instead brought with it a heavy burden of guilt. In the early 1960s it was still considered selfish, or at best eccentric, to opt out of motherhood. Women's Lib had not yet gathered momentum. Whatever the climate of opinion, however, I am sure I would have felt the same, for the conflict came from within myself. My wish to devote myself to a career seemed abnormal to me; it was also inconvenient, since I had no career to speak of at that time, having drifted into becoming a secretary. I wanted very much to want motherhood, even going to the lengths of attending National Childbirth Trust films and lectures in an attempt to over-come my resistance. I sat, pink with embarrassment, amongst heavily pregnant women, feeling both jealous of their condition and sorry for their plight. Nothing was resolved. My husband was tolerant and sympathetic but he did not want children himself and found it difficult to understand my feelings of guilt.

Eventually I started a degree course at the local polytechnic and found the course stimulating and exciting. But my obsession did not fade; instead it grew to a pitch where I could no longer even look at a woman's magazine without wishing to tear it up, nor listen to a woman's radio programme without feeling enraged. At the end of my first year's studies, I plunged into a breakdown of such gravity that it took six years of treatment before I emerged into the beginnings of a healthy personality. Three of these years were spent as a day patient at a psychiatric hospital. From the relationships with my fellow patients and the affection of a maternal ward sister I began to learn what being part of a family meant. Somehow, with the aid of sympathetic and generous tutors, I completed my studies and gained my degree.

But by this time my marriage had given way under the strain of the long years of illness and I found myself alone, still receiving psychotherapy, with a new life to build. Gradually, I gained in confidence and, after many set-backs, obtained a well-paid and challenging job as a polytechnic information officer. I had at last climbed out of what had been for me a secretarial rut and I was satisfied. I did not think much about children because, having reached my middle thirties and having achieved some measure of self-respect if not happiness, I did not contemplate re-marrying. Most of my contemporaries had young families and I blush now to think how little interest I showed in their offspring.

It was therefore to my complete astonishment that I met a man who I not only wanted to marry but with whom I wanted children. He had also been married before and had not wanted children so we were both surprised at our desire, this late in the day, to reproduce. Looked at rationally, it might not have appeared very auspicious to start a family. We were both thirty-five, only children, used to pleasing ourselves, and I had a history of mental illness. All the arguments I had once used to convince myself that motherhood was not for me were dismissed in favour of an intuitive feeling that I wanted to extend the happiness I had found to a family. In the first flush of my new-found love I questioned no further.

I became pregnant shortly after I re-married and found my romantic idea of pregnancy rather spoiled by morning sickness, which in my case was inaptly named since it lasted all day. Once this tiresome phase was over, however, I felt marvellous. I longed for the pregnancy to show and began wearing maternity clothes long before it was necessary. I walked surreptitiously around Mothercare gazing at hitherto unknown articles like nappies and baby vests. It was the long hot summer of 1976 and every lunch time I left my work to laze on the beach and swim. I experienced a sense of well-being I have never known before or since. My hair shone and my skin glowed. The only interruption in my happiness was the visit to the hospital where long delays, clumsy interviews and a rough and unpleasant doctor reduced me to tears. But, this over, I continued to bloom and prepare for the birth.

I attended National Childbirth Trust classes and happily accepted the dogma that pain-relieving drugs were not only unnecessary but a hindrance to the joyous process of childbirth. Any thoughts of the pain I might face were quickly suppressed. I might be termed an elderly primigravida by the medical profession but I was fit and happy and envisaged nothing going wrong. When I was seven months pregnant I left my job with no great regrets. I had achieved my modest ambition and I had no wish to tear myself in two by attempting to combine career and motherhood. I thankfully stayed home, decorated the nursery and waited eagerly for the impending birth.

I was surprised, when labour at last began, at the strength of the contractions. The National Childbirth Trust lecturer's use of the term 'discomfort' seemed woefully inadequate. After only five hours in labour I had reached the 'emergency' level of breathing and was beginning to wonder if I would last out. After much argument with the midwife and doctor, I eventually accepted a shot of Pethidine and was thankful to sink into oblivion for a while. When, some hours later, the second stage of labour started I was expecting the pain to ease but, on the contrary, it seemed to intensify. After an hour of red-faced and fruitless pushing, I was told by the doctor that the baby was facing the wrong way and that forceps were necessary. My husband was sent out of the room, my feet were placed in stirrups and to my horror the baby was wrenched around and forcibly pulled out of my body. I let out an involuntary shriek and a gas-and-air mask was clamped onto my face. In my eagerness to get the birth over, I pushed as hard as I could and the baby shot out, tearing me badly in the process. But for the moment all this was irrelevant, for a warm, bloody weight was placed on my stomach and the midwife exclaimed 'You have a daughter!'

A daughter! I had convinced myself, no doubt to avoid disappointment, that I was expecting a boy when, in fact, I dearly longed for a little girl. I was ecstatic, and the pain and violence of the birth seemed temporarily unimportant. When I looked at the baby I felt overwhelmed with joy and tenderness, for she seemed so tiny, helpless and precious. I was drunk with excitement – it was like falling in love all over again. My euphoria, however, was short-lived as complications set in soon after and I remained in hospital for a miserable three weeks. On my return home I felt weak, ill and unable to cope with the new baby. The birth injuries did not finally heal for seven months and, as I could only sit comfortably on a rubber ring, my social life was somewhat curtailed.

The birth had left me feeling a failure. My unhappiness seemed to convey itself to the baby who was fretful. Walking was painful, yet pram-pushing was the only way to achieve some peace. I missed my job more than I anticipated and I felt lonely and inadequate. Depression finally overwhelmed me and I was sent for psychotherapy. Under treatment it took some time for me to accept that the unpleasant birth had not been my fault and that the doctor had been incompetent both in his handling of the delivery and in his aftercare. I had to come to terms with the bitterness and anger that remained and it took two years before I could even contemplate having another child.

Despite all these difficulties I had never regretted having a baby. By this time she had developed into a delightful child. Yet I still felt there was something missing. After my experiences as an only child I was anxious that my little girl should not be put in the same position. I also wanted to put the record straight by experiencing a birth that was normal. My husband, who had enjoyed being an only child, was not keen to try again. He felt he would resent the time taken by another baby and was concerned that another birth might bring in its wake further ill-health and depression for me. I was now nearly forty at which age the risk of a handicapped baby is greatly increased. I could not avoid the unpleasant fact that I had a first cousin born with Down's Syndrome when his mother was over forty. But once again I allowed my instincts to overrule my reason and I persuaded my husband that we should try for a second child.

To my dismay I found that I did not conceive. I resorted to temperature charts and an ovulation thermometer, but found my highly irregular cycle difficult to chart. Apart from the acute disappointment that accompanied the onset of each period, the necessity to everlastingly calculate dates did not have a beneficial effect on our sex-life. We considered adoption but knew that our age would prohibit this. My little girl was now at nursery school and I had some time on my hands. All my friends seemed to be producing babies. To stop myself brooding I took up some outside part-time work.

On a visit to my doctor, about a minor foot complaint, I mentioned just as I was leaving that I had tried unsuccessfully for over a year to conceive. To my surprise he sprang into action and said that at my age there was no time to lose – I must attend the infertility clinic. Arrangements were made on the spot and I was ushered out of the surgery weakly protesting that I had only come because of my feet. Reluctantly, therefore, I attended the clinic where a coldly matter-of-fact doctor embarrassed me by his questions and comments on my sex life. I was relieved to be passed on to a more humane consultant who suggested I try a fertility drug. He assured me that the days when five or six babies were conceived at once on these drugs were long past. Rather apprehensively, I agreed to go on a low dose to start with.

After only a month, to my amazement and delight, I found I had conceived. My pleasure, however, was somewhat marred by the morning sickness which was more severe than the first time. I could stomach little food, yet unless I ate something every two hours I became ill and faint. I noticed, too, that I seemed to be rather large for such an early stage. As I had decided that there was no way I would go through an experience like the first birth, it was arranged that the consultant I had seen at the clinic would deliver the baby. At my first antenatal visit he carried out an ultrasound scan and after a pause said chattily 'I think I can see two in there.' All I could say was 'Blimey,' which did not adequately sum up my horror at his bombshell.

I returned home in a daze and was almost incoherent when I told my husband. He went white, said nothing and disappeared to his study. Friends, when they heard the news, either roared with laughter or asked worriedly how would I ever cope. I found neither reaction very helpful. Here I was, over forty, expecting twins. The thought of the birth frightened me, but not as much as the worry of how I would manage afterwards. The pregnancy, difficult from the start, did not get easier. I had decided to have amniocentesis, the test of the amniotic fluid surrounding the foetuses, to see if there was any abnormality. The thought of my cousin, shut away in an institution since he was two years old, haunted me. The consultant asked me to seriously consider what I would do if the tests revealed that one foetus only were affected. Would I agree to an abortion of both babies even though one was normal, or would I let matters stand and give birth to a handicapped child? There would be little time for decision-making once the results came through. Both eventualities seemed appalling to me. While I could not bear the thought of killing my babies, neither did I believe I was of the calibre to bring up a handicapped child. I spent sleepless nights thinking about the possibilities and could come to no conclusion. Eventually, aware of my distress, the consultant sent me to a London teaching hospital where some success had been achieved in killing one foetus in the womb without aborting the normal baby. There the amniocentesis test was carried out before a large audience of students. The professor in charge gave me a lecture on the necessity for rest and despatched me home to Sussex without one. I then waited anxiously for a month before I learnt that both foetuses were normal and that they were little girls. I cried with thankfulness.

Despite my relief, the pregnancy continued to be tiresome. I felt exhausted all the time yet I could not sleep at night. My sexual relationship with my husband ceased, as the babies' obvious presence seemed to inhibit such contact. Despite the consultant's assurances that an epidural would ensure a painless birth, I worried about the complications that might arise. I was relieved when I had to be admitted to hospital two weeks before the babies were due. The birth was very quick, straightforward and happy, even though the epidural did not provide the painless experience I had been led to expect. I felt a great achievement in being able to push out both babies unaided and my husband's delight in seeing his daughters emerge into the world was good to see. For me the experience of producing two new human beings within minutes of each other seemed a privilege I was fortunate to be granted.

The rest of the time in hospital was not easy. The babies weighed well over seven pounds each and my womb pained me. I took some time to regain my strength and there was little help with the babies. While I had happily breastfed my first child, trying to feed two babies at once became a nightmare, particularly since I was not producing sufficient milk. Eventually I was advised to give up the struggle and thankfully changed over to the bottle. On arriving home I found it difficult to walk without pain and twenty-four hours later haemorrhaged and was bundled into an ambulance with the twins and returned to hospital. After a hasty operation (for a partially retained placenta) and a blood transfusion I was allowed home again some days later convinced that childbirth in the 1980s ought to be less traumatic.

Afterword

Two years later I look back in thankfulness that I do not have to go through the process again. I have my family and I am content. The twins are a continual delight and I am pleased to find how very much more relaxed I am with them than with my first child. Whether the difficulties of childbirth were in any way attributable to my age I am not qualified to say, although the doctors never suggested so, but I do know that the babies were worth it. I remember from reading accounts written by first-time mothers how easy it is to identify with all the problems they recount but not with the pleasures. All of us know what irritation, tiredness and depression are like but there is no way to appreciate the joy of holding your own child unless you have experienced it. Fulfilment is not an easy state to describe.

Whatever my relationship with my children in the future, and I do not look upon them as an insurance policy for my old age, they have given me a sense of continuity through the generations. And, for the present, there is the pleasure of seeing them develop and of enjoying their freshness and fun. What is indisputable is that life can never be the same as it was before the children arrived. Friends change, attitudes alter and everyday life is transformed by a multitude of small details. My relationship with my husband has indeed changed, or perhaps I should say developed. Caring for children leaves no room for starry-eyed idealism of one's partner – we have seen each other at our worst and our marriage is, I believe, the stronger for it.

Whether or not I am a better person for being a mother I cannot say; I am certainly often overtired and short-tempered. But while my stamina may be less, there are considerable advantages to being an older mother. Twenty years ago, beset with uncertainties and anxieties, I would have been bewildered by the flood of well-meaning but conflicting advice handed out to mothers. Today, I am able to use my own judgement and not mind so much when I'm wrong. Perhaps most important, I do not resent the children for having prevented me from achieving certain ambitions, for I had had time to do most of the things I wanted to before they were born. This is not to say that I have not minded the small everyday irritations – the inconvenience and clutter of prams and push-chairs; the palaver of organizing outings; the running noses; the dirty bottoms; the impossibility of doing what I want when I want. The children's needs always have to come first and it is difficult to organize the time to myself that is essential for my own well-being. I am fortunate in having a husband who understands this and also in being able to have some outside help with the twins. Had I neither of these benefits I might well be telling a different story for I do not find being a mother easy. I have always found staying at home more challenging than working outside it, as it takes a certain amount of inner discipline to retain order throughout the day and to keep up other interests and activities. I may well return to work some time, but being with the children when they are young is, for me, important. Above all, the restless unhappy searching of my twenties has gone, and in its place is a measure of self-knowledge and some sense of achievement. I have come in from the cold at last and joined the human race.

Margaret Edwards

'During the last five years my ideas and values have been turned upside down. No longer do I seek a career as a means of fulfilment. That competitive, aggressive world has become alien. I have not opted out of society, but I want to fight for a new set of priorities, which acknowledge those who give life, who nurture, who want peace . . .'

Understanding myself as a mother has inevitably involved a reassessment of my own childhood. I was an only child, born at the end of the war. My parents were both teachers who never quite achieved their own academic ambitions. From my earliest childhood I was influenced by their concept of Fabian Socialism, particularly of improvement through education. Academic achievement and a successful career were continually presented to me as desirable goals.

My mother continued teaching after my birth, taking a four-day-a-week job at a private convent school. I was cared for by an elderly neighbour until I was three years old, when I joined the infant class at my mother's school. Looking back, I realize that I had virtually no contact with mothers or young babies. We must have been an isolated family: both parents were fully involved with their careers, they had few neighbourhood contacts and casual visiting was limited to grandparents. I never experienced the visits to friends' houses, the toddlers and playgroups which my own children take for granted.

I was a solitary child. Both my primary and secondary schools were far away from my home, over an hour's journey. I left home early for school, returned late and had little contact with local children. When I started Grammar School, homework occupied a lot of my spare time. In my teens, my parents made it clear that any distracting ideas such as boyfriends, marriage or motherhood were to be avoided at all costs. Babies prevented a successful career.

At convent school I quickly sensed the ambivalence about sexuality and motherhood and puzzled over the unattainable ideal of the Virgin Birth. Occasionally, curiosity overcame fear, but early furtive sexual encounters were dominated by a dread of pregnancy. Leaving school for university was a watershed: I rejected Catholicism for ever. The freedom of the Sixties, the sexual revolution, the contraceptive pill, opened a new way of life for me. But the deeply engrained ideas about achievement, the need to have an unimpeded career, the fear of pregnancy remained. After university I married, and embarked on a career, first in social work, and then in teaching social science. At work it was frustrating to see so many capable young women in my department leave to have babies, and to see so many senior posts filled by men. I stood by, perplexed and confused as ex-colleagues visited the department with their new babies and were surrounded by excited and admiring women. Pregnancy and parenthood were synonymous with problems, an unnecessary diversion from the main business of life, a career and freedom to enjoy myself as I wished.

In my twenties I had become increasingly committed to feminism and had joined a local Women's Group. Many of the women of my age were mothers and were struggling to re-enter careers. Some regretted this early commitment to motherhood and there was much discussion about the problems of having dependent children. The woman's right to choose not to have children was continually emphasized. My childlessness was in itself a refutation of the idea that a woman's biology must be her inescapable destiny.

And yet... and yet... I was restless. My work was dominating my time, in fact I was rapidly becoming a workaholic. However, I knew that further promotion would lead to increasingly bureaucratic and administrative work, which I disliked. Much of the time I felt tired and depressed. On my thirtieth birthday I was forced to acknowledge that I could not carry on. In a trap of my own making, tearful and exhausted, I succumbed to a week's sick leave and a bottle of Valium.

One of the new, liberated generation methodically taking my contraceptive pill every day, the rejection of motherhood had been easy. But a positive decision to become pregnant was something for which I was totally unprepared. My friends, my husband, my parents all had an image of me as an independent, childless woman. I found I was trapped by this image. To change was to betray their hopes and expectations.

The struggle to develop new ideas and to acknowledge new needs was painful and frightening. I became increasingly dissatisfied with my job. My father died and I suddenly realized that I was entering a new stage of life. My partner and I wanted to put down roots, to explore a less superficial aspect of living, to develop more mature relationships.

Why I wanted a child was a difficult question to answer. Certainly I had no realistic idea of what pregnancy and parenthood would involve. Yet the desire for a baby was strong. I felt as though a whole part of myself was undeveloped and unfulfilled. It was, I suppose, an essentially selfish feeling; the idea of a real live demanding baby rarely entered my mind. I wanted a child. I was thirty-four years old. I became increasingly aware that time was running out. Desperately, I looked around for information and guidance. 'If you want a baby, dear, you had better hurry up,' was the curt response from the Family Planning doctor as she briskly prodded my vagina.

Surprisingly, I conceived quickly and without difficulty. However, adjusting to the idea of pregnancy was difficult. Friends did not help. Some automatically assumed that the pregnancy was a mistake, some were openly hostile, feeling that I had abandoned a feminist stance. A few men were smugly triumphant that I had at last succumbed to my feminine role. The pregnancy had an air of unreality. Neither my husband nor I could accept what was happening. I was still looking for another job and to a large extent ignoring what was happening to my body, angrily rejecting any suggestions that I should act differently because I was pregnant. I think I was fearful of being submerged into the cloying, sentimental picture of motherhood.

As the pregnancy progressed I became increasingly conscious of my age. At the antenatal clinic I sat in the familiar long queue, but my hair was beginning to show grey and my tolerance of both the heat of that long hot summer and the impersonal inefficiency of the hospital set me apart from the younger, cheerful women who surrounded me. Some had toddlers with them and grumbled amiably. For me each visit was a grim and frustrating confrontation. I entered the consulting room with a list of questions. 'Ah,' said the doctor, on one occasion, 'You are the lady who reads all those books.' He was right: my one concession to maternity was appropriately academic. I read avidly and soon had a formidable collection of books on the subject. My insistence on information, my persistent questions, first provoked a placatory, soothing response and then overt irritation. Clearly, this elderly primigravida was an eccentric nuisance.

In contrast to my theoretical knowledge, my practical information was nil. I had no friends with young babies who could offer advice. A week before the baby was due, I rushed around the local shops, panicking at the idea of a nappyless baby. I stared in total confusion at vests, gowns and suits. It was all so complicated! Finally I bought one of everything in the blind hope that something would be right and crept home exhausted and feeling totally inadequate.

John and I had been to the National Childbirth Trust classes and had practised the breathing exercises in a halfhearted way. However, I was overwhelmed by anxiety at the prospect of giving birth. It seemed unacceptable for a woman of my age to lose control, and I was frightened that I would be unable to cope. In fact, I had a comparatively straightforward labour and, much to my own and my husband's surprise, the breathing techniques did help. Suddenly, there we were, staring at a baby.

I had a baby. For the next few hours I sat in the hospital bed smiling broadly and proclaiming to all around that I had a daughter. My strongest memory is one of sheer surprise. Emotionally, I had not adapted to the idea of pregnancy. So many years of adult childlessness made adjustment difficult. My body had known that it was pregnant, but not my mind.

The period of adaptation was long and difficult. I found it hard to accept and trust my emotions. Often I would try and deny my own strong feelings, distrusting behaviour which was not rational and considered. From the very beginning I was completely infatuated by my daughter. This experience of being totally overwhelmed was, and still is, the central pivot of my life. For the baby's first year I lived in a confused attempt to combine these strong emotions with a lifestyle which, to a large extent, ignored my daughter's existence. I took a series of temporary part-time jobs whilst feeling increasingly strained whenever I left her with a childminder. Later I applied for, and got, a full-time job but panicked at the thought of increasingly difficult child care arrangements and sent a last-minute telegram of withdrawal.

I suffered from increasing bouts of anxiety and depression. Much of my life seemed artificially divided into two spheres. At work I felt the pressure to ignore the fact that I had a child. At lunch time I would secretly rush away to phone the childminder and check that all was well. At the end of the day I would dread any delay, driving tense and anxious, back through the rush hour traffic. In contrast, my life at home was lonely and isolated and doubly frustrating. I was unable to use my time to pursue interesting home-centred activities: it seemed impossible to read or garden or paint in peace and without interruption from the relentless demands of a baby.

Many of these problems were inherent in my situation, but

some were certainly exacerbated by my age. Many of the women who I met at local clinics and toddler groups were at least ten years younger than myself. Contemporaries from school and college tended to have much older children and be unwilling to rekindle any interest in teething or potty training. Feminist friends in particular showed scant sympathy to a woman who had chosen to live in a nuclear family with a small baby.

My relationship with John certainly changed radically. Ideas of shared child care proved unrealistic as job opportunities declined and we became increasingly reliant on my husband's salary. We were gradually pushed into the traditional roles of father out at work and mother at home. At times my frustration at this situation was inevitably unleashed at John. Alone with a fractious toddler, bewildered and inadequate, I made increasing demands on him, wanting more time and emotional support.

Five years after Ruth's birth, we have not resolved these problems, but I certainly feel that I am able to understand and accept my present needs, and the kind of life I now lead. Instead of now holding a senior post in a large department, I am at home with two children. My second daughter was born at home six months ago. I wanted her, and fully accept that I will probably be housebound for several years to come.

During the last five years my ideas and values have been turned upside down. No longer do I seek a career as a means of fulfilment. That competitive, aggressive world has become alien and with hindsight I wonder whether much of my early feminism was paradoxically devoted to the pursuit of masculine standards. I no longer decry as 'soppy', 'sentimental' or 'silly' the feelings of love, care, and tenderness. So often women themselves will tend to underplay the strength of their feelings for their own children. Only occasionally when women trust each other will they express the sheer ferocity of their maternal bond.

I am in a relatively privileged position. Because I had my children in my thirties I had already achieved some financial security. I now have a home-based part-time job and my husband is employed. I am able to relax into a relationship with my children which I now see as the central focus of my life, the climax of my emotional career. I have rejected the pursuit of an equality which is measured on male values. I have not opted out of society but I want to fight for a new set of priorities which acknowledge those who give life, who nurture, who want peace.

Sometimes I wish I had had my children when I was younger. I will be fifty when they are adolescent. But I know that I would not have been able to cope when I was in my twenties; even now I need every ounce of patience and maturity.

I have had a successful career. I do not need to prove myself to the outside world. But I am constantly aware that I could easily have remained childless; that I could easily have missed so much joy and fulfilment. Occasionally I catch the expression of an elderly woman looking shyly at a new baby – it is a glimpse into a hidden emotional dimension which I discovered late and which changed my way of life and my understanding of myself.

Afterword

Rereading this now, I am conscious that my generation was perhaps the first to be able to make a positive decision to have children. Pregnancy did not automatically follow marriage. I and, I suspect, many others were totally unprepared for this new role. The long and painful decision to have children in my late thirties involved a very conscious commitment to motherhood – perhaps I share the fanatical devotion of the late convert.

It would be wrong to give the impression that I have a placid and contented life. I am frustrated and constrained by the demands of two small children. 'My' life begins after their bedtime, by which time I am usually too exhausted to enjoy my freedom. Many women of my age have grown-up children and are re-embarking on their careers. I have little hope of ever re-entering the job market on a full-time basis.

And sometimes, in the early hours of the morning, soothing a whimpering child, I feel very, very old.

Pat Rolfe

'A bonus for me that came out of having a baby late in life was the fact that, having made a break in my secretarial career, I felt that I could pursue something I had always wanted to do . . . to take up full-time study.'

It would be difficult not to remember the day that I discovered I was supposed to be having two babies instead of one. It was the day the bomb went off at the Old Bailey. In the hospital for a check-up, I was being examined on the scanning machine at the time and the dull but reverberating thud I heard was dismissed by the machine's operator as being due to demolition work taking place close to the hospital. I soon discovered the error of this remark. The scanning machine room was on the other side of the hospital to the Out-patients Department and, in order to get back there again, it was necessary to walk along the road that runs around the outside of the hospital. Imagine my horror when, on nearing the main part of the hospital, I discovered pandemonium in the form of ambulances rushing about and pedestrians wandering around in various stages of distress with all sorts of wounds. It became clear to me that demolition work of a very different kind to that envisaged had been taking place.

The Out-patients Department became a casualty clearing centre and it was in this havoc that Dick (my husband) and I searched for one another, not knowing if either of us suffered any injury. He had been looking for me amongst all the pregnant ladies who had been shepherded downstairs from the Obstetrics Department, amidst broken glass from the blast-shattered windows. They insisted I sit down whilst they sent Dick off for a cup of tea for me. I assured them that I was okay and that they should look after the injured. However, I was firmly pushed into a seat between a woman with a head wound and someone with a cut arm. Thus, the knowledge that I was having twins was somewhat overshadowed by the more sombre news of the bombing and, in retrospect, it almost seems to have been an omen for, from that time onwards, things did not go so well in my pregnancy.

I may well have wondered what I was letting myself in for at the age of thirty-nine, and why I had waited so long to have a baby, and there is certainly no easy answer. Although brought up in a working-class home where the norm was to get married and have children (preferably in that order) at a fairly early age, I wanted neither. My childhood at home was extremely unhappy and it may well be that, subconsciously, I did not regard the family unit as a happy one. However, at twenty-seven I fell in love and married within the space of six months. That was not as hectic as it sounds for we had known one another for some years and it was just a question of a rather sudden coming together! I had already said that I did not want children and Dick had pointed out that he was not marrying me for any children I might have. Thus, we had twelve years of married life before we, or I should say I, initially, decided to have a baby. My husband's first reaction was that we might have left it too late, and to this day I cannot remember what prompted me to decide to have a child at thirty-nine. However, we decided to go ahead and it did not take too long to conceive, although when I had not done so after the first couple of months, Dick suggested temperature-taking etc. But I was obviously not too desperately concerned because I decided that if it did not happen quite spontaneously, then that would be that. All these decisions were basically mine because Dick felt that it was my body and my life that would alter drastically (just how much I did not realize at the time!), far more than his.

I had it all so beautifully planned; I would work right up until I had the baby and then find a suitable babyminder, so that I could go back to my secretarial job on a full-time basis. Since Dick worked shifts at that time, and was prepared to look after the baby too, it would not have been necessary to employ a babyminder for the whole of the time I would be at work. So much for my plans! Once the hospital discovered that I was going to have twins I was given all sorts of extra advice in order to avoid going into premature labour, part of which necessitated giving up swimming, which I had been doing every day in order to try and keep in shape and which was an activity that I enjoyed. I finished working at the end of six months, as the doctors said that it would be dangerous to go on any longer.

I was looking forward to a few weeks of peace and quiet but it was not to be, for a couple of days after I had left work I woke up one morning and, as I got out of bed, discovered water running down my legs. I immediately thought that I had gone into premature labour and, on ringing the hospital, was told to go straight to the antenatal ward, which I did. To everyone's relief I was merely slightly incontinent, which does sometimes happen in pregnancy, but once admitted to the hospital the decision was made to keep me in. Twin pregnancies require two weeks of bed rest in hospital prior to the birth, and so, since I was there, they decided I should stay for the fortnight. Had I known that those two weeks would stretch to the actual birth and afterwards, I might not have agreed so readily although, looking back, it is difficult to see what else could have been done. I was a mother 'at risk' and although I have some criticisms of parts of the treatment, which I shall discuss later, I have no doubt that the constant care and attention I received from the staff not only saved my life but that of one of the babies too.

Thus, part one of my plan did not materialize – there was no question of working until I gave birth. In fact, I very soon became 'institutionalized', with every decision taken for me, occasionally being let out at the weekend like a prisoner on parole. However, there were lighter moments in the hospital when I was used as a 'live' exhibit in lectures and during medical exams. I would hasten to add here that one is not forced to do this but I was always keen to help in any way I could and the staff were always most grateful and courteous. One day, after a rather large lecture at which I had even risen to such dizzy heights as to answer students' questions from 'the floor', I received an enormous bouquet from the doctors and medical students, which I thought was a delightful way of showing their appreciation. I also made friends, not only with some of the doctors, medical students and nurses but with patients too, who were having twins and were in for bed rest. One of these friends and I made a 'dummy patient' in her bed and, starting with the junior nurses, went right through sister to the house doctor and initially fooled them all. I felt more like nineteen than thirty-nine but it was great fun and everyone had a good laugh, in fact I thought my friend would give birth on the spot, she was laughing so much! However, this levity did not extend to the consultants and, whilst understandable up to a point, nevertheless the almost 'god-like' atmosphere they create around patients' beds during ward rounds makes an impersonal and cold impression.

I shall never forget the day when my particular consultant said quite matter-of-factly that one of the twins was failing and would probably be born dead. How much kinder it would have been had they drawn the curtains round the bed and allowed someone like the Sister to tell me, who could perhaps have held me whilst the sobs that I tried to control forced themselves out. Instead, that care did not come until later when the initial shock had worn off. I learnt from the medical students that 'my' consultant was a brilliant surgeon and basically a kind man (having his medical students home for dinner, etc.). It is a pity that this caring aspect was not more manifest in his dealings with patients. I have noticed on previous visits to hospitals that once doctors become consultants, the personal touch is lost (at least with National Health patients) and one becomes a symptom or a cipher. I have not seen my husband cry very often in our considerable time together, but the other clear memory of that day is of his evening visit, and the tears streaming down his face once I had passed on the consultant's bad news.

We had been delighted at the thought of having twins for we thought it would be an instant family with no more pregnancies, as ideally we had not wanted an 'only' child. However, this was not to be and, with this news, a period of sadness set in for both of us. Constant checks on the scanning machine and the foetal heart machine in the labour room only confirmed the diagnosis and, at about thirty-eight weeks, the Registrar tested some of the fluid in the placentas and decided to perform a Caesarian Section the following day (a Sunday). I had known for some weeks that I could not give birth normally and was not unduly worried about it. I merely thought it a minor operation from which I would soon bounce back. Again in retrospect, it might have been helpful if someone had been able to explain just what was involved in having a Caesarian but then, conversely, I can see that such information could be seen as being alarmist and not everyone reacts the way I did, thank goodness. However, on Saturday evening, unaware of what was in store for me, my husband and I sat out in the square of the hospital by the fountain and talked over the knowledge that one of the twins was possibly already dead and that something might be wrong with the other one. We comforted one another as best we could and arranged to meet at 8.30 the following morning, the time set for the operation.

Before 8 a.m. I was wandering about the ward in my operation smock, making last-minute plans and packing my things for removal from the antenatal ward to the postnatal one. Everyone remarked on my calmness and Dick was allowed to be with me all the time. In fact, he sat outside the operating theatre and thus saw our daughter within minutes of birth. The first shock came when I discovered that I was not allowed a 'pre-med' jab, the sort that makes you feel you 'couldn't care less'. It would be bad for the unborn child and this, of course, I immediately accepted. So I was wheeled into the anaesthetic room stone cold sober! They asked me to take deep breaths of oxygen from a mask – good for the unborn child – and that was my last conscious action before my ordeal began; an ordeal that was to affect me both physically and mentally.

Before I go any further I must emphasize that what I am about to relate is a very personal experience, and my mental state no doubt affected my physical progress, and that there were patients in the ward who had Caesarian Sections who seemed to recover quickly and easily and made nothing of the operation.

I think the anaesthetic I was given must have been very light, again probably for the baby's sake, because I seemed to be semi-conscious at times. The particular medical student assigned to my case told me afterwards that he had been so intrigued at watching my wriggling toes that he did not concentrate on the operation. I assume the operation could not have lasted very long but I had the feeling of being flat on my back, unable to move or speak (which of course I was) with, on either side of me, what I can only describe as telephone lines. I was being propelled along these lines, very much against my will, and with an awful humming in my ears. I felt I could also hear voices in the background. I remember feeling terrified and thought that I must be dying. How I wish someone had discussed the question of an anaesthetic with me, for I feel I would have been better perhaps having a local one that numbed the lower part of me but left the rest of me, including my mind, conscious and thus able to take a more rational view of things.

When I became fully conscious after the operation, I found that I was not in the postnatal ward but in a room on my own for observation. Dick was by my side and told me that we had a little girl and I suppose I dimly realized that the other baby must have died. The awful thing is that at that time I did not care! I remember feeling terribly guilty but the only thing I could think of was the awful pain I was in. I did not want to see the baby and longed only for the injection that would knock me out again. However, oblivion did not last long and after a day they moved me into the postnatal ward, which I dreaded. I desperately wanted to stay on my own and could not bear to see anyone. Something seemed to have gone 'click' inside me and I just could not communicate.

Physically, at least, things began to get better; I gradually got back on my feet and the pain began to lessen. I remember my first shower, looking in the mirror afterwards at what seemed the whitest possible face with two dark-rimmed sunken eyes (which seems incredible after only a few days), surrounded by long, lank hair (I had not had the sense to have it cut). I could not believe that it was me. I had no interest in my appearance and slopped around in hospital nighties – for some reason I had got it into my head that I would not be going home. I felt utterly depressed, worn-out and exhausted. I just wanted to be left alone to get well but I had a baby to look after and I made myself go into the nursery. I nearly passed out a couple of times and would have given anything for help. Had I asked it probably would have been forthcoming, but the nurses always seemed so busy and everyone else seemed to cope beautifully.

In the meantime, the question of the dead baby arose and I was horrified to learn that the baby had to be buried officially! The hospital made the arrangements for the actual burial but my husband still had to go along to the Registrar, and to me it just seemed to be rubbing salt in the wound. I remember thinking, again quite irrationally, how cold it would be for him under the dark earth.

However, I also had to concern myself with the living baby; all was not going well in that quarter. Some women are able to breastfeed after a Caesarian but my milk just disappeared. I remember once trying desperately to feed the baby with a bottle, but she seemed to be taking ages and I felt so utterly inadequate that huge tears welled up and poured down my face on to the baby's head, at which point the Matron happened to discover me. She was a super person, very understanding, but also very busy. She took the baby from me and immediately Sarah began to feed. I was so screwed up that I could not even give her a bottle!

In addition to the problem of feeding her, Sarah was in and out of intensive care. She was badly jaundiced and they placed her in an incubator with her eyes heavily bandaged so that she could have the necessary treatment. It was not effective and, on the eighth day after birth, they decided to change all her blood, which I was assured was a routine procedure but, for something routine, there seemed to be a lot of interested people wanting to watch. After the change of blood they said that everything was okay, so I was not prepared for the shock that greeted me. Although jaundiced, she had looked quite healthy, but now she was so pale and she had a tube in her nose which made her look worse. She was back in intensive care but, thank goodness, she did begin to pick up and, just over two weeks after she was born (which seemed a life-time to me!), we finally made it home. However, she was having three lots of medicine nine times a day and I had to keep a chart to make sure I gave her the right amounts at the right time. There followed three months of 'demand feeding' and such tiredness I did not know existed! There was no one I could leave her with, even for a short break. How I would have loved the opportunity of a few hours uninterrupted sleep; I lost count of the number of times I fell asleep feeding her, but there was a light at the end of the tunnel. After three months she began to sleep through the night and although I was still terrified at the thought of unexplained cot deaths, we decided she could move into her own room.

Life began to take on some semblance of normality. I returned to part-time work; there was no longer any thought of employing a baby minder. I had a very caring boss who allowed me to work hours that suited me and allowed me to fit in with Dick's shift work, so she was looked after by either her Mummy or Daddy. I could not possibly have left her all day as, by this time, I had become besotted with her. I know it sounds ridiculous but I feel that the bad time we both had at the beginning of her life created a strong emotional bond between us. This has become even more apparent as she has grown older. She did not want to leave me and it took hours of coaxing and patience to get her used to Play School, which I felt was essential, particularly for an only child. I knew it would prepare her for school, too, and thus we got used to being apart for some of the time.

A bonus for me that came out of having a baby late in life was the fact that, having made a break in my secretarial career, I felt that I could pursue something I had always wanted to do, and once our daughter started school I was able to take up full-time study. I have just completed my fifth year of studying and have enjoyed every minute of it, except for the exams involved. Trying to fit everything in was difficult at times but my husband was very supportive and fortunately enjoys cooking. I did an initial year's course called 'Fresh Horizons' at the City Lit in London and from that was able to get into the North London Polytechnic without A levels. Both at the City Lit and North London Polytechnic, mature students received sympathetic consideration, and most of the lectures and seminars were timed to coincide with school hours. After three years as a full-time extremely mature student I managed to get my degree in English, despite some interruptions along the lines of 'It's cuddling time, Mummy.' And, since there's no answer to that, the books would be put away whilst we had a cuddle.

The past year has been spent studying again, this time for a teaching certificate in Further and Adult Education, which I have just obtained and hope to use in part-time teaching. I have also embarked on a two-year drama course which I hope to incorporate into my teaching. Certainly, my limited teaching experience helped me with Sarah's tenth birthday party recently. Instead of the haphazard free-for-all which usually develops, I had worked out a plan, as I had been taught to do for teaching practice, and it was much easier to cope with ten high-spirited youngsters! Sarah's ten years have not merely flown by, they have been engulfed, leaving behind some hundreds of photographs and memories. Two memories particularly stand out: a very early one of her first real smile at me, as a tiny baby, when I was in the middle of changing her; and a far more recent memory, only the other day in fact, of Sarah sitting out in the garden one evening drawing some roses. She seems to have inherited my love of the theatre and accompanies me to some of the plays and ballets that I go to see. Sarah also likes to act herself and has just finished playing an elf in an open-air production of *The Merry Wives of Windsor*.

I now feel that I have the best of both worlds: the ability to be with my daughter most of her free time and yet to pursue my own life too, which I think is vitally important for both mother and child. How we go from now only time will tell, but I know that despite all the pain and worry involved in having her, I would not be without her. When she puts her arms around me and says; 'Mummy, I love you so much I wish we had been born at the same time so that we could grow up together,' I cannot imagine anything that would move me as much as those few words.

Has Sarah lost out by having an 'elderly' mum? I don't think so, because I seem to do far more things with her than many younger mums. We share the same hobby of acting and I have taken her swimming since she was only a few weeks old. My latest venture is to start ballet classes (amidst much laughter from my contemporaries!) but at least I can learn the steps and, whilst it is good discipline for me, I can also help Sarah when she has to practise her steps. In fact, I hope that we will be able to practise together.

My only regret is for the son who should have been growing up with Sarah. However, Sarah herself has a realistic attitude to the situation. I waited until she was well into her ninth year before telling her briefly what had happened, as I felt she ought to know but that the time had to be right. Her immediate response was that, whilst she would have liked a brother or sister, by being an only child she did not have to share our love for her. Have I lost out by being an 'elderly' mum? From what I have said it is obvious that I do not feel that I have. The only drawback is one of physical exhaustion. I am sure I reach saturation point much earlier than younger mums! Age may well have contributed to my peculiar experiences during the Caesarian birth. However, although I thought I was on my own regarding this incident, I have since discovered other women who have had similar reactions and difficulties and I would like to be able to help, even if it is only just by listening to their problems, but by the time any such problems come to light, it is often unfortunately too late. If there is a lesson to be learnt out of all this, it is mainly for women who feel that they cannot cope after Caesarian births and that this is not a feeling of which to be ashamed.

There is no doubt that having Sarah changed my life, dramatically so at first, but now that the early traumas are fading into the background, what is left is a life enriched.

Ann-Marie Monteith

'The day my first story was broadcast on Listen with Mother
. . . we drank white wine to celebrate something that went
far beyond that cheerful little tale being piped across the
nation.'

I was thirty-three years old when I left the convent, twelve years
after entering. They had been good years, varied, vigorous and
purposeful, but eventual disillusionment with the way religious
life was going – or, more accurately, not going – combined with a
vague inner dissatisfaction led me to ask for a dispensation to
return to the world. At the time I had no intention of marrying.
Indeed, my main purpose in leaving had been to search out some
alternative, more relevant way of living a life devoted to God and
to people.

Ours was a close family. Father could best be described as a
benevolent despot. A solicitor and an ex-major in the army, he
had three things in life which he valued: his family, his religion
and education. As the eldest child I carried much of the burden of
his love and his hopes. He was of Scots-Irish descent and, despite
the fact that we were several generations removed from Ireland,
he still spoke with pride of our Irish ancestors who had come over
to work on the railroad and who, by perseverance, hard work and
natural ability, had pulled their families away from the potatoes

and into the professions. By the time I was five I knew that I was going to be a teacher. I clearly recall the scene in the baby class when we were sitting on little painted chairs, discoloured by generations of little wet pants and the teacher asked us what we were going to be when we grew up. 'A teacher,' I piped at once. Father believed in sowing the seed early. When I was about nine he told me that he would rather see me dead than married to a Protestant. No threats; simply a statement of fact. Not that he had anything against Protestants, amongst whom he had many friends. It was simply that long observation of life had showed that those who marry outside their religion often lose their faith. He obviously made an impression on his children since the three girls became teachers and his son followed him into insurance. In addition, we are all married to Catholics.

In all this he was supported by my mother, who is descended from old Highland Catholics. She was quieter, but in the end more tenacious about her ideals. She would let my father talk on for hours about his marvellous Irish Catholics and then, as she rose to go about yet another chore, she would quietly cap his story by remarking that the Scottish Catholics held on to their religion against much greater opposition and that they therefore were the superior lot.

It was these strong beliefs that led my parents, penniless though they were after the war, to find the modest fees necessary to send my sister and me to the Franciscan convent for our education. The convent was short on qualified teachers but rich in the love of God and children and those nuns gave us an incomparably rich start in life. No doubt we had an excess of religion and a deficit of biology and geography. We were, however, happy and though I have since moved far from traditional Catholicism, I regret the passing of that precious thing which religion gave, namely the experience of living out poetry in action. In my later years I was among the iconoclasts who cried for a return to reason: abolish the angels and statues! Away with candles and incense! Out with Latin and in with precisely balanced English! How foolish and ignorant we are to bypass the senses. Each Corpus Christi feastday there would be a procession around the convent grounds. Waxy rhododendron bushes held up purple torches to light our way. With great reverence the priest, together with imported altar boys, carried the Blessed Sacrament around the grounds. We girl children, in white dresses, went ahead. In our hands we carried silver baskets piled high with rose petals. Parents who lined the way sang the ancient hymns whilst we lifted the petals, kissed them and threw them onto the ground in the path of the oncoming Lord. The entire year was punctuated with events like this. Sticky sweets were saved during Lent, cardboard cribs appeared at Christmas time and flowers, flowers, flowers and rosaries were everywhere during the lovely month of May.

Having passed the Eleven-Plus exam, I found myself a pupil of the much larger and sterner grammar school of Notre Dame. Here the nuns were exceedingly highly qualified, some of them pioneers in child development and scientific research. The atmosphere was stricter, the work harder; success was the goal, religion was taken for granted. Each day began and ended with prayers; indeed each *lesson* began and ended with prayers. But these were as remarkable to us as were the chairs or the walls. Only before exams did we squeeze our eyes tightly and beg God to do his stuff.

We were never pressurized into becoming nuns. Indeed, one could say that the sisters erred on the side of over-respect for the private conscience. On the other hand, they had good reason to believe that daily religious lessons, annual retreats, the weekly confessions and the monthly masses would probably reap some kind of harvest and that they could safely leave any further individual approaches to the Good Lord.

Personally, I had, then, no desire or interest in becoming a nun. If truth be told, whilst I admired the sisters' integrity, I was repelled by their men's handkerchiefs, men's shoes and by the smell of the not-too-frequently washed habits. The boys of the nearby Jesuit college, and sixth form gossip about hopes and conquests, were much more my line.

Eventually, I reached university. I felt deeply honoured to be there, following in the footsteps of my father and uncles before me. I could have kissed the very bricks of the dear building, representing as it did to me all that was most noble, most honorable, most worthwhile in life. This, however, did not make me work any harder. I was an average student and knew it.

The one subject in which I did most effortlessly excel, however, was moral philosophy. Whilst others floundered amongst the thoughts of Socrates and Plato, I sailed easily along. After all, since primary school we had been quite clear about the no-goodness of doing the right act for the wrong reason. Good and bad, right and wrong were familiar terms and any six-year-old Catholic was well aware that it profited a man nothing to gain the whole world whilst suffering the loss of his own soul. I have to admit that it was an enormous relief to me to discover that people other than Catholics were concerned about these matters. Perhaps this realization was my first step towards a wider world outlook.

Life at university was concerned mainly with the exciting social life. The thirst for knowledge came a long second to the hunt for boys. In a novel of those times, *How Far Can You Go?* by David Lodge, the answer to that question posed was 'not very far!' Never mind impure *actions*; I and my Catholic boyfriends were concerned about impure *thoughts*. Not that life was any less exciting for that. In my second year I met the boy whom I thought I would eventually marry and days passed in dreams of him and occasional anxieties about work.

I left university having obtained a geography degree, having loved and been loved, a little older and a little wiser. I was at that time restless and disturbed, hungry for something. I did not go on for my teacher's diploma. I broke off my relationship with my boyfriend and I went to find a job in Cambridge, in a convent grammar school. It was here that I discovered the thing that I was looking for: inwardness. It was in the eyes of the nuns with whom I worked. Each sister was at one with herself, was at peace, was *self*-possessed. In an instant I knew I wanted to join them. As well for me that this was a feminine order. Everything was colourful, clean, tasteful. Within the year I was a postulant in their mother-house in London.

The reaction of my family and friends to this unexpected move was varied. My father was immensely proud and saw it as a blessing on their marriage. (He was equally proud and loving when I came out twelve years later.) My mother was pleased but sad. The sister to whom I am closest was, and remains, immensely loving. To the majority of my friends, indeed to all of them, with the exception of one who is a scientist and an atheist, I was simply boring. In short, they dropped me. Never wrote and, with few exceptions, never called. Nuns are a weird lot, even to Catholics.

The biggest sacrifice for me on entering the convent was in giving up any hope of ever having a family of my own: no suppers by the fire, no babies or dogs, no hot soup or late night chats and, most significantly of all, no person with whom I would be able to share an intimate life-long companionship. It was necessary to surrender all thoughts, hopes and dreams in this direction. Besides being the right thing to do under the circumstances it was also the most practical, since to allow one's thoughts to wander was to be condemned forever to a lifetime of torment. Nevertheless, mentally to surrender family life was a kind of inner mutilation. Thereafter, in the years that followed, I never referred to the subject again and, on a day to day basis, it did not trouble me. I was, nevertheless, relieved that the convent did not allow us to attend social functions like weddings. I was happy to let sleeping thoughts lie!

I began my novitiate with about twenty other sisters aged between sixteen and twenty-five. We were given new names, new habits. In the early days we were not allowed to read the newspaper, listen to the radio or make social visits. Even family visits were restricted. It was a form of brainwashing, but one which we gladly embraced because we sincerely wanted to love God and to serve his people in the form of teaching, nursing, caring for the incurably ill and working on the missions. The disciplines which we underwent separated us from our own desires and from the tug of the material world and set us free to work wholeheartedly for others. Strong and lasting bonds were formed among us: we truly became sisters.

As a nun one has ample opportunity to pursue one's career; in my case, teaching. Time is available before and after school, at weekends and in the holidays. Superiors encouraged us to attend courses and conferences so that we might be better able to help the children in our care. We never saw money but, under those circumstances, we never felt the need of it.

For six years I taught in our schools and then for the following six in state comprehensives. I feel it is relevant here to explain the kind of work I was doing since it will go some way to explaining the kind of difficulties I experienced when I was confined between four walls with a crying baby. Under both systems I held Head of Department posts. I would not say that I was fanatical about work, simply that I got on with the job and on the whole enjoyed it. Outside the classroom there were geography excursions to be organized and religious conferences to be undertaken. One of the most exciting of these was the Search for Christian Maturity movement which I had met in Jamaica. The American Jesuits are very active out there and they had introduced 'Search' to the island. I had been thrilled by the power, the beauty, the dynamism of the movement and, on my return, began the same in England. Although I am no longer involved in 'Search', it is still going strong today.

In short, I enjoyed the life. I liked the challenge it set and I thrived on the company and conversation of those highly motivated and intelligent women.

It was probably whilst in Jamaica, however, that the first seeds of discontent and doubts about religious life began to grow. For the first time I saw people with several cars, swimming pools, beautiful houses, living right next door to people who lived in wooden shacks, who had no running water, no electricity, no shoes on their feet. Those with the swimming pools kept guns as a matter of course to protect their belongings from the poor. And our Order was identified with those who owned the swimming pools. They were our friends, our customers, our protectors. My closest contact with the ordinary Jamaican was through our school maid, Violet, a beautiful woman of about forty. Through her work at the school she supported her grandmother, her mother, her own children and her daughter's child. There were, of course, no men to be seen. On several occasions I went to visit her. The hard mud yard outside her house – a two-roomed wooden shack – was swept clean; the inside was as clean as her goodwill and conditions would allow. But nothing could eradicate the smell – that hot, sharp sour smell that hit you at the door. In my honour Violet would produce a bottle of coke from the fridge (which, of course, was not connected to any electricity) and, as she handed it to me, she would laugh a warm gurgling laugh at her own foolish vanity. At that time we paid Violet five pounds per week, and when I suggested raising the sum I was told that this could start some undesirable revolution amongst the working classes. I am pleased to report, however, that the sum was eventually raised to seven pounds. Again, whilst I taught twenty children in a spacious classroom, through the window of that very classroom I could see seventy children packed into *each* room of the state school across the way. I honestly could not understand why, with all our principles and ideals, we were not over there with them.

After two years in Jamaica I returned to England to find the Church struggling to come to terms with the ideals of Vatican II as outlined by Pope John XXIII. In some ways it was like watching a dinosaur trying to become a ballerina. In our Order, the old long black habit was abandoned and the sisters, unused to modern fashions and lacking hairdressers, wore embarrassing, botched-up modern dress. More importantly, the silence of our days was eroded. Everyone could talk pretty well everywhere. We now had recreation at most meals. Instead of a particular community working on one particular project, many sisters, including myself, began to work outside the convent in state schools and hospitals. In the evenings, instead of all being present at the final prayer and then retiring to bed, many of us were out at meetings and conferences. As time went on some were also out at films, restaurants and on social visits. It was claimed that all these changes were 'good things' in that they contributed to a growth in personal maturity but, for my part, I could not see the value of making the tremendous personal sacrifices of poverty, chastity and obedience for the sake of the half-cocked life we were living by 1970. I had been one of those in favour of change but I had envisaged such a change to take the form of a united onslaught on the problems of contemporary society. Perhaps I was simply naïve.

Whilst the experiences in Jamaica and the reawakening Church formed the background to my thoughts of leaving, in my mind and heart changes were also occurring. When I first entered the convent I had had no doubts about the 'worthwhileness' of religious life. But even in those first years I used to waken in the night and think 'soon I shall be dead' and the thought brought comfort – not a reason for leaving – but certainly comfort. Living was hard, death would be a release and I would have done what God wanted me to do. And that was sufficient. As time went on, however, I felt more and more that my inner self was dying; that if I did not move in the direction in which my life force was pushing me, my spirit would indeed die. At that point it became necessary to approach superiors in order to set in motion the painful task of extricating myself from the religious order. During the period that followed there were many tearful talks with friends, many long letters exchanged with home, many admonitions from superiors, a few 'you are making a big mistake' warnings from priests. The emotional climate lasted for a good six months but did not really disturb me. Having made my decision, I knew at once that it was the right one for me and my inner self began to breathe again.

Fortunately, there was a job waiting. The headmaster of a comprehensive school in Birmingham phoned the convent and offered me a post teaching religion in his school. After a year or so in the school I found myself head of the department and enjoying the work and the staff. Not to mention the blessed anonymity of being able to walk around in mufti! It was during this time that I met my husband-to-be and a whole new, unexpected world opened up.

Peter is general manager of a Housing Association. He is the same age as me and in the past had been a priest. He is six-foot-three and very English; a product of prep and boarding school, a graduate of Oxford University. I think it was his gorgeous English voice and his laugh that won my heart. The magic of being able to laugh! I had lost the talent. At the time of our marriage Peter's job necessitated our moving around the country. Along the way, I took temporary teaching posts in Glasgow, London, Birmingham and Cardiff. Looking back I do not see what else we could have done, but the fact remains that within a month of being married my work, which constituted an important part of my identity, had been trivialized. We were so involved with one another at the time that we hardly noticed the fact. We were to feel the backlash later.

Even after marriage I still had no thoughts of having children. My husband, my work, our social activities were enough for me. At the time I was using the Pill – something which would surprise only those outside the Catholic Church. Almost every Catholic I know uses some form of contraception (and I am not here referring to the so-called 'safe' period!). Certainly Rome and the media make a great deal of noise but in Britain most couples simply use their own judgement. It was Peter who first suggested having children. He would have liked ten! I had difficulty enough getting my mind round the possibility of having *one*. To create a totally new human being; to have a little companion and friend; to help shape someone's life and future – the idea seemed too astounding to contemplate.

But what about the risks? I was then thirty-six and would, on our timetable, be thirty-eight when the baby was born. We approached the business of having a baby with a great deal of care, with a great deal of planning. First there were the three months off the Pill, then the rubella tests, then the temperature charts – there was little time to lose. Then, finally, the pregnancy tests. I was in school when the results came through. Peter phoned at break. 'Congratulations!' he sang down the line. 'You're pregnant!'

In that instant our perception of the world and of ourselves altered. No longer were we free-wheeling achievers, we were parents-to-be. The wonder of it all has not yet left us, almost five years on. I did all the things necessary to give our baby a good start: ate well, drank gallons of water, rested daily. I attended all classes and clinics.

In the fifth month, the hospital doctor put a microphone to my abdomen. 'We shall just listen to see if the baby is okay,' she said. As she turned up the volume, the cubicle was filled with the sound of a valiant little heart beating away. Independent of me. *De-boom, de-boom, de-boom.* The sturdy little life filled the room and I wept, tears trickling from my eyes to my neck. 'This is a precious baby,' the doctor said gently. I nodded. It was not necessary to speak. (Precious baby is the term used by doctors for the child of an older mother.)

I have always doubted the truth of the maxim that 'all the world loves a lover', and am inclined to believe that it is the arrogance and self-absorption of the lovers themselves that deludes them into thinking that they are so highly rated. There is no doubt, however, that all the world treats a pregnant woman with protective tenderness. Once, when I was crossing a road, a juggernaut lorry shuddered to a halt and, with all the courtesy of an old-world knight, the driver waved me across. Bus drivers waited for me to get on the platform; elderly men and ladies rose to give me seats, school children inundated me with toys. All seemed to be touched by the miracle that was happening.

I had been prepared for the bump in the front – everyone knows about that. What I had not been prepared for was to discover that my body, that faithful and reliable servant, disciplined with diets, supple with yoga, cosseted with eight hours' sleep and Revlon creams would suddenly take a mind of its own. Overnight, I became heavy and slow, varicose veins threatened, breasts grew, back ached. I was being taken over: where was the 'Me' that I knew? Most deadly of all, and most extensively experienced with my second child, was the terrible exhaustion. No one who has not been pregnant and had a house and a lively toddler to look after at the same time can know the devastating effects of total exhaustion. It was as though lead had been poured into my limbs. I would look at the stairs in our home and wonder if I could make it to the top; vacuuming had to be planned so as not to use up minimal energy supplies too early in the day; every street came equipped with hills to rival the Pennine Way. Iron tablets helped but I would never, never wish to experience those times again.

Gradually, the nine months passed. Because of disproportion (i.e. the baby's head being too large for the pelvic gap), I was down for a Caesarian Section. I know that many women feel a loss at not being able to go into labour and give birth naturally. Not me! By the time that the nine months were up I had had enough of pregnancy to last me a lifetime. Without feeling a single labour pain I was told to come to the hospital on a particular day.

On the morning of the Caesarian, I was labelled, gowned and cathetered and then, holding my husband's hand, was wheeled to the operating theatre. We kissed goodbye at the door. I felt no fear. Curiosity would more accurately describe my feelings. The theatre was small and white-tiled. The doctors and nurses appeared to be wearing white aertex vests. A curly-haired woman came up to me. 'I am your surgeon,' she said. I was amazed that she was so young. Two seconds later the anaesthetist approached. 'I am going to give you an injection,' he said, holding my hand. I was about to ask him not to do anything till I was properly unconscious when I must have passed out.

Meantime, my husband, Peter, was waiting outside. He saw the nurses hurrying to fetch something. 'What is that?' 'Blood,' replied the nurse, 'just in case we need it.' It was at that moment that Peter realized that this was a serious and possibly dangerous operation and was afraid. Twenty minutes after I had gone in, he heard a baby's cry, loud and strong. They brought out our son, David, weighing 7 lb 4 oz, for him to hold.

It was some time later that I came to, to hear Peter say in my ear, 'We have a son!' Through pain and drowsiness, I was amazed. The whole thing was difficult to assimilate, no doubt because I had missed out on the actual birth. A son? Ours? Astounding! The pain at that time was colossal. I felt as though my abdomen had been replaced by a black hole fringed with golden edges – the thing was very visual. I would have been surprised to have looked down and found my body intact. As it was I could not move an inch. A doctor friend thought later that I had not been fully sedated. Certainly the second time around I asked for every pill and injection going and did not feel anything like that first discomfort.

During my twelve-day stay in hospital there were moments of incomparable beauty. David had been born at Christmas time. My husband visited each evening and, whilst he held David, we would chat over the day's events. The window was on the fourth floor and we were able to watch as huge, silent snowflakes floated by. In the distance the dock lights twinkled. One evening, as we were talking, we suddenly heard the sound of a male voice choir drifting down the corridor. 'Silent night, holy night,' their voices came full and warm and faceless. 'Sleep, O baby king,' they sang, 'Sleep in heavenly peace.' It was a moment of profound bliss. The present, the past, the future made one. Our child, the Christ child, every child – precious beyond belief.

If being a pregnant mother in Britain is to be one of the most cossetted and cared for members of society, being a mother at home is to be one of the most neglected. Both our children were born by Caesarian Section but only David was put in the intensive care unit. It was to this fact that we attributed his ceaseless, heart-rending crying. All day and most of the night he cried. Nor would he stop even when lifted. He even cried between spoonsful of food, for this went on for ten months. He was thirteen months before I felt his love coming back to me, whereas with Clare that loving response had been there from the first week. The only way of calming David was to walk. Frequently Peter was to be seen striding along by the canal at 4 a.m. or at 11 p.m. at night, and rain, hail, snow or gale I walked the pram each morning and each afternoon.

The following years were the hardest I have ever experienced. Up till then I had always had control over my life. Now all was chaos. At two, four, six in the morning we were awakened by the sound of crying. Instantly the adrenalin started pumping. We took it in turns to rise; sometimes we slept in shifts or, if one were too absolutely exhausted, the other did the whole night. The official morning rise would be between 4.30 and 6.30 a.m. It was imperative for me to be showered, dressed and mascara-ed before Peter left. I felt that all would be truly lost should these last remnants of civilization be neglected. At 7.30 a.m. Peter left for work. The housework was already done. Still David cried. Always it seemed to be dark. Always it rained. I had few friends and no relations in the area. I was quite simply desperate.

How urgently I needed contact with others in those days. Being an older parent means that family ties have become tenuous and, anyway, one's own parents are often beyond the age when they could or should be asked to look after a lively infant. I shall never cease to be grateful to one neighbour who stepped out of the mist one day and said, 'Would you care to join our coffee morning?' Apparently, the nurse at the clinic had given her my name. God knows what the nurse said – 'Do include Mrs Monteith, she's going round the bend!' However, I was beyond pride by that time and my independence no longer seemed so important. I attended those coffee mornings regularly for a year and if those dear ladies felt anything about having to guard their coffee cups and sugar bowls from David's charges, they never said anything to me.

It was not possible to work against the screaming. Housework and meals were done at 90 m.p.h., whilst the baby slept. At times I would attempt to do something interesting like baking a cake or making bread. I would be halfway through, at the point of no return, when the screaming would start again. The frustration was such that I felt physically sick. It has taken me a long time to adjust to the exacting discipline of the housewife, namely, to do *what* you can *when* you can. I had been accustomed to spending hours at a time on projects and to carrying on conversations without being sicked on, wee-ed on or mauled about. I am still slowly mastering that other talent of the housewife whereby she attends, at any given moment, to a *minimum* of four unrelated demands. There were days when I was stunned into depression and withdrawal. I could not blame the children; my husband had to work; I would not leave the children with anyone else. There seemed to be no way out.

All this put a strain between Peter and myself. Ours had been very much a joint decision to have children. How was it then that I had finished up isolated in the house whilst he went off merrily to build empires and meet fascinating people? The injustice of it all made me very bitter at times. I grievously missed not only mental stimulation but also mental space – and I am convinced that one can actually suffer from adrenalin withdrawal symptoms. I am afraid that I see no preordained reason why one person in a partnership should be allocated all the menial work whilst the other corners all the interesting side. When I mention this in public, I am chided, frequently by *women*, 'Oh but this is different – a wife does all this for love.' It would appear to me that a love that demands such a contraction of another person's life is not worthy of the name, and that those who undertake such sacrifices are simply storing up sorrow for themselves. To be fair to Peter, it had not been his intention either that things should have worked out this way, but once having had children it is not easy to change course.

The solution that most people in my position take is to employ a child-minder, but I could never do this. Living with the children has taught me that they have three absolute needs of their mother: the womb need, the breast need and the emotional need, and that the emotional need is just as real as the other two and that only the father or the mother can truly respond to it. David has reached the stage when he has gone beyond those three needs. Clare has not. For me and her father to be absent from her just now would cause her intense pain and loss. The time will come when she is ready to go from *us* and it is then that I shall think of working outside the home again.

In the meantime, at Peter's insistence, I began to try my hand at writing. At weekends, apart from breast-feeding duties, he took over the children, the house and the meals. I spent Saturdays writing in the library and Sundays typing up. I have no doubts that this kept me sane because it gave my starved and ravenous mind something to feed on. Output was necessarily small but there was enough success in newspapers, magazines and radio to keep me going. The day my first story was broadcast on Listen With Mother, Peter came home early from work. We fed David strawberries one by one to keep him quiet and drank white wine to celebrate something that went far beyond that cheerful little tale being piped across the nation.

David is now four-and-a-half and Clare is two-and-a-half and things are so much easier that I can hardly believe it. The physical pressure is more or less off. It is conversations now that never stop, usually conducted simultaneously. Fairly typical was the one we had yesterday on the way down to the nursery. Because of the tankers and double-deckers rumbling by we all have to shout, of course.

David:	Are you going to die soon?
Me:	I hope not.
Clare:	Have I got a bagina?
Me:	Yes. *Vagina.*
David:	*When* are you going to die?
Me:	Not till you're a big man.
Clare:	Has David got a bagina?
Me (*bellowing*):	VAGINA! (*passing man's head jerks up*)
David:	I'm not going to grow up, then. I'll be like Peter Pan.
Clare:	Has Peter Pan got a bagina?

They can sustain these conversations from 6 a.m. till 6 p.m. – given the chance. This is where parks come in handy!

So there it is. Coming late to motherhood, for me, has been the entry into a new and hitherto unknown world. It has been a gatecrashing of ideas, habits, outlooks, even of beliefs built up over 35 years of living; it has been the unleashing of emotions of love and tenderness, of fury and despair; it has been the extension of a vision of the future far beyond my own personal lifetime. I

now view the Earth as a place to be cherished for our children –
and for our children's children. There have been hard times but,
like my parents before me, Peter and I see our children as the
crown, the blessing, the incredible gift of married love.

PART TWO

Maintaining Careers

Phoebe Delafield

'I had established an identity based on an awareness of my own capabilities. I was not prepared to give all this up in the name of motherhood.'

I was no more than four or five when I first talked about having children. I played at breastfeeding my dolls and took them for walks in a wheelbarrow. But it was not until my mid-thirties that I was able even to consider the reality of having children. I was just thirty-seven when I had my first child and nearly thirty-nine when my second was born. It was not that I made a conscious decision to wait to have children. It was rather that my life unravelled itself somewhat differently from the way I had envisaged when I was a small child. Then, I had taken my mother as my model. I would marry late and, if I could bear the pain, have several children. 'Labour hurts as much as a third degree burn,' I had been told by a school friend, and I had lost a lot of nights' sleep thinking about what such a frightening statement might really mean.

On reflection, I think I must have been a very uncertain person in my teens and twenties. I didn't have a clearly worked out life programme or a career. I knew I wanted to work – my mother had done so for many years before her marriage and then again after I and my two brothers started school. After my A Levels I worked abroad for a year, then spent three years at University before taking a job as a secretary, first in London and then in the United States. It was not until my late twenties that I started to build a career for myself, first in industrial training and then in adult education.

I still had not met anyone I wanted to live with, or whose children I wanted to bear. Somewhere in the back of my mind I imagined I would, sooner or later. It was later, in that I was thirty-two when I met a man whom I liked a lot and felt I could live with. I knew by now that I was tired of short-term relationships and that I wanted children, but I had persuaded myself that if, after fifteen years as a sexually active adult, I had still not conceived – even if by mistake – then I must be barren.

I had come to the conclusion, consciously at least, that motherhood was not for me. I was enjoying, for the first time in my life, living with a man. We spent our holidays travelling, our evenings out. We lived as free a life as our jobs would permit and experienced a sense of well-being from sharing each other's company. But this man, who is now my husband, did not want more children. He had two, already in their teens, from his first marriage and he knew what having a family involved. I, on the other hand, did *not* know what having children involved and, now that I was into the last quarter of my child-bearing years, began to want to know very much indeed. It would be hard to give the true reasons why, for the conditioning to become a mother starts very young indeed and persists in subtle ways throughout one's formative years, but I think that uppermost in my mind was the simple desire to be pregnant and to give birth. In short, to fulfil my biological function. I did not think much, then, about what it would be like to bring up children, what I would have to give up, or what a strain having children places on a relationship. I wanted babies.

My man was honest with me about his own feelings from the start. He said that, since I wanted them so much, we should stop seeing each other so that I could meet someone else who felt differently about having them. This was the hardest time of those early years of our relationship. I realized that I would rather stay with him than have children. I persuaded myself that I had outgrown my desire to have them. But I was less honest with myself than he was with me. As we became more involved with each other the thought of leaving him became more unbearable. But I wanted both what we had and what we might have. I thought perhaps he would come round to the idea of our having children. But I was wrong and I was unfair to him, and having children almost put an end to our relationship.

It was not that I consciously decided to have children against his wishes. A large part of me was convinced of my incapacity to conceive, and then there was the scare about the dangers of women over thirty-five taking the pill. In fear of a thrombosis I gave up the pill. We avoided sexual intercourse during the middle of each month, but this is a very unreliable method of contraception and I soon became pregnant.

My excitement at being pregnant was unlike anything I had ever experienced. I started to feel the changes within my body before not more than a week could have elapsed after conception. I bought books on pregnancy and visited the clinic for a test well before the appropriate testing time. I mentioned some of these new sensations to my husband – we were decorating the top floor of the house we had just bought, and I had several dizzy spells at the top of a ladder. He agreed that it was possible I was pregnant.

The day I got the results of the test was unforgettable. It was August and very hot. My husband's teenage daughter had just been to stay with us for the weekend, which had not gone well for any of us. It seemed to me that my husband was still feeling the effects of separation from his children. More than seventeen years had elapsed since they had been born. They were still a worry to him and probably always would be. To start a new round of child-rearing, just when he was beginning to experience the first period of freedom and self-fulfilment of his life, must have been very hard indeed. His anger and despair on learning of my pregnancy now seems to be wholly understandable. He felt that this had not been a joint decision, and I had taken our future into my own hands. A great deal of thinking now had to be done. There was my job to consider, the house too, and our marriage. I so much wanted this child that I was prepared to do almost anything to make things work. I didn't see why we shouldn't still spend time going out, time abroad, or why our lifestyle should drastically change.

Other people thought differently. 'Will you give up your job?' This was the kind of subtle persuasion that started to test my sense of identity and my nerve. I made it clear to everyone that I intended to carry on working full-time. It was particularly important to both my husband and me that I should do so, for much of our good feeling for each other was based on our mutual independence and our interest in each other's work. We had bought a house together and we needed to continue to pay for it and maintain it on an equal footing. 'Ah,' people said, 'you don't know how you will feel once the baby is born.' I didn't know how I would feel, but I did know that there was an insidious pressure to consider giving up work, particularly from those who had done so themselves. Even my doctor, a woman, had said, 'But won't you need time at home to enjoy your baby?'

What they didn't seem to understand was that at thirty-six I had worked for fourteen years, I had slowly and painfully established a career for myself. In the first three or four years of my teaching job I had worked seven days a week, and almost as many evenings, getting the job into shape. I had established an identity based on an awareness of my own capabilities. I was not prepared to give all this up in the name of motherhood. And I did not. I worked a full timetable until I was eight months' pregnant and then took my maternity leave. But it is telling that, in that month, I suffered the worst depression of my life. For the first time since I had become pregnant I began to consider the implications of my new condition.

What had I done? Had I ruined our marriage, had I embarked on motherhood too late for myself, and my child? I had never felt more tired in my life. I had never felt more directionless, nor so old. It embarrassed me that I should be pregnant for the first time when some women of my age or a little older were grandmothers.

If people asked me if this was my first child I'd sometimes say, 'Yes, but I have two stepchildren,' as though this would explain away the peculiarity of my situation! But probably the most difficult aspect of this change in my life was, temporarily at least, being without a job and not knowing whether I would ever be able to take it up again. I had arranged to return to work eight weeks after the baby was born, but would I be able to do it?

Certainly there is nothing like the exhaustion one experiences after the birth of one's first child. Labour itself is a strenuous activity and mine went on for a very long time. Night feeding also seemed to go on and on. And then there was the enormous emotional adjustment to make to being a mother. My husband helped, but only I could feed it.

When the baby was a month old we went out for the first time since his birth. I remember the elation and amazement I felt as we mixed with the crowd at the cinema. 'I am a mother! I am a mother!' I kept repeating to myself. There was nothing, so far in my life, which had given me this kind of satisfaction. Leaving the house on that first evening out had been hard. I felt that I had cut through a bond connecting me to my baby. And I still feel this to some extent when we go out in the evening. But the pain of severance never lasts long and I have to admit that when I started work again and left my child with a minder I felt a great sense of relief. I did not experience, as many people said I would, anxiety about the child or jealousy of the minder. Instead, I felt enormous gratitude to her, and not a little guilt. Why should she do my job for me? Why should I be allowed to enjoy my life instead of paying the price people all around me had paid and were assuming I should pay? Of course, there were times of great worry. My child was not getting enough sleep in the day. After six weeks I changed the minder and began to worry less about his sleep. I began to experience great elation and a sense of achievement. It was possible to have a child and to work full time. It was hard – often very hard indeed. There was a lot of work like writing, marking essays, and class preparation that had to be done at home. I would count on the child sleeping and feel such frustration and anger when he woke half way through a piece of writing.

And there wasn't time to go out, or we hadn't as yet found a sitter to give us the freedom to go out together. But one has only so much energy and, by the end of my child's first year, I found that I was very, very tired. The hardest thing was going in to college and doing a day's teaching and seeing numerous students and fitting in administration, all after weeks and weeks of broken nights and early rising. Yet somehow the energy to do so was there.

Friends of mine have said that one must inevitably have less energy in one's thirties than one's twenties, but I think that the more fulfilled you are the more energy you have and, in my own case, I feel that I can cope with far more than I could have managed ten or fifteen years ago. I have been able to do the job as efficiently or as inefficiently as in my childless state. Of course there is no chance to have a drink with a colleague after work or to drop in on a friend on the way home. Nor is everything rosy when I do get home. The baby might be unwell, or overtired, or difficult. My main aim has often been to get him to bed as quickly as possible so that I could eat something and then do some work. But then there are the other times when I and my husband and child feel so close to each other, and enjoy each other to the full.

Because I was an elderly mother by anyone's standards, there was pressure on me to have a second child very soon. My husband, an only child himself, had always said that if we were going to have a child, then we would have to have a second. I had argued with this, but once my child was born I began to feel differently. Didn't he need a sibling? Why should he grow up with two elderly parents and no live-in playmate? This question worried me for a long time. It was something that my husband and I needed to discuss. But before we had got round to discussing it, and before my son was one year old, I was pregnant again.

And now life began to be very difficult indeed. I was thirty-eight, and I was extremely tired. My second pregnancy was much less enjoyable than my first. I was constantly depressed. I was unsure about the validity of having another child. I could just about manage one child and a demanding job, but how would I manage with two? I saw less of my husband, we talked less and I became more and more unsure about the desirability of two children. I also feared for its well-being. The hospital had advised against an amniocentesis test in both cases, as I was under forty, but I knew of other hospitals which gave it automatically to anyone over thirty-six. I'd been lucky enough to have one normal child. Would my luck extend to two? And I had taken less care of myself second time round. I had eaten less, slept less and worried more. All this changed when the second baby was born. The labour was much shorter, the birth much easier and she was a normal, healthy child. I could not believe my good fortune.

And now I am thirty-nine years old. My baby is three months old and I have been back at work for a month. There have been many difficulties and there will be many more in the future. What I am discovering, though, is that they are surmountable. The hardest thing to cope with is, perhaps, fatigue. Two babies waking at night instead of one does take its toll, physically and mentally. And, when one is tired, relationships suffer and so does work. And yet the sense of satisfaction and achievement is something I had not suspected possible. I do wish I had had my children a little bit earlier, so that I'd be that little bit younger while they are growing up, and perhaps more energetic. But I wasn't ready to have children sooner, either personally or professionally. I wish, too, that I knew more mothers with young children. Most of my friends had their children many years ago. But, since I work, it is inevitable that I have little contact with other mothers, and before long my children will be going to nursery school and mixing freely with other children.

What does amaze me is how defined the children's personalities are, and how defined they were at birth. It seems to me that the mother's age – whether it is seventeen or thirty-seven – isn't going to make much difference to the child's character. Her maturity, or lack of it, might well affect the child's emotional development – and in this sense I am glad that I am as old as I am. I know myself better than I used to, and have a much stronger sense of identity.

I am also surprised at how readily small children adapt to other people. I took my son out to a minder for over eighteen months and he was always happy to go to her. I now have found someone who comes into the house each day and both children are thriving. Perhaps because the children are cared for by several people I have the sense that I am not the children's mother, rather their guardian for a few years. On the other hand, I have had this feeling since the moment the eldest was born. They need me very much at the moment and I enjoy their dependency, but I am also very aware of their individuality and their capacity for independence.

I would not have missed having my children for the world, not because I hope they will look after me in my old age – who knows how long any of us will survive? – but because they are the result of an emotionally satisfying relationship and a deeply fulfilling biological process. They are also two beings who, although their lives started so recently, already know what it is to enjoy themselves and to respond joyfully to all those around them.

Afterword

Six months later, as if in answer to something I had wanted before the children were born, a job was advertised which appeared made for me. Completing the application was an effort. While the competitive part of me wanted to succeed, emotionally I didn't feel ready to take on the additional responsibilities. On top of moving house, because I would have to live in or near the college, I'd be away from the children yet more as this was a full-time, five days a week post with evening work besides.

The interview took place before a governing body of fourteen and continued into a second day. It was searingly painful. Much of one's professional confidence is lost, I am convinced, as a consequence of repeated broken nights and a complete absence of time to reflect or draw breath. Although I had a good job, I was intellectually 'getting by' because it was so familiar. Faced with the prospect of a new one I felt out of practice, as if I'd been away for a long time. The issue of having children didn't enter into the interview, not, I suspect, because the governing body had a progressive attitude so much as that it didn't occur to them that someone of my age would have small children. I was changing Anna's nappy and Thomas was crying when the phone rang. First I had to say, 'Hold on a minute. I need to calm the children.' Then, when I heard that they were offering me the job, I was stunned and horrified. After I said yes, I would accept it, I felt worse. I experienced depression and was unwilling to consider the consequences of my actions. First Thomas, then Anna, then this, in hardly three years.

Fortunately I needed to work a six-month notice before taking up the post which gave me time to accustom myself to the prospect of change. Now that I've completed my first academic year, I can look back at what is probably the most difficult year I've had to face and say that somehow we have all survived.

Moving meant selling the Victorian house we had spent over five years renovating and had just made comfortable. My husband was willing and able to commute from either place but finding a suitable house took over a year. That meant, for the first eleven months, I commuted and so spent even less time with the children. Some of that little time was spent in rushed car journeys across London house-hunting. And much of it I was tense, preoccupied with my job. At the same time I felt guilty about not involving myself enough with the children. At work I faced staffing difficulties and tended to personalize hostile reactions. Tied to the issue of moving and selling the house in which we had invested so much of ourselves was the question of continuing to live with so much strain. Perhaps this was the time to split up, to live away from each other in an attempt to simplify life. I thought of taking the children with me.

In April the four of us moved into a large ground-floor flat which has a garden, is in good decorative order, and easy to manage: the antithesis of our three-storey Victorian terrace. It's now August and we have adjusted more quickly to our new surroundings than I had imagined possible. Since it's August, we have a chance to catch our breath and time to be together as a family: to make plans together, to tell each other stories, to have picnics on the lawn, to take a boat trip on the river and, to do it, as the children are always asking 'again tomorrow'.

Michelle Jones

> 'On 6 April 1977, the maternity pay provisions of the Employment Protection Act 1975 came into force. This meant that after two years in full-time employment, I would be entitled to several months' paid leave and up to a year's absence without losing my job.'

I always wanted to have a child. I had a healthy body and expected that, when I was ready, it would reproduce. At the same time, from the age of nine or ten, I planned to be a writer. I was especially influenced by my father, who assured me that I was Superwoman. He sold me his dream of a bohemian paradise in which babies suckled without so much as nudging the hand which held the pen. Mates were soul-mates and lovers. Marriage was an archaic institution. The job of the woman-artist was to create in two forms. Somehow, essentials would be provided. Perhaps he, a hardworking employee, would continue to care for me. We would see. As for the newborn, they quickly matured and sat to compose symphonies or great works of art. Behind him was my mother, reminding me to take care of myself and my body, and to save myself because one day I would become a mother.

I suppose it was after I had finished university and was living in New York, supporting myself with odd jobs and writing early and late, loath to miss a single day, that I began to see the gap between my father's vision and some realities. At the same time, by now his dream was mine and I wanted both an artist's and a domestic life. But first one, I thought, and then the other.

So for a few years I was an obsessive, unpublished (unsuccessful) Lower East Side writer. Then, for a few more, I was an obsessive, similarly unsuccessful, diary-keeping wife, kept sane by the things I did outside the home such as studying dance and teaching English. Yet I suppose I would have had a child then if my husband hadn't been sterile. Or, if he had agreed, we might have adopted one. I came to understand slowly, but eventually saw that, joined with him, I could become neither a writer nor a mother.

At twenty-seven, I started out again. This time I moved to London where I met someone at a comparable crossroad. Approaching thirty, Andrew had a left a wife, child, dog, house, and nine-to-five on a career ladder in order to try his hand at poetry. It was 1970, neither the best nor the worst time to set up a separate-but-equal household to give shape to private ambitions.

Looking back at our first five years, I see how endlessly we were distracted from our primary goals: by one another, yes, but also by the search for part-time work and a place to live. In those years we moved six times and between us collected per hour wages from more than a dozen educational institutions. All that time, despairing at the fragments I produced, I wanted to have a child. I felt two things: (1) suspicious of myself because, failing to complete a novel, wouldn't I fail with a child? and (2) that it was impossible. Without sufficient means, and with no more of a home than a temporary double bedsitter, or a three-room flat lacking a private toilet or bath, how could I bring a child into the world? On top of that, my companion, in whom I had fully invested myself, spoke of living quite happily without a child. His former wife, who had already remarried and had a second, teased him that he was a long time getting round to it. At the same time she warned him not to make the same mistake twice.

Finally we were both dissatisfied. We seemed to have lost on all fronts. We lived poorly in worse and worse accommodation. The cost of living was rising. Opportunities for the kind of part-time jobs we sought were shrinking. The autonomy we had hoped to find together did not exist. Squirrelled away, our intellectual and creative life remained essentially private. Although we lived in the city, we were short of the time, the means, and the energy to participate in much of the artistic culture it offered. Moreover, notions of another style, in particular the memory of what he had left and his former wife reclaimed, stirred Andrew to take a stride backwards. He rejoined the world of the full-time professional employee. In doing so, he took me with him and, inadvertently, led me towards the fulfillment I sought.

The steps were these. Because of his appointment, we both left London for a town in the Midlands and purchased an eight-room semi-detached house. I was able to cover the down payment, which bought me time to find work in the area before having to meet my share of our monthly expenses. At first, I sought part-time work imagining I could earn sufficient for our new bourgeois existence and still leave myself partially free. Within a few months, however, I realized my error. By then I was teaching in three institutions, travelling up to eighty miles in a single day, and away from my own work five days a week. For this, the salary was half (if that) of a full-time wage when you took into account holidays, sick leave, etc. So I, too, decided to seek a post. It was 1976. Although the British economy was already in trouble there were still occasional openings and, by chance and luck, I slid into one of them.

So, finally, I met the practical requirements I thought necessary. I had sufficient space, money, and job security to take on motherhood. Signing the contract, I made a secret pledge to myself. As soon as I had earned the right to maternity leave, I would take it.

On 6 April 1977, the maternity pay provisions of the Employment Protection Act 1975 came into force. This meant that, after two years in full-time employment, I would be entitled to several months' paid leave and up to a year's absence without losing my job.

I explained this to my companion who congratulated me on my

good fortune and left it at that. He had his reasons. A year further on, he had had enough of his full-time post and was wondering how much longer he could keep himself at it. At the same time, he couldn't think what he could do next except to return to part-time work and writing poems. In a way my revised career decision gave him the opportunity to abandon his; and within a year of my appointment, he had resigned. His time his own again, he reasoned, since he wasn't doing anything better with his life, we might as well have a child. At the same time, he refused to discuss it. He didn't 'feel like it'.

It was difficult to know how to interpret his reticence. Our normal practice was to discuss things endlessly and repetitively. Certainly it contained hesitation and, partly in response and partly in face of my own fears, as the marked time approached, I hesitated. It was December and bitter-cold and everything around us looked grey. A friend with an eighteen-month-old came to stay for a few days. She was altered beyond repair, I felt, endlessly haunted. With eery and painful clarity, I suddenly recalled my mother's post-partum depression and the breakdown which followed, then my friend Sue's, her body starved beyond recognition, helpless to carry on with the life it had brought into the world; and I imagined myself destroyed in the same way. I would live beyond childbirth, yes, but as one dying, bloated beyond return, exhausted into a nullity. Premenstrual at the turning of the year, I looked hard at myself and reversed my decision. No, I wouldn't have a child. I would never have a child. I announced it to my companion as final because it felt final and he seemed to accept it as such. At least he offered no argument.

How I felt afterwards was that I had become my own executioner. With feigned calm, I described myself: 'The decision not to have children made her feel as if the crises of her life had passed, and the pinnacle too, without being noticed. The depression which followed seemed to have all the characteristics of a post-partum, only there was no infant to drown in the bath, save her devolved self.'

For my own salvation, I had no choice but to do an about-face.

Six weeks later, with Andrew's acceptance, I put my diaphragm away. The next month, as if on the dot of the appointed time, I was pregnant. Looking back, these facts stand as a memorial. They mark the end of what might have been an easy onset to a full-term pregnancy and birth and the beginning of what real life is far more likely to offer.

By now I was thirty-four. At this point my age began to play a part; and I began to learn about it. Healthy as I was, careful as I had been, I had never stopped to consider the logical processes of biological growth. Designed for reproduction, the mature female body prepares itself month after month and, if unseeded, goes unchanged. Or does it? Fibroids, tumours of the uterus, consisting of smooth muscle and connective tissue, are uncommon before the age of thirty and tend to occur in women who have not given birth. Fibroid tumours may contribute to miscarriages or prevent conception.

I miscarried twice before my tumour was diagnosed. In June, I was 'had in' for 'shelling' via abdominal surgery; a week later, tumour-free, I was released. I was told to stay home six weeks, given six months to heal, and then, the consultant said, I could try again.

It was not an easy time. On more than one level it played havoc with former assurances. Hyped on drugs and the confusion of the hospital experience, I became loud and assertive, perhaps, in some primal way, rising to the occasion. Although Andrew could find some justification for it, it affected him badly. He had neither the emotional nor the psychological resources to engage with me as I then was. It was all he could manage to stay put and withdraw. This contributed to his long-lived-with uncertainty about having a child with me, or at all; and, as the time of healing crawled forward, he faced me with a forbidding muteness.

At this point we had been living together for nine years. For several reasons, including a reluctance to start again, I wanted to believe this meant permanency. And it might, I saw, if I forsook motherhood. But could I? Or did I have to choose between him and it?

Bogged in indecision, I could seem a fool. After all, the only real act to alter was contraception; or to stop acting against Nature. There were women who couldn't understand. 'Get pregnant,' they advised. 'He'll come round.' But these were women who lived by different codes. For me, such a pregnancy would have been devious beyond forgiveness. In moral terms, it would have been a sin.

Andrew never completely recovered from his first separation, his departure from his former wife and infant. Neither of us believed he could survive a second such severing without dire consequences. So we stalled; we stalled. Again it was December. According to the consultant I was healed and, at thirty-five, should get on with it. But how could I? I looked at myself and I saw failure. There was nothing left but a job in which I was required to resuscitate works written by the dead. Seeing this, I chose.

It was like a last ditch attempt to retrieve ourselves or, worse, a ritual enacted after the real ending because, on one level, we had terminated our coupledom. Burying memories of innumerable connecting threads, we declared ourselves moribund and, since we were opposed in our thoughts about a child, we ceased to be lovers.

In this condition we set off on a pre-booked pre-Christmas package holiday to a two-star hotel at the desolate end of Majorca. On the flight over I warmed to the idea of myself as a single parent and began to see glimmers of an utterly different life set up far from my companion and far from England. In this imagined life, I would be part of a communal household, one of several one-parent families. In the enormous house which we would share, I would be tucked away high up in a little room on my own. But then, alas, on the heels of this idyll I saw rushing towards me the steaming kitchen, vats of stew, mountains of laundry, dishes that never ended, and children of all sizes and ages left to my care. There were other scenarios including a single bedsitter in Birmingham, again in an attic room, this time with a blazing gas fire, and a baby's wicker basket tucked under the eaves. For a fleeting moment, there was even a return to my parents' three-room flat. In flight for two and a half hours, anything was possible.

On land again, however, things felt different and, still together, we staged a farce. On the one hand we carried on in our normal holiday manner: we trudged and climbed, plunged and explored, ate oranges, drank brandies, and even swam in the sea. On the other hand, we were pouting, shouting, declaring ultimatums. 'If you haven't decided by New Year's Day,' I threatened, 'I'll be gone.' 'With you gone,' he encouraged me, 'I can get social security to help with the mortgage payments.'

In this way we reached the last night and somehow, after agreeing to write lists upon lists to determine what we would and would not expect of each other, came to an agreement. Relieved and terrified, we made love.

This time I failed to conceive until the second month. In the annals of childbearing, it is no time; but in the circumstances it seemed an eternity. Day by day, hour by hour, moments expanded. I was so obsessed that I suffered the delay as if I had been fixed on pregnancy since the first egg had formed in my unborn body. Travelling to work, at work, shopping, everywhere I went I collected statistics: how frequently they had done It, how long It had taken, what complications arose, if any. And at home, I worked for It. Every other night, I waited for him to come to bed, waited through midnight, my face to the bedside light to keep me alert. At the same time, I was panicked that he might change his mind or, perhaps worse, out of an unconscious resistance, be unable to perform. Despite both of us, I feared, the seed might be withheld. Each time this didn't happen (and it didn't at all) I trembled and wept inwardly with relief. Meanwhile we did not (perhaps could not) speak of it, as if we had a pact.

Of course it altered our love-making. The frequency and persistence roused our long-programmed bodies to new thresholds. And the idea of the child stirred us to acts terrible, frenetic, and redundant, echoing our beginning and leading us towards an uncertain future.

One Monday in February I came home with a headache. I scowled at the supper table, took one look at a glass of water, and crawled upstairs to vomit. All I could think was, 'Thank God, we don't have to make love tonight.' Another week of routinized love-making passed before my temperature chart convinced me that that Monday must have been the day.

Because of my previous miscarriages, I resolved to keep this pregnancy quiet until I had passed the three-month mark and the placenta was formed. I might have succeeded if I hadn't been told yet another tale of an ectopic pregnancy – an egg fertilized and settled in a Fallopian tube which, about the ninth week, burst, endangering the life of the woman. By the fifth week I felt a distinct aching on my left side and, during the sixth, doubled over in the garden one day convinced of doom. The next morning I carried a urine sample to my GP and, presenting my neurosis as fact, insisted on being probed. I left the office dazed and exalted. It was not my fallopian tube but my uterus that was palpably enlarged.

Once I had been to the doctor, professional anxieties moved in on me. After the ectopic scare, there was the possibility of twins; first, because there were two dips on my temperature chart, suggesting that I had produced two eggs that month; second, I was within a year of the prime age for twin production; third, I swelled quickly and remained large for my dates. By the seventh week, I had been to see a consultant and she, like my GP, recommended hormone injections as an aid against another miscarriage. (I did not have them.) During the middle three months things quieted but, in the last trimester, problems arose. My creature remained in the breech position into the ninth month, turning the very week of the due date. Then I reached the due date and the head wasn't engaged. (Perhaps my pelvic bowl was too small.) My due date passed, a week, ten days, two weeks. At my final antenatal appointment, the doctor who saw me said he'd like to book me for an induction but couldn't see any available time until the next week. Fiercely opposed to any interference, I continued to practise my breathing exercises.

Three days later, labour started by itself, slowly and with no more than mild cramping. From that point until the end of the second stage, things went well. Andrew drove me to the hospital where I spent the pre-dawn and early morning hours alone in various rooms resting, musing, listening to the rain and, intermittently, reading. Midwives kept a check on me. I felt at once terribly excited and dead calm.

Someone had advised me to have everything I wanted written across the top of my file. Because of this, the midwives persisted in supporting a natural (no drug) labour and gave me what I asked for beyond my ability to know the steps. For instance, at about 7 a. m., a doctor arrived to break my waters. He argued that it would get things moving. I shrugged, thinking he knew best, but the midwife interfered: she said that I wanted it to be natural and the membrane would give in its own time. The doctor departed and left us to await the flooding which occurred six hours later.

I was in labour for almost a full diurnal cycle. At the twenty-one-hour mark, the consultant's registrar suddenly appeared. I recognized him from the antenatal clinic where once or twice he'd examined me. At the same time I *didn't* recognize him, because his friendly calm was gone. Counting me high-risk because of my history and age, he shouted at my midwife, including in his attack the junior doctor who happened to be there, and Andrew, 'Why isn't she on a monitor? I'm not having this one born dead.'

Within minutes, my freedom was gone. I was unbent from my semi-lotus, laid back and connected, an electrode 'down there', a band around my thigh. Andrew was set the task of reading the graph of the heartbeat and its correspondence to my contractions. I remember glancing at him and seeing nothing but green: his green paper hat, green smock and the length of greenish paper unreeling in his hand. Whatever he felt was locked away and I lost any signs of it as I dived again into the rising constriction. Breathe and count, breathe and count, breathe and count; and then there were no seconds left. Suddenly I was nothing but a body maddened to push.

Everyone else saw her first. The cord was cut, she was wiped, weighed, wrapped in a towel, and then placed face to breast. I sensed rather than saw her, felt rather than held her. A wet, reddish head so briefly with me, she was more like an illusion than anything remotely connected to my body.

One minute they were there, the team of them, my companion, and my child; the next minute, gone. The show was over. Still on my back, I waited to be stitched, waited through an eight p.m. tea which was going on elsewhere, waited while in my head a voice sang over and over the mute refrain: born! born! born!

My joy was a delirium which continued for two sleepless weeks. Then the exhaustion set in, bringing with it the waking which does not end.

Among the many feelings I had then was the one of at last being like others. I was Everywoman. As such, I looked back through my pregnancy and saw how double-edged it was. During the first half I felt sick and alien, during the second, buoyant and unapproachable. It was then, I believe, that I saw our relationship alter. I felt as if all the masculine element had ebbed out of me. This didn't mean that I felt weak, but that I had no need, and hardly any notion, of my independent self. Distanced from my companion by the prodding creature within, I came to know him as an atmosphere, like the air I breathed, replete with oxygen to sustain life.

This feeling persisted for some time after the birth and brought in its wake a permanent change. As we progressed from duo to trio, we were no longer separate-but-equal in our domestic partnership. It's here, if anywhere, that I would point to the birth of my feminist consciousness; here, too, is the origin of my remade self.

Afterword
This was first drafted when my daughter was eighteen months old. At that time I wrote: 'The effect of parenthood is such that, if I were to wake to wonder what has happened to my last decade, I would be interrupted before thinking it through. Becoming a mother, I've become a rota system of small accomplishments and

failures against the background of those long, large lines I still see in the distance. Now I am living the reverse of the slow time of conception and pregnancy. Now I live with the loss of months and years. The need for sleep, or, at best, the idea of sleep haunts me and, with it, the idea of waking rested. In between, I try to value those moments containing my daughter's constant discoveries, and my own. Fatigue has sobered me, these early stages of motherhood lashed me in some unpredictable way, and my daughter both excites and defeats me. Still in the process of becoming, I find myself thinking, yes, this is what I wanted, but only once. This once. It is as if I have fallen from a high cliff and keep bounding through a landscape whose contours I can barely see. I'm neither broken nor wounded and I don't expect the earth to give way beneath me, but I can hardly catch my breath.'

Two years later, with a three-and-a-half-year-old, it's different. Despite continuing broken nights, and days which frequently begin at dawn, I can look back.

The clocks changed the week before Eleanor was born. The darkness was everywhere, electrically-lit. I might have been living in a cave. It was as if there were no days, only the hardly interrupted winter of breast-feeding which held me as I held her, a child who would rest in my arms but howl awake the instant she was lowered into her cot. Secure and obsessed with my daughter, I lived utterly self-absorbed. The only crises I experienced had to do with her: nappy rash, unpredictable sleep patterns, two- to three-hour feeding sessions, a tracery of blood in her faecal matter, an unrelenting objection to the carry cot. This psychological enclosure was made painfully clear when a friend described her father's dying and I saw myself mouthing condolences I meant but could not feel. It seemed as if all my feelings were exclusively related to Eleanor. If I had any concern for anything else in the universe, it was only because it related to her.

When Eleanor was four and a half months old, my father had a heart attack. That I did feel and, because it was important to me that he see her and I him, I took her to the States. When we returned, ten days later, she pulled herself into a sitting position which meant she acquired a new world view. About then, so did I.

By then my maternity leave was over and, in a limited way, I was back on the job. Coming and going, I learned new sequences of paranoia (triggered in part by leaving Eleanor with a day-time nanny) and completed the first steps of the ongoing business of organizing my domestic and work lives. Dedicated to breast-feeding and wary of allergies (such as eczema) said to be bred by cow's milk, I continued to reply to her demand and managed that first year because my colleagues were supportive. At no time was I required to be away from home for more than four hours. By the following September, when the length of my working day reverted to the norm, Eleanor was nearly a year old and eating homegrown and homeground foods with gusto. Still I breastfed her last thing before running for my train and first thing upon return; and she continued to demand 'mummy's milk', especially in the evening and during the night, until her third birthday. Although this was not something I had been prepared for and, by eighteen months was uneasy and somewhat embarrassed to admit (as well as aware of Andrew's feeling that it insured my primary position in her life long past time), I argued inwardly and outwardly for Eleanor's right to make her own decision.

Because she breastfed so long, and because in the interim Andrew succeeded in finding and settling into a job which interested him, its ending seemed to mark the end of my coming to motherhood. By then we had succeeded in living as a family for three years and, out of countless heated discussions, unprecedented eruptions, accusations, incidents, and tears, were growing confident in ourselves as parents, as professionals, and, to a lesser degree, as writers.

Although it is a more decisive factor in my case, since I am the primary caretaker, I believe it is true for Andrew too that Eleanor's birth carried in its wake new temporal imperatives. Moved forward a generation, we saw the future shrinking and went to work. At last he has completed and seen published a volume of his poetry and is musing over the completion of another. For my part, I'm better able to accept my own imperfections and, in the last two years, have managed to decide on final drafts for eight or nine stories which (like Andrew's poems) had been hanging about for a decade waiting to be finished. These I've sent out and seen in print. At the same time, I've redesigned longer works to make them more reasonable under-takings and given myself different kinds of ultimatums. The myth of having a lifetime for writing and rewriting is extinct. There are some hours available on some days and either I use them well or accept that I do not. Moreover, whatever I hope to achieve has to be viewed within the compromises that that time imposes. If Eleanor interrupts me half a dozen times, I can but shout. So I find myself both better disciplined and able to work more intensively; and less severe, able to reschedule for another week, month, or year what I had hoped to complete during this one.

Having said this and acknowledging that the long lines of my life are being fulfilled, perhaps I should add that there are recurring moments when I am filled with disbelief. Can it be real? Am I a mother and a 'wife'? Perhaps we are on a Sunday outing. In the daypack on my back is a stash of fruit, sandwiches, and juice. Ahead of me, laughing and chasing a cavorting coloured ball, are Andrew and Eleanor. Watching them, I could be a stranger. The phenomenon is strange. It's almost as if the better I know myself as integral to the family, the better I am able to contend with my separateness. Emerged from the early stages of motherhood, I find myself returned to a former skin. Within this, looking in and looking out, I live alone. So I can be unbearably moved by recognizing that I have a familial place. Suddenly I, too, am running after the ball, catching up to the pair of them and laughing while the pack bobs between my shoulders. This releases me from my earnest tempo, and I am grateful to be given, however briefly, such respite.

I should add too that, returned to my former skin, I'm again an eager sexual partner. This has come about after the five years during which my body was primarily concerned with other business: the two miscarriages, abdominal surgery, pregnancy, birth, and breastfeeding. Only this past year have I found myself reawakened, and in this, an ardour and excitement I had all but forgotten. And, with the childbearing issue resolved, I feel freed to be a lover as I could not quite when the idea of saving my body for childbirth lingered as a warning.

This doesn't mean that I've become reckless. On the contrary, childbirth completed means that parenthood remains and, because I hope to live to a ripe old age, for Eleanor's sake if not my own, I feel obliged to take care of my body – to nourish it well, to rest it as I can, and to take it out for daily exercise, almost as if it were a domestic animal in my charge. At three and a half, Eleanor delights in this latter and sets out for her own jog each morning along a route she has planned. Referee, I stand at the finish line watching her speed on strong thin limbs and imagining us together in another decade and another, collaborating as we set out on our chosen tracks.

My life may be pieced-out and hardworking and, no doubt, I shout more than I like to admit, and have more advantages than I will count, but it serves, satisfies, and enriches me. No, I can answer Andrew now, there isn't anything I would change.

Eleanor looks at herself. 'Mummy, my belly's getting rounder. Do you have babies at my age? I mean little tiny ones you can't even see.' She laughs, but she's only half-joking. 'You'd have to have binoculars to see them. Mummy,' she adds, because she sees I am writing it down, 'Are you writing this in your book?' I nod, read it back to her. She nods in reply. 'Yes,' she confirms, 'that's what I said, isn't it? I'll be four in October, won't I? 'Mmm.' 'Then I'll be going to nursery school. Will I be able to write then?' 'You might start,' I say, 'we'll have to see.' 'Oh that's all right,' she concludes, and runs off to see if her father isn't doing something more interesting, like snipping at his beard.

Jacquee Storozynski

'In theory I have organized my life very well, exactly as I said I would, before the baby was even a possibility. I have resumed my career and I have found a registered child-minder to look after Natalie during the day. It has all worked out very well: I am still the same outgoing person I always was. I look the same, but inside I have completely changed . . .'

I had my first baby when I was one week short of thirty-five years old. I had always been thought of as a career girl, in fact I thought of myself as one. I had worked for the same company for sixteen years and had worked my way up to Assistant Technical Information Officer, and I was well thought of. I was judged a capable sort of person, somewhat dominant and well organized.

I don't believe that all women have maternal longings. I had never had them. I never billed and cooed over other people's children and in most cases I could take them or leave them. It was only when my brother became a father that I began to feel maternal longings, as I watched my small niece grow from babyhood. My desire for a baby was not an overwhelming longing, more of a wondering what sort of child it would be. What colour hair, who it would look like, etc. My mental picture was always of a blonde blue-eyed flower child. Completely unrealistic.

I married late, at thirty, and it was at about the age of thirty-two that I actually thought positively of being a mother; but something else always seemed to crop up that took priority. My husband bought a car and we couldn't afford both that and a child, so I again pushed the idea to the back of my mind. Then, when I was thirty-three, my mother died. That almost made me decide to never have children, especially as my mother would never see any child that I might have. The whole decision was tossed around, on and off, for about four years. Even so it was always a mental thing and not an overwhelming longing.

At thirty-four I was plucking up courage to have the coil, that I had had for two years, removed and finally take the plunge, when fate took a hand. I began to bleed heavily and had to have the coil removed. The trauma of its removal sickened me, the indignity and the manhandling appalled me and I had a feeling that childbirth was going to be far worse.

I became pregnant almost immediately. I knew I would. When I saw that small ring that denotes a positive result, I had a sudden feeling of panic. The decision was made; it was out of my hands now; for once something was about to happen to me that was out of my control. I was just a tiny bit scared. Putting my fears aside I assumed a breezy, confident air and, somewhat embarrassedly, told the world that I was about to become a mother. My feelings changed to annoyance when people reacted with absolute surprise and mutterings that they never thought I would have a child, and back on the grapevine came the fact that people were wondering if it was an accident. I began to feel like a creature from another planet, not thought capable of producing a baby.

Being very conscious of appearance, I was dreading the actual state of pregnancy. The thought of waddling around feeling unattractive for nine months was not very appealing. Surprisingly though, I began to enjoy every minute of it. I felt well, looked well, and relished the attention and consideration I received from friends and relatives. The consideration did not extend to the tube, where I was only offered a seat on two occasions.

People told me I was blooming and I received so many

compliments, it was wonderful. Most people told me I would have a boy because some old wives' tale decreed that if your face looks nice you have a son. In fact, I had a girl, Natalie, so I wouldn't set much store by that. I had many compliments from men, which surprised me. The question of being an older mother-to-be did not seem to affect my appearance at all. In fact, I looked and felt better than a twenty-one-year-old colleague who was pregnant at the same time.

Having decided that I would continue working as long as possible, I felt it was essential not to be a burden on my colleagues by continued absences and therefore I decided that I would have no morning sickness, thinking that all things are conquered by mind over matter. It worked! I never suffered any of even the most minor ailments. Although, strangely, as soon as I arrived home in the evening I felt queasy, as if it was all right for me to be ill at that time. However, it soon passed and I was never sick. I never had any strange longings except once when I had an overwhelming urge to eat a pair of dirty, white, dusty gardening gloves.

Feeling full of energy and happy with my condition, I was put out on my first visit to the hospital when they asked me why I had left my first pregnancy so late. As I had had no desire, previous to my marriage, to be a one-parent family, I was most offended. In addition, the young nurses kept running to tell me that there was another woman of my age in a nearby cubicle and she was having a first baby too. It seemed to be such a strange occurrence. I remarked that it was a shame to be so old and they commiserated with me, not realizing that I was being sarcastic. The final insult came when I looked at the notes and written across them was 'Elderly Primigravida'. It sounded like a decrepit monkey! I was also surprised to be examined by the doctor with a young boy in tee-shirt and jeans looking on.

I was given no special treatment and sat happily among the young ones waiting to be seen. I always went early, so I didn't waste a whole day. I was happy to see that I looked a good deal better than most of the younger mothers-to-be, who seemed to have let themselves go. I had a scan and the usual blood tests and blood pressure readings, and everything was all right.

I gave up work at eight months and sat at home bored stiff. The highlight of the week then was the relaxation class at the local clinic. Once a week six of us, me the eldest, went through our paces. It mostly degenerated into hilarity after we had seen ancient films about free orange juice and National Dried Milk. There was a father's evening when we were shown a film on the actual birth. When they waved the placenta at the camera I was horrified. The butterflies began to set in, thinking about what I was letting myself in for. My husband was definitely against being at the birth. Again, I put the thought of the birth out of mind. In fact, the midwife told me that I had the look of someone who hadn't actually realized that they were pregnant. I must admit that, until the baby arrived, I could not visualize myself as a mum. I knew one thing though and that was that I was going to insist on an epidural. This always made the younger girls laugh because they thought that having that would be far worse than the actual labour.

At last, being two weeks overdue, I was taken in to be 'started off' as they put it – a castor oil cocktail, enema and prostaglandin suppository as well, and twenty-four hours later I started to get slight labour pains. I rang for my husband to come to the hospital as he had promised to be with me until the later stages. As I was wheeled into the labour ward I asked about the epidural and was told that it was not available at that stage because the staff were busy but that I could have it later if I wanted, when the anaesthetist was free.

I was in labour fifteen hours altogether, the first five hours having mild contractions at four-minute intervals that lengthened to ten minutes after I was given Pethidine. The rest of the time I was in screaming agony. I was told I was only an hour away from the actual birth and then that I had been wrongly assessed. Doctors kept coming and going, arguing around the bed, nurses kept changing shifts, the baby was put on a foetal monitor. At last, after begging them, I was given an epidural and it did not have any effect. I had a saline drip that made the contractions so severe that I wanted to jump out of the window and put an end to it all.

My husband was trying to help whilst arguing with the nurses. The relaxation exercises did nothing. One of the nurses said, 'Childbirth is painful; that is why men don't have babies.' I had always thought that it was for physiological reasons.

At last they decided on a Caesarian. As they wheeled me into the operating theatre I thought that I was going to die. When I came round I could not believe that I was still alive. I heard voices telling me that I had a daughter and I looked across and saw a small face peering through a plastic crib. I felt nothing. All I could do was croak, 'Isn't she ugly?'

I say croak because I lost my voice and went stone deaf with the shock. The effect lasted for over a week. The whole birth had been the most traumatic experience of my life. I kept weeping when I thought about it. I felt abused, as though my innermost soul had been assaulted. I did not feel any sense of achievement, just degraded and invaded.

Although I felt awful I forced myself to get up and about which surprised the nurses, who said that the young mums lie around ringing the buzzer all the time. The night that I gave birth there were five other Caesarian Sections although mine was the only unplanned one. Apparently I had made no progress in the fifteen hours of labour so, although the drip had induced severe contractions, they had achieved nothing. The doctors would not commit themselves as to whether age was a factor and seem to think that it was a perfectly normal birth.

For the first few nights the baby was taken away to the nursery and I was relieved that she was not my responsibility. I didn't feel any love toward her, nor animosity – just numb, no feelings whatsoever. I breastfed her, but even that did not bring any feeling of closeness, or the bonding process, as they call it. I had so much milk that I joked that I was going into the milk marketing business, whereas another older mother had no milk and was told it was because of her age. I did not see how it could be. I did not enjoy the feeding; I felt dragged down with the commitment. My body was not mine any more. The aches and pains of cracked nipples etc., irritated me. I breastfed because I had been brainwashed into thinking it was the best thing for baby.

The first night that the baby was left with me I nearly had a nervous breakdown. She cried and cried; nurses kept coming in and offering conflicting advice. Every time the baby breathed I thought that she was wheezing and ill and demanded to see the doctor. Finally she and I fell asleep from exhaustion.

It was like that every night until I came home, having been in hospital eleven days. As we left the hospital my husband asked me if I loved the baby and I answered of course I did, although I wasn't really sure. He was over the moon with her, kissing and cuddling her, although of course she did not respond.

The first day home I briskly fed, washed and changed her and then cried for half an hour because I couldn't cope. I was overwhelmed by the responsibility of it all. Her life was in my hands. It was only later that I realized that I *had* coped.

The next day I developed a breast abscess and had to give up feeding until the abscess healed, whilst maintaining the milk. The baby was to be on the tinned variety as a stopgap. I made up the bottles in paranoid distress in case I made the feed incorrectly, the bottles weren't clean, or I had compressed too much milk in the scoop; I was like a crazy woman. I resented my husband when he tried to advise me, in fact I really hated him. Every decision I made concerning feeding, changing, etc., he challenged. Although he was trying to help, I saw it as interference and, when he played with the baby whilst I was dressing her, I wanted to smack his face. It all seems so irrational now but, at the time, small things took on overwhelming importance. We clashed over the silliest things, even over whether the baby should wear rubber pants. An edge crept into our marriage. He seemed to resent the fact that I was making the decisions for the baby and I resented him for challenging them.

As time progressed he began to resent the baby interfering with his lifestyle. He was annoyed if she cried in the night, although it rarely happened, and if she cried when he was watching television it was almost the end of the world.

To add insult to injury the baby became ill and was taken to hospital with suspected gastro-enteritis. All my paranoia about germ-free bottles etc., and she had still become ill. I felt as if the world was against me. I kissed her goodbye as we left the hospital and my husband said that it was the first time that I had kissed her; and it was. She was two weeks old; it felt like a lifetime. The trouble (which was thought to have been caused by an allergic reaction to the penicillin I was taking for the abscess) recurred until she was nearly three months old. I had to keep pumping off my breast milk with a hand pump so that I could maintain it whilst she was on glucose and then, when the symptoms disappeared, I breastfed her and back came the symptoms again. I dreaded feeding times; I felt like a cow being milked, the chore was tedious and, after I had resumed breastfeeding, I was on the watch for problems the whole time.

I used to visit the GP and the clinic in tears only to be told that I should continue to breastfeed as that was not the problem. The baby was small and frail-looking although she was perfectly happy, no trouble at all. Each night I crept into bed dreading each day. I felt awful, looked awful, and was touchy and irritable. I felt that I had lost my identity, that I was no longer an individual. I remember that I visited my office for the day and made a concerted effort to look nice so that nobody could say that I had let myself go. In fact everyone said how well I looked but it was all superficial. I enjoyed myself so much I did not want to come home.

When Christmas came Natalie was inundated with presents and, although I was pleased that she received so much attention, I felt sad inside. I felt as though nobody cared about me any more. I kept checking the mirror to see if I had suddenly aged or become ugly. My husband could not see any difference and just thought I was being stupid.

Suddenly things changed; I decided to think positively. I decided to stop being pressurized into breastfeeding and put the baby on modified milk. Although I dreaded the actual making process and the bottle-washing chore was the biggest bind of my life we have never looked back. Almost overnight the baby began to blossom, and I blossomed and we began to enjoy each other. I relaxed and then I knew I loved her. Everyday things were done spontaneously because I wanted to, not because I had to. The pressure had gone, it was marvellous.

I have now found a baby-minder and returned to work to the same company, although not the same job. The money and the grade are the same and it is not a pressurized job so I am finding that it is no strain to arrange my commitments around the work. The slower pace suits me for the time being. The baby is happy with the minder and although I am glad, I sometimes have twinges of jealousy when I think that someone else is having the pleasure of my baby.

How has the experience affected me? Well, I am again the bright and breezy well-organized person that I was before, but I have changed. I have become an inveterate worrier. Everywhere I go I hear of someone with an illness and I worry in case the baby catches it. I never realized before that there was so much disease around. Someone told me that they can tell I am an older mother because I worry so much; whether it is age that is the reason I don't know. I have become over-protective to my baby and to other people's. I worry if I see a child out with no coat or on its own. My husband has settled down and the edge has disappeared. The baby is eight months old now. She is a happy, well-adjusted child and I think that we are happy, well-adjusted parents. I know that I only want good things for her, I want her to have lots of love and sensitivity. Strangely, she *is* a blonde, blue-eyed flower child, just like I imagined, and she was worth all the pain and torment. However, would I go through it all again? I don't think so.

Afterword

It is now nearly two years since Natalie was born. In theory I have organized my life very well, exactly as I said I would before the baby was even a possibility. I have resumed my career in Information Science and I have found a registered child-minder to look after Natalie during the day. It has all worked out very well. I am still the same outgoing person I always was. I look the same but inside I have completely changed. I have lost my peace of mind. I brood all day over what the minder might or might not be doing, I badger her with do's and don'ts. According to her, this is an 'older mother syndrome', everyone says so – whoever everyone is! Being worldly wise I see dangers everywhere, not only for my child but for complete strangers and I worry for them. I am turning into a neurotic worrier.

The hardest part is having to leave Natalie every day: nobody warned me about the guilt I would feel, and as she gets older the guilt gets worse, not better. Even holding the job down is difficult, because the baby seems always to be sickening with colds and coughs and I have to wrestle with my conscience whether to stay at home with her. I usually do, using up holiday or working at home, and then I catch the bug myself and have to have time off. It is a constant round of guilt. Guilt at letting work colleagues down, not doing the job properly and worst of all, not being the central figure in Natalie's life.

To balance all this I have gained enormous pleasure. I feel as if all these years there has been something missing and I never knew. I wasted years obtaining material things and wanting a career only to find what I enjoy most is a spontaneous kiss or cuddle from my child. I can't imagine why I waited so long to have a baby. At the ripe old age of thirty-seven, well nearly, I feel like a twenty-year-old, I want lots of children, I've found a whole new side of me that didn't exist. I enjoy being a mum.

Dervla Murphy

> 'I longed to have more time to be in physical contact with Rachel . . . and often I looked enviously at Amala, settling down to give Rachel her bottle while I settled down to disentangle the latest chapter.'

For thirty-six years, I never even glanced at the possibility of becoming a mother. Babies and small children have always bored me – I much prefer animals. Also, I like to organize my life to suit *myself*: a reaction, no doubt, to sixteen years of drastically restricted freedom. My invalid mother was totally dependent on my nursing from 1946 to 1962, when she died. I then did what I had always wanted to do – travelled and wrote – and by 1968 I had published four moderately successful books and was an established writer living (when not abroad) in the home that had been left to me by my parents.

At that stage I began to feel that something was missing; there is a certain aridity about living, however enjoyably and successfully, for oneself alone. Marriage, however, was not the answer; I would have found such a curtailment of freedom intolerable. There was, however, motherhood. A young woman of the 1980s might then have thought about A.I.D., or some other advanced-technology method of reproducing the species. But my mind and heart work on old-fashioned principles. I felt I couldn't truly love a baby unless I also loved its father, so without Fate's intervention I might have remained forever childless. Fate, however, soon looked after that problem. In 1967 I fell deeply in love (again) and the following April, to my undeniable joy, found myself pregnant. It was impossible at once to visualize myself as 'A Mother', yet motherhood did seem to offer a satisfactory compromise between matrimonial shackles and selfish solitude. The impracticality of my having a baby was obvious but – I felt – irrelevant. As my parents had left me no income, I was financially dependent on my work; and it would be irresponsible to drag a baby through Himalayan gorges or across Ethiopian plateaux. Therefore I would have to stop working for a few years, apart from my regular book-reviewing for the *Irish Times*. But my temperament is Micawber-ish; I can't ever worry about money, even when I feel that it is my duty to do so. And the wondrous glow of physical and emotional well-being induced by my pregnancy made me still less inclined to dwell on that sordid subject.

My first physiological reaction to pregnancy was a sharpened appetite, apparent even before the pregnancy had been confirmed. I had no faddy cravings, but an omnivorous yearning for every kind of food, with the emphasis on meat. As neither morning sickness nor heartburn afflicted me, there was nothing to counteract this greed and I weighed exactly fourteen stone, instead of my normal eleven and a half, the day after giving birth. It took me six months to get back to my normal weight.

Inevitably, I felt occasional spasms of apprehension when I realized that the total freedom I had enjoyed for six years was about to end – for some twenty years, by which time I would be fifty-six. This realization prompted me to pack my rucksack in June and set off to spend the middle three months of the pregnancy walking through Armenia and Turkish Kurdistan. But of course, this had to be a relatively sedate trek; I was no longer at liberty to risk physical shocks or injuries. Already my freedom was less, but this didn't irk me; I was awed and exhilarated by the consciousness that another *person* was dependent on me. And yet, not having a strongly maternal nature, I felt more like a caretaker than an expectant mother. I was not looking forward to nappies and teething, but I *was* looking forward to meeting that mysterious individual who, in December, would emerge – incredibly! – from my body. Possibly this dwelling on the marvel of birth is one of the main differences between a young and an elderly mother. Very likely most young women take the miracle of creation more or less for granted, as part of the average woman's destiny. But I, who had never thought of myself as a potential mother, was continuously and joyously astonished to find my body engaged in propagating the species. I recall standing one evening in front of a mirror in an Erzurum doss-house bedroom, gazing at my portly nakedness with a curious objective reverence. From this child's point of view, the advantages and disadvantages of these differing attitudes probably balance out.

For every mother, the first kick of her first baby must be memorable – as the first tangible *communication*. At that moment I was sitting on a sun-warmed boulder in the Seljuk ruins of Ani, on the Turkish-Russian border, being glared at by a sentry in the Soviet watch-tower: the only visible human being for many miles around. There was a powerful contrast between the narrow pettiness of a political watch-tower and the universal grandeur of a first kick . . .

As the kicking progressed, my Turkish friends said, 'You have a son! A World Cup player!' I smiled and said nothing. I was convinced I was carrying a daughter. Had she indeed proved to be a boy, I would have had to do some drastic readjusting.

B-Day was to happen at the beginning of December and I spent October at home, in the little Southern Irish town where I was born and bred. Several of my friends questioned the wisdom of this move. Surely an unmarried mother would have problems in a society not yet much influenced by the Permissive Sixties? But I love Lismore, and I intended to bring my child up there, so why not be seen bulging? After all, post-birth, I would be seen pushing a pram. Some people urged me – 'For the child's sake' – to move house and start afresh where nobody would know whether I was married, single, divorced or separated. To me this was unthinkable, apart from the fact that a writer's domestic life is too public for such a deception to be possible. It was also a stupid suggestion. Although my neighbours might be shocked, initially, they know (Lismore is a *very* small town: population some 800) that I am not promiscuous. And there my child would obliquely reap the benefits of being my much-respected parents' grandchild. A tortuous point, but valid. In the event, I met with nothing but kindness and moral support.

On November 1st, I moved to London to share a friend's flat and be checked regularly by my gynaecologist, a sensible man who had seen no reason why I shouldn't spend the middle months of pregnancy romping through the Hakkari Mountains. By then I was, mentally, at the bovine stage: contented and slow-witted. I was still writing (mainly book-reviews) but I couldn't concentrate on work for more than an hour or so. Yet my physical stamina was unimpaired; I could – and often did – happily walk twelve miles at a stretch in four hours, despite my enormous bulk. By December 1st I could scarcely reach my food if I sat on a normal dining chair at a normal dining table. And then, at 1.40 a.m., on December 9th, the curtain went up.

The ambulance arrived half-an-hour later and, as it sped through night-quiet London, from Holland Park to St Teresa's Hospital, Wimbledon, I was euphoric. Also, I felt increasingly curious about the physical adventure of childbirth. Yet my excitement, though intense, was calm. A great, almost contradictory, stillness seemed to envelop me, now that those nine months of waiting were over.

However, the waiting wasn't quite over. I lay all day in my cheerfully soothing room, reading two Edmund Crispin novels while nothing much happened except short spasms of mild pain. I was, as usual, very hungry and felt rather aggrieved because big meals were taboo. At intervals, amiable nurses investigated the goings-on inside me and asked solicitously if the pain was too much. It wasn't, until 8.30 p.m., when a masked figure wheeled me off to the labour ward, which bore an unexpected resemblance to an aircraft hanger. One of the older nurses, with whom I'd established a Special Relationship, confirmed my growing suspicion that athletic elderly women, with massive muscles in every direction, often have Hard First Births. How hard I was soon to find out.

By the time Rachel had fought her way through, to appear at 3.40 a.m., on December 10th, I had endured seven hours of neat hell. But that seemed irrelevant as I looked at the emerging head – and then at the whole person being held by its heels, all purple and yelling, in front of me. 'It's a girl,' someone said. 'Of course,' I replied complacently. A moment later I was given an injection and passed out while innumerable stitches were being inserted.

I came to at 5.30, in my room. For that incomparable moment there are no words. The emotion was unique. A total, flawless, profound, simple happiness is the nearest I can get to it. Few emotional experiences are so uncomplicated. I lay and looked at the ceiling and remembered the purple yelling object. And no number of successful books could give me the illogical sense of achievement I felt then.

Soon Rachel arrived for her first feed. She was no longer purple and yelling but pink, smooth, plump, golden-haired and apparently content with what little she'd seen of the world. I looked at her and said, 'Rachel,' noting delightedly that her head was her father's head and that her hands were my mother's hands. As I spoke I realized the significance of a *name*. From now on I would be dealing with a separate, distinct individual instead of with an anonymous hidden mystery. While the individual discovered the dairy, I appreciated for the first time the peculiar nature of mother-child relationships. Every other relationship is conditioned by past experiences on both sides; but the responsibility for placing *our* relationship on sound foundations would be entirely mine. I gazed down at my new challenge and hoped that the vague attribute known as 'maternal instinct' would come to the rescue. And then I noticed that although babies have never switched me on, *this* one somehow seemed different . . .

'She weighed exactly nine pounds,' said the nurse. Later, I

reminded my gynaecologist that he had advised me to give up
smoking (twenty a day was my average) because nicotine can stunt a
baby's growth – advice which I ignored. He then admitted
(unofficially) that perhaps, for some mothers, nicotine has a
certain shrinkage-value.

I spent the forenoon triumphantly on the telephone, spreading
the good news to Rachel's father in Ireland, and to various friends
near and far – some of whom remarked that I spoke as though the
routine arrival of yet another human being were an event
unprecedented in the history of the universe. Rachel was allowed
to spend the afternoon with me, being admired by a stream of
visitors. I assured them all that within twenty-four hours I'd be back
in my friend's flat, preparing to return to Ireland. But in fact I had
to spend six days not only in hospital but in bed (I was forbidden to
stand up) while a clot in my left leg was being dissolved. As I have
had varicose veins all my adult life, this was not – from the
doctor's point of view – an unexpected complication. Much more
serious, and grieviously disappointing, was my inadequate milk
supply which meant that Rachel had to have supplementary feeds.
This, presumably, was a result of comparative old age.

Fortunately, our friend was out when we returned to her flat on
December 18th; so I was spared the embarrassment of a witness to
my behaviour during the next hour. I had never before had
anything whatsoever to do with a European baby, because I make
a point of arriving at baby-ridden households *after* the children's
bedtime. But I had taken it for granted that my work with Tibetan
babies, in Himalayan refugee-camps, would have sufficiently
prepared me to be a moderately competent mother on the
practical level. This illusion was rapidly dispelled when I found
myself for the first time solely responsible for my own daughter's
welfare.

We arrived at the flat soon after 5 p.m., at which hour Rachel
was accustomed to being fed. She reacted accordingly and I hoped
the neighbours were out as I flung open her gigantic suitcase. The
fact that she was on both bottle and breast was adding to my
confusion. Since birth she had acquired an inordinate amount of

property, and her bottles, teats, milk powder, napkins, creams, pins and cotton wool were now lost to view amidst a welter of tiny garments, teddy-bears, Beatrix Potters and various nursery labour-saving devices. As I excavated frantically she lay on the bed beating the air with clenched fists, kicking like a full-back and roaring like a wounded tigress. Then suddenly she turned crimson all over – plainly convulsions were upon us – so I dropped everything and seized her. She hit me in the eye, glared at me with unfocused hatred and opened her mouth still wider to reveal within it a lump of wool sucked off her jacket. Trembling all over, I removed the wool and put her to the breast. But she was smelling like an open sewer and at once I visualized septic nappy-rash. Replacing her on the bed, I began to fumble with safety-pins; these were of a kind unfamiliar to me, known as 'double-safety', and they refused to open.

As the decibels increased I remembered that bottles must be sterilized and fled to the adjacent kitchen to put a saucepan on the cooker. Back with my terrifying daughter, I wrenched the pins out by brute force, lacerating my left thumb, and unravelled the arcane complexities of the nappy. It was our joint misfortune that Tibetan babies do *not* wear nappies . . . Rachel promptly kicked much of the contents onto her face and hair. Racing to the kitchen sink for a basin of water, I passed the boiling saucepan and raced back to the bedroom for the bottle. When I returned with the basin Rachel had evenly distributed the remaining contents of the nappy (a lot) over the counterpane and wallpaper – and she was purple from head to toe. *Pneumonia!* I desperately wrapped her – unwashed – in the nearest woollen covering, which happened to be her swanky christening shawl. Thus attired, she abruptly stopped yelling, but only because she had resumed wool-collecting. Tucking her under one arm like a rugger-ball, I grabbed a packet of milk powder and sprinted to the kitchen. When the one-handed mixing of a feed defeated me I laid her on the table and thrust an (unsterilized) teat into her mouth by way of weaning her off the shawl. By this stage I was sweating with terror and could hardly hold the milk packet steady while reading the instructions. These conveyed that death would claim the average European infant if *everything* connected with the feed were not sterilized. Throwing a spoon and mixing-cup into the boiling water, I thought wistfully of Tibetan babies, who consume dirt by the ounce and flourish on it. Then the noises within the shawl changed; Rachel had discarded the teat and reverted to her old addiction.

Consulting my watch, I calculated that all the relevant articles must now be sterilized and seized the Napisan that my kind friend had left on the table; I was about to measure it into the mixing-cup when I realized that the smell was wrong. During the next five minutes, while I was filling the bottle, Rachel achieved a crescendo of protest against neglected malnutrition. As I struggled with the intractable new teat the bottle skidded off the table into a basket of earthy potatoes and my meticulous sterilization was all undone. Retrieving it, I pretended that Rachel was a Tibetan and thrust it into her ever-open mouth. My morale was slightly restored when she finished that first mother-mixed feed without registering any disapproval, then burped dutifully and fell into a deep sleep. Returning to the bedroom, I washed and dressed her while she lay supine. And for the next five hours she slept without a whimper, while I put down several double-whiskies, sponged the wallpaper above the bed, steeped nappies and other casualties, made four feeds to go in the refrigerator and laid a rubber sheet and a clean nappy on the bed.

By the time our hostess returned all was serene. 'How are you getting on?' she eagerly enquired. 'Fine,' I replied casually. 'Really there's nothing to this baby-care business – it's just a question of establishing a routine.'

Before our return to Ireland on December 23rd Rachel made her first media appearance when Maureen Cleeve interviewed me for the London *Evening Standard* and mother and daughter were photographed together. I then saw a danger signal flashing. Limelight at ten days old is harmless, but I vowed that Rachel must henceforth – until adolescence – be shielded from the media. On occasions this has been difficult, especially at the end of our

Andean trek when international pressmen in Lima sniffed the fact that a nine-year-old had just walked Pizarro's 1300-mile route from Cajamarca to Cuzco. But the effort was necessary. An elderly single mother with an unusual career and only one child runs the risk of involving that child too deeply in her own life, and thus unwittingly slowing or distorting its development as an individual.

I had never, since becoming pregnant, thought of motherhood as a full-time job. Obviously, Rachel would have to come first, but for both our sakes she must not be allowed to dominate my life. So at the beginning of January I was joined in Lismore by a dear Tibetan friend, Rinchen Dolma Taring – 'Amala' to her friends. Amala was taking four months off from running the Tibetan Refugee Children's Home in Mussoorie, Northern India, to write her autobiography (*Daughter of Tibet*, published by John Murray in 1970). My task was to edit, but not ghost, her manuscript. Ghosting would have been simpler; the editing of that book was more demanding than the writing of most of my own. And all the detailed preparatory work *had* to be done within the four months. During that time, Amala – an experienced mother and grandmother – virtually monopolized baby-care while I devoted ninety per cent of my day to her book. This was an ideal practical arrangement but, emotionally, I found it frustrating. I longed to have more time to be in physical contact with Rachel; for the first six months of her life that was a powerful need and often I looked enviously at Amala, settling down to give Rachel her bottle while I settled down to disentangle the latest chapter. But Amala and I are so close that I never resented this situation. I only regretted it, and wondered how some mothers could voluntarily, for no reason, relinquish the care of their small babies to others.

Rachel was three years old when she first went abroad, to France, Germany and Switzerland – where she enjoyed a mini-trek in the Jura Mountains. A year later we went camping and trekking in the Dordogne where she happily walked ten miles a day, in easy stages. I reckoned then that she was ready to leave

Europe and a month before her fifth birthday we travelled to Coorg, in South India.

I was now back on course as an earner. My book about Coorg was followed by one about Baltistan, in the Karakoram Mountains of the Western Himalaya, where Rachel (aged six) rode a retired polo pony for hundreds of miles while I walked. To the astonishment of many, we had survived the impecunious static years, though in retrospect I can't think how . . .

In the summer of 1978, when Rachel was nine, we set off on what may have been our last long journey together. Rachel is now at boarding-school, and post-school she will doubtless want to travel with contemporaries rather than with an ageing Mamma. For reasons explained in my book *Eight Feet in the Andes* (John Murray, 1983), this trek was exceptionally gruelling – a three-month walk through the remotest areas of some of the toughest mountain terrain in the world. And that shared experience had an unexpected effect on our relationship. I didn't at once realize what had happened. But after our return it gradually became apparent that the relationship had acquired an extra dimension. Rachel was now something more than a daughter. Her response to extreme hardship – which I would not have inflicted on her could I have foreseen it – in a subtle way made us *equals*. Companions first, mother and daughter second. However, this shift of emphasis, though fundamental and enduring, *is* subtle. It has not affected my imposition of old-fashioned maternal discipline, or Rachel's tolerant condescension – now that she is adolescent – towards a non-with-it mother who knows nothing about the latest fashions and has never heard of Neil Young.

PART THREE

Another Generation

Isabel Marney

'When, at the age of nineteen, my son had one ear pierced and wandered around wearing an ear-ring, I wondered what he was trying to prove to me'.

I was a shy, withdrawn child with no close relationship with either my father or my mother, who was excessively possessive. My brother was born when I was eight years old. I was pleased to have a brother, but the difference in age was too great for us to be companions until we were adults. I never resented his arrival, or felt that I had lost my 'only' child status. He was born at home and, although I knew that we were to have a new baby, I did not appreciate that it was actually happening. I was very worried, and frightened by my mother's moans and cries. I went outside and played far enough away from the house not to hear her.

I grew up with no love of dolls, and my favourite toy was a teddy-bear. I adored books, and read avidly. Christmas and birthdays were always a time for more books, most of which I still have. I was devoted to our dog, two cats and rabbits. Living in a small village, a swing in a tree afforded great pleasure. From six years old I went to school in the nearest town, so did not mix a great deal with the local children, most of whom came some distance from farms in the area.

At the age of ten, my father was made redundant, in the 1930s slump, and from then on he had a series of jobs, not only in England, but in Wales and Scotland as well. I began a period of changing schools which did nothing to help my lack of self-confidence. No sooner did I succeed in making some friends, than we moved hundreds of miles away. I believe that it was as a result of this that I found it increasingly difficult to form friendships. I looked forward to the day when I would leave home to go to college, and when I eventually qualified as a teacher I took a job a great distance from home. Boys were not interested in me, nor I in them, and I only went out with two, for short periods before I married. However, I made two life-long girl friends at college, and through one of them met my husband.

It was soon after the war, and we were married when he was twenty-four and I was twenty-five. I had no wish to have any children. For five years I had been teaching five- to seven-year-olds, and was quite happy to see them in a classroom, but failed to imagine having any of my own. In any case, my husband had to complete his training, interrupted by the war, and get his qualifications before he could get a job, so we decided that I should continue teaching for at least another three years. I had taught in a city, far from home, sharing a flat with another teacher, and was happy to be financially independent. I never relished the idea of being dependent on someone else. The years slipped by very rapidly and I continued my career. Then, because we had begun to be less careful about contraception, at the age of thirty-eight I became pregnant. I was shattered, and for some weeks very upset. Abortion never entered my head.

I felt sure that a child would come between my husband and myself. However, by three months I had grown accustomed to the idea of being a Mum. And then I had a miscarriage. It might be supposed that I would be relieved, but, perversely, I now felt extremely inefficient that I had not succeeded in producing a child. Soon I was pregnant again, and my son was born when I was thirty-nine, and, as I did not wish him to be an only child, my daughter followed twenty months later. My husband and parents were all delighted, though later I found that anything that went wrong my mother attributed to my age!

It was a strange coincidence that at the time of my first pregnancy both my sisters-in-law were also expecting babies. One had been married for twelve years, and was having her first child. The other, also in her thirties, was expecting her second. Of my two college friends one had had no children, but the other had had both of hers in her thirties. Another friend had produced three between thirty-two and thirty-seven. So my age did not seem in any way extraordinary to me. At this time I made friends with a younger girl who was ultimately to have four children, and for several years pregnancy seemed to be the order of the day. I seldom saw my sisters-in-law during my first (successful) pregnancy, as we lived far apart, but when we did meet we had plenty of comparisons to make.

My only concession to 'old age' was to book an amenity room for myself in hospital. I did not feel that I would have a great deal in common with the young mums who would probably enjoy the radio going all day.

During both pregnancies I attended the antenatal clinic at the local cottage hospital, run by my own doctor. At no time was I treated in any way differently from the bright young things who attended with me – some under twenty. But this was in 1961, and I understand that, after thirty, one can be made to feel ancient these days. Sometimes I looked around the clinic and smiled at myself as I thought, 'I could be your mum!' Neither doctors nor nurses ever drew attention to my age, and I was not made to feel in any way unusual. Everyone was extremely kind.

I experienced persistent nausea up to five months of my first pregnancy and, later on, heartburn. Fortunately, neither plagued me during the second. But I continued to teach until six months, and managed to push these discomforts into the background.

Both pregnancies were quite normal, but my son arrived fourteen days early, appropriately on Passion Sunday! My daughter was ten days early. Both were born in the local hospital. Unfortunately, at a late stage of labour it was discovered that my son was facing the wrong way – face up – and he was delivered by forceps, under an anaesthetic. My second confinement was a very speedy affair. I arrived at the hospital at 5.30 a. m. and my daughter was in my arms by 7.15 a. m. My doctor was a gentle, elderly man, full of reassurances that I was in safe hands, but I was not given any details of the actual birth, and no relaxation classes were held. I read books and talked to friends. I felt that the pain must be bearable – after all everyone survived it! As it happened, the first time I was not put to the test. The second time I was only given a very small pain-killing injection. I had made a pledge to myself that no matter how bad it was, I would not utter a sound. I was able to keep that pledge quite easily. I did not find it a beautiful or inspiring experience, as I have heard some women claim. It seemed rather messy, and I felt that I was in a very undignified situation. I was very glad that it was not common practice in those days for husbands to be present!

I felt a sense of achievement, similar to passing a driving test, but no overwhelming love for either baby. In fact, I was considerably deflated at the news, 'It's a girl.' I had wanted boys on both occasions.

At no time during either pregnancy did I ever consider the possibility that, because of my age, I might give birth to defective children. It simply never occurred to me, although I knew a woman of thirty-seven whose second baby suffered from Down's Syndrome.

There were two features of pregnancy which took me by surprise, though both were unimportant. I had, of course, heard of morning sickness. No one had ever suggested that it could well be morning, noon and night sickness. Not that I was often actually sick, but the sensation of nausea stayed all the time.

I was also familiar with the craving syndrome. I had heard of women demanding anything from kippers to strawberries in January. But I was unprepared for a turning against things. I found I was unable to face tea and coffee, and could not have smoked a cigarette if I had been paid. This was probably a good thing as now smoking is considered harmful. I drank cocoa, which

I could face. These phenomena were common to both pregnancies. My sister-in-law could not touch any hot drink, and survived on fizzy lemonade. Yet, as I was still in the labour ward, waiting to be stitched, I drank a cup of tea with great relish, and it tasted like nectar!

A strange thing happened during my first pregnancy. There was a room in the cottage where we were living in the first six months which, to me, had a dreadful mouldy smell, and if I was forced to go into that room I held my breath and made a mad dash. It was not a room we used, and we had quite a lot of furniture stored in it. I was horrified that our things must be getting ruined with mould, and no amount of reassurance on the part of my husband could convince me that there was no smell in that room. When the things were moved out they were perfectly sound.

Now I was alone I had to cope on my own. I had never been particularly interested in any one else's babies, and had never had any urge to nurse or cuddle them. I was content to look in the pram and make suitably complimentary remarks. I felt no differently with my own. Secretly, I was afraid of handling them, and felt totally inadequate. Both cried a great deal and I felt helpless to do anything about it. I had been accustomed to being able to communicate with children in school. There was no way to understand a small baby. I worried a good deal about the crying, but other people's advice was to ignore it. I couldn't.

Then came the worst part. I know now that I must have suffered from severe postnatal depression after both births. The second time lasted right on to the menopause which I experienced at forty-four years old. Then, at last, I was revived by antidepressants. The Health Visitor called regularly. She told me not to worry about the crying. I took both babies regularly to the clinic for weighing, injections etc. I tried to appear cheerful, and I suppose I succeeded. But, at home, I cried a good deal. I would stand at the sink, rinsing the interminable nappies, with tears dripping off the end of my nose. Life, as I had known it, had come to an end. I could not visualize a time when it could return to what I considered normal.

It hit me very forcibly that, while my life had changed out of all recognition, my husband's had stayed exactly the same. This, I resented. He still spent the same amount of time on sport. Golf at weekends and badminton during the week. I felt trapped. I was unable to drive, and too depressed to make the effort to learn. My husband used to say, 'Don't grumble at me doing what I enjoy. You are free to go out whenever I am at home.' But where could I go? The nearest cinema or theatre was many miles away, and the bus service almost non-existent. I had never been interested in sport, and, without a car, I had not got a friend near enough to visit in the evening. I had loved reading, but even that relaxation was denied me because, owing to the babies crying, and my own depression, I could not concentrate. I joined a women's organization which met once a month. It was not quite my scene, but it forced me to do something different. When my husband and I went out together I often had to come home early because I felt so shaky and unwell.

The second thing which contributed to my sense of desperation was peculiar to me, and I do not think would affect most new mothers. It was the loss of what I had always prized, my financial independence. Three months before my son was born we had moved into our newly-built house, and I had put most of my money into it. Now I had nothing to fall back on. The situation I found myself in, I have never really been able to understand. It remains a mystery that my husband, who is normally a generous man, refused to give me any allowance, no matter how small, and would not agree to a joint bank account. It could not have been because he thought I was careless with money. On the contrary, born of Yorkshire and Scottish parents, I was thrifty in the extreme. If I tried to discuss the situation he would pick up the newspaper, or turn on the TV. I learned for the first time how stubborn he could be, and how reluctant to enter into a discussion. I cried about it, but the only response I could get out of him was, 'If there is anything you want, you have only to ask, and I will give you the money.' It made me feel untrustworthy, and I refused to ask for a penny unless it was a case of dire necessity. So, for three-

and-a-half years I survived on the family allowance which, in those days, was about eight shillings a week. It usually went on presents for the family.

Then a heaven-sent opportunity arose. I was asked to return to teaching for three mornings a week. It was the light at the end of the tunnel. From then on things started to improve. I had nine hours a week away from the house, a cheque at the end of the month, and I learned to drive. After a while I graduated to fifteen hours a week, and bought a small car. The children went to a nursery school, and I had a woman in two mornings a week to help with the housework. Later, I returned to full-time teaching.

What did I expect of motherhood? I think I imagined a sort of miniature school with only two pupils. I liked to teach children, but did not enjoy looking after their physical well-being. Dirty nappies, sicky bibs, etc. repelled me. I did not feel close to the children. I looked on them as I might on two children in a class. In the past when I had said I was not interested in having children of my own, friends and relations always assured me that one's own were quite different. I did not find this to be true in my case. I read to them both a great deal, which was something I really enjoyed, and was always ready to do. I looked forward to the day when I could start to teach them to read. It came as a disappointment to me that they did not want to learn to read, and have never developed a love of books. As they grew older they were so totally unlike me, in appearance and ways, that I could hardly believe that I had ever had any part in their creation. We seemed to live on different wavelengths, and I have never come to understand them better. When, at the age of nineteen, my son had one ear pierced and wandered around wearing an ear-ring, I wondered what he was trying to prove to me. I said nothing at all.

My husband liked to be able to pursue his interests peacefully, and avoid any unpleasantness. My daughter was a naughty, wilful child, given to tantrums if she did not get her own way, even at the age of fourteen. I was often cross with her and smacked her. My husband always took her part, and whatever she did he said it was my fault. He was not prepared to elaborate. This caused a good deal of friction between us over the years, and we grew apart. However, now that both children are away taking three-year B.Sc. Hons. Degrees, I feel more calm and relaxed than I have done for years, and my husband and I are closer than we have been since they were born.

I have learned that I expected too much of my children. Because my husband and I had achieved a great deal more than our parents, in that we had O and A Levels, professional jobs, and a middle-class standard of living, I wanted my children to be much cleverer than we were. They were simply good-average. They took for granted the cars, dancing and music lessons, the horse etc. I know that I was totally inadequate as a parent, and that I let my children down. My early decision was the right one. I should not have had children. But they have made my husband very happy. And, if I had never had them, perhaps I would feel that I had missed out on a great experience.

Mature mums – do not despair. I am sure that my experiences are by no means common, and they had nothing to do with my age. There was something lacking in me, which made them unable to confide in me, and discuss their problems. They probably found comfort and companionship in each other.

Lois Heiger

'My daughter came to motherhood much younger, had two children close together, and is relieved to be at home. Whereas I felt the loss of my career, she proved not to be career-minded. I admire tremendously the way she works in the house and is vastly patient and friendly with her two small boys. As a grandmother, I try not to swamp her. Once a week we pay each other a visit. A present matter for discussion is whether she should try for a third child at the ripe old age of thirty-six.'

We had an extraordinarily Victorian upbringing – starched pinnies, governess, regular church, a lot of punishment and pi-jaw. But I will say that we had good play opportunity and four weeks by the sea each year in a furnished house, which was great. And the parents really bothered to make it fun. Our house was suburban, not the grand affair, with a seldom-used drawing room. The kitchen was my 'best place', as the maids played with us there in the evening. We had a big nursery upstairs, rather cramped bedroom space, a garden for jumping and bubble-blowing, hardly any visitors apart from aunts. Dinner at the weekends was a very well-behaved occasion. I did *not* have a great sense of being loved, though my father talked sentimentally and we had to kiss him at breakfast. My sister complains that they used no terms of endearment. However, we didn't have to treat the furniture as holy, there was always the noise of the piano going and quarrels. Our education was good and we all worked hard at our homework, which I rather enjoyed.

My mother was an efficient person. I think she protected father, who was not too robust. Their marriage was a devoted one, the children coming second in affection. She had a cheerful nature, but was very hard on one's sex-curiosity or rudeness. When I became a mother, I did not model myself on her at all. I don't like needlework and I tried to be available for my daughter and not be stuffy and grown-up with her. We have a pretty good relationship now. I ought to mention that my first four years were during the Great War; we had bombs and went into the lower hall for air-raids. I imagine that the parents and maids were anxious, but I don't remember being frightened.

My mother died when I was twelve. My father was a particularly uncommunicative kind of person and very Church of England. He so disapproved my marrying a Jew that he didn't even give me a wedding present. His two sisters stayed at home to care for their mother, as did my mother's younger sister, so I surmise that he visualized his old age being attended to by his 'three jolly girls', as he called us. My two sisters went to a domestic science college and did stay at home, unmarried.

I never learned any child care or chores (except dusting) and did not want to know. I was distinctly academic. I couldn't cook at all when, at the age of twenty-seven, I took a flat in order to house a Jewish girl that my brother had befriended in Czechoslovakia and wanted to find a home for before the Nazis arrived.

I really never thought of myself as an 'older mum'. I'd always had good health and was confident in my body, though in no way a sporting type! I remember Hazel saying, when staying with me (we were about twenty-nine and were abluting), 'What a waste of two perfectly good females. We'd better look out, or it will be too late!' Before that, I'd assumed one was pursued, or not (not much in my case as I was not a flirt), and that proposals and affairs lay with the man to initiate. After this conversation, I believe I went to the Fabians' Summer School with a hope that there might be young men to meet. It was there I met 'my fate', but he was not a very young man!

I'd been engaged secretly to a probation officer when I was about 24; he was tough and very left wing. Although we kissed (and I fell over in the process pretty often!) it went no further, even when we shared a bedroom in a friend's house. He said he couldn't trust himself. I think I wasn't very provoking either, as I was definitely inhibited about dancing and had had a traumatic passage of arms with my mother over exchanging sex information with friends (facts prised from a medical dictionary), which I guess left me rather awkward, though I'd read enough to be reasonably sophisticated. Well, in the end David called it off: no explanations given; me weeping but accepting.

First intercourse was with an oldish, clever, but rough working man, who got little reaction out of me. We were together many years. His mind I enjoyed, not his body. Then I fell for a married man who made a very heart-stirring friend. Sitting next to him at a concert, I'd feel very sexy. After many years of abstinence, he said, 'Tonight's the night.' I was dead tired that day, so, although he seemed delighted, I wasn't – except to see a loved face on the pillow in the morning. He told his wife and it was all over!

Iz, being fourteen years older than me, made no snide comments on my age. He was well up in all the manuals, got me fitted with a cap and went through the motions for arousal but, till one night when he performed twice, I can't say I was properly gratified. Then I said, 'This is the one.' But it never happened again like that, alas! I've had a few lovers since then, but though they made me feel good and I admired them, I wasn't properly in love. I think with all this, I'm trying to say to myself that I'm not a success as a 'bird', what with a Victorian upbringing and not a very good selection of blokes to pick from. Though none of the chaps failed to perform, I'm sure we could have done better. This makes me puzzle over the fact that I found pregnancy and birth so easy. You might think I'd be stiff in that department.

I didn't think about having children when I was in my twenties because marriage seemed an unlikely happening. At university there were very few affairs going on and there wasn't much social life for me in the town where I went to work afterwards. I was in my thirties when I met my husband and the war was on. He'd had no children by his first wife and we didn't even discuss the matter of having some ourselves. I was working as an almoner in a hospital and taking the Mental Health Course. One assumed that having children during air-raids was not the done thing. I thought he didn't want kids as he's rather academic and eccentric but, after the war, he said, 'What about a family?' I had no objections but, as nothing happened, we went to get medical advice. They lost the specimens of sperm and said vaguely that a holiday might do the trick, which it did! I realized during a lecture that I was pregnant. I felt absolutely thrilled.

When I got pregnant, I kept at work till three months before, though it was quite tough home visiting on a bike in the snow. I did not *need* the money, but felt aggrieved that Iz never gave me a dress allowance when I stopped work . . . not till *much* later! My health has always been good and I had a good pregnancy. I had had considerable difficulty adjusting to Iz, as he is a first-class neurotic and had a hangover from his failed first marriage. I feared he'd not shine as a dad, but in the event he helped over night crying and played with Ba, though he had abusive moods.

I did cycling and gardening up to the very day. I had performed all the Dick Read exercises very thoroughly, so I felt confident and well-prepared. Mind you, I'd not listened to any horror stories about birth. The clinic sister used to laugh that I sat there reading while the other mums were in a gruesome huddle! Looking back, the baby books I read seemed to be written by older women and one felt they were aimed at sensible mothers, not flibberty-gibbets. The mums I knew in Child Guidance (this is where I was working) were on the whole not youngsters. I believe my mother had good confinements as she was wide-hipped, like me. She had no disasters associated with giving birth and I didn't expect any myself, though I knew about cords round babies' necks and eclampsia etc.

The clinic doctor was a remarkable, mature middle-aged

person. She had a sense of humour and she egged me on to be confined at home, which suited me fine. She said to me, 'Many tribes believe that the older mother will produce warriors.' This was meant as a light-hearted encouragement and it was the only comment on my age that I recall. The GP and midwife bleated a lot about the anaesthetics they would inflict; I didn't contradict, but inwardly I thought, 'Not if I can help it!' Giving birth when you are overdue, in nice hot weather, in your own home, with the evening sun coming in the window, your husband cooking the supper and nobody interfering is my ideal of how it should be done. I wasn't anxious.

The birth itself was terrific. I was two weeks overdue and Iz was due in America for a conference. I started after a hard day's work, with the plumber in the flat. I took raspberry-leaf tea (Swedish tip) and sent for the midwife. She mopped up my vomit at 5 p.m. and said she'd return after another visit: I should be delivered at midnight. I threw myself about in the most original way and was sitting on the loo, fully-clad, when the head crowned at 7.30. I waddled to the bed. Iz said, 'Let's have the rest of it!' I ran through the obvious cautions needed, gave one push and she came out. We just sat and laughed. We phoned for the doctor, who was furious! 'Give her the gas and air,' says he to Midwife. 'She's torn. I'll have to stitch her.' I say, 'No need. Dick Read says you're anaesthetised there for thirty minutes after.'

So it proved, to their amazement!

Knowledge had been my midwife, an excellent one. I hadn't been put off by the grisly warnings; I didn't have to worry about getting to hospital in time. I was eager to prove that Dick Read was right and, though I was alone, I wasn't left alone unpleasantly. Iz was on call downstairs. If Ba had arrived during the day, the story might have been more harrowing. So my main feeling during the labour was the satisfaction that I could manage myself; but also that I was in the hand of a mighty power, who squeezed me like a sponge. During the ensuing night I was sleepless, with tired legs, and viewed the baby with amazement as it lay like a soap doll in its crib.

Looking back, I see I hadn't thought of myself as an elderly primigravida. The handicaps of age didn't enter my mind until Iz suggested a second child. I said, 'No, there's not room.' When we got a larger flat later, I agreed to try for a year, although I knew that my hearing problems (otosclerosis) would increase if we succeeded. As I was already thirty-seven, I had misgivings about the fatigue of picking up toys and I was quite relieved to call off the enterprise.

Today I do feel sorry for poor mothers who are past enjoying their babies, but I can't envy the very young mums who still seem keener on the pram than on its contents.

The breastfeeding began well. Then Iz went to America and, as the midwife's husband had just killed himself, I had no one to consult. By the time Ba was three weeks old, I felt I had insufficient milk. No one in the flats had children, nor anyone in my family. A doctor friend of Iz's happened to be over from the States. He made a call. This gave me a boost and I managed. I fancy I had as little anxiety handling Ba as I did because the birth had gone so well and I had studied psychology.

I didn't go back to work. I had a home help to cook and clean for two weeks. No one else helped, but I was grateful to Iz for responding to night crying (we did share the time) and for coping when I was making supper and the baby wouldn't hush.

I have always jibbed at housework. In fact, when Iz proposed to me, I retorted, 'I'm a bad choice, I'm utterly undomesticated.' However, I stayed at home and did chores till my daughter was eleven, when I got a char and took a part-time job. My husband retired when I was fifty and after a while took over the cooking and shopping. About three years ago, I lost my energy and sense of humour and stayed in bed all day. He then took over the cleaning, too, as he had offended the char, who left! Actually, I was brewing up an immense brain tumour. My personality returned to normal when I'd had it removed. During the same year, I had a mastectomy, meningitis and an operation to remove a carunculus of the ureter, so he was considerate and kept on his housework jobs. I have managed to regain the washing up, ironing, window-cleaning and part-time jobbing gardenership, but he won't let me touch *his* new washing machine and Hoover! So I don't, nor do I really want to!

Relationships with people did change because of Ba. Life with Iz improved because of his sharing the birth and because he took part in the baby's life. Yes, I feel that a father is more likely to be devoted, even if annoyed, than a childless husband, and that presence at the birth does bond a couple, though I must admit that I catch myself feeling that our child is my child only. I also got to know women at the clinic a bit and one in the court who returned with a child. This kid is still a friend of Ba's. My family was very pleased with me. My dad was good with Ba and knitted for her! Several friends called more often and were warmer. They enjoyed the baby.

Other men weren't in the picture. I made more friends when Ba started in a nursery group, which was very early so she wouldn't be spoilt. One of these is a major friend though living in Scotland now. I suppose I had to stop going out, because of the feeding, though I did go to the flicks alone sometimes. When Ba was weaned, I used to do evening classes, which rather annoyed Iz!

I hit Ba once for emptying a bowl of hyacinths. I resented her complaints about food, which Iz pandered to. I learned I was capable of hard physical work, and patience. I even learned to sew for her. I loved the breastfeeding, which continued till nine months. The neighbours were querulous about Ba crying outside in her pram, quite unrealistic and unsympathetic. People in general make a fuss of mothers, but can't comprehend their tensions and fatigue. When Ba was two, she was ill in hospital. There was only weekly visiting. I was upset and tearful about this and fought quite hard to get it changed. I also reacted savagely when she was hit by a teacher. I am now more aware of mothers getting fed up and I don't feel housework is a soft option. My daughter came to motherhood much younger, had two children close together and is relieved to be at home. Whereas I felt the loss of my career, she proved not to be career-minded. I admire tremendously the way she works in the house and is vastly patient and friendly with her two small boys. As a grandmother, I try not to swamp her. Once a week we pay each other a visit. A present matter for discussion is whether she should try for a third child at the ripe old age of thirty-six.

Alison Satterthwaite

'I am as old as, or even older than, the mothers of many of
the wives around me. I get along with them, but I'm a
different generation.'

I was thirty-seven when I became an 'elderly primigravida', not
because of medical problems or a career, but simply because I
didn't get married until I was thirty-four.

I was born in Perth, Western Australia, in 1936 and, a vicar's
daughter, lived at home until I was twenty-six. Why I didn't leave
home earlier is difficult to explain. Perhaps going over some
events might help.

My brother joined the Australian army at eighteen, married, and
that was him gone. At the same age, my sister got a job with Civil
Aviation who supplied a hostel for employees, so that was her
gone. A few years later, my father, having itchy feet, moved my
mother and me to Melbourne. Two years later, they moved to a
country parish. My mother took ill, was not properly diagnosed
until too late and, within a few months, died of cancer of the liver.

When she first became ill, I gave up my typist's job in
Melbourne and went down home in the country to keep house – a
job at which I was terrible as my mother had never taught me very
much. My mother died in November 1956. I was then twenty and
had found work on the country telephone exchange. My father, in

his usual way (thinking of himself first, so everyone just had to fit in), went on holiday to Perth. So I decided to transfer to the Perth Exchange. For the next eighteen months I lived with one of my aunts there.

My father, meanwhile, had moved back near the city of Melbourne, not far from my sister's job, so she moved in with him, kept house and went to work. She then met and wanted to marry Robin. She wrote me an impassioned thirteen-page letter, saying that it was my turn to live with Dad, she'd done her stint, etc. So I came home, got a transfer with the G.P.O. again, worked full-time shift work (which I loved) and kept house for five years. I had two boyfriends and lots of time when I had no one at all. I seldom went anywhere, had very few friends, except a few of my older friends, now married, and led an extremely dull life, because I just never had the guts or whatever to go to a dance on my own and I just didn't know how to meet people. I was not a party type; smoking and drinking and so on didn't appeal to me. I would get depressed at my life and possible future. Every so often I would think about going to another State, but was too afraid. You can be even more lonely in a big city living in a bedsit when everyone in your office goes home to their own lives. So I never had the courage to leave home, until chance led me to going to Ocean Island.

I spent the next seven years working as a typist on two very small islands, twenty-three miles south of the Equator, due north of New Zealand. It took eight days on a company ship to get there. And here I finally had my 'youth' – parties, drink, sex; but the real me came out before very long, and I realized that none of that interested me very much. I preferred a nice steady relationship, quiet home life, and my idea of a good night is at the theatre or a small group of friends talking.

The money was marvellous, but I couldn't live this life for ever, so I had a last fling before settling into being an 'old maid' living in a bedsit in Melbourne. I did a month's flying holiday around the Far East and, as fate would have it, on the first stop, which was Singapore, met up with my husband.

He was thirty, I was thirty-four; we got talking. He was tired of living in British Army Barracks, ready to settle down in his own home; I was tired of being odd one out amongst my married friends. He suggested we marry each other; and the joke became reality. Three weeks later (just in case) I bought my wedding dress in Manila and two months later, having been with him only three days (and being carried away with the whole romantic aspect of it – like a Barbara Cartland novel) I went back to Singapore to be married. It seems I was out to prove the truth of the old adage, 'marry in haste – repent at leisure'.

I had been terrified of the pain of childbirth for as long as I could remember and had never been particularly interested in other people's children, nor in having my own. My husband, I found out after we married, just loved little babies and dearly wanted at least one of his own. So for his sake, and because everyone around me had them, and I felt rather out of things, I told myself that millions of women have had babies and lived through it, and even gone back for more. It's not likely to kill you in this day and age.

When we first married I stayed with my in-laws in Yorkshire until I could join my husband on base in West Germany. Three months later, after I had joined my husband in Hameln, a little village where we were based for the next four years, I went to the gynaecologist at the Military Hospital. Because of my age, they ran me through the usual fertility tests and told us there was nothing wrong. The fact that my husband and I didn't have sex all that often didn't help me get pregnant. He never seemed to be all that terribly interested. It was as if, once we had sex, he'd get the taste and look for it every day for the next couple of days, and then go three weeks without wanting it. As you can imagine, I felt extremely embarrassed to tell the doctor this, especially in view of why I was seeing him. When I finally did, he said, 'We'll soon sort that out.' So we had to make love on certain days. I became pregnant after two and a half years.

To my surprise I had a trouble-free pregnancy. The baby was very still all along: in fact, twice I thought he had died as I felt no movement for a few days. But, apart from raised blood pressure towards the end, it all went very well indeed. My husband was away for the first six months, but I like my own company and could please myself if I wanted to go back to bed in the day. I had the car, so could get out, and I had a girlfriend who checked on me every day. So, on the whole, especially with no aggro at home, I had a very peaceful and serene pregnancy.

For antenatal care I went to the Army Doctor and SSAFA Sister. I gather it's pretty much like many British civilian set-ups, only our clinic didn't have any relaxation or mothercraft classes, nor did the hospital, which did the usual 2 p.m. appointment thing. The difference with us was that, if a bus came in from a distant army garrison with twelve pregnant ladies on board (a common occurrence), whoever got up the stairs last was the last to be seen.

I had been told that I would be well looked after at my age but I never found this to be so. In fact, I would call it neglect. As soon as the test proved positive, I asked for an initial check-up appointment and was given a date when I would be over three months pregnant. I was appalled and extremely upset. I got so hysterical, in fact, that they quickly changed it to the following week. They consolidated this neglect after the baby was born, as I would wake up every night for weeks after with my nightie and my hair wringing wet. The clinic sister said it must be some kind of fever that built up by day and broke at night, but nothing was done about it.

I was in labour for twentyfour hours. Two hours before the birth, the anaesthetist came in and, seeing the state I was in, gave me such a dose that from then on I was completely without any feeling from the waist down. Consequently, I didn't know if I was pushing the right way or the right strength when the baby came. This probably contributed to the many stitches I needed ('How many have I got?' 'Too many for me to count.'). I also had massive bruising, and for four weeks after the birth could sit on nothing without a rubber ring cushion – I had to drive the car sitting on it. Going round corners I nearly took off. Only the seat belt and clinging to the wheel kept me there.

The hospital made us look after our babies by our beds from 6 a.m. until 10 p.m. David developed jaundice and needed two-hourly feeding. I was supposed to have salt-water baths. We had to eat in the dining room. Nappies needed changing. And when he cried I had to investigate. I seemed to be up and down off that high hospital bed hundreds of times a day, and it was absolute agony every time. I would lie there shaking, clinging to the edge of the mattress. I'll never forget the sister who called down the passage – 'Now then, Mrs Satterthwaite. Straighten up and take your hand off the wall. You don't have to walk like that.'

By the third day, I couldn't stop crying. I couldn't bear to talk to anyone, or go into the dining room and mix with the others. I, who had been the life and soul of the maternity floor for two weeks before the birth, had a case of post-natal depression. I felt as if I was going insane.

I was put on Valium in a side ward on my own and within thirty-six hours felt I could cope better. So they gave the baby back to me to care for. Unfortunately, one sister told my husband that I had just been looking for attention, there was nothing wrong with me. For years afterwards he would throw this up at me in a row when I got upset over anything.

I came home on Christmas Eve, which was the seventh day. Luckily, my husband adored David so much he would do anything for him – even change nappies, and get up for the two o'clock feeds.

Normally I'm the one to sit up until midnight, but I felt so ill, so exhausted and in such pain, for weeks afterwards, that I fell into bed by nine at night. David was a 'sickie' baby for the first nine months. My husband did the feeds, nappy changing, cleaning up. I *hated* handling the baby; I would rather wash nappies, sterilize bottles – anything except have to feed and bath and change it. Once he went back to work, of course, I had to and, of course, I did. But I handed the baby over with pleasure at 5 p.m. every day. In fact, for the first few months, I could have easily walked out and left the two of them without any regrets.

David was four months old before I felt I loved him. I showed him off to people and I looked after him and I worried over him and was pleased when people admired him, but I didn't love him. I used to look at him sometimes and think, 'You poor little thing – I just don't feel anything for you.' Luckily, I'd heard that this sometimes happened with new mothers and also told myself perhaps his father's love made up for it.

I have often wondered why I felt like this – or perhaps, didn't feel would be more like it. When he was born, they showed him to me for a few seconds. I don't even remember if I held him or not. Then he was taken away until the next morning, I think. So was it due to lack of 'bonding' that they talk so much about? Or was it just that I felt so ill and exhausted that it killed off any other feelings – perhaps I subconsciously resented him for being the cause of the way I felt. Suffice to say, I wouldn't have wished my worst enemy to go through those first few months of pain and I vowed I'd never go through it again for anyone. At least my husband had the baby he wanted, I told myself.

One of us had to be sterilized. John wasn't keen to be himself. Perhaps it was the idea of losing his fertility/manhood type of type of thing. I didn't mind being sterilized. I just wanted to make quite sure that I could never get pregnant again under any circumstances. We had to go before a specialist who had to approve of our application. And so I was sterilized in July 1975, two weeks before we came back to Britain.

As soon as we arrived in England I got a message that my father had died, never having seen David who was named after him and who looks so like him.

When David was four months old, I had a frightening dizzy spell, the only time I'd had such a symptom of hypertension. Since then, I've been on a rather high dosage of tablets daily and I expect I will remain on them for ever.

I found having a baby, with all the extra work and broken nights, tiring as everyone does, but having been at home with not so much to fill my days, I didn't have the shock of someone who has left a busy job with pleasant company, for a baby and no one else around all day. But I came to understand why some mothers batter their babies – until then I just couldn't comprehend how anyone could do such a thing. If you don't feel well yourself, if you're tired because of lack of sleep and exhausted with all the heavy work, when you've tried everything to sort out the crying or whingeing, you can easily reach snapping point. And I only had one child to look after. How much worse with two or three little ones to cope with!

Being older than most mums hasn't given me any extra patience – on the contrary. I just can't be bothered with little ones nowadays, and blow up frequently with poor old David. Is it due to my basic personality? The menopause? Pre-menstrual tension? Or just old age? At forty-seven, I feel I have not 'grown up', just aged bodily and slowed down. I worry that I might have a heart attack or a stroke. (Don't let me be crippled. Just let me live long enough until my son is eighteen or twenty and could look after himself if he had to.) I wonder if I will live to see him married or to see my grandchildren.

When David was small, it felt as if I had an extra leg always attached, dragging along behind me, a burden always there. I resented, and still do, the ways in which having a child tie me, or stop me from being free to do certain things. I would never shirk the responsibility. He is my child, after all, but men do get off easier in this world. If I had a bigger income, perhaps it wouldn't be so bad. I could afford to buy myself some freedom, though I do feel strongly that my child needs me there when he comes home from school, to come and see him in the school concert, needs the security of knowing that if he is ill at school, I will be there if they bring him home.

Having no one to help me from the beginning, except my husband, has sometimes made it harder. All my family have remained in Australia where I still feel I belong. I don't like asking people to look after my child, unless it is for something important, such as a medical appointment or an emergency – not so I can go to cake-icing classes, or shopping or to the movies on my own. I never quite fit in either. In all the army quarters where we've lived, I've been the oldest wife in the patch. Anyone in their thirties has teenage children – and I am as old as, or even older than, the mothers of many of the wives around me. I get along with them, but I'm a different generation. I can't just go out on the spur of the moment at night, as my contemporaries can with their teenagers – I have to get a baby sitter. Even a mother who has her second or third or even fourth child over thirty is different from me. For one thing, the other kids take some of the work off her – fetching and carrying, keeping an eye on the baby/toddler, checking up on it and then acting as baby-sitters at night. And they seem more 'adult' than me too. It must be having these older children and their problems.

I greatly resent the way my husband can just go off to the pub on the spur of the moment, and stay out as long as he likes, knowing I will stay home with our child. He says, 'I don't stop *you* going out' – which is true, and he will stay in to babysit, though I usually have to organize it in advance. But where can I go? Especially on the spur of the moment – on those occasions when I feel fed up to screaming and want to get away from it all, I can't go and sit in a pub, I hate bingo, classes are an organized thing, I can't land up on someone's doorstep for the evening and it all costs money that I feel we can't afford. But all this is common to any mother – not just the older ones.

Over the years I have gone to Adult Education classes (in the day if possible). I have religiously attended the Army Wives' Clubs (only because there was nowhere else I could go out at night) and, of recent years, the National Housewives Register groups, which I find more my style since it is more of a discussion group, meeting in our homes with people taking part in the evening's topic. I have done some voluntary work; I have helped at the school; I knit for the school fête – in desperation (for money and the interest); I've done party-plan selling – twice! It is hard for army wives to get work. Outside firms know you're not staying too long and there is little work on camp. Husbands are often away for weeks on end, so there is difficulty in covering the children then. Most army quarters are full of young wives with young children and I do strongly believe that you should be home when your own children are that age. My mother would have been seventy-one years of age when my son was born – so, even if she had lived near me, the help she might have provided would have been limited.

I still believe that men and women can never be considered equal. Having a child has just confirmed this for me. With money available, a woman can pursue her own interests still, whether in a career or otherwise, by handing over care of the child to someone else, leaving her free both physically and mentally to do other things, if she so wishes. But the social system still means that lower-income mothers are either tied to their children and their homes and get out, if at all, with difficulty – or, if they go to work, have all the extra hassle of organizing cover for their children, or else neglecting them, as some do. So how can we be 'equal' in every way? It's impossible. As my mother, a vicar's wife, used to say – 'It's easily seen God was a man.'

Having a child of my own has made me care more about all other children, though I'm afraid I don't go to the lengths of joining pressure groups or marches – but I feel more for children in trouble or pain, and for the parents too, and I bother more about the safety and welfare of any children I see at play near me. I've also become more of a pacifist (not the best thing for an army wife to be!) as I realize the dreadfulness of wars, the killing and maiming of men – some of them only boys themselves, others with young children left fatherless – and the terrible consequences children suffer in war-torn areas.

If I was asked now if I am glad that I had a child – I don't know what to say really. I love him very much. God knows how I would feel if anything happened to him. And yet, I don't think I would have minded very much if I'd not experienced birth and motherhood. I only wish I could have got married ten years earlier and had my baby when I was younger. I reckon it has taken a lot out of me physically. I feel so tired all the time. I feel like a grandmother instead of a mother of an eight-year-old. But then, maybe I'd feel like this anyway, and at least I can now use David to fetch and carry for me and save me getting up from my chair or tackling the stairs.

Afterword

A year after writing all this, I was asked to bring my story up to date – so perhaps the worst is yet to come. At Christmas, the day before our son's ninth birthday, my husband told me he was leaving me. He had often said this – drunk or sober – through the years, but when he had to start thinking about his future out of the army after next year, he realized he couldn't spend the rest of his days tied to a life of misery with me. He also luckily met someone (divorced with two children) and fell in love for the first time in his life.

So now I am being pushed into the one-parent poverty trap – and I'm terrified, depressed, frightened sick, worried, in a terrible state some days – and likely to be for some time to come, I guess. I will not be sorry to be parted from him. I won't miss him at all, thank goodness – but I feel bitterly resentful that he is not prepared to stick it out for David's sake, as I have been, bitterly resentful that he is condemning David to a childhood where money will be lacking, where he may have to do without in various ways. For myself, I don't care as much – I could survive in a bedsit sharing a kitchen, but how do you bring up a boy into puberty in those conditions? It has been an unhappy twelve years for both of us. We are two completely incompatible people who should never have married.

Five years ago, I nearly decided to leave John. I took David out to Australia for four months to think about things. I spent many sleepless nights sitting, drinking tea in the small hours in the kitchen of my aunt's house, wondering what to do. I kept feeling not only that I ought not to part David from his father, but also that I wouldn't be able to cope, physically or mentally, with working and being a one-parent family, afraid I would go down under it all if I tried, either with a nervous breakdown, or else bad health. So I decided to come back and keep trying.

I now feel that I must think of my future first, and that David must take his chances with his life still before him. Things are as bad in Australia as in England as far as work goes – either for myself or for David later on; and although my family is dwindling in numbers, and they have their own problems of redundancies, no jobs for the school leavers, etc., I feel I badly need some people near me who care, who can give me the love and support I've not had for many years. I always thought David would travel to Australia when he was nineteen or twenty to work; now it is likely to be the reverse, with him coming to see his father and his roots. At least if he does and I'm on my own, near sixty, I hope to have some family, nieces and nephews at least, around me.

So, at the age of forty-seven, my life is changing drastically and so is my son's. He is scared of going to a strange country, strange children, strange schools. He knows all about the Norman Conquest and wants to be a medieval historian. How will he survive? Australia has no castles!

PART FOUR

Facing Infertility, Handicaps and Death

Jill Hepwood

'She is a child first, and handicapped second . . . at times I feel it is a privilege to have her.'

I suppose I had always known that I would want a child one day, but I was in no hurry. I went to the City of Birmingham College of Education and trained as a teacher. Peter and I married soon after I left college when we were both twenty-two years old. I started teaching at Oak Meadow Junior School in Wednesfield and found the job very hard work but immensely rewarding and enjoyable. After training for three years, I was doing what I wanted to do. Two years later I was given a Scale Two post with responsibility for music and later became lower school co-ordinator.

We had started married life in the upstairs of my grandmother's house but, during our first year of marriage, we moved to a modern semi-detached house. Three years later, we moved to an older, detached house which needed quite a lot of work done to it.

When I had been teaching for five years I successfully applied for a Scale Three post at Dovecotes Junior School, on a new estate about ten minutes' walk away. As the school was brand new, the job was very demanding. Most evenings were spent in marking and preparation. There were lots of extra-curricular activities to join in, such as youth hostelling, but again it was very satisfying. We had lots of friends of a similar age to ourselves and led a fairly active social life. We bought a tent and spent our holidays under canvas. The house was gradually, room by room, being decorated to our taste. We were doing nearly all the work ourselves and taking our time. Most of our spare money was spent on the house, buying carpets, curtains and furniture, and a new car. We never spent our money extravagantly on ourselves. We didn't buy lots of clothes, go out for meals, or have holidays abroad. We spent our money on the things we wanted. Life was coasting along.

I suppose it was as I approached the age of thirty that I thought if we were going to start a family we shouldn't leave it too long. Thirty seemed to be an important age, not only from the point of view of my body getting older, but also of the age gap between us and any children we might have. We were beginning to reach a stage where the major spending on our house had been completed. We had a fairly new car, and we could just afford to live on one salary. I had thoroughly enjoyed my nine years of teaching but had definitely reached a stage where I could give it up.

I knew, without them ever saying anything, that my parents would be thrilled if I were to have a child, despite the fact that they never once during our marriage mentioned the subject. In fact, after being told I was pregnant, my mother said she had thought we had decided not to have children. I was not at all sure how Peter might react to having a baby. He was an only child and had not had any contact at all with babies or young children. He showed little interest in them when we did see any and seemed quite awkward in their presence. All the time, whenever we had discussed the subject he always said that he would like a family one day.

One day! I often wondered when that one day would come, or if we would keep putting it off indefinitely. I had never shown any interest in other people's babies and couldn't see why people always wanted to hold and cuddle them. I certainly couldn't understand why couples had children early in their marriage before they had had some time on their own. I suppose there was a vague worry that while we had a happy marriage, would having a baby perhaps change that? For many years a baby seemed like an unnecessary complication and it was much easier to do without. Most of my friends were similar to myself in that they had satisfying careers and no plans for a family.

Now I was beginning to think positively about starting a family. When some close friends told us that they were expecting a baby that influenced me even more. I started mentioning it to Peter and we discussed it for the next two months. I knew he wanted a baby but would need some gentle pushing into making the decision. I am sure the fact that our friends were expecting helped him. We worked out our finances to make sure we could manage. Luckily they are quite straightforward. Once we realized we could just about manage on Peter's salary, and we had decided we definitely *did* want a baby, there was nothing to stop us. I suppose we jokingly thought, 'Well, let's have a go and see what happens.' It was rather a strange feeling after years of taking precautions. As things turned out, I conceived the first time we tried and we were absolutely thrilled – nearly as thrilled as my parents and Peter's mum! Unfortunately, Peter's dad had died two years before, but we know he would have been absolutely over the moon.

Peter and myself talked a lot about what changes it would mean to us when the baby was born. Our main worry was the loss of freedom we would feel: not being able to go out wherever and whenever we wanted to, but we were prepared for that and ready to accept it.

We also felt we had reached a stage in our lives where events like holidays and Christmas had lost their excitement. We were looking forward to experiencing the wonder and excitement of these things again through the eyes of a child. Peter is a lover of nature and he talked about how he would be able to share this with the child as it grew up.

I thoroughly enjoyed my pregnancy. I looked forward to leaving work, then cried buckets when I did. But then I settled down to enjoy the last three months before the baby was born. I can remember the frustration of being at home and having all the time in the world to do all the jobs that I couldn't physically do like gardening and spring cleaning. I did enjoy being recognized as pregnant by everyone. People who passed me in the street would smile. Men gave up their seats in pubs for me. I enjoyed being cossetted.

At the back of my mind there was always this nagging anxiety that there would be something wrong with the baby. I never really voiced my fears – particularly to doctors – because I knew I would be told that it was a perfectly natural fear and common to every mother-to-be. I told myself this and tried to rationalize the fear. I did know, however, that whenever I had seen programmes on the television about Down's Syndrome it had always meant something special to me, and I had vaguely thought to myself that I would have a child like that. When Peter and I discussed all this after Gemma was born he had thought exactly the same thing.

My pregnancy was absolutely perfect, no problems at all. No high blood pressure and no need for scans. In fact, I used to joke to a friend who had had to have hospital rest for high blood pressure, that no one took any notice of me, they just kept saying that everything was fine. I was never treated differently by anyone because of my age. Gemma was born on the day she was due, 13th August 1982.

My contractions started the evening before while I was at my last National Childbirth Trust class with Peter. This caused a great deal of excitement. By going to the local authority's antenatal classes and the N.C.T. classes I felt I was quite well prepared for the birth of the baby. I certainly understood everything that was going on, but I don't think anyone can prepare you for how painful the contractions are – perhaps I have a low pain threshold! I was determined to stay at home as long as possible, until the contractions were coming about every ten minutes. Peter eventually took me into New Cross Hospital in the early hours of the 13th, complete with book to read, flask of coffee and sandwiches, as recommended by the N.C.T. classes. There were no complications with the birth, but the pain! I did all the breathing to no avail. I used gas and air from the moment I went into hospital and eventually asked for pethidine, which didn't seem to have any effect at the time. After much pushing and getting nowhere I had an episiotomy and Gemma was born at nine a.m., twelve hours after labour had started. I now know why it is called labour!

As soon as Gemma was born we knew she was a Down's baby, although we didn't say so to each other. The reaction of the midwife to the birth of a new baby seemed strangely subdued, which helped to confirm our private fears. I can remember Peter saying, 'I want someone to tell me she's all right. I thought babies had large round eyes.' I pushed my thoughts away. The pethidine injection was working, I think. I seemed to be just drifting. Peter went home to phone our parents and friends. After having my stitches I was taken down to the ward and put into a single room. I woke up once feeling extremely woozy and vaguely thought that perhaps I should ask for my baby, so I pressed the bell and the sister told me that the baby would be brought in after the dinner trays had been round. I accepted this, but sensed that all was not well, and drifted back to sleep.

When the paediatrician eventually came into the room and told me that he feared Gemma had a chromosome defect I accepted it quite calmly – what I had always feared had happened. I can't remember when I started crying. I do know that it was wrong of the paediatrician to tell me when Peter wasn't there, because then I began to worry about how Peter would take the news. We had had so many plans for the baby when it was born and now everything seemed hopeless. As it turned out, Peter came in and said, 'It doesn't matter, Jill. It doesn't matter if there's anything wrong with her.' And from that moment on it didn't matter. She was our baby and we had each other. The nursing staff on the ward were wonderful. They allowed Peter unlimited visiting which really helped. He usually came just after lunch and stayed until cocoa time.

The paediatrician saw us both together and explained that they would take a blood sample from Gemma and send it to Birmingham for analysis. Not only would they be able to confirm that the extra chromosome 21 was present but also whether the condition was a chance occurrence, which was most likely, or a defect in our chromosomes. The results could take about a month, but we told him there was no doubt in our minds that Gemma had Down's Syndrome.

I thought I knew Peter, but even I was amazed at the way he took to fatherhood. He loved to hold and cuddle Gemma and when we got home I wasn't allowed to bath her for a fortnight.

Our parents, understandably, were stunned at first. Books I have read say that when a handicapped child is born you go through the stages of bereavement. You mourn the child you were expecting and lost and learn to accept the child you have. I think grandparents must go through the same process. Our family and friends have in fact been extremely supportive, although I think they were more shattered at first than we were. When we first came home my mother came every day for a week to help me get into a routine.

From a practical point of view she was marvellous. I didn't have to do anything but look after Gemma and talk to the many visitors. At that time, however, my mum and other close family were clutching to the fact that the condition had not been confirmed. We all had only a superficial knowledge of Down's Syndrome, because we had never needed to know anything about it. The paediatrician had explained that there were some characteristics of the condition that Gemma had got, and others she had not got. For example, she has normal creases on the palms of her hands whereas some Down's babies have only a single crease. We all realize now, of course, what a complex condition it is, and that doctors have identified up to 300 clinical characteristics which might be related to Down's Syndrome. The majority of children with Down's Syndrome will have only a small number of these characteristics.

When the condition was confirmed, there was no problem at all with Mum accepting it, and she absolutely adores Gemma, as does everyone who knows her.

Almost immediately we were put in touch with the Down's Children's Association in Birmingham and, by becoming members, we were sent much information and advice on what Gemma needed – in one word STIMULATION! From Day One!

We do realize that we are spoilt with Gemma. She is placid and undemanding. She has never woken for a night feed since she was born. Consequently we have never had broken nights and the bleary-eyed, haggard look that most new parents get. Just wait until the next time, I tell myself.

I don't feel there have really been any changes in my relationships with anyone. When I am with friends who do not have children I do try not to talk about babies. I can remember not being able to understand why people with babies were obsessed with time – they always knew at exactly what time the baby had woken, what time it had its feeds, and what time it went back to sleep. Now I understand why but try not to talk about it.

Those first few weeks at home were quite difficult. I was determined that everyone would know Gemma and hopefully accept her. I quite understood that people didn't know what to say, especially if they didn't know how we felt. It was our job to make it easy for them to talk about it. My most upsetting time was when I went into the local newsagents, and nothing was mentioned about the baby. It was as if I had never been pregnant. He obviously knew about Gemma but didn't know what to say. The longer I was in the shop the more difficult it became for me to mention it myself, yet I knew it was important that I could talk to him about it. A newsagent is such a key figure in the community, and I felt he would be able to let many people know how we felt about Gemma. We both took Gemma with us the next day and explained about her and how we felt. He was really relieved that we had done so.

It was, and still is, important that people know that we accept Gemma as she is, and the fact that she is mentally handicapped is not a problem to us. She is a child first and handicapped second. She is now becoming well known in the neighbourhood.

I made a lot of new friends at my N.C.T. classes. I met a girl who happened to live just around the corner who has become a very good friend. The N.C.T. hold local coffee mornings every fortnight in each other's homes, and we meet other mothers and other babies and toddlers.

The thing I would hate most is if other people felt sorry for us and said, 'Oh, isn't it a shame for them?' I know they must do, because I have said it many times myself. But we do not feel sorry for ourselves at all; at times I feel it is a privilege to have her. People who know us well just accept us as any other family now. Other people take their lead from us. Our readiness to talk about Gemma makes people feel easy with us.

What effect has having a baby had on me? I can now understand the wonder of babies. I see babies as tiny miracles. Motherhood definitely took some getting used to for me. For quite a few months I kept thinking how strange and frightening it was that there was a baby upstairs who was our total responsibility.

Naturally, because Gemma has Down's Syndrome it has opened my mind to all sorts of handicap. It makes me realize that you only really understand how people feel when you experience something yourself. Everything is relative, and when I see the handicaps other people live with I feel lucky that Gemma has Down's Syndrome.

Gemma is ten months old now, and progressing extremely well. Fortunately she has none of the physical defects which can be present, like a congenital heart condition. So far, she has reached her milestones at about the same age as other children.

There will be many problems in the future, as with any child. Our problems will just be different. We don't worry about what might happen. Events have taught us to take each day as it comes. At the moment we are enjoying the rewarding experience of bringing up Gemma, a child with 'a little extra'. This poem is pinned up in our kitchen:

> One day at a time
> this is enough.
> Do not look back
> and grieve over the past,
> for it is gone,

and do not be troubled
about the future,
for it has not yet come.
Live in the present,
and make it so beautiful
that it will be worth
remembering.*

* Ida Scott Taylor

Ann Conway

'We felt nervous as we drove to the nursery, carrycot in the
back . . . When we arrived at the institutional building, we
were shown into a bare room with chairs arranged round the
walls . . . The ten-week-old baby was brought in. Our first
glimpse of him was from behind – his bald head and his ears.
He was unwrapped and seated on a nurse's knee. He had big
bright blue eyes. He began sucking his fists. We both knew
immediately that he was for us.'

I was born in 1943, just over a year after my parents' marriage. My
father was a solicitor and my mother a secretary. She continued
working until she was six months pregnant and did not return to
work until I was twelve. Both my parents were, and still are,
active Christians and accepted that marriage was 'ordained for the
procreation of children'. They also have conventional views
regarding the roles of men and women and accepted that my
mother would stay at home to care for their offspring.

My elder brother was born fifteen months after my birth. My
mother told me quite recently that he was conceived before she
started menstruating again, while she was still breastfeeding me,
and that she was shocked to find herself pregnant so soon. My
younger brother was not born until 1950 when my mother was
forty and she has often hinted that she had not wanted another

child and that a third child was my father's idea. Indeed, she has often said that before her marriage she did not like babies – 'ugly little things' – and never had any desire to coo over them. I have never known whether she derived much pleasure from our babyhood, although she has often told us of all the difficulties she had to contend with: 'I had two of you in nappies and had to light the copper before I could boil them.' I was seven when my younger brother was born but have no recollection of my mother enjoying him, indeed my clearest memory of that time is the distressing one of my mother getting angry with him and shaking him because he would not take his feed.

One of my most vivid childhood memories is of going, often unwillingly, to church and Sunday School and of family Bible reading sessions, which I hated. Sex was never talked about and, as I remember it, my mother used to exclaim 'Humphrey!' in shocked tones whenever my father showed any physical affection towards her. I remember asking her why only married women had babies and she replied, 'Because the egg has to be fertilized,' and left it at that. I could only imagine a chicken's egg and had no understanding of 'fertilized'. She used to send me to buy sanitary towels but did not explain what they were for until I was about twelve when she told me, briefly and with embarrassment, about periods. I learned about sexual intercourse from a schoolfriend at about the same time and remember feeling incredulous and horrified.

I went to Grammar School when I was only ten and was the youngest and also very much the smallest girl in the school. From the beginning I was seen as a joke and christened 'Tiny'. Some of the other girls in my class already had breasts. They would get together in little groups and whisper about secret things which they said I was too young to understand. I felt very much the odd one out and was very unhappy that no one seemed to take me seriously.

This feeling became more acute as the years passed and all my classmates became physically developed while I remained a little girl. I grew a little taller but was still the smallest in my class. I would lie in the bath contemplating my flat chest and longing for it to change. I longed to be able to talk in knowing tones about periods. But nothing happened and I continued to feel that I was a peculiarity. I had friends but never felt that I was really accepted on equal terms with them. The fact that I was good at school work – a 'swot' – was, of course, no help at all.

I do not remember anything at all being said at home about my physical immaturity but my mother took me to see the doctor when I was fifteen and again when I was seventeen. He said 'She's just a late developer,' and the matter was left at that. The only references I can remember my parents making to the matter were comments that I was the sort of person who would have a career rather than get married. They took pride in my academic achievements, although my mother also complained frequently that I always had my head in a book. Certainly, by my late teens, I saw myself as someone who would not have children, although I have no clear memory of how this came about.

When I was in the sixth form my feelings of being different and inferior became more acute. By now my friends were preoccupied with boyfriends, clothes and parties; I felt excluded from all this, not only because of my physical condition but also because my parents seemed more old-fashioned than other people's – they would not allow me to go out late and were reluctant even to let me wear nylons and lipstick. We had weekly dancing classes with the Sixth Form from the boys' Grammar School and these were an excruciating experience for me. I particularly remember a bilious yellow sweater which my mother chose and a green tweed skirt which she 'ran up' for me. Other girls seemed to choose their own more fashionable clothes. I was horribly aware of my flat chest and I was often the last to be asked to dance, if I was asked at all.

My only other social activity was the church youth club, and I even had to come home from that earlier than others. I found that boys took little interest in me. There was one who sometimes put his arm around me and with whom I considered myself 'in love'. However, when he gave me my first 'real' kiss (I was sixteen) I found it a revolting experience.

One of my school friends, who considered herself very knowledgeable in sexual matters, tried to help me. She showed me how to put on mascara and how to flutter my eyelashes. She also suggested that I wear falsies. I remember going with her to buy the nylon bra with its foam rubber pads and trying it on. I was quite pleased with the effect and went home wearing it. I felt extremely self-conscious but no one in the family said anything about my changed appearance, then or later. Sometimes when I had left my clothes in a heap, with the bra at the bottom, I would come back from the bathroom and find it on top of the pile. I suspected that my elder brother was thus showing that he scorned my attempts to look mature. Although I was pleased to look more normal, the bra did not really help my confidence. In fact, it became the subject of deep anxiety. I was very much afraid of anyone finding out the truth and this greatly added to my inhibitions about any sort of physical relationship with a man. I went through agonies whenever I went swimming; I had a padded swimsuit but was always afraid that someone would catch a glance of my undeveloped chest. Similarly, whenever I had occasion to share a room with some other girl I had to keep my bra on all night.

I went to University at eighteen, painfully aware of my undeveloped body, my falsies and my fear of physical contact with men. I longed to be normal, to be attractive to men and to have a boyfriend. In spite of my physical condition and my belief that I would not have children, I very much accepted the prevailing belief among my fellow female students that one's first aim should be to 'find a man', to be loved and to get married. I had no idea what career I would follow if I failed in this aim. Until I actually acquired a 'platonic' boyfriend in my third term I felt that something was sadly lacking in my life. As far as I can remember, my fantasies about what was lacking were rather vague. I imagined an emotional, romantic affair rather than a physical one and, above all, I wanted to be seen by my women friends as someone who could attract a man. I vaguely believed that once I went to a hospital specialist my physical immaturity and aversion to sexual contacts would be 'cured'.

I told no one about my physical problems until the beginning of my second year, when I told two women friends about my lack of periods. It was at this time that I also nerved myself to see the college doctor about the matter. He referred me to a gynaecologist who saw me several times and carried out various tests. Then he dismissed me. 'We have been unable to establish the cause of your condition. Come and see me again if you want to get married.' Throughout, he showed no understanding at all of my feelings of inferiority, my difficulties in relating to men, let alone getting to the point of marriage. He even made a telephone call in my presence when he said, 'We have to establish whether or not this patient is female.' (In spite of this I did not for a moment accept that I could be anything but female and chromosome tests in fact established that I was). I was still much too subservient, too imbued with the idea that a specialist knew all the answers, to challenge this pronouncement. Instead, I shelved the problem, thinking that I would seek another opinion when I had finished my exams.

I had very little help from women friends at that time. I remember the two I had confided in laughing at the idea that I might be a man. 'You'll have to go to a men's college.' 'But you can't be a man if you've got breasts.' With much embarrassment I told them the truth and felt that they were curious and amused but not very sympathetic. In fact, I had more help from two men friends. The first was very understanding about my aversion to sex (even kissing) and we had a happy platonic relationship for over a year. The next boyfriend was a very gentle, loving person who helped me discover the pleasures of a physical relationship, though we never got further than 'heavy petting'. When my relationship with him ended I concentrated on working for my degree and then for a certificate in social studies. For two years I had only short-term relationships with men, although my prime aim in life was still to 'find a man'.

During my fifth year of University, when I was studying for my professional qualification in social work, I met Michael. Within a short time we were very close, intellectually and emotionally, and my physical problems soon became apparent. We decided I should again seek specialist help but, by the time I was sent an appointment, I was about to begin my career as a social worker in a London Borough Children's Department (now Social Services Department) and saw that gynaecologist only once. As far as I remember he seemed uninterested and unconcerned about my condition but did suggest a London endocrinologist who might help.

It was some months before I could obtain an appointment to see this specialist. Meanwhile my relationship with Michael continued and deepened, though we were a hundred miles apart and only saw each other every other weekend. Thanks to Michael's initiative we spent a lot of time reading books about hormones and sexual development and when I saw the endocrinologist we had already decided I needed hormone treatment. This specialist was, however, even less sympathetic and helpful than the previous ones. After carrying out various tests (including twenty-four hour urine sampling which involved my carrying bottles from one social work visit to another!) he announced to a group of students, without any prior warning to me, that he could reach no conclusions except that I appeared to have no uterus or ovaries. He referred me to a gynaecologist for surgical enlargement of my vagina.

In response to this development Michael wrote me a supportive and encouraging letter, but when I next visited him for the weekend he was very distressed. He was torn between his love for me and his need for a normal woman who could bear children. He very much wanted to have children of his own one day.

When I saw the gynaecologist I at last found a specialist who showed some interest and concern for me as a person. I sat up while on the couch and asked whether I could have hormone treatment and he said, 'Of course, I can't think why it hasn't been tried before.' He put me on a large dose of premarin (oestrogen) and norethisterone (progesterone). I have continued to take these, at a much lower dosage, ever since. He deferred the question of surgery.

I was overjoyed when I began to develop breasts and even more delighted when I had a period. I realized I must have a uterus. After a few weeks my vagina had developed sufficiently for Michael and I to have intercourse, which was a great relief to both of us. It was obvious that I did not need the operation for which I had been referred to the gynaecologist.

However, there still remained the question of whether or not I could have children. It was a matter we felt should be clarified before we made a decision about marriage, particularly as we were unsure about adopting, not only whether we would want to but also if we would be able to. Because I worked in the Children's Department I was well aware how few babies were available for adoption.

The gynaecologist explained that the only way to find out what was wrong with me was to carry out an abdominal operation. I therefore went into hospital for the operation and it was discovered that I had 'ovarian agenesis' or 'streak ovaries' – something had gone wrong at the foetal stage. I felt no surprise when I was told I would therefore be unable to have children. The fact is that I felt I had always known this, although I have no memory of how or when this knowledge came to me. The distress I felt was connected with Michael. Could he reconcile himself to never having his own children?

In fact, I learned afterwards that he had begun to come to terms with the prospect of childlessness before the operation but had decided to wait and see how he felt when, and if, this prospect became certain. Soon after I came out of hospital he asked me to marry him and we were married eight months later. That was in 1968.

For the next three years we lived in rented accommodation and both followed our careers. Although we referred now and then to the possibility of adopting children, this seemed remote and of no immediate relevance to us. We found that we could lead happy, fulfilled lives without children and were much more interested in finding a permanent home, preferably in the country. Our main motives were to become independent of landlords and to live in congenial surroundings. We did not visualize our home as a family home; if we had any vision of the future it was of ourselves as a couple enjoying a settled country life – growing our own vegetables, perhaps rearing animals, going for walks, earning enough to be comfortable. We hoped to find a house where we would be happy to live for many years since we were both unambitious as far as our careers were concerned and had no desire for promotion or for the moves which that could entail. We eventually found our present home, just the sort of place we had envisaged, and moved here in November 1971.

When the legal process of buying the house was under way we began making tentative inquiries about adoption, although we still saw this as an unlikely and very much a future possibility. We obtained a list of national and local adoption agencies from the Association of British Adoption Agencies. These are nearly all charitable organizations, many with specific religious connections, although local authority Social Services Departments also act as adoption agencies. We wrote to all the Protestant societies which covered our area and to local Social Services Departments. As we expected, we received a stream of letters saying that their lists were closed. 'I am very sorry but due to our very long waiting list of prospective adopters, and the great shortage of babies being offered for adoption, we are unable to help you adopt a child.'

By the end of 1972, when we had been in our home for over a year, we were beginning to lose hope. By this time I was working as a hospital social worker and part of my job was to help unmarried mothers and to refer them to adoption societies when they wished me to do so. During a conversation about a client with a worker from one of the church societies I mentioned our interest in adopting and said we had not applied to her society because we were not active churchgoers. 'Oh, that doesn't matter,' she said. 'As long as you get a vicar's reference you'll be all right.' So we applied and were duly vetted by a social worker and an understanding vicar supplied a reference. We approached the process of being vetted with detachment, still not expecting that we would ever be offered a baby, or at least not for several years.

When, in June 1973, we received a letter accepting us as adopters, we were amazed to read, 'We will probably offer you a boy and we hope you will have your little son by the end of the summer. We note, however, that Mrs Conway is still employed and, as we do not offer a child while the wife is still working, we shall be grateful to know when she intends to retire.' It had not been the practice of any agency I had come across to require the wife to retire in this way. Indeed, it would have been unrealistic in view of the length of time which often elapsed between acceptance and the offer of a baby. We did not feel that we were in any way ready for a baby so soon, or for me to stop working, and wrote to the society saying that I would prefer not to 'retire' until March 1974 as we still had expensive repairs to carry out on the house. We were relieved when the society replied, 'We fully appreciate your reason for asking that we do not look for a baby for you until next spring.'

It was only now that the implications of adoption really hit me. I was enjoying my job – though I often found it worrying – and I was not sure I wanted to give it up. Did I really want children? What would it be like to be at home all day, committed to children for many years? I believed that child rearing was the most responsible and difficult job one could undertake and was not sure I could cope with it. Moreover, I had a vivid picture of the unpleasant side of child rearing: the fact that once we had children there would be no escape from the responsibility, from the constant demands for attention, from the practical tasks of feeding and clothing them. I imagined how awful it would be having to go on coping with a noisy, messy toddler when one felt ill or tired. I was well aware that when relatives or friends who had children came to stay with us, I was always relieved when the house was once more free of their noisy voices, their screams and demands, their clutter. How would I cope when I could not get away from them, could not go for a walk or for a drink with Michael on the spur of the moment, could not stay in bed late when I felt like it? I found it difficult to imagine the pleasures of having children and was not convinced when a friend told me they gave meaning to life.

By this time Michael had come to a gradual, almost subconscious, realization that he did want to adopt children. He was used to my being apprehensive about any new undertaking so was not inclined to take my doubts seriously. Early in 1974 I finally gave in my notice (an event I cannot recall) only because I was unable to come to a decision *not* to adopt children, and as Michael especially wished to go ahead.

During my last few weeks at work I felt increasingly ambivalent about giving it up. I would be glad to see the last of my boss with whom I was constantly at loggerheads. I would be relieved not to have to deal with hospital doctors who saw me as a menial whose task was to empty beds rather than to provide a professional service for patients. It would be a welcome change not to have to cope daily with the severe shortage of vacancies in old people's homes, home helps, housing for the disabled and other services which my clients needed (and that was in perhaps the heyday of the welfare state!).

But I would very much miss the daily contact with my colleagues, the satisfactions of helping others (despite the frustrations), the pleasure of having a role (even if misunderstood) in a large and interesting institution.

I remember feeling very depressed after leaving work in March 1974. I was no longer a person of any consequence; I had no role or purpose in life. I would no longer have easy, companionable relationships with people I saw daily. Surprisingly, these feelings only lasted a few days. I remember having to call in at the hospital to collect some belongings and somehow this seemed to exorcise my regrets. From that day onwards I began to feel glad that I was no longer employed, and ever since have felt grateful to be free of that daily treadmill.

I expected to be at home for several months before we were offered a baby and planned to do a lot of decorating and gardening, to settle myself gradually into being a housewife. However, only a few weeks after I had finished work the adoption society worker telephoned to say they had a nine-week-old baby for us to consider. Michael answered the phone but I gathered what was being said and whispered, 'Not yet, not yet, we're not ready . . . '

However, Michael agreed that we would go to see the baby in his nursery in five days' time. I felt very shocked and full of panic. I could not cope with a real baby yet, had not painted the room, had not learned enough about feeds and nappies. True, we had obtained all the necessary equipment – cot, carrycot, nappies and so on. True, I had spent a day with a friend who had a baby and seen how she mixed feeds and changed nappies. But I knew very little about the physical care of babies and I had no other local friends with children.

The next few days passed quickly. As already planned, we spent the weekend in Wales. The day we arrived it was foggy and I remember leaning over a bridge gazing through the mist at the stream below. I was still full of uncertainties about saddling ourselves with a baby but Michael said he had a feeling that this was going to be our child and that he would bring us happiness. The next day, a golden Sunday, we walked in the hills. I felt very melancholy, aware that this could be our last weekend alone together for many years, our last unencumbered walk.

When we got home we tried to get ourselves ready – practising mixing feeds and folding nappies. While I grew increasingly apprehensive and excited, Michael remained calm.

Several weeks earlier my parents had arranged to visit us for a few days and arrived the day before we were to see the baby. Both they and Michael's parents had seemed pleased that we had been accepted as adopters although none of them had said very much about it. Now my parents seemed calm about the matter and I was glad they were there to help us.

We felt nervous as we drove to the nursery, carrycot in the back. How would we feel? Would we like the baby? What would we do if we didn't? Could we cope with a baby anyway? When we arrived at the institutional building we were shown into a bare room with chairs arranged round the walls. A little boy came in and said, 'You're the people who've come for baby John.' Then the baby was brought in. Our first glimpse of him was from behind – his bald head and his ears. He was unwrapped and seated on a nurse's knee. He had big bright blue eyes. He began sucking his fists. We both knew immediately that he was for us.

The social worker told us as much as she could about his mother, both her background and her feelings for the baby. She told us that his mother had cared for him during her ten days in hospital and had been very distressed when it came to handing him over. I had shared that agonizing ten days with several mothers while I was a social worker and was vividly aware of how she would have felt. I wished then – and still wish – that we could meet her. It seemed so artificial that she was completely cut off from us and we from her. Surely it would have helped both us and her to have met. But this was not the policy of our particular adoption society.

After the talk with the social worker I gave the baby a feed, whereupon he was immediately sick. Then I changed his nappy and saw that he had runny green stools. This hardly increased my confidence. But when Michael and I were left on our own we agreed that we wanted him and a little later set off with him in the carrycot.

He was quiet for most of the two-hour journey but when we stopped for a few minutes he began crying. We had no idea what to do. I was filled with panic. To our relief he stopped crying as soon as the car moved again.

I felt nervous when we arrived home and had to feed him and get him ready for bed. My mother was helping with getting the tea but clearly felt she should let me care for the baby. I half wished she would feed him and change his nappy but knew I must do so. He took his feed easily and brought up some wind with no trouble. Both my parents and Michael held him for a while. They all said what a nice baby he was. I began to feel a little better but my nervousness returned when I took him upstairs to change his nappy. I lay him on the floor of his bedroom and fumbled with the safety pins. I managed to get his nappy off but then didn't know where to put it. I daren't leave him to put it in the bathroom so dumped it on the carpet. Then urine spurted from him all over the floor. I realized I should have put a plastic sheet on the floor and had a bucket handy for the nappy. I was frightened by the sight of his tiny, thin legs and his sore bottom. He began to cry. With trembling hands I finally managed to clean him up, dab some cream on his bottom and pin a nappy on. I was relieved when Michael appeared, picked him up and cuddled him.

I escaped to the bathroom. I remember sitting there overcome with fright at what we had done. Our house, this bedroom, the countryside outside were so familiar and unchanged. Yet everything was changed. We had taken on a tremendous and frightening responsibility.

But as we put the baby to bed – wrapping him tightly in a blanket as we had been shown in the Nursery – my feelings began to change. The love I had felt on first seeing him flooded back. He fell asleep straight away. He looked beautiful and I ached with tenderness for him.

He slept all that evening and we kept wishing he would wake up. We wanted to repeat the pleasure of holding him but waited until he awoke for his ten o'clock feed. Michael gave him this feed and changed his nappy, much more calmly and efficiently than I had done. From that moment on he was as involved as I was in caring for the baby. I felt that the three of us were very close to one another.

I lay awake all night waiting for the baby to cry. I was excited and happy. Already I was terrified that his mother might change her mind, although it was some comfort that he was now ten weeks old and she had stuck to her decision so far. I felt grateful to her but also distressed at her grief. I knew that it was often the most caring and sensitive single mother who stood by her decision to have her baby adopted after the birth. I could not delude myself that she did not care.

As I lay awake I was amazed at the intensity of my emotions. I had never expected to feel like this. I realized that this was a special part of my life and that I ought to be writing about it as it was happening. I now regret that, in fact, I did not find time to write anything at all!

The baby slept until five o'clock next morning. Michael woke too and gave him his feed. The baby got hiccups afterwards and we were both worried until he 'recovered'. I felt that Michael and I were close in a new way, that our relationship was already enhanced by this third member of the family and the concern we both felt for him. We decided to call him Philip John, keeping the name his mother chose as his second name. We also decided to begin telling him straight away about his natural mother. We thought that if we did this while he was a baby it would seem easy to do so when he was old enough to understand.

For the next few days my emotions see-sawed wildly. The predominant mood was one of euphoria but I also found myself unpredictably bursting into tears. My feelings about my mother were contradictory: I wanted her to help me and yet leave me to cope on my own. I realized she was trying to support me without interfering too much, but I felt dissatisfied with her efforts. When she and my father went home I felt both relieved that Michael and I now had Philip to ourselves and resentful that my mother had not offered to stay and help me for longer than three days.

My emotions continued in this pattern for the next few weeks. There was one occasion during the first week when Philip kept crying instead of going to sleep; I was tired and anxious and felt a desire to shake him. I realized then how mothers come to batter their children. There were many other moments when I was ecstatic. I had never expected to feel such emotional and physical pleasure in a baby so quickly. Michael and I greatly enjoyed handling him and particularly feeding him. My one regret – which I still feel – was that I could not breastfeed him but this was mitigated by the great advantage of Michael's being able to share in the feeding, which both strengthened his bond with Philip and enabled me to have alternate nights off. On our nights 'on' we slept in the baby's bedroom and gave him his ten p.m. and six a.m. feed so that the other could have a night of uninterrupted sleep. Without this arrangement I would have found the intensive round of washing and feeding harder to bear and my pleasure in Philip would have been diminished. We were also fortunate that he was an 'easy' baby, well settled into the Nursery's regular routine of feeding and sleeping.

After the first few weeks of high emotion we settled into one of the happiest periods of our lives. Our relationship became closer than ever and we both took increasing pleasure in Philip. Michael's parents came to stay with us and, like my parents, immediately accepted Philip as their grandchild. We also enjoyed the interest and support of two social workers – one from the adoption society and the other from the Social Services Department. The latter was carrying out the welfare supervision legally required until the adoption went through; she was also acting as 'guardian ad litem', preparing a report for the Court on the adoption arrangements.

We were overjoyed and relieved when after two months Philip's mother signed her consent to the adoption. From then onwards we felt fairly sure that nothing would go wrong. Five months after he was placed with us we went to the County Court for the final adoption order. In was a very brief procedure and seemed an anti-climax. This also marked the end of visits from social workers and I found I missed their concern for us.

From the beginning, Michael was happy for me to go out when he was able to be at home. I remember how relieved and free I felt the first time I went out, although it was only for a social workers' meeting. Philip had been with us for three weeks. It was marvellous not having to worry about him – to forget the intense, domestic routine for a few hours. I kept up my involvement with the local Shelter Group for some time, then became a member of the National Housewives' Register and of a local choral society. After a few months I began delivering Meals-on-Wheels once a month and was lucky to become a visiting social worker for an organization which helps families with handicapped children. This involved about one visit a fortnight.

For the first few months I felt a lack of women friends, particularly women with babies. We live in a rural area and I knew no other women with whom I had anything in common. The Housewives' Register, based in a town twelve miles away, was invaluable in this respect and then I gradually began to make friends in my own locality. These friends were, and still are, of great importance to me in that I very much need to discuss my children and my problems with other women in the same position. Inevitably, there were discussions about pregnancy and birth. I felt left out but not distressed and, after hearing how badly they seemed to have been treated, I could not help feeling a certain relief that I had not had to go through the process. Furthermore, I was glad not to have had to face the decision of whether or not to bring more people into our already overpopulated world. Instead I had the privilege of choosing to care for a child already in existence.

As Philip became a toddler I found that my pleasure in him was increasingly mixed with irritation and frustration. Michael continued to be as involved as ever and was often able to be at home for two days a week. Philip was not a particularly difficult toddler, but still I found the continual mess, his need for constant supervision, the noise, very wearing. In fact, having a child was becoming more as I had imagined it before we had Philip, although never a day went past without a few moments' sheer delight in him. It was at this time that a certain amount of tension developed between Michael and myself. He did not find Philip as wearing as I did and found it difficult to tolerate my negative feelings. There were times when I felt his love for Philip was greater than his love for me and my own love for Philip seemed somehow inadequate by comparison.

When Philip was two-and-a-half we applied to adopt a second child. Again there was a stage when it seemed unlikely that a baby would be available. Again I had very mixed feelings. Did I want two children? Could I cope with two, especially with the sibling rivalry? Both of us wondered how we could love another baby as much as we did Philip and could not imagine having another equally easy baby. Michael was much more sure this time that he wanted to go ahead and my doubts were again not definite enough for me to say no.

One day, when Philip was three-and-a-quarter, I had a phone

call from the social worker to say that they had a baby girl in mind for us. At the time I was in the middle of washing my hair, was suffering badly from sinusitis and had just discovered Philip 'writing' with lipstick on a newly painted wall. A few days later Michael and I set off to see the baby in her foster home. This time, it had been agreed that we should not bring her home straight away. We felt that we needed to decide whether to accept her and then have time to prepare Philip.

Again, it was love at first sight and it was the baby's beautiful large eyes which first struck us. Again we had a useful talk with the social worker who had worked with the baby's mother. We wished we could take the baby straight away. Instead we drove back to tell Philip about her and waited impatiently for another week before taking him with us to collect her. We were delighted with his reaction to her – he seemed to take to her as we had done – and we were all happy to be driving home with her.

To our surprise, she was as easy a baby as Philip had been and we found that our pleasure and joy in caring for her was as great as it had been with Philip. The only difference was that I felt calmer and less anxious. It was, again, as she grew into a toddler that I found things more difficult. She demanded a great deal more attention than Philip had done at this stage and it was now that he began to show signs of jealousy. As before, I found the next year or so difficult and more as I had imagined motherhood would be, although I still enjoyed the children. As in Philip's case, Michael did not find this stage as demanding as I did and this again caused tension between us. Although it is not a major problem, this tension has to some extent persisted, in that my feelings about the children continue to be much more ambivalent than Michael's and he finds this hard to understand.

Afterword

Now that both children go to school I am enjoying life. Thanks to W.E.A. classes, my interests now include women's studies and creative writing as well as choral singing and I am gradually becoming involved in the peace movement. I have continued to deliver Meals-on-Wheels once a month and kept on with my fortnightly social work visits. These visits have been invaluable, in that I have been able to retain my identity as a social worker as well as that of housewife and mother, both in my own and the family's eyes. They have also enabled me to have a small but valued income of my own, provided a good reason for half a day's break from the family and given me a sense of proportion about the problems of bringing up normal children. Furthermore, Michael has had regular opportunities of having the children to himself and the children have learned that I am not always available to them. At present this is as much paid employment as I want. I have lovely free mornings when I can garden, write, walk, do housework, call on friends, as I please. Michael is at home one or two days a week and on those days we much enjoy being a couple on our own again.

We derive great pleasure from seeing the children change and develop, from hearing our daughter Laura announce that it is a 'lovely bird-tweeting morning' or Philip comparing hailstones falling on the lawn to 'little volcanoes erupting everywhere'. We still regret not meeting their natural mothers. In both cases we wrote detailed letters about the children for the Society to pass on to the women once the adoptions were finalized but were never sure they received them. Now and then we write about both children to the Society in case either mother inquires about them. We find that our thoughts turn to them particularly on the children's birthdays. We feel sure they must wonder what the children are like and we, for our part, would love to know how much the children resemble them, both physically and in other ways. I tend to believe that their present environment has more influence on their behaviour than inherited characteristics but it would be fascinating to know, for example, whether either of Philip's parents were difficult to toilet train, as he was, or whether Laura's mother was a noisy, cheerful child, as she is. It would have been nice to have had letters for the children from their mothers or some item they had specially bought for them. Typed sheets of information about their background (which the Society provides) are not enough.

Because we talked to both children about their natural mothers while they were babies we find it easy to refer to the fact that they are adopted now that they can understand. They both seem to accept this without difficulty and while Philip says little about it, Laura chats about her 'first' Mum and how she would like to see her one day.

I cannot deny that at times I still find child rearing difficult and worrying or that I am sometimes depressed. However, I suspect that I might have been far more worried and depressed if I had continued in full time social work rather than adopting children. Moreover, Michael and I would have missed a deeply satisfying and pleasurable experience.

Jay Kleinberg

'Just before we were married Nic had another infertility
test done . . . He was again told his sperm were not viable.
Upon hearing the results of the test, I cried for hours.'

I came late to motherhood because, like many women of my
generation, I wanted a career. I devoted my twenties and early
thirties to obtaining a Ph.D. in American History and teaching at
various universities in the United States. Few friends of either sex
had children and even those that did were very career-orientated.
There were two other factors which made our having children
unlikely: Nic lived in England while I remained in the States for
most of the year to teach, and he is paralysed from the chest down
as the result of an automobile accident in 1969. We met before he
was disabled, continuing our friendship by post and occasional
visit, and marrying in 1979.

Marriage resulted in a number of changes in our lives. Living
apart, pursuing our separate careers, no longer made much sense,
though neither of us wanted to cease our complicated professional
lives. We both travelled frequently, went scuba diving as part of
our work (Nic is an oceanographer and marine archaeologist and I
had a side-line in archaeological and underwater photography),
and enjoyed a diversity of intellectual interests. As we were both
up for promotion, we decided to determine who moved where by

which promotion came through first. Nic's did, so I moved to
England in the summer of 1980. I could not get a job teaching
history. As I had always enjoyed working with figures, I got a job
as a trainee accountant. This involved studying, travelling around
England auditing clients' accounts, and commuting to London.
The work given to first-year students was not particularly
interesting and studying in the evenings and at weekends,
combined with commuting, left me tired most of the time. Still, it
was a job.

We had previously talked in a vague way about having
children, but it hadn't seem feasible whilst we lived apart. Now
we wanted them in earnest, but had to confront two biological
facts: our ages and Nic's disability. I was thirty-three and Nic was
forty-four when I moved to England. It seemed that we were
running out of time. Moreover, Nic had been told in 1972, by
doctors at Stoke Mandeville Spinal Injuries Unit, that he was not
fertile. He did not accept that, even though received medical
opinion is that paraplegic men are not capable of having children
because they do not ejaculate naturally and many of them either
have low sperm counts or the sperm are not motile if they can be
obtained.

Just before we were married Nic had another infertility test
done at Stoke. He was again told that his sperm were not viable.
Upon hearing the results of the test, I cried for hours. Nic was
more stoic, but determined to investigate further. Our honeymoon
consisted of a camping trip across Europe, visiting archaeological
sites, and some diving in Israel. We stayed there with a doctor
friend who had taught a course in diving for the disabled with Nic
several years earlier. He knew of a doctor who was concerned
with paraplegic fertility, with whom we spoke. It seemed that a
group in France had managed some pregnancies amongst couples
where the man was a paraplegic. The Israeli doctor gave us a copy
of a brief article written by the French group, which stated that
they had achieved several successful pregnancies with their
technique of obtaining semen from paraplegics. Nic's confidence
in his ability to have children was enhanced by reading the French

paper, but I didn't think we were much closer to our goal. While having a check-up at Stoke Mandeville, Nic spoke to a visiting doctor who knew of a professor at London University who was studying fertility amongst male paraplegics. At last we had a person closer to home who was actively concerned with the problem.

We saw Professor Brindley in March, 1980. He had devised a method of obtaining semen from men with the type of spinal cord injuries which prevent their ejaculating in the normal fashion.* After testing Nic's nerve reflexes, Professor Brindley used his machine to obtain semen, which he examined under a microscope. We were thrilled to see all those little sperm lashing their tails and scuttling about: millions of tiny swimmers, one of whom might someday impregnate me! Nic was capable of fathering a child after all!

As it was not practical for us to continue travelling up to London during my fertile periods, we obtained a machine from Professor Brindley which we could use at home to obtain the semen and do the insemination. The charge for loan of the machine was a nominal £25.

For most people, the physical acts of making love and procreation are the same. For couples with fertility problems such as ours, they are separate processes. Although we did not construct temperature charts, etc., we took the approach that ovulation occurred in the middle of my menstrual cycle, give or take a week or so. At those times, we concentrated on obtaining semen and, if successful, insemination. Sometimes it was extremely frustrating, as the procedure was not always successful. It was horrible to let a 'good' day go by because we couldn't get the machine to work, knowing that we would have to wait a few days to try again. I decided not to construct temperature charts to time ovulation precisely because the method did not always work. It would have been even more exasperating to know *exactly* when the best date was and then not be able to get the method to work. Amazingly, I became pregnant about four months after we got a machine to use at home.

Pregnancy was a time of joy, uncertainty, and adjustment for us both. Nic had some reservations about how he, now forty-five, with limited mobility and problems of access, could cope with a baby. He wanted to participate fully in all aspects of parenting, but there were some physical obstacles to overcome. He can't bend over without bracing himself because he has no waist muscles to provide balance and stop himself from falling. This means he can only pick things up with one hand. How would he manage to pick up a baby safely? Since he needs his arms to push the wheelchair, could he carry her from one place to another? We didn't know anybody in similar circumstances, so we tried to envisage the problems he might encounter and find ways around them. Elaborate changing tables were out of the question, as was a changing mat on a chest of drawers. In neither case would he have been able to get the wheelchair close enough to them to put on a nappy. Nic's brother and sister-in-law put up a wide shelf in the baby's room, supported by brackets, which he could wheel under.

Throughout my pregnancy we had faith in our ability to cope and hoped we would be able to find solutions to whatever problems presented themselves. From habit and necessity we approached the impending birth and childcare problems as if they were research problems. We bought books on pregnancy, childbirth, and childcare. We asked people how different kinds of nappies performed. Nic watched how parents with young children managed them on long airplane voyages. In short, pregnancy made us both much more aware of child-raising and other people's approaches to childcare.

I was uncertain as to how I would react to being at home after so many years of working. What would it be like to depend upon someone else for support after fifteen years of financial independence? I worried about preserving my own identity in a society in which role expectations seem more rigidly defined than they are in the United States. What would having a child do to me, even a child we wanted very much? Having rejected the housewife and mother role at twenty, I was understandably nervous about what it would be like to come into it at thirty-four.

It was important to develop a local support network. My parents and sister still live in the United States. Although I had some very close friends there, I hadn't met many people since moving to England except those connected with my job, some thirty-five miles away. Fortunately, my sisters-in-law are warm and encouraging. Nic's youngest sister had her first child in her late thirties and was pregnant with her second at forty. She passed on her own very positive feelings about motherhood, which helped me through some of the less pleasant aspects of pregnancy, including my 'morning' sickness which lasted all day and for most of the pregnancy, and was made worse by commuting daily on the train. She also passed on clothes, equipment and toys, as did other relatives and friends. This both eased the financial burden of having a baby and made us feel part of a community. Pregnancy (and later, birth) helped root us in time and place as nothing before had done.

I was struck that the transition to motherhood took place during pregnancy. Decisions about work and travel had to be made in the light of my condition, age, and the difficulty we had in conceiving. Both my general practitioner and the Registrar to whom I was assigned because of these factors, stressed that there was much less margin for error in our case. Clearly, being an elderly primigravida and pregnant through A.I.H. (artificial insemination by husband) resulted in a very conservative approach to my pregnancy. We tried to find a healthy balance between what seemed to be the needs of the baby and my own. Yet, having been on my own for so long, I'd got into the habit of just picking up and doing things as my work or mood took me. Now each event had to be considered in terms of its impact upon the baby, and being pregnant ruled out some activities altogether, so that when I did some scuba diving, I was careful to limit it to shallow water, rather than get involved in decompression diving which might endanger the baby.

Although I stopped working as an accountant at the end of my fourth month of pregnancy (commuting made my morning sickness intolerable), I hoped to carry on writing, photographing, and lecturing. In fact, I travelled exensively during the first two trimesters of my pregnancy. The first trip was to the United States in June, when I was three months pregnant, to attend a conference and stay with my sister. I discovered that the sticky heat made me even more nauseous, but it was really good to see Carol and to compare notes with her (she had just had a child). The conference, on Women's History, was an eye-opener: it seemed that a dozen historians my own age or even older were pregnant for the first time. Many of us had discovered our biological clocks and were racing the same deadline.

I had my doctor's blessing on my first overseas trip, but there was some suggestion that the second one might not be such a good idea. We were scheduled to do some underwater archaeology at the end of my fourth month. Nic is very interested in human settlements which, because of rising sea levels or land subsidence, are under water. Being in a wheelchair has not stopped him from participating in expeditions or scuba diving to observe underwater archaeological remains. I have gone on expeditions as photographer, diver, and data recorder. This particular expedition was to Aghios Petros, a small island in the Northern Sporades, Greece. Even though I had already discovered that extreme heat exacerbated my morning sickness, it was too good an opportunity to pass up. I discussed matters with my doctor, who understandably felt that there were more risks involved in living rough in rural Greece than in staying at my sister's house in suburban New Jersey. But, as things were going well with the pregnancy, we decided it was an acceptable risk. So off we went to spend three weeks on an uninhabited island, two-and-a-half-hours by fishing boat from the nearest doctor. The Greek women on the expedition thought I was very valiant to accompany Nic to such a remote and primitive location. My parents thought I was crazy. It certainly was uncomfortable to live in a tent with the nearest fresh water a mile's walk from our campsite, but I'd done a lot of camping and rough living before and have always found it exhilarating. Not surprisingly, being pregnant made it heavier going this time. I needed to be careful of the old traveller's enemy. The doctor warned me not to take any anti-diarrhoeal preparations without medical supervision. I had one or two bouts of 'runny tummy' but nothing serious. I got some good photographs underwater and spent a lot of time doing a photo catalogue of the material from the land and underwater sites, and was very glad I went.

As my pregnancy advanced, I carried on with some freelance work, doing a computerized analysis of a diving club's membership, and planned to go off on another foreign trip. Nic had organized a symposium in California, where I had taught some ten years earlier. I arranged to give a few lectures to subsidize my airfare. The doctor agreed it was not too late to travel (I was late in my sixth month and would be seven months pregnant by the time we returned). We had lovely weather, I enjoyed seeing friends, and felt certain that all this travelling was making a very cosmopolitan baby. But, when an opportunity arose to do some photography in the Middle East at the beginning of the eighth month, the doctor refused to countenance the trip. He said it was too risky and that no airline would let me fly without a doctor's letter this late in the pregnancy. I'm glad I took his advice. I went into labour three weeks early, the day after I might have flown.

Despite antenatal classes, I was not prepared for labour – not for this labour at any rate. I woke up early in the morning with my waters broken, but it was three weeks before I was due and I couldn't really believe I was in labour already. I'd cut up a ton of wood with my chainsaw a fortnight earlier. Had the baby decided life would be easier on the outside? We rang the hospital who told us to come in straight away. I wasn't having contractions at this point, just a bit of cramping. The admitting process at St Luke's wasn't as bad as I'd feared; I even had a delicious hot shower before being popped into bed. I began the breathing exercises as practised at the classes. Time passed quickly at first. The doctor told us my cervix was between 3 and 4cm dilated, but that the baby's head hadn't engaged yet. A foetal monitor was rigged up. Nic kept likening the traces to geological formations which variously amused me or made me cross depending upon the strength of the contractions. By noon I had done so much heavy breathing to keep the pain at bay that I felt hyperventilated. I decided to have an epidural as the labour showed every sign of dragging on. The epidural procedure was painful as the anaesthetist had trouble finding the right place and had to wait for a contraction to pass before he could start again. At 4 p.m. the contractions were still irregular and I was still only 4 cm dilated, so I agreed to a syntocin drip to speed things up. The day and night passed with the epidural being topped up until 4 a.m. when the cervix finally opened completely. The baby's head still was not all the way down, so the doctor and midwife could not determine which way she was presenting. After half an hour of futile pushing, the midwife sent for the consultant obstetrician and house doctor. They poked and prodded in an excruciatingly painful fashion and concluded that the baby was transverse (head sideways) so that there was no way I could push her out. The delivery had to be by forceps, although I pushed as the doctor pulled. An episiotomy was done without discussion – I heard rather than felt it.

Kirsten Erika emerged dancing and singing into the world at 5.31 a.m. Nic and I were both exhausted and thrilled as we had never been before. Her birth had been a lyrical, if painful, experience. The physical pains of the aftermath went on for weeks. I was tired beyond what I ever imagined possible. My mother said that was because I was older and lacked the resilience of a younger woman. I don't know about that, but many of the women in my antenatal class were older first time mothers, and most of them had a rough time in labour. Was our age a factor – we were mostly in our late twenties or early thirties?

I felt like a zombie for the first few months after Kirsten's birth. Breastfeeding, whatever else it does for the mother-child bond, ensures maximum exhaustion in the early days, when the child wakes up twice a night. I still hadn't finished the computing work I had hoped to complete before Kirsten's early arrival, so I took her to the computer centre with me. I felt very strange taking her there and hoped she would not wake up for a feed while I was logged on the computer. She did, of course, so I fed her while trying to get my programme to run. Until her feeds became more predictable, I didn't feel I could leave her with anybody else. Nic took all his accumulated holiday leave so that he could be at home with us, but it was a very busy time for him at work, so most of her day-to-day care became my responsibility. Kirsten sat on my desk in her bouncing chair while I wrote. She was good company and sweetly distracting as she tried to focus on the mobile hung from a convenient curtain rod.

Nic discovered that he could pick Kirsten up safely by scooping her up with one hand. He would lay her across his lap when she was tiny. This was reasonably secure, though she did roll off once or twice, fortunately with no damage done. Although he does a lot of paperwork at home on the weekends, this was relatively easy to combine with taking care of Kirsten and thus gave me time to get on with my own work. The only thing Nic could not do was bath Kirsten. His own lack of balance made this simply too dangerous. Nevertheless, we found that this handicap did not really interfere with active fathering.

We had another expedition planned for April when Kirsten was four months old. This one was a complicated project, involving British and Australian scientists interested in the submarine geology and archaeology off the northern coast of Australia, where it is thought the Aborigines crossed from Asia. Nic was chief scientist, I was data manager, surface photographer, and diver. Kirsten went along as baby-in-chief, though not without considerable protest from the owner of the boat we had chartered. He refused at first to have a baby on board, said I should leave her with someone if I wanted to come, or we should both stay ashore. As Nic wouldn't go without me, and I wouldn't go without her (I was still feeding her myself), Kirsten went, too. We were very cramped on the boat for the first part of the trip and could not take anyone to help with the baby (by now four months old). She reacted to jet lag and the heat by waking up once or twice every night. I could not let her cry for more than a minute or two for fear of waking up the others. Fortunately, at least some of my duties were vaguely compatible with looking after a baby. The one that wasn't, diving, could usually be scheduled when either Kirsten was asleep or there was someone else to look after her. Nic tried to take care of her as much as he could, given that his ability to manoeuvre on board the ship was restricted by the cramped quarters in which we had to work. When I did surface photography, I could usually position Kirsten within sight and well away from any potential danger sources. She still had several major sleeps during the day, so that, with someone always within earshot of our cabin, I was able to get on with my jobs. A young woman joined us on the last segment of the trip to look after Kirsten, who had become more active and needed less sleep. It was such a relief to have someone whose attention didn't have to be divided amongst four or five different activities at the same time. I realized how stressful it had been to look after the baby and work under such awkward conditions.

I'm no superwoman – nor do I think any woman should *have* to be one. Kirsten (all children) should have quality care, though I think every person means something different by that term. I knew after that trip that I couldn't look after the baby and do much else. Baby care is very time-consuming and being tired reduces efficiency. We hired a nanny when Kirsten was ten months old because we felt I should continue to do things outside the home, even though they can't be said to be financially profitable yet. Nic feels as strongly as I do about this. In fact, his encouragement makes it possible for me to carry on, trying to find photographic, writing, and lecturing assignments. I desperately want to find sustained employment. Since that seems unlikely in the current economic climate, I cobble together little bits and pieces and hope something will pay off some day. Since we don't have relatives nearby who might look after Kirsten regularly and since we are just getting to know our neighbours, having a live-in nanny works very well for us. We are very fortunate to be able to do this. This arrangement has something of the feeling of an extended family to it. It means we both can get on with our work, but still spend plenty of time with Kirsten at weekends and in the evenings. We have a distribution of chores which suits our talents (such as they are) and interests. Even with three of us to divide up the work, we are all exhausted by the end of the day.

Parkinson's law as it applies to housework and childcare is that they expand to fill the time available – and then some! Nic works at home in the evening and at the weekends, but manages to look after Kirsten by moving his typewriter and papers into the kitchen cum family room, where he has a pull-out table he can wheel under. I work bits and pieces during the week and at the weekend, but am with Kirsten for parts of several days during the week and at weekends. Kirsten's nanny works five days a week and tries to recoup her strength over the weekend. Sometimes life seems very intense, as when both Nic and I have deadlines to meet or when he is away on business for several weeks on the trot. Then the sun comes out, we sit outside playing with Kirsten and feel recharged and refreshed. It's fabulous to watch her discover the world and to be a part of that process.

The changes in my relationship with Nic, occurring as a result of Kirsten's birth, are due to having a demanding third party present, frequently being tired, and rarely being alone with each other. Our life is lived in shifts; when one of us takes care of Kirsten the other is usually working. The weekend lie-in is a thing of the past. A leisurely Sunday morning cuddle is now a group affair, with Kirsten drinking her juice in the middle of the bed. Her presence strengthens our relationship, even though it gives us much less time together. We feel bound to each other by her, through her. She came from our love for each other and reinforces it.

Motherhood has changed the basis of other relationships as well. Previously, most friends were work-related, now they are mostly baby-related. I attended antenatal classes in our village and met women in the village through them. We get together weekly now, to get out of the house, to have a break from the domestic routine, to chat, and to give the babies contact with people the same size as themselves. These morning coffees or afternoon teas were especially important when the babies were tiny. I felt lost after Kirsten was born. I hadn't a clue what to do with her and it helped to compare notes, if only to find out that she wasn't the only one who woke up twice a night or would only eat food if it had been slathered with yogurt.

Even though I've met people through having a baby, the geographical range of these contacts has been restricted. At first we took Kirsten everywhere with us. She went to meetings, restaurants, dinner parties. Of course that became more difficult when she outgrew her carrycot. She's more fun to be around now, but much less transportable after 6 p.m. Sometimes we ask Kirsten's nanny to stay with her for an evening, but we don't go out very much. To some extent, we've reorganized our social activities because of her, but we seem to have so little time anyway, that what we do have is devoted either to Kirsten or work. This isn't any sacrifice on our part. It's just the way we choose to spend our lives.

The single most dramatic change that came with motherhood was never being alone again. My work tends to be solitary in nature. I lived alone for about ten years before we got married. I'm used to uninterrupted stretches of time and lots of peace and quiet. All that is a thing of the past. The other thing about motherhood that came as a surprise was the continued sleep deprivation. Kirsten is eighteen months old today and still sleeps through the night only occasionally. She's been back and forth to Australia and the United States. Her response to time shifts is to wake up in the night. Her response to teething (and she has almost all her baby teeth) is to wake up in the night, her response to most upsets is to wake up once or twice a night.

Motherhood has to be lived through to be comprehended. It is an intensely emotional experience. I fell in love with Kirsten as soon as I saw her. She looked so pleased with herself for surviving the birth trip, yet so vulnerable. I feel more emotional about children in general because I am a mother. Life has become more poignant.

Being responsible for a child frequently means putting aside one's own wishes and needs. That can be very difficult without a lot of support from family, friends, and community. Having a child can be a very isolating experience, particularly in the early days when one is recovering from the actual delivery and trying to establish a routine after the structured days and assisted nights in hospital. Despite routine visits from the local GP, midwife, and health visitor in the week or two after leaving hospital, there is no follow-up beyond physical care. It is ironic that the local surgery sponsors antenatal classes which teach how to give birth, but doesn't have mothering or parenting classes to help postnatally. Our society seems more interested in the birth process than in life after delivery for parents or baby. I feel fortunate to have found a group of mothers who provide moral support for each other over coffee. That has eased the transition from full-time work to motherhood and occasional freelancing.

I don't view women or men differently than I did before Kirsten was born. But, as an occupation, motherhood is undervalued tremendously by our society despite all the lip service paid to it. It's hard, but very rewarding, work. Whether one stays home, returns to the labour force, or, as in my case, works from home, one has a responsibility to the child to be the best parent possible. For women, the problem is to know how to achieve this, given the conflict and tension between the job one does outside and that within the home.

Nic and I came late to parenthood, and that has made it more precious to us. We want to share all aspects of childbearing. I've gone away for weekends leaving Nic in sole charge of Kirsten. He was thrilled that they both enjoyed themselves so much and that he could cope with taking her shopping and to a neighbour's for lunch. Since we were both childless for so long her development is all the more fascinating. We both want to spend more time with her, but strive to balance work with parenting. I'm glad I became a mother when I did, that I had a chance to develop on my own before I began helping someone else to grow. I hope we can pass on to Kirsten some of the richness of our experiences and involve her in our adventures. Being a parent, regardless of one's age, is an awesome responsibility.

After the birth, as during pregnancy, I've tried to balance my own needs and desires with the baby's. I would not be a happy person if I did nothing but childcare seven days a week. My pregnancy was hectic and unconventional, perhaps, but it produced a healthy, happy child. Kirsten is relaxed amongst strangers, interested in the world about her, and generally an easygoing person. Perhaps exposing her to so many different people and experiences has had a positive effect. We are off to Israel to do some archaeology this week. Kirsten will come along, as will her nanny. They'll sit on the beach while I photograph and Nic attends his conference and we'll all explore in our own way. Parenthood has enabled us to combine different types of exploration and discovery. We feel that this benefits all of us and makes our lives richer.

*The interested reader is referred to G. S. Brindley, 'Physiology of Erection and Management of Paraplegic Fertility' in T. B. Hargreave (ed.) *Male Infertility* (1983), for clinical details of the method used.

Doreen van Hiley

'The hospital had told us to treat him normally and I always
bitterly regret having taken this advice. If only they had
said, "Treat him as if you were going to lose him." Then I
could have spoilt him more . . . They say when you lose a
child, part of you dies with it . . .'

My mother was already separated from her first husband when she
met my father during the war. He had been torpedoed in the
Mediterranean whilst serving in the Dutch Merchant Navy and his
convalescent home was near the shop in which my mother
worked. I was born before my mother received her decree
absolute and was two-and-a-half years old when they married.
Because my father was an alien and unable to work in Britain, they
opened a tobacconists in my mother's name. This they ran
together for several years, until my father found employment with
the Netherlands Embassy. After that my mother continued to run
the business until, after fifteen years, she was sick to death of it.
When a friend needed help, she went to work for her part-time.
So, initially, I was brought up 'behind the shop' and, by the time I
was eight or nine, had my own key to let myself into the house
after school. Both my parents had large, extended families but I
came to know only my father's, spending most of my summer

holidays with them in Holland. I was the youngest by far and, since my parents did not have any friends with young children, this meant I had no real contact with them.

I was born with a congenital hip condition, probably inherited from my maternal grandmother. This, on top of a difficult labour, influenced my mother's feeling about having any more children. As for marriage, she couldn't see it as the be-all and end-all of a woman's life. When she was asked what I would do when I grew up, she always replied, 'She's not getting married.' I took this to mean, 'She's not *only* going to get married.' So I always felt that marriage wouldn't be the first thing, but would come eventually.

Both parents supported me as I plodded my way through my education. At first I hoped to go into teaching but, after an operation on my hip, I was told that teaching would be too strenuous for me. So I decided on social work. I finished my training in 1969, having worked for a year and done a secretarial course between school and college.

Before taking up my first post, I fulfilled a long-held ambition to go on an overland trip to India. It was on this that I met my husband. We travelled in a convoy of two trucks; I saw him from the back of mine. Before we married eighteen months later, I was careful to make it clear I was not keen on having children – certainly not for a few years. My husband agreed, but I always knew that he wanted to have a family.

He is a Midlander and his family has a history of losing babies. His maternal grandmother lost her first child when he reached the age of seven. She lost a second, my mother-in-law's twin, shortly after their birth. Similarly, my mother-in-law lost my husband's twin sister shortly after birth. When I first learned about this, I didn't give it any extra thought.

I was born when my mother was thirty-two. When I reached her age I began to think seriously of starting a family. Somehow we thought it might take a couple of years but I became pregnant immediately. As I had a small show in my second month I did not seek confirmation until I missed my third period. My GP worried I would have problems in labour and delivery because of my hip condition so he referred me to an obstetrician. The latter didn't foresee any problems and sent me back to my GP, who then undertook my antenatal care. The GP insisted I have the baby in the local maternity hospital 'just in case'. I attended an antenatal class which taught relaxation and breathing techniques and which reinforced my determination to breastfeed. *Breast is Best* became my bible.

When I was about fourteen weeks pregnant we went to Paris for a long weekend and visited Notre Dame. There I mistakenly placed a candle on Joan of Arc's tomb. From that moment I felt it was an omen of bad luck and that something would go wrong with the baby. I tried to push this to the back of my mind and continued to work until eleven weeks prior to my due date. I was ready to leave work by then, as I had started to nod off at my desk. I had decided to resign rather than take maternity leave as I really had not considered that I should or could do anything else. I certainly felt that I could not combine the job I was in with being a full time mother.

Nearly five weeks before the baby was due my waters broke in the middle of the night. We called the ambulance and hurriedly threw things into a case. I was admitted and given the compulsory shave. I didn't need the enema, as my body had taken care of that before the ambulance arrived. I was given an injection to prevent the baby having trouble with its chest (this is apparently a precaution with premature babies) and then my husband and I were left alone – it didn't occur to us to call anyone. I put my breathing exercises into action and a nurse popped in now and again. It was only just after transition, when I was having terrible cramp in my leg and as the baby's head started to engage, that we called for help. I was wheeled off to the delivery room as my husband was given a plate of porridge in the corridor from a passing breakfast trolley. He was still eating this when Richard was born with the aid of an episiotomy. He was a good size (7lb 6oz). My husband telephoned both sets of parents, returned home and went to bed. I was stitched up, bathed and put to bed to sleep. Richard was taken to the nursery. The midwives, to my surprise, congratulated me the next morning for managing mostly on my own.

Later on a very young nursery nurse came to bring a bottle of milk which I asked her to take away. She protested but agreed when I accepted the bottle with sugar and water as a prevention against jaundice. Richard was then brought to me and, when I had a chance to have a good look at him, I was frightened. He looked for a moment so much like my dead father-in-law that I thought he was a ghost. Then as I said hello he looked at me, and I got a strong feeling that he recognized my voice.

I didn't feed him in the nursery, preferring the privacy of my own bed space. It seemed as if I was managing but I don't think my breastfeeding was properly begun during those twenty-four hours.

The next day I was transferred to the local GP unit. By then Richard had become jaundiced. I thought I was being transferred to a better environment but, once there, my problems really began. They stuck to the routine of feeding every four hours which, in my case, was a disaster. I was having difficulties feeding because of very tender nipples and engorgement and I was obstinately refusing bottles of milk and insisted on being woken at night to feed. I continued to supplement with water as Richard was now very yellow and being called Ho Chi Minh by the staff. Things finally came to a head with a Staff Nurse shouting at me, 'You do realize you're putting the baby's life at risk? When I first came on duty I looked at the notes, which said you're a difficult mother.' In reply I dissolved into tears which lasted the whole day. My husband found me sobbing in the staff room. I gave in and allowed them to give Richard a bottle during the night so I could get some sleep. The next morning I discussed the problem with a different Staff Nurse who, on discovering Richard was four-and-a-half-weeks premature, immediately initiated a programme of feeding two- to three-hourly and enabled me to feed even during visiting time, which was unheard of. From then on everyone, including me, relaxed and I took full advantage of the pampering and stayed until Richard started to turn a normal pink!

At home I was followed up by the midwife and my GP, but

when the Health Visitor came I could sense that she was a little concerned. She said 'just to be on the safe side' I should see the Community Physician. He duly saw Richard and felt that there was nothing to worry about. He was obviously premature but he would catch up in time. I was not to worry if his motor development was a little slow as this was a common thing with premature babies.

Breastfeeding occupied most of my day and night as he was a very slow feeder. But we persevered and gradually established a comfortable routine.

My mother enjoyed being a Granny, despite her earlier protestation to the contrary, but my father, we heard later, was constantly worried that there was something wrong with Richard 'from the chest up'. We decided not to have Richard christened, mainly because I felt this was hypocritical as we are not churchgoers. John's family were upset, though, I think because they thought this would bring bad luck.

I missed work desperately at first and compensated for my isolation by attending regular meetings of the local breastfeeding group. This provided me with much-needed help and advice and a new circle of friends. I also took up adult literacy teaching and, when Richard was one year old, I approached my old employers about obtaining a one-day-a-week job. While I was at work my mother looked after Richard.

Although Richard's motor development was slow and he did not learn to crawl, soon after his first birthday he stood up and walked. But about a month later we noticed he had difficulty keeping his balance. At first we put it down to tiredness but then he crashed into the doorpost of the bathroom. Still I didn't attach much significance to this; however, my mother, when she had him on the following Monday, noticed he was not using his left arm properly. Then his squint became much more pronounced and I was worried enough by the Thursday to take him to the doctor. My doctor was on holiday so we were seen by someone else. Richard had perked up while we were in the waiting room and the doctor could find nothing significantly amiss except for the squint, which he had always had. As the weekend progressed I began to get frightened. His eye started really rolling in his head and, by the next Monday, he had lost the use of his left side and could not sit up properly. I went to the doctor first thing in the morning saying Richard looked like someone who had a stroke. I didn't realize that I had made the right diagnosis. The GP sent me straight to the paediatrician's clinic. As I had no appointment I was kept waiting until last. Richard was given a thorough examination and an X-ray, which showed nothing conclusive, and we were referred to the regional hospital for a brain scan. As I left the paediatrician said things were very serious and wished me good luck. The regional hospital rang later in the afternoon and arranged for us to attend the next day.

This was to be one of the most horrendous days my husband and I have ever had. We arrived, as requested, at nine-thirty in the morning. It was two or three in the afternoon before we were through. For the scan, Richard's head had to be kept perfectly still so he needed to be sedated. Given his condition, the doctor decided that the drug should be administered intravenously. They couldn't get the needle into his veins, even with me lying on top of him. After each attempt we had to walk him round outside in his pushchair to wait for the drug to take effect. There was nowhere to get a drink, or sit down quietly and, because only small amounts were getting into his bloodstream, it took five attempts before Richard was relaxed enough. Although he was sedated he was still conscious as they pushed his head slowly into what looked like a large washing machine.

By now he was terrified and I was physically and emotionally exhausted by all the previous failures and had to come out and leave him with my husband for the final run. We were not told anything then and refused permission to look at the scan. After what seemed an interminable wait, we were told he was to be admitted to the children's ward. They put Richard in a cot and I collapsed crying in a chair. We were moved to the visitor's room and given a cup of tea, but were not allowed to finish it or take it with us, as we were summoned to talk to the doctor who wanted some family history. Then we were left alone with Richard who had been put in a cot. Nobody came to see us.

Finally, I went to ask if we were to speak to the consultant. He called in at about five-thirty on his way home and explained that he was not sure, but the possibilities were that either Richard had a brain tumour, which meant we would lose him; or that he had an arterial condition, which would mean he would live but be severely handicapped and we could still lose him at any time. Although I pressed the consultant, he was not prepared to commit himself. He pointed out that Richard had not yet showed any of the classic signs of a tumour, such as headaches or vomiting.

He obviously found this conversation as difficult as we did. When he left we stumbled out into the grounds, sat under a tree and, clutching each other, cried our hearts out. I remember saying 'I bet it's a tumour.' Eventually we gathered ourselves to break the news to our families. John's mother had intuitively felt that something was wrong, while my mother was speechless.

Richard was discharged from hospital about a fortnight later. He immediately perked up when he was put into his car seat. He'd obviously missed his own environment and so, momentarily, things looked brighter. The hospital had told us to treat him normally and I always bitterly regret having taken this advice. If only they had said, 'Treat him as if you were going to lose him.' Then I could have spoilt him more. Instead, I tried to carry on as normal, taking him shopping and visiting. I insisted he try to use his good hand to do everything with, and smacked him when I thought he was naughty. I held back, clinging to the hope that he might live. Now I would give anything to have that time over again. How I longed to have him sleep in our bed! But we reasoned he was better in his own room, and certainly he seemed content in his cot – although gradually I started to bring him in with us in the morning.

He began to deteriorate, but he hadn't started to vomit so there was still a chance. But in my heart, I knew there was no hope. Gradually he lost his ability to walk and became drowsy. Looking back, I think he was in pain on occasions. Our health visitor arranged for a physiotherapist. This lady was a godsend. She had doubts about his prognosis right at the beginning but was full of practical advice. She asked me to call on her one evening and told me frankly what would be involved in bringing up a handicapped child. Until then I had been putting a brave front on things, but I cried solidly all the way home and then for most of the night. After that I truly hoped that all of us would be spared that kind of suffering. One thing she said which helped me through and has remained with me since was 'There are worse things than death.'

Richard seemed to comprehend that he was ill and to know how upset I was. On one occasion he fell over after I had put him on the floor. I scooped him up and sat with him in my lap on the floor. I was rocking him backwards and forwards and he was stroking my eyes and wiping away my tears with his good hand. By then he could no longer speak.

A month after the first hospital admission we had to have another scan. As soon as Richard entered the room, he started hitting me. On seeing this, the doctor arranged for him to be sedated orally on the children's ward and all then went smoothly. The scan showed nothing more conclusive so we went home again to worry. Then I received my warning. For me, the breaking of glass without cause is always a sign that someone close is about to die. One morning I picked up my heavy glass mixing bowl to find a large chunk had chipped off by itself. My husband tried to pass it off as a legitimate accident but we both felt we knew.

All Richard was now able to do was lie on the settee without moving and just follow us with big eyes.

Our doctor, who had been on holiday and just caught up with developments, called to see us. He was moved and upset. He prescribed antibiotics for a possible infection. I asked him if there was really any point, but complied.

Richard couldn't keep this medicine down and started to vomit. This was the symptom we were dreading. We telephoned the doctor and he came out straight away, took one look, and asked the regional hospital to re-admit Richard. Before we left I wanted to take a photo but my husband said it would only remind us of when it had been taken. Richard was admitted again to the children's ward and they arranged for us to stay overnight.

We couldn't stay at the hospital indefinitely so we travelled the fifty miles round trip each day. We had a letter from the hospital allowing us to have meals in the staff canteen. This arrangement enabled my husband to continue going to work.

A day or so later Richard's breathing became irregular during visiting and, as a nurse tried to regulate this, it stopped. In rushed everyone with the rescusitation equipment. At the same time, the duty consultant was called. We were pleading through sobs for them to let him go, but they rushed him off to intensive care. Then he had another scan. We were sent off to lunch and, in the afternoon, asked to present ourselves at the intensive care unit. We were standing in the public area just outside when the duty consultant told us honestly and clearly that Richard had now a massive tumour situated in the mid-brain, where it was virtually impossible to treat. Some treatment was available but, in his experience, had never been successful in a child under two years old. Besides, the side effects were devastating. There was now the complication of the brain damage caused when his breathing stopped. They would treat him if we wished, but the prognosis was still extremely poor. We decided on no treatment. Sister then came to ask us what we wanted to do. We wanted his kidneys to be donated. She explained this meant waiting for brain death. As he was not yet in that condition, we agreed for him to stay in intensive care on the respirator.

For the next few weeks our lives became dominated by the sheer strain of coping. My husband went to work each day and in the evening I would drive us both the twenty-five miles to the hospital. We would have a meal at the canteen, visit Richard, drive back twenty-five miles, and collapse into bed, often crying ourselves to sleep. Things were made even worse because his condition would fluctuate from day to day. One day he would be close to brain death, the next in an oxygen tent with his eyes open. Mercifully for him, he never regained consciousness. We were encouraged to speak to him, however, and hold him, just in case something was getting through.

On hearing about things, a neighbour of one of our friends referred us to the local Vicar. His was the only counselling we received. I was initially very hostile and unable to accept his help, especially when he offered 'healing'. His proposal was that Richard should be christened, and then anointed, and that we could have a healing service. After much heart-searching I agreed. On the day, we put on our best clothes, and the nursing staff washed Richard's hair and spruced him up. I took along a shawl John's mother had made for him to be christened in. Afterwards my husband and I went out to dinner as a sort of celebration. We'd been grieving continuously since the first admission, concentrating on surviving from day to day. The christening somehow brought us some peace and acceptance.

We'd been told that Richard would not come out of intensive care but, soon after his christening, to our surprise, he came off the respirator and was moved back in the children's ward. Although he had been unconscious for several weeks, he could now breathe on his own. He was subject to jerky, involuntary movements and teeth grinding, but his condition was stable. At this point I asked for him to be moved to our local hospital to relieve the strain on us; and this was done a week later. What a godsend that move was. Whereas previously we were housed in a goldfish bowl, we now had our own private room. They dressed Richard and gave him different-flavoured food by nasal tube and arranged for him to have a radio, as hearing is the last faculty to go. Again we were encouraged to talk to and hold him. We could visit when we liked, so could my parents and friends if they wanted. Because he was still grinding his teeth and jerking his limbs, they tried him on non-convulsive drugs but stopped them when it became clear they had no effect. I went to see him every afternoon and again with my husband in the evening.

The afternoon of the day before Richard died I held him, cradled in a pillow, in my arms. It was the first time I had cried with him for a long time. I remember saying, 'Don't hang on too long.' The end came suddenly the next day. The hospital had been trying to ring me all morning, but I had been doing a bit of shopping. I telephoned my husband to come from work. My parents called in by pre-arrangement and stayed until late afternoon. It was about nine p.m. when he died. We didn't call anybody. We just cuddled him and waited for him to stop breathing, telling him to stop fighting and let go. The doctor came with his trousers on over his pyjamas to sign the death certificate. We asked about donating Richard's kidneys but, because a chest infection was the actual cause of death, they couldn't be used. We'd hoped they would give some other child life and that something positive would come out of his death, but it seems his death couldn't even bring this small gift. We stayed with him a little while and then gathered ourselves to break the news to our families.

I coped with the funeral, which had been planned during sleepless nights, by holding in, and holding everyone else together. I knew that if I broke down so would everyone else.

The fact that I no longer appeared with Richard obviously puzzled some of his little friends. One, a four-year-old, asked point blank what had happened to him, and another kept looking at me strangely, obviously wondering where Richard was. One friend asked me to help with her daughter's birthday party. Why she asked, and why I went, I really don't know. I remember handing round sandwiches in a trance.

I had been keeping my friends at the office in touch with events so I knew there was a vacancy. Two days after the funeral I went back to work. The routine of work was in itself therapeutic, but I had my setbacks. One day a mother came to ask me to remove her eighteen-month-old boy from her care. I did so, but was left feeling physically sick.

Mid-brain tumours are a spasmodic occurrence – about one in 25,000. We had been assured that this was not a hereditary condition. There was no reason why we should not try again. We had no doubts about wanting to be parents for a second time. My husband duly wore himself out for a week when I was pretty certain the dates would be right. A month after the funeral we went on holiday. I knew by then I was pregnant again. This time I felt sick for the first three months. I asked my doctor about amniocentesis and he agreed to refer me on condition that I would consent to an abortion if it was necessary. I had no qualms about that.

So it was back again to the regional hospital, although to a different building. At first the consultant refused to help on the grounds that Richard had been a one-off occurrence and there was no family history. He told me to return in a fortnight. That time he performed the test. I didn't enquire what had changed his mind.

I lived in a state of suspended animation until the results of the amniocentesis test showed that the baby was all right. I asked which sex it was, and was overjoyed to learn I was to have the replacement boy I dearly wanted.

And yet I couldn't completely relax. My Rubella test proved positive and I panicked, knowing I had never had German Measles. I only calmed down when I learned it was too late to do any tests and I realized I might have picked up an immunity without knowing it.

Also, my mother had taken Richard's death very badly. Whenever I visited her she poured all her grief out on me and, because of my own feelings, I was not able to help her with hers. All I could do was soak it all up. This usually left me feeling sick as I drove home afterwards. Eventually the strain exacerbated the illness she had had for a long time and her strength gave way. There I was, six months into my second pregnancy, making funeral arrangements again. It was only my work and the hope of new life that kept me going, but I cried in the night when my husband was asleep.

I went into labour seven weeks early. I was having contractions at work in the morning but attached little significance to them. Luckily, I had a hospital appointment that afternoon. The drive must have raised my blood-pressure because they refused to let me go home. It was feared I would give birth to another premature baby, so I spent a very uncomfortable night attached to a monitor and a drip in the delivery ward, cared for by largely unsympathetic staff. This was followed by two weeks of blissful cossetting upstairs in the 'waiting' ward. I was finally allowed home with some unpleasant medication and with strict orders to do absolutely nothing and certainly not drive.

Three weeks later (two weeks before my date) I went into labour again and I was admitted during a busy period. It was clear no one had read my notes and I was treated in quite a rough-and-ready way. The baby came all in a rush when no one was prepared, and I was torn during delivery. My first question was, 'Is he all right?' He was, and after a quick suckle, he was whisked upstairs. I was left for over four hours waiting to be stitched up.

I stayed in the postnatal ward for the maximum time again, to sort out my recurring breastfeeding problems. This time a pumping machine did the trick, but I was in agony each time David fed, so the midwife prescribed a nipple shield.

I was a much more confident mother this time so there were no real problems while David was younger, but whenever he became ill my husband was terrified. I forced myself and him to be calm, telling him if something was meant to happen we couldn't stop it anyway. As David grew older we became more relaxed.

Of course he was a different baby. He was bigger for a start and had hamster-like cheeks, but on occasions he bore an uncanny resemblance to his dead brother. This became very apparent when we put a portrait photo of each of them into one frame. Unless you knew the story you'd never have guessed they weren't twins.

We bought a house in a nearby village as I wanted to be somewhere with facilities for mums and children. Initially the house needed a lot of rebuilding so I was kept busy with builders and plumbers etc. I attended the Mums and Toddlers Club twice a week and generally settled down to being a mother again. The need to work felt less urgent this time and I didn't seek it as before. However, when David was eighteen months old, I was again offered a one-day-a-week job. Since my mother was gone, I found a local child-minder for David. She introduced me to a baby-sitting circle and the local group of the National Housewives' Register. This gave me a new set of friends. When David was two I took him to meet the family in Holland. My husband telephoned every night to make sure he was all right. David celebrated his third birthday there this year. He is now the baby of the family and is allowed to get away with murder, just like I was.

I have just returned to full-time work and a picture of both my boys sits on my desk. Even those who know the story ask me if they are both of David.

They say when you lose a child part of you dies with it, and certainly the death of two of the closest people to me knocked me for six. But I don't cry inside all the time any more. I only ever wanted one child so perhaps this was the only way David could have been born. Perhaps he is meant for some special purpose – who knows? I only know that, when I look at him sometimes, I see glimpses of Richard and the Grandfather they both never knew.

PART FIVE

Single Parents

Susan Lyons

'I think there are things that make life easier as a single parent. There was nobody else expecting anything of me, even in terms of having a meal on the table at the end of the day . . . I did not feel I needed to be achieving other things all the time . . . I have found that living on my own, I have coped with all kinds of situations, and I would much rather be on my own than making hopeless compromises.'

Ben is twenty years older than me, married with children. I had always hoped that he would leave his wife, but he has other children, so it just did not work out that way; and I live on my own in a flat, but see him regularly. I had known Ben for about six years before I had Wendy. We talked about having a child for quite a long time but, because the circumstances were not really right, it was not until I was about thirty-five that I began to think really deeply that it might be something that I would do.

I suppose I had always grown up thinking of a man and woman having a child whilst living together. I am not particularly brave about going against social pressures, although it does not really worry me deep down. When I was thirty-five it just became an instinctive issue: I wanted children, and it was beginning to be a question of soon or not at all. I have always liked children although I have not had a lot of contact with them. Education and child development interest me a lot.

I wanted to be an architect when I was about eleven, but I questioned that, and went off into other things at about O-Level time, but I came back to it. It was partly because I was being a bit bloody-minded, as no one at school wanted me to do it. It was not quite what people planned. It did not relate to anything I had studied at school, and nobody could give any guidance on it. From the age of sixteen onwards that was what I wanted to do. Architecture involves a long training: five years at college, with a couple of years afterwards on the job. So it does impose a very set pattern on your life. London has a great pull and people tend to train and stay here, so that was another aspect of my life which was fairly set.

My life would not have been without meaning if I had not had a child, because I am too committed to my career, and I have a very tangible end-product to my work. It is possible though that, without a child, I would not have known quite how to structure my life and might have become more and more career-orientated in a slightly obsessional way. If that does not happen, then it can simply become a question of earning as much money as possible, and indulging interests like travelling. It becomes a conscious choice of how best to enjoy oneself. If there are children, the element of surprise and risk comes into one's life: there is no way of knowing what the child will be like, or what life will be like with them. I did not see anything pushing my life off into a different course.

It took me about two years to decide that I was going to get pregnant, because there were so many complications. I had to work out financially whether I could do it; whether I could afford to have the time off work. There were some really unpleasant experiences initially with social security. I had assumed that through taking unpaid leave, I would become unemployed, but discovered that, technically, I was still employed. So then it was a question of finding out about supplementary benefit: I needed some hard figures to be able to work out if I could do it.

First of all I went to the local Social Services, and that was an awful experience. I went up to a counter where there were lots of people around and spoke to a dreadful woman. I was trying to say 'How much would I get, being on my own?' and she said, 'Where's the father?' She was terribly moral about it: it was horrible. After that I decided to continue the investigations over the phone, and I got the same kind of reactions from people who asked questions that showed no understanding of the situation at all. On the other hand, when I was actually on supplementary benefit, I was all prepared for unpleasantness when they came round to check if there were any men hiding in the cupboard, as I had been warned they would. In fact, they were very nice, but I suspect that they took a cue from the fact that I was an architect. I think there is a nasty side to the whole business and they might give other women a much harder time. As far as I was concerned though, there were no problems. I was interviewed by a man who treated me as an equal. He took everything at face value and I got exactly what I expected.

I knew that I had got to work out my finances in quite a lot of detail. My employers would give me paid maternity leave for about eight weeks into the period I would have off. I wanted to take the full twenty-nine weeks. My employers give a period of half-pay: an awful situation because I knew I would be unable to claim supplementary benefit, but still not have enough money. That left about three months in which I would not be getting any pay at all.

Eventually I managed to find out everything from the National Council for One-Parent Families, who sent me some useful literature. But, because I had all the information in dribs and drabs, I went through times of thinking I could afford it, worked it all out, and then decided I could not. It was a time of great ups and downs. I think it was the worst part of the pre-planning. I had already bought the flat, so there was not much else I had to do in terms of changing my life. At work I had been working for two-and-a-half years on little projects, nothing very interesting, so I thought: now is the time. Then, the minute I got pregnant, I was given a new building to design!

I was rather concerned about people's reactions at work if I had a child on my own. I suppose I was not really sure how they would react, but hoped people would say, 'Your private life is your own.' I was more worried about the area I live in, and the neighbours. We are not close but I see a lot of them. They are very traditional: upper working class with rather set attitudes. And then, of course, there was the question of my parents; I felt they would be really worried, not from the moral point of view, because they are fairly open, but worried about me doing such a thing on my own. Now, since I am happy about it, so are they. They are very supportive. We are quite a close family and they would see Wendy every weekend if they could.

There was a point at which I thought I really should be brave enough *not* to have a child, because of the effect on it. I do feel that a child should have male and female influences in its life. There was also the fact that I would be working: there is a pressure for the mother to stay at home during the first five years of the child's life. It is only since the war that there has been a lot of literature on the subject and I have read most of it! There was one particular book I had read which was reassuring. It was a collection of studies on children in differing circumstances which really came out saying that as long as the difficulties were met and talked about with the children they would be okay. Having read that I felt I would not be just indulging myself or, at least, not unreasonably so, and not to the detriment of the child, and that it was all right to go ahead.

There are so many children who are born without being planned or considered, and I thought that, as I had planned it all almost into the ground, it would be all right. And really, if you feel strongly that you have to do it, then you have to do it. It is a leap in the dark, but . . .

Ben accepted the decision immediately and quite quickly became very supportive about it. I think he wanted me to have a baby but he was a bit frightened about the complications of the situation, particularly in relation to his job and his wife, as she does not know about our relationship.

I was convinced that, because of my age, it would take a long time to get pregnant: at least a year. But, in fact, it took a month. The temperature method worked fantastically well. So it did take me very much by surprise, really, when I found I was pregnant. I was thirty-five when I started trying, and I thought I would be thirty-six by the time I got pregnant, and thirty-sevenish by the time I had her. That would just about leave me room for one more child before I was forty, if that was what I wanted. So I was a bit younger than I expected to be.

The first visit to Social Security reinforced all the social pressures, real or imaginary, and I probably did not progress any further for about three months. It was a very slow, stop-start process. During the last three months I was reading a tremendous amount of literature and trying to find out about the problems of being older and the possible ill-effects on the baby. I was very worried about the fact of being an older mother, mainly because of old wives' tales: it was more an atmosphere than hard concrete facts. It was all part of the slow build-up, since the age of thirty, of trying to find more information. I talked a little to my doctor about it. Most of the literature which I read seemed to suggest that there were not too many difficulties, and that amniocentesis was available, and that seemed to cover the one really major problem, so I calmed down my worries over that. The real worries were that there might be something wrong with the baby. I was not concerned about being unable to cope, as I did not have enough of a picture about what having a child was like. I have one close friend who had a child eight years ago, and then another child about a year before I had Wendy. He was the only small child I had seen growing up.

I had all sorts of ludicrous fantasies about what it would be like to have a child. One of the most ridiculous ones was that, after having had a career and always been busy, there would be a wonderful period when I could sit at home and read cookery books. I bought books about home-baking and saw myself floating around, being domestic, wearing dreamy clothes. The child was always sleeping! If I had really sat down and thought about it, I would have said that such ideas were absurd, but they linger at the back of your mind. It was a strong reaction against having a career: I saw myself in a maternal role at home indulging all those aspects of life I had missed out on.

During the time I was working out finances, Ben was waiting to see what the decision would be. It was very much in my hands. I had been working out the temperature method for about six months. I was sure that it would take a long time to get pregnant so I felt I really had to concentrate on it in a very positive way. Ben is so much older too, and we both were very aware that our fertility was decreasing. Everything I read indicated that becoming pregnant would be quite a long process. Ever since the age of thirty I had a growing conviction that I must be infertile, even though all the time I was using contraceptives. I had decided that if I was unable to have children I would have concentrated on my career. I would have liked to adopt, but it is so difficult. I would probably have re-arranged my work so that I had more contact with children.

I came off the pill when I was thirty. I decided I did not like it for some reason; it was not very rational. It was before there was the big fuss about stopping over thirty-five. I was happy with the cap so continued using it.

I began to suspect that I was pregnant very early on. It was not really morning sickness – just odd sensations. I went to the local family planning place and they confirmed the pregnancy. The nurse came out and said, 'I'm terribly sorry to say that you're pregnant.' And I said, 'Well, I'm very glad.' I think she was a bit astounded. She had said that because she knew that I was single.

Then I went to my doctor, and he was very helpful. He had a long talk with me and gave me a week to think about having an abortion. I had not even considered it, but he said, 'If you want to have the baby I will support you all the way, but I really think you need to think about it.' It was a very good thing, because I absolutely eliminated any ideas of going back on the decision after that stage. That meant that it did not hover as a possibility. After the decision had been made, the doctor was very supportive all the way through. That was an area that was, perhaps, different from normal. He was supportive because I was single, not because of my age. He never treated me as being different because I was older.

There was a traumatic two weeks early on in the pregnancy when I hoped that Ben would leave his wife, and he decided he could not. He wanted me to have an abortion at this stage. It shook me rigid. Therefore I had to decide to have Wendy on my own. It had always been my decision but I had vague imaginings that things would be different when it came to it. So I just said, 'Well, I am going to have this child, I don't care what you think.' From that moment I was very glad about it. And I was lucky, because I had a terribly easy pregnancy. I have never felt fitter, and I was working like mad and had so much energy. It was just coming out of my ears! It was absolutely extraordinary. I have never felt better. It was just luck and could be different another time, I believe. Age had no effect at all.

Telling my parents was a real trauma. I waited until I was four months pregnant, when there was not much chance of anything going wrong. It was very difficult, even though we had talked about it in principle before. It actually came up one meal time because another friend of mine was thinking of having a child. They said, 'What's Liz doing about this idea about having a child on her own?' and I said, 'Well . . . ahem . . . !' and everybody guessed! They did not take a moral attitude, but they were just worried about me. There was no difference between my father and mother on that. They had not met Ben until Wendy was born, but anyway they related to it very much from the point of view of knowing me. I had lived with someone else before and they realized that I was just not going to go down the straight and narrow. They had not brought me up to be like that anyway, so I do not think that they could really expect it! If you bring people up to question everything then you are bound to get results like that!

When I told people at work that I was pregnant nobody questioned me, nobody said a thing. This was apart from my few close friends whom I told quite separately. People were very good. My boss just said, 'I don't agree with it, but it's your life.' He did feel he had to say he did not agree with it! Most people were initially surprised, but then thought it was really good!

Early in my pregnancy I read Sheila Kitzinger's book about hospitals and childbirth. I went to Westminster Hospital first of all, but did not like it. It was a fantastic situation in London at the time because you could pick and choose. West London Hospital is out of my area, but I went along for the interview. It really did feel like an interview there. They check to see if you are the kind of mother they want! At the most basic level they wanted someone who was interested in breastfeeding and wanted to have the baby by the Leboyer method. That was what they were trying out, so there was no point in having women there who did not want that system. A close friend of mine who had a baby the year before was very keen on the Leboyer method and I learnt a lot from her. It was not until I was pregnant that I started to think about how I wanted to have it.

I was initially worried about the labour being more difficult because of my age. Talking to doctors and reading books quietened that fear down. Two friends of mine had children at the same time. The one who had the easiest labour was the eldest at thirty-eight; I was the middling one, and the third, who is about a year younger than me, ended up by having a Caesarian, having laboured away for twelve hours. So it was actually quite the reverse, as far as ages went.

I talked to my mother about labour and having children. I think she had a fairly easy time as she was noncommital about it. I did not talk to her about having a handicapped child, because I knew she was probably worrying about it anyway. My doctor was the only other person I could have checked it out with, but I had been reassured by the hospital. In fact, on the question of age, the hospital had been very supportive and positive. However, I was unsure about the hospital's attitude towards me having an amniocentesis. I was very keen to have one and they more or less refused, saying that there was too great a risk of harming the baby. I was unsure of the statistics and uncertain of their reasons for refusing me. Perhaps they could not afford to give amniocentesis to everybody, or perhaps there really was a risk in having it. The things I heard and read were conflicting. I really feel that something more clear-cut ought to be known about it.

I was worried by the logistics of getting to hospital on my own. At Hammersmith, the hospital administration insists that everyone goes in by ambulance. In fact, the waters broke at night on the day she was due. I rang up and they told me to ring back in three hours. When I did so they told me to come in. So labour was starting when I arrived at hospital at seven o'clock in the morning, and I had her at seven in the evening, which was not a very long time.

I was very frightened of the outcome of the day – not for myself, but I was terrified of losing the baby. My brother and two fairly close friends all lost their first child at birth without there being any previous problems. Two had the cord round the neck and the third was brain-damaged. I know that many people complain about being strapped up to all the machinery so they can listen to the heartbeat, but I must admit I thought it was marvellous. It was just terrific to know all the time that the baby was all right. I kept wondering whether she would be okay.

That anxiety was related to my age. Having read so much about it all beforehand, I thought I knew more about it than I actually did. I knew roughly what the pattern of things would be. I was a bit nervous that it would be painful, but I am not that frightened of pain: I always have my teeth done without an injection, unless it is going to be really bad. But it was not as orderly as the classes had led me to believe, even though they did stress that all sorts of things can happen. There was no point at which I was frightened. I knew what was going on: it was just a lot more uncomfortable than I had expected.

I had an epidural, which I waited too long for because I wanted to see if I could give birth naturally. I would not do that again! I had the epidural at midday, so I had been going for about five hours with quite strong contractions. There were quite a lot of people all having babies almost simultaneously, all wanting an epidural, so I had to wait for about half an hour before the man could get round, and things were building up fiercely. The epidural had an immediate effect, and also instantly stopped the contractions. So then they put me on a drip, and that changed it somehow. Instead of having a peak with the contractions then receding, there was continuous pressure all the time. I had not been trained to cope with it. I believe that backache labour is like that: there is just constant backache all the way through. I could not tell when the contractions were coming because of the epidural. But the epidural did help enormously. I had one top-up and then wanted another one, but was told I was too far on. By the time I was giving birth, in fact, the effect had worn off, except that my legs were useless, which is a standard thing. I was not getting any pain relief by that stage, and was very tired.

I felt marvellous when Wendy was finally born. I was totally exhausted at the last minute when I was actually pushing and I had to watch the machine to tell me when the contractions were so that I knew when to push. I did not have any natural pushing feeling. They warned me of that in the classes: it can happen with an epidural. I was really terrible, screaming and swearing! I just lost all my inhibitions. I was given the baby immediately to feed. They did not clean her up beforehand – the classic Leboyer thing! I just felt completely uninhibited and kept talking to her all the time. I discovered I was thrilled it was a little girl. Half of me had known that I would prefer a girl to a boy, but I was not really aware of it. Bringing up a girl interests me very much, because things are changing so much for women. It is also important how boys are brought up to cope with the ways things have changed, with the women's movement. But it affects a girl so much more directly.

After holding her initially, the recurring worry returned: was she okay? I could see that she had all her fingers and limbs, but the fear of Down's Syndrome came back quite strongly at that point. I voiced it to the student doctor immediately and he said that he had checked for it straight away. He was very reassuring and said that there were no problems. All the time I was in hospital I was visited every day by the student doctor. I discussed all my worries with him. I think it was the same with the other mothers who would talk to him about the most pertinent worry they had. When Dr Jolly came round he had been briefed by the student. The hospital really worked at reassuring me on all fronts so that by the time I left I really felt that everything was as good as it could be. Obviously, new worries develop over time, but there were no obvious problems then; it was just as well, because if I had not been totally reassured I would have been very nervous and worried at home, and it is not always clear where to go for advice.

The delivery was at the weekend and Ben came to see me on the Monday. He would actually have been at the birth if it had been a week day. He was very brave in coming to the men's classes even though he was in a different age group. He felt rather out of place. He did not participate in the birth of his other children, so I think he was disappointed not to be at Wendy's birth. Anyway, he appeared on the Monday morning as visiting hours are very free at the hospital. I explained to the doctor that we had not seen each other and they let us have a room so that we could look at her and talk.

I had quite a strange time whilst I was in hospital. There were several private rooms which were available after the first few days and I had one for a while. I have always been an eight-hours-a-night sleeper, and being woken up at all hours was very disruptive. I found it very, very peculiar. I used to have weird dreams: I did not know if I was a baby or a grown-up. I found myself lying in the same position as the baby in the womb when I slept, and I would get confused between myself and her. It was very surreal and I find it difficult to explain. It continued for quite a while after I left hospital, although it was most extreme whilst I was there. It was probably some memories of myself as a child that were churned up by the experience of giving birth. On the whole, though, it was a very reassuring time for me in hospital.

I found coming out of hospital traumatic. Ben came home with me; my parents came to see us and my mother stayed for a week or so. I found suddenly having to cope with even the standard everyday things absolutely terrifying. I was constantly turning to my mother, not really for advice, but wanting her to look after

Wendy. Nothing I had read prepared me for what that time would be like. I just felt at the beck and call of this tiny thing that needs feeding every two hours, and the stream of nappies seemed to be never-ending. I was used to a job where I was pretty much in control and then, suddenly, I found someone was in control of me, all the time. I had felt previously that I could cope with life and suddenly, I was being shown that I could not. There was no time to reflect. So this was the spontaneity and risk I had been looking for! It was a long time before I could even start thinking about such things. I feel that even now I am still in the middle of the confusion brought about by the change from being in control in my job to being at the beck and call of a small baby. I am only just beginning to come out of it and see her as separate; for a long time I was interlinked and unable to separate myself. It took quite a while for me to realize that all the visions I had of motherhood were unrealistic, also that even basic things that I needed to do, such as bits of painting around the flat, just would not get done. I would start off the week with a mental list of things I was going to do and end up not achieving any of them by the end of it. It took me a long time to adjust to that. I had seven months off work and it was only after six months that I realized I would have to stop thinking about trying to achieve anything other than looking after Wendy. I found that was the biggest mental step: just to let things go. So I decided that I would have someone to do the cleaning and use all the assistance I could get. Before, I had coped with everything, basically because it was easy to cope with.

During the early months I had phases of wishing I had someone with me all the time to whom I could turn. It would have been lovely to have had someone there to help so I could sleep uninterruptedly. I found the fact that I had to deal with her singlehandedly very difficult at times. At times I wanted to shut the door and walk away from it, but of course, was unable to; dealing with her demands was an absolute imperative. I had never had anything in my life that made such demands on me, that I could not walk away from, or at least discuss!

However, I think there are other things that make life easier as a single parent. There was nobody else expecting anything of me, even in terms of having a meal ready at the end of the day. I just could not have done that! My mother was sure it was easier in that respect. It had been the bane of bringing up children for her. My father was not terribly demanding, but he did feel that a meal should be on the table when he got home.

It was quite nice not to have to account for my day to anybody; I did not feel that I needed to be achieving other things all the time. I do not think that being a single mother is all problems by any means. I have seen stresses in other people's marriages as a result of having children, that have proved to me that is the case. This is especially marked in a marriage where both partners are working: the woman tends to feel hard done by, that she does all the nasty chores whilst the man does all the pleasant ones. I have found that, living on my own, I have coped with all kinds of situations, and I would much rather be on my own than be making hopeless compromises.

On balance, I feel fine about bringing Wendy up on my own, but there are situations where it can be a problem. Shopping for clothes is virtually impossible, because she pulls everything off the shelf. I just cannot make any decisions with her there, and I cannot take time off to shop on my own very often. It really would be nice to be able to switch off sometimes and have time on my own. On the other hand, things are getting easier in that there are more places I can go to with her; exhibitions, for instance. If I pick the right kind, she is quite interested. Obviously, I cannot appreciate them in the same way as I would have done before: I cannot really look critically as one eye is always on her.

Soon after I had Wendy and returned home, there was a week when I was really terrified of going out with the pram. I was absolutely inept with it. I walked into Marks and Spencer and knocked coats everywhere; I was so cack-handed. People would say, 'Whose baby is this?' thinking that I was an aunt or distant relative.

I did not know any other single mothers before having Wendy, and think it would have been a great help if I had. I had read as much as I could about single-parenting, but there is not a great deal written about it, and what books there are concentrate on the idea of the poverty-stricken single mother. I could not find anything in books about someone who is in my position: someone who undertakes single-parenting after consideration, and with enough money and resources to carry herself through.

I have not made many new friends since having Wendy. I met a few at first through the National Childbirth Trust and that was very pleasant. But as I got back into work, and life became more normal, it took all the spare time I had to keep up with old friends, and I found that I did not particularly need new ones. My established friends at work with families had more in common with me, in that their time and energies were divided between career and children, as opposed to those from the National Childbirth Trust, who were often home-based. The N.C.T. meetings were very useful in the early days though, as they meant I got out of the house and I was also able to discuss practical problems connected with breastfeeding and changing nappies. I found it extraordinary that there is a whole area I knew nothing about, and there is very little help given on it. When I first used non-disposable nappies at home I had to ring up a friend to find out how to sterilize them, as the instructions on the label tell you nothing about it! There is nothing written about actually scraping dirty nappies!

I found fatigue particularly hard to cope with. I still get woken by Wendy at least once every night. There has not been a night that I have not been woken by her since she was born, but I seem to have managed to adjust to it. It took about eighteen months to adjust: at first I felt as if I was being tortured. It was the biggest of the problems. It does not seem to have any connection with age, but depends on the child. The friend who had a child just before Wendy was born had exactly the same problem, even though her first child was very placid and slept well, so I knew that it was not really my fault. My mother said that all of us had been similar. People who have children who sleep well make me feel terribly guilty though. I feel that I am not looking after her properly; that there must be something wrong with the way I am treating her.

Breastfeeding was easy. I think the hospital helped a lot as they were very keen on breastfeeding, and by the time I left there were virtually no problems. However, there was one big worry on the subject: I developed a lump in my breast and had to go into hospital. I was referred to St Thomas's, and they were absolutely fantastic: they arranged a special anaesthetic, gave me a private room, and I was not even kept in overnight, so I could continue breastfeeding. They were virtually certain that the lump would not be malignant and they trusted me not to eat before the operation. The anaesthetic wore off very quickly so that Wendy could feed straight away. It was all very impressive! The lump did prove to be non-malignant, so in the end it turned out to be a fairly ordinary incident, although I was frightened by it. I must say that I have found hospitals very supportive in many ways. There were no eyebrows raised about the fact that I was a single mother. The only unpleasant experiences I had about this were the early ones in my dealings with the Social Security people.

I felt very positive about my sex life whilst I was pregnant and in fact was incredibly randy the entire time! Since then, the circumstances of life have changed things, but I do not think it is harming our relationship. We are both aware of the joint responsibility of having a child and are affected deeply by it. There is a lot of mutual enjoyment in the child and it has brought us closer together, so there are compensations. I certainly do not want to swap sex for the joys of having children, though! I can imagine that my relationship with Ben would still be quite close even if we had not had Wendy, as we had already known each other for a long time. However, if I hadn't had her, I would have been getting very panicky by the age of thirty-eight. The big question now is whether to have another child. I would like to, but think I will have to shelve it for a while as it is difficult enough coping with one. All indications are that it is best to wait until the first child is about four. I am quite positive, though, that I would like another child. I would like her to have a brother or sister as she is rather limited in her number of relatives. I have two brothers, and she has one set of grandparents, which is not a lot. This is one problem of being a single-parent family. I think that as she gets older it will be very important for her to have a brother or sister. I have one friend who was brought up by a single mother without many relatives. She is my age, and very much alone and frightened about what will happen when her mother dies. It does not matter whether you love or hate your brothers and sisters, the important thing is that there is always someone who you have a special kind of contact with. I cannot really imagine coping with two children at the moment though. Possibly I will contemplate it when Wendy is older and out of nappies and not needing to be carried and the physical difficulties of coping are reduced. I am not making any decisions now though!

I am very glad that Wendy's child-minder is Marie, who has a family. She is far better integrated into family life than if she was being minded along with many other children. I find it difficult to accept Wendy being partly dependent on someone else, but it is all part of the process of letting go. It takes a long time to adjust to, but is very good for me to learn, and I do not know whether it is ever possible to do it completely.

There are many advantages in being an older mother. I have never been concerned about the possibility of there being a large gap when Wendy is a teenager. I have a friend who was adopted by a couple who were in their fifties or sixties. He is very close to them. There is obviously a large gap in terms of ideas, but that does not necessarily mean a gap of love exists between them. I think I am much more aware of how I operate now than when I was in my twenties, when I had a lot of stresses within myself. I am calmer now with children.

There were certain aspects of motherhood that came as a surprise to me. I feel very differently about peace. I have always been against nuclear weapons, but before, it was more through concern for myself. Now I get very angry because I am afraid for Wendy. It is quite different: an awareness, through the child, of a whole new area of vulnerability. I have a dread of something terrible happening to her. There are some things, like leukaemia, that are terrible but one has to accept them. But problems that people can actually deal with, like war, social problems and unemployment make me furious, angry and militant. We have created the problem and we have got the power to deal with it . . . and it threatens Wendy. Before Wendy, I probably would have had the same reaction, but there is much more strength to it now. I am astounded, because surely all parents must feel like this, and why hasn't something been done about it? It makes me much more impatient with the world.

At the moment I do not have time to be involved with organizations on a daily basis. I belong to CND and the Labour Party and sometimes join a protest march and do what I can. I do not have time to attend meetings, though, so am left with the difficulty of having stronger feelings, but less time to do anything positive with them. I suspect that there are many women who feel like this; women who are tied by the home who have *very* strong feelings, political feelings, about how they want the world to run, feelings that are all suppressed within the home. I am sure that the majority of women are not heard; the voices that are heard are the voices of women who have opted for a different kind of lifestyle, so maybe these women are not really helping the silent ones. I do now feel much more militant and the urgency of the need to push more for equal opportunities; and I am much more aware of how having a child affects me, the future and the way events happen.

It would have been extremely difficult to get very far in my career if I had broken off at twenty-five or so to have children. At that age I would only just have qualified, and if I had then stayed at home and stopped working I do not think I could ever have really acquired the self-confidence to push for a career. It would have taken me a long time to do it. Whereas, as it was, I just went straight from college, side by side with men, and worked from there. It has not affected my career to have a child later. I think men over-emphasize the impact of a child on one's career.

I wanted a child partly because of a feeling about the importance of the continuation of things: that if one has immortality, then it is manifested through one's children who, in turn, pass it on to later generations. I am very close to my grandmother, for example, and she may have been close to hers. This feeling of continuing relationships with people is quite strong.

I adored Wendy as a baby and just did not want time to pass! I took hundreds of photographs of her. I found the physical quality of our relationship surprised me as it was not something I had expected or thought much about beforehand. I had not realized how lovely babies are physically and how good they are to cuddle. I have been very surprised at how early Wendy became a companion, and at her responses.

I think you enjoy your own childhood again through your child. That is particularly true when you are in your thirties: in your twenties, childhood is that much closer. I find it is great fun, very refreshing, a mid-life phenomenon to see snow, for instance, through your child's eyes for the first time. I expect that it is always exciting, but it must be more so in your thirties because you are further away from the original experience. So the spontaneity and risk elements in having a child, that I mentioned before, have certainly fulfilled themselves: they are completely new areas in my life and provide something to respond to: I love doing things with her that she enjoys. Having a child has brought spontaneity into my life in a much more positive way than I ever expected.

Rewritten by Wendy Bastable from Sue Gee's interview with Susan Lyons.

Iven Spicer

'There have been times, particularly in the first couple of months, when I've felt I might burst with joy, and longed to be able to share this feeling . . . I suppose I still would like someone to share the intense pleasure she gives me . . . However, I have often felt there are advantages in bringing up a baby alone . . . I can bring her up the way I feel is right for her, without trying to reach agreement with anyone else.'

My father was a soldier during the Second World War so he wasn't around much until I was about three. I remember him coming home from the war and *feeling* he was a stranger while *knowing* he was my father. During this time my mother and I lived at the seaside – my memory is that she had plenty of friends and was always ready for a party. Once the war was over the three of us went to live away from the city (this was in Australia) in a fairly isolated area. For the next two or three years, except while I was at kindergarten, my mother and I spent most of our time together – my father left for work early in the morning, coming home late in the evening, so I only saw him at weekends, and my mother seemed to have no friends.

Then we moved again; this time to another beach suburb. Over the next three or four years my parents' lives changed again.

There were new friends (mostly met in pubs) and they began leading more separate lives. At the beginning of this period the three of us moved a couple of times. Then there were some moves for just my mother and me (and sometimes a male friend of hers). At some point my parents were divorced. Then it was I who was moved, to live with different people (an aunt, and a woman friend of my father's), and my contact with each of them during this time was intermittent. It stopped altogether with my mother when I was around twelve.

At about this time I moved into the boarding house where my father was living, and after a year we had a flat together. When I was fifteen my father remarried and I lived with him, my stepmother, and her two young sons until running away just over a year later to make a new life for myself at the other end of the country.

I think my parents were married when my father was around twenty-four and my mother twenty-six or so, and I was born a couple of years later. One early memory of my mother is of closing time in a hotel and her placing some chairs in a circle, standing in the middle, and singing 'Don't Fence Me In' to a group of her friends. Another is of waking from an afternoon sleep and being taken by a familiar woman on the short walk to the beach where we found my mother with a couple of friends.

The next stretch of memory is of a warm, loving woman who shared her life, it seemed, with only me (with my father somewhere on the periphery – he was the man who came on walks with us, and with whom she sometimes fought in the nights) and whom I came to know intimately. Still, even though I believed she was the most beautiful lady in the world, and adored her, I felt she was different from other mothers (not that I recall knowing any others!) and once didn't pass on an invitation to parents to come to a kindergarten Christmas concern – in case she embarrassed me, I think.

After this period my mother was involved with a particular man (at one stage I was made to use his surname at school, which I didn't like) and started drinking heavily. Although at the time I didn't feel she loved me less, I certainly was no longer the centre of her life, and by the age of twelve I had no part in her life. I was in my early thirties before I could admit that she had rejected me. I thought I had come to terms with this but after the birth of my own daughter I realized that I haven't.

During my early teens I consciously rejected her later life as a model for motherhood – the heavy public drinker, leading a noisy and volatile life (I was right to suspect when I was younger that she would embarrass me!), but for many years used the period when my mother and I were more or less alone together – she cooking delicious food, making nice clothes, amusing me and always there – as my ideal model. Yet, at the same time, I often sensed an unnamed threat to this idyll and tried to be very good so that everything would be all right.

During my last two years at school my father and I shared a flat together. I was excited at the prospect of being with him, but by this time he had met my future stepmother – his emotional needs were being met, and mine were not. I was very unhappy without understanding why and, unknown to anyone, made a serious, but obviously abortive, suicide attempt. While living in the flat I did all the cooking, cleaning and washing, and when my father remarried it seemed natural to us all that she take over these duties, although it was my father who insisted that I keep my room to the same standard as the rest of the house.

My father wanted me to have plenty of friends of both sexes. I wanted to be, but wasn't, popular with boys, though, and the few I found attractive were too grown up and experienced for me. He was keen that I should have a good job, though I think this was as much so that I'd meet suitable friends as for my own fulfilment or advancement in a career. One of my less conscious reasons for leaving home was probably that I suspected I wasn't going to want, or be able, to meet what I thought were his expectations of me – to be popular and settle down with a husband and raise a family. Some people tell me it was a brave step to take. I never felt this as, for me, it was easier than being face-to-face with the disappointment I felt he'd have in me.

My working life started when I was fifteen, as a shorthand-typist in a bank, and I loved every moment of it. My colleagues were older, and I felt very inexperienced in comparison and was eager to catch up. Within a year I had started smoking and had lost my virginity – I was out of my depth, though, and it was almost two years before I continued my sexual education but I did feel extremely smug at the time. The most significant event was going to visit a relative on the other side of Australia in my holidays. I felt free, relaxed, more confident and in my right element. When I returned home I asked my father if I could go back there to live and he said no. Until then I'd been discontented at home, but now I'd had a taste of an enjoyable life and I was even more miserable. Somehow I found out that jobs were going in the Public Service in the area I wanted to live, and that fares (it was two thousand miles away) and accommodation were taken care of. I applied and was accepted, so resigned from my job, which I was sad to leave, but didn't dare tell my father as I believed he'd try and stop me, and was sure he'd succeed. I did think of leaving a note on my pillow, but was frightened it would be found before I was safely on the plane, so I posted a letter the day I left. For me it was the right thing to do and I have never regretted leaving when I did. Curiously though, I sometimes felt extremely homesick. After the initial recriminations, I felt, and continue to feel, very close to my father and he, my stepmother (of whom I am fond) and I have always corresponded regularly. However, I have only seen him three times since then, and I find it a great strain because if I behave as myself we end up arguing, and if I behave as he seems to want I feel resentful.

The town where I was living was physically and psychologically isolated from any other town or cities in the country. It was a landing point for travellers from Europe, many of whom stayed for a while, and a large proportion of the population were people from other parts of the country who were generally working in the Public Service (the area was an administered Territory instead of a self-governing State). Whereas, in other parts, the norm was to get engaged during one's late teens, marry in the early twenties and have a child a year later, here were plenty of people my age (I was seventeen when I arrived) and older who weren't even 'going steady'. Again I loved my job, but now I also enjoyed my surroundings and felt I fitted in. After a couple of years, even though I was still having a good time, I wanted to explore more of the world. At that time (the year was 1962) it was almost as if Asia and the Indian sub-continent didn't exist for young Australians – London was the place to head for and Britain and Europe the places to be visited. The usual method of getting here at that time was by sea so I set off on the long voyage, expecting to be away for about two years on a working holiday.

I had almost no money on arrival in London, so found a job straight away – it was my third in an office and this type of work was beginning to pall. Within a year I was engaged to be married. When he asked me my heart sank, but I didn't know how I could say no. Also, I felt that I had to get married some time and, as I liked him, I went along with the idea. For a time I convinced myself and others that I loved him. Deep down I knew I didn't, although I did love the new status of being engaged. I would have been happy to take it no further, but I became pregnant so we put our names down for a register office wedding. But I miscarried very early so we didn't bother to get married then. After this I left my job and spent the summer working with a girl friend in holiday camps in Scotland and England, and went on to hotel work in Wales at the end of the season. I liked it there and, when the hotel job finished, found a job in a petrol station nearby. By now I had to face the fact that I would not be happy married to my fiancé so I wrote and returned the ring.

Eventually, I made my way back to London again and went back to office work, but before long found this didn't satisfy me. Another important factor was that I wasn't meeting people that I particularly liked. I was on the lookout to try and change this situation when I noticed a card in the library asking for volunteers to help in a youth club, so I went along and helped each week. The person who ran the club worked in a large hospital, and she encouraged me to apply for a vacancy there, co-ordinating volunteers. I had little idea of what the job entailed but liked the sound of it, applied and, by great good fortune, got it. I enjoyed it, learned a tremendous amount, and stayed for four years. Then I saw an advertisement for a two-year full-time course in community and youth work and, from the course description, just knew this was right for me. I was accepted on the course and sure enough I was correct.

During all this time my emotional life was often at sixes and sevens. I'd feel very upset whenever a man didn't want to see me any more, which usually happened sooner or later, but there was only one who I would genuinely have wanted to marry.

Perhaps I should say here that I did not want to make the same mistakes I felt my mother had made, yet for some time believed it was almost inevitable that I would. As often happens, I spent several years trying to fulfil this self-imposed prophecy. It took more time to find a clearer identity of my own, yet I still saw having a child only as a possible development in a long-term loving and stable relationship with a man. Some of my relationships have been long-term, a few have been loving, none have been stable. The ingredients I'd selected were never together at the same time and so I didn't think seriously of having a baby.

I did get pregnant again, in 1965, and this time had an abortion. I liked the man concerned but he didn't want to be a father. I didn't want him to stay with me just because I was having a baby, and I felt unable to cope bringing up a child by myself, and at that time had no close friends. My over-riding feeling was that I wouldn't be able to give the child a secure and happy life, but I didn't think I could face having the baby adopted, so I was determined to have an abortion. I tried the old wives' tales I'd heard about but none worked, so I convinced a doctor and a psychiatrist that I'd commit suicide if I had to go through with the pregnancy – abortions were more difficult to obtain on the National Health Service then and neither I nor the man concerned had access to any money for it to be done privately. My stay in hospital was horrible and I felt depressed and guilty afterwards. I didn't regret my decision but even now, eighteen years later, I sometimes think of that baby and what she (as I was convinced she was) would be like now. It wasn't an experience I'd repeat so I started using the Pill. I liked the feeling of control this gave me – not only in preventing pregnancy but also in altering the timing of my periods when I wanted.

I felt the most pressure to get married (whether real or imagined I don't know) in my middle twenties. However, by the time I was twenty-seven I was doing a job which interested me, followed by a course which was full of variety, and then by demanding jobs which I'd chosen. Consequently, my single state wasn't always uppermost in my mind. Added to this was the fact that most of the men I met of around my age had involvements or responsibilities which prevented any uncomplicated relationship. By now I also had a number of good friends.

During the autumn when I was thirty-five I emerged, a little scathed, from a long but intermittent relationship. At the time I had no urge to be in another relationship, but I wanted to be pregnant and have a baby so I stopped using the Pill (by the way, enjoying finding my natural menstrual cycle). I didn't want to pick up any man just to try and get pregnant so I started fantasizing about how I might have a baby – artificial insemination was one half-hearted idea. Then my last affair was rekindled but I didn't become pregnant. Each month I was disappointed because I so wanted to get pregnant, and at the same time relieved because I wasn't sure of being able to cope with this particular man being my baby's father.

After a few months the affair ended again permanently and I felt I was back to square one. Then I went on a short holiday outside London with some friends and casually met a man whom I found physically attractive. I had a very brief, but pleasurable, encounter with him a few weeks later, and became pregnant as a result. I was overjoyed but didn't expect, or particularly want, to see him again. My friends seemed pleased for me, and those who already had babies or young children were particularly delighted with my news. I wrote to my father and stepmother and they said they were pleased for me, with the expected reservations about my coping alone, the child growing up without a father and so on. I told my colleagues at work and they went along with my plan to keep working as long as possible before the birth, and to come back soon afterwards and then to just play it by ear.

During the twelfth week of my pregnancy I had a sudden, heavy loss of blood. I looked in a woman's health book and was appalled to read that according to my symptoms I was having a threatened miscarriage and that nothing could be done about it, other than resting and hoping for the best. The only time I'd prayed (in the sense of a desperate call for help to whoever *could* help) in my adult life was when I had been pregnant before and wanted to have a miscarriage. I was aware of the irony of this as I prayed again – this time for the foetus to remain intact.

I had expected to feel glowingly healthy right through my pregnancy, but although my general health was good I had some trying side-effects. Nausea set in fairly early on, then I had a six week period when I felt great before severe heartburn, which was more or less continuous, developed. I also suffered from quite painful piles and constipation. Still, although these were all unpleasant, I knew there was an end to them and this made them bearable. My doctor had a shared-care system with the local hospital so thankfully I only made three visits to the hospital antenatal clinic.

Initially, I wanted to have the baby at home, but after some discussion with my doctor, and thinking about it, I decided to go into hospital. I went to antenatal classes, run by the National Childbirth Trust, with a woman friend who intended to be with me at the birth. On the whole I did enjoy my pregnancy. I felt proud of my growing body and found the changes themselves fascinating.

I wasn't entitled to maternity leave but, by taking holiday due to me plus a little sick leave, I reckoned I could have the necessary time off work and still get paid. Two of my co-workers got together and planned how they could cover during my absence and then showed me their ideas which I presented to our management committee who fully supported the plans. These went a little awry when, six weeks before the expected birth, it was found my cervix was almost fully dilated and I was taken into hospital. Still, I carried on with some paper work while there and then went back to work again when I was discharged two weeks later, although by this time I was taking things pretty slowly.

When I was around five months pregnant I felt I should let the baby's father know. I had thought about this very carefully, and in the end felt I should at least try to maintain some kind of contact with him. I believed it was important that the baby could grow up knowing that she or he did have a father (albeit a distant one) and my hope was that if, at some time, she wanted to have some independent contact with him, that he would be willing to foster this. I wrote and explained myself as best as I could, leaving the matter as open-ended as possible so that he could choose his degree of involvement. As a result we did see a little of each other during the rest of my pregnancy.

On the evening of 19th March 1980 we went out for a meal and he came back to my place for the night. It was two weeks before the expected birth. I felt extremely uncomfortable through the night but did not realize I was in labour until I had a show of blood early the next morning. I rang my friend to come and meet me at the hospital and then started packing. I was on the verge of panic. Then my waters broke and Christine's father drove me to the hospital and agreed to stay with me. By now the contractions were frequent and overwhelming. I was taken direct to a delivery room, shaved, and then started pushing. It took a couple before I got the hang of it, and then a few more (tiring but *almost* pleasant) and suddenly there was a tiny little baby between my legs, forty minutes after I'd been admitted. The baby was given to me but the only feeling I had was a faint one of anticlimax. Everything had happened so fast that my mind hadn't adjusted to the new circumstances. Still, my instinct was to not show what I felt and I tried to play the role of a delighted new mother. When the nurse brought the cleaned up baby back to me she suggested I put her to my breast. I'd really looked forward to this moment but my nipples felt so tender that I let out a yelp of pained surprise. It seemed all my illusions were being shattered and when the nurse took the baby back I felt she had nothing to do with me. My friend had arrived by now and they let her in to see us so I had the added feeling of regret that she hadn't been able to see the birth. I needed a few stitches and that was painful – another surprise as I'd expected the only pain to be the birth itself (which wasn't).

Still, by the time I was wheeled back onto the ward with my baby following in her cot, I was feeling high. Early that afternoon I thought maybe I'd pick the baby up, and when I did a huge joyful emotion surged up and spilled all over that perfect little being. Over the next few days I realized I'd shared an experience with an untold number of women, yet it was unique to each of us. I still wonder why something so commonplace does feel so miraculous. I enjoyed my eight-day stay in hospital – the flowers, cards, presents, playing with my baby – but felt ready to go home when the time came.

I was still finding breastfeeding difficult and might have given up, as did most of the few women in my ward who tried it, if I hadn't had a book on the subject to encourage me. The nurses were either indifferent to, or ignorant of, the problems, or else gave conflicting advice. I realized early on that my only hope was to stick to one source of advice, which was the book. After a few weeks it became easier, and after a few more weeks I didn't wince at all as Christine latched on, and after that it was as simple as breathing. She was five or six months old before she had anything but breast milk. By the time she was about a year old she was only having one or two feeds a day, and her last one was a couple of months later, when we both seemed ready for this.

After Chris was born I stayed away from work for two weeks and then did some work from home before being project-based again. I was breastfeeding on demand, so just took Christine with me wherever I went, first of all in a quilt-lined basket with handles and then in a carrycot. I fed her whenever she cried and became an expert at doing this discreetly. On the odd occasions when I sensed someone would be upset, or I didn't feel comfortable about it, I'd either leave the room to feed her or, if this wasn't very practicable, I'd turn away slightly. Because I was confident, people seemed to quickly accept Christine and her needs. When she was three months old I needed someone to look after her for some of the time, so I rang Social Services and was given the name of a child-minder who looked after her for two afternoons a week initially (I'd feed her when we arrived and before we left the minder's) which was increased to three afternoons a month later. I felt she was safe there and she seemed to settle in okay – at least she didn't show any signs of distress.

Then we moved to another part of London so I could share a cheap house with someone I knew, and be nearer some close friends. Christine was now five months old and it was becoming difficult to bring her to work at all, as she needed pretty constant attention. My job was coming to an end the following March and I wanted to continue in it until then – not only from a professional point of view, but also to use the wages it paid to save a return fare home to Australia. I rang the Social Services in my new area and this time was given a list of child-minders, most of whom weren't on the phone. I found the prospect of choosing someone daunting, and continued leaving her with the same minder for another six weeks despite the extra travel. Then for the remaining four months I left her from nine until five with a woman from the child-minders' list. I felt guilty about leaving Christine, and the exploitative situation whereby I was able to earn enough to pay £17 a week, the standard rate at that time, to someone who wasn't able to earn a good wage. Added to this were my reservations about the sort of care Christine was receiving. Still, I felt it was essential to complete my job so I just tried to suppress these feelings. I should mention here that it was only possible to continue working in the way I did because of the support given by my colleagues in the project. This was on a practical (taking me, and then me and the baby, to work and back by car when I felt unable to drive, helping out with the carrycot and plastic bags I used to cart around, being willing to come to meetings at my place and so on) as well as on the emotional level. Having a car made the fetching and carrying much easier, too.

In retrospect, I found the period from when she was about three months to around nine months the most difficult, because I really didn't know how to amuse her. Carrying her around, feeding her and changing her all felt very natural, but they didn't take up the whole day, and if I'd been at home with her all the time I would have found it much more difficult to manage. I needed to make quite large adjustments in my attitudes, and was able to start this process with less difficulty than some by easing my way into a spell of full-time motherhood.

For about a year after Christine was born I didn't feel quite myself emotionally – it's difficult to describe but, for example, I'd get upset over things which wouldn't normally bother me, or I'd feel defeated by some small obstacle which I'd usually surmount. The marvellous thing is that although I feel back to normal, it is almost as if a part of myself has been unlocked. Again it is difficult to describe but, in the past, I've often gone through the motions of expressing what seems appropriate in a particular situation – compassion, interest etc. – because, intellectually, I've understood this is appropriate, but without actually feeling very much. Now I really feel these emotions.

I have no regrets about not having a baby until I was thirty-seven. I just didn't feel ready before then, and if I'd had one earlier I doubt that it would have been the happily awaited event that it was. This is partly due to the network of friends I've built up over the years (several of whom don't live in a nuclear family), so there is a degree of support which just didn't exist in my early twenties. The only real difficulty was acknowledging my new identity. It has taken me all these years to come to terms with 'me' and then to incorporate 'mother' into this – Christine was nineteen months old before I referred to myself as 'mummy' to her! Now she is just over three and she still calls me 'mummy' (although she has cottoned to the fact that I have a name like everyone else) and it doesn't sound strange to me any more.

I knew it would be important to keep some small part of myself separate and, although I was besotted with my daughter, I managed to maintain and develop some interests separate from her. Fortunately, we live in a street where there are other children around her age, and in fact she has spent a great deal of time with a boy who is just a couple of days younger. I didn't go out much without her when she was smaller, but when I wished to there was no difficulty in having her looked after by people she knew. I do have more commitments outside the home now and it is hard work to arrange and maintain a system of swaps with other parents, but the effort is worthwhile from my point of view, and I think possibly from Christine's as well – she is growing up aware that she is an important *part* of my life.

There were times, particularly in the first couple of months, when I felt I might burst with joy and longed to be able to share this feeling. Not just with someone who knew it because they'd felt it for their own baby, but someone who felt it for Christine, and ideally this would have been her father. By the way, our contact with each other petered out after Chris was a few months old to the point where he occasionally rings to see how we are. I'm still not sure whether I should be making an effort to maintain contact. Occasionally Chris asks if she has a 'daddy' and where he is and I answer matter-of-factly that he doesn't live with us but lives with some other people. If the questions become more curious then I'll play it by ear. He did sign her birth certificate, although we used my surname, so I suppose when she is older she may like to see this.

From my point of view, the only real disadvantage has been, from time to time, having to respond to Christine's needs (particularly when she was younger) regardless of how I felt. It would have been nice just occasionally to have had a bit of time off knowing there was someone else on the spot, rather than making arrangements in advance for it. However, I often feel there are many advantages in bringing up a baby alone. For example, while I was breastfeeding I could enjoy the closeness and share my bed with her whenever I liked, or she liked, which was most of the time when she was younger, without worrying about excluding anyone else. I can also bring her up the way that I feel is right for her without trying to reach agreement with anyone else, which saves me some possible split of loyalties.

I stayed at home with Chris from when she was a year old until she started at a local community nursery a couple of months before her third birthday. For the eight months prior to her starting nursery I had a complicated system of child-swapping so that I had two free days a week to work with another single mother of a three-year-old girl. We wanted to create work for ourselves and formed a co-operative to sell non-sexist children's books through a mail-order book club. Chris has settled in well at the nursery and I'm now working most of the time on this project. We haven't any funding yet (the State is supporting me meanwhile) although we hope to have this in time to start selling children's books in October of this year. I thoroughly enjoy being a mother and am continually fascinated and charmed by my healthy and delightful daughter. I also like the work I'm doing and my involvement with various community activities. Money is tight, but I feel very satisfied with my life now.

If I had my life over again there are some things I would have done differently, but having Christine how and when I did wouldn't be one of them.

PART SIX
Lesbian Mothers

Marie Ely

'To a number of people in this society, it is a total outrage
that a person such as myself should want a child.'

I waited. The woman swished the liquid slowly back and forth in
the container in her hands. The liquid was clear. She said it would
turn a milky colour if the test was positive. My thoughts turned to
the hundreds of women who must wait praying that the liquid did
not change colour. At last I saw the swirling mass seem to thicken
and whiten. I turned to my partner and smiled. We had done it. I
was pregnant.

I guess I had always wanted to have a child. It was a thought
kept well to the back of my mind, emerging at irregular periods
which I labelled 'clucky'. Throughout my twenties I said, if asked,
'Oh, I will do it later. I'll just wait until I have a secure job.' The
future, if I gave it much thought, rolled out endlessly.

The first friend I knew of who became pregnant had to get
married within four months of leaving school. My mother seized
on the situation to warn me in no uncertain terms that that was *not*
going to happen to her daughter, was it! Although I was already
trying to break away from the restrictions of our mother-daughter
knot, I absorbed the message and took care not to go too far with
the boys I was going out with. I took care until I was twenty and
then, well, somehow it no longer seemed to matter either to me,

or the boy, or to my friends. Needless to say my mother still cared and neither of us really forgot the confrontation that took place at the front door of my flat at eight a.m. one morning, me in my duffle coat and the obvious signs that Jim was upstairs in my bedroom. 'A rose is a rose is a rose and would never be the same,' she said.

In the first few weeks of the relationship I relied on beginner's luck not to get pregnant. I was lucky and, after my first period, found a co-operative doctor who agreed to give me the Pill on the basis that he could not stop me ruining my life. 'If you are stupid enough to go ahead then I can't really be held responsible for your morals, can I?' he said. My relationship with Jim lasted nearly three years. When I finally gave up and realized that he was not going to change, and that his selfishness and general desire for other women would never take my feelings into consideration, I recognized that I had been sensible not to have given in to any of my 'clucky' feelings.

My next relationship included an exchange of gold rings, and a new surname for me. We shocked his parents on several occasions by talking about swapping parental roles when we had children, but we never got serious about when this 'revolutionary' event was going to happen. Thank God. The bitterness of our marriage breakdown was comforted by the thought that I was not fighting about child custody as well.

I do not remember my thirtieth birthday very clearly. I don't recall a strong awareness of passing time and the consequence that I would have to make some decision soon, or my body would betray me with age. In that year I was still engrossed in my job, my political commitments as a feminist and my friends. My mother had died suddenly two years earlier and I was, on the face of it, free from her desire for more grandchildren. Life without children was still an appealing proposition. There was also an added consideration. In my late twenties I had come to terms with a changed consciousness concerning my sexuality. I was a lesbian. There was therefore no possibility that I would accidentally become pregnant. However, as I said, I was not really worried. I could still do it later.

During my thirtieth year I began a relationship with a woman eight years older than me. She had two children of her own who were at the threshold of adolescence. Whilst they did live with us alternate weeks, my commitment to child-raising remained essentially on a part-time basis. We retained the emotional and physical time to still have our own lives. Indeed, the fulfilment of the relationship, as well as the thought that she would not want to go back to night feeds, wet nappies and the responsibility of a pre-school child, had resulted in me shelving the concept.

One day, however, an old friend asked what I now thought about having a child. I mumbled that I had not given it a lot of thought lately and we left it at that. That night, however, my partner asked me the question again, only she posed it in a way which gave the space to make a serious answer. For several months I pondered the question. Did I? Or didn't I? Should I? Or shouldn't I?

The circumstances which I had considered basic to me deciding to have a child were now, to a large extent, existing. I had always believed that parents had some responsibility to provide a secure environment for their children, and to assure them that they were wanted. My partner and I now jointly owned our own home and had some financial security behind us. Furthermore, I was optimistic that a degree of career fulfilment to date had given me some security in analysing whether I would be content to put a major part of my energy into the early years of child-raising. It remained for me to decide if I really wanted to have one of my own. Throughout this time my partner wisely insisted that consideration for her should not be paramount in the decision. She said that she would support me whatever I decided, and would take on a co-parenting role if I chose to go ahead. She argued that if she had come into the relationship when I already had a child there would have have been no such choice for her. The decision was therefore mine and mine alone.

In the May after my thirty-second birthday I made up my mind. I would, if physically possible, have a child. Looking back, I can't remember what finally tipped the scales in that direction. It was true that I liked children. However, I suspect that the conditioning absorbed during the 'fifties, which emphasized that I would not be complete until I had a child, was firmly entrenched in my irrational belief system. During my teens and twenties I had challenged much to do with my politics and sexuality, but this one sat quietly on the sidelines waiting to spring into action. From the experience of living with school-age children I felt I knew a little about what this decision entailed. I clearly understood some aspects, but overall I underestimated the disruption and challenges which our 'little scrap of nonsense' was going to cause.

The first problem which arose was just how I was going to become pregnant. Immaculate conception was beyond my resources. As a lesbian in a loving relationship I had no desire to go out and find a man. Indeed, as I was already living in a home and sharing the responsibility of bringing up my partner's children, I did not want to consider sharing the responsibility of bringing up the child with a natural father. One-night stands in the hope of falling pregnant seemed a most undesirable option, and Fertility Clinics have been established to assist the heterosexual married couple with difficulties; not the woman who might choose to have a child without engaging in sexual intercourse. To a number of people in this society it is a total outrage that a person such as myself should want a child. Indeed my choice has since been labelled by a member of the Festival of Light as 'an abomination and a sin'. In some minds it is preferable that I be raped and refused an abortion than to choose to have a child without engaging in sexual union with a man. I had read that there were several doctors and medical centres able to provide the information as to how I could inseminate myself, and who would secure donors on my behalf. On contacting these people I discovered that they were now able to provide only the information and that it would be up to me to secure the donors.

My partner and I spent many hours making a list of suitable donors. For medical reasons we were advised to find four as this would facilitate my chances of becoming pregnant during the most fertile period of ovulation. This was acceptable to us as a means of ensuring some anonymity with regard to the father. I did not want another person to feel responsible for the child, or to make any paternity claim.

It was important that donors be of good health and have no known adverse genetic history. Further, we were looking for the maturity in them (and their partner) to handle the situation. We eventually concluded that the most effective way of testing these requisites was that they be in a secure relationship and that they already have children of their own.

We were very fortunate in having understanding friends who were prepared to contribute something towards fulfilling my decision and, after several months of thought and discussion, we settled on our choices and gained their assent.

In the meantime I had been taking the temperature of my anal and vaginal passages each morning to ascertain the exact time of my ovulation. As I was extremely regular we were able to assess the time of ovulation at the tenth to the sixteenth day, and that the best times for me to introduce the sperm would be the tenth, twelfth, fourteenth and sixteenth days of the twenty-six day cycle.

The decision to go ahead during my next fertile period was made at the beginning of July. We juggled times and dates with the prospective donors, in accordance with their social commitments. We were now fully prepared.

It was with no small nervousness that my partner and I set off on the tenth night to meet up with the first donor. Thanks to a sympathetic doctor I was armed with a diaphragm of my size and a syringe (without the needle point of course). We agreed to meet at his place at 9.30 p.m. To relieve the tension we stopped and bought a large, family-size block of chocolate to eat on the way.

Thinking that the donor might be too embarrassed to face us we arranged for a split second pick-up involving his partner bringing the 'goods' out to the car in a sterilized jar. She handed them over amidst some embarrassed laughter. We backed the car out the driveway and vanished off into the night.

On the assumption that the fresher the sperm the more potent it would be, we pulled up the car in the nearest back street. In the darkness I nervously endeavoured to draw the sperm into the syringe, inject it as far up as I could into my vagina and then seal the contents in with the diaphragm.

With shaking hands, and in the dim glow of the street lights, I didn't feel very confident. My partner drove home and I sat in the passenger seat with my legs resting on the dashboard. Twelve hours later the diaphragm was removed and positive thoughts willing conception abated. The sequence of events was repeated at two day intervals. On the sixteenth day, however, we did go inside and I inserted the semen in a bedroom after a friendly cup of tea.

The feeling of waiting, so intrinsically tied with pregnancy in my mind, now began. I didn't become pregnant and experienced a keen sense of loss when my period arrived one week late. I was away from home the next time of ovulation, and so it was with optimism that we planned another round of nocturnal visits for the following month. By now, vanishing into the night had been proved unnecessary and we were able to treat the situation with some sense of social normality.

This time we placed (or at least tried to) a lower priority on the results. We felt unable to handle alternating anticipation and disappointment on a regular basis. We were also increasingly aware of the difficulty of asking the donors to continue each month. We resolved that we could probably ask them two more times at the most, and then we would have to take a break and work out what might be going wrong. After all, for what period of time could we expect donors to co-operate with us in this way? We knew of one lesbian couple who had been trying for over twelve months, and wondered whether we could implement the decision to have a child if anything like that were to happen to us.

As previously, the first day of the next period passed without event. And the second, and the third. We began to hope that the changes already occurring in my body were a sign of something other than false hope. Ten days later we agreed that a pregnancy test was in order. The result was positive.

From that time onwards my partner and I lived with a reality which differed considerably from our expectations. We were prepared for inconvenience but at no stage anticipated the somewhat 'tumultuous' nature of the baby's coming. We do not regret the decision, but feel immeasurable relief knowing we do not have to live through the pregnancy and the year that followed again. Of course, we had had to deal with negatives in ourselves and in the relationship previously, but this time there was a certain relentlessness about the way things were, and about the way we so frequently turned from two reasonable and normal people into nasty, unpredictable monsters.

Firstly, there was the reality of the pregnancy. I experienced severe hyperemesis (to call it morning sickness is an understatement) from the beginning to the end. I lived with an overwhelming sense of nausea twenty-four hours a day, which could only be abated by the drug Debendox. Throughout those nine, long months I sought alternatives including vitamin and mineral supplements, acupuncture, special diets, chiropractice, naturopathy, homoeo-pathy, even colonic irrigation, but nothing else had any effect. I did know there were risks involved in taking Debendox, but then there was a certain inauspiciousness in not even being able to keep down a glass of water and in losing a stone in weight within two days. From time to time I would try to reduce the dosage but always ended up back in bed staring at the inside of a bucket. Meantime I tried to maintain a normal life working on the publishing and distribution business my partner and I were running. However, for all that time, I dragged the chain and our personal life and relationship had to become a poor second to the advent of the baby. So much for the blossoming and rosy pregnancy I had envisaged!

The birth, when it finally came, exceeded my expectation. As I was over thirty, I had assumed that a home birth was out of the question. We'd therefore set about finding an obstetrician or GP who could accept our belief that a woman has some rights in the making of decisions during pregnancy and labour, and who could allow that my partner was an intrinsic part of the birth. After several weeks it was patently clear that no such person existed in our city.

On the off-chance we decided to look into home birth. We were lucky. We found a midwife who did not see my age, our lifestyle or the fact that it was a 'first birth' as problems. From the first conversation when Maggie said that she would *like* to be our midwife, the medical aspects of the pregnancy and birth went far smoother than we could have wished for. She was only as far away as the telephone, and her support ensured that we never had to confront any discrimination. She couldn't eliminate the pain of the labour but her skill and care guaranteed that the long and gruelling ordeal was at least manageable. Whilst the pain did exceed all my expectations, I was as prepared as any novitiate could be. My waters began leaking away at 8 a.m. on the Friday morning, the first contraction occurred on Friday night, and Susanna came screaming into this world at 2.21 on Sunday morning. My partner literally and emotionally held my hand throughout, and at the time I could only be grateful for being in a trusting relationship with someone who had been through it herself.

The next divergence between expectation and reality was Susanna herself. Given the supportive environment of the birth, we were both prepared for an easy relationship with Susanna. We reasoned that, without hospital intervention, there would be no unresolved feelings to deal with. This reckoning, however, was without Susanna's digestive system. Told time and time again by medical 'experts' that there was no such thing as colic, neither of us could so summarily dismiss the distress which she continuously experienced. After every feed the crying would begin again and we each walked the floor night and day trying to settle and calm her. At times we lapsed into intense depression amidst the sleepless nights, the protracted crying and the feeding problems. Miscommunication between us was rife. Furthermore, being 'strong' women, we pushed ourselves to cope while maintaining our home, our family and our business. Although we never ultimately went under, we still bear scars from those first few months.

One of the greatest disappointments in that period was myself. I had talked easily and glowingly during the pregnancy about sharing the child. Not only was Susanna a child of the relationship, but we were genuinely going to divide the responsibility and decision making. But in the reality of a constantly crying child there seemed no time to talk about, let alone work through, the different perspectives we had. I found it difficult to accept the validity of my partner's experience, and to let go of gut-feelings as to what was right. Our realities spiralled off in different directions, and we easily lost sight of each other. In our despair we feared the end of the relationship.

Ironically, the solution we found was a return to the traditional pattern. My partner stepped back a bit and it was agreed that I would take on the major role in Susanna's life. We resolved to begin from where I was, rather than from where I wanted to be. As a result, Susanna (like most babies) saw her mother as the centre of her universe, and related to my partner as the secondary or back-up person.

It has taken nearly two years for this to change and only now does the reality resemble our original expectation. During this time I have been reasonably successful in confronting and dealing with my possessive feelings and enabled my partner to respond with increasing spontaneity on matters of parental responsibility. My partner's reality has altered too, and with Susanna herself now broadening her needs and wanting input from other people, a certain flexibility is emerging. As with the other two children, we are now able to share the parenting and enjoy the benefits of joint responsibility. This is not to imply that there are not periods of pain, but nowadays we seem to reach the light at the end of the tunnel quicker.

In retrospect, I feel that my possessive feelings arose in part from a conditioned belief about what a mother should be. I believed that I had all the solutions to Susanna's problems by virtue of being her mother. I took the role very seriously and came to almost enjoy a situation which gave full play to maternal feelings of responsibility, nurturing and self-sacrifice. There was also the validation which this role gave me – people related to me as a *mother* rather than a person. For a time I didn't have to look at myself as I was, but rather could evolve my life around this little being who accepted in innocent trust that I was 'a bit of all right'. I was content to make the role virtually my number one priority.

Two years later I still fully accept and, I confess, enjoy being a mother. I do, however, have a stronger feeling that the rest of my life is important. My ability to make Susanna such a priority is changing, and I am giving more energy to my relationship, my friends, my political commitments, my writing and to studying as a homeopath. It was necessary for me to wallow in the role for a period of time to learn that a balance with other things would give me a greater contentment in the long run. I believe that this contentment is now reflected in my relationship with Susanna and is giving her a sense of security.

My partner is a writer and a teacher and works with a flexibility of time which ensures that she is there for Susanna. Her deep commitment is separate from our relationship and is in the form of a sort of life-long guarantee. Her role, however, has a certain greyness in the eyes of society. As surrogate parent she is not mother, father, sister or even fairy godmother. There are some who would find it preferable if she did not exist, but for Susanna she provides the balance, the other half to her mother.

The reality of having a child does now resemble my expectation, but the 'challenge' to achieve this has been exactly that, again and again and again. It's one of those things you look back on and wonder where you found the strength. Our day-to-day lives have changed completely and we sometimes sit down and wonder what we did with our time before it was punctuated by Susanna. I remember having a constant sense of busyness but also have fading memories of sleeping in on Sundays, finishing conversations without interruption, and of going out without a bagful of equipment. No matter what preparation we make I'm convinced that none of us can ever anticipate the total impact of the change. However, I do feel that in having genuinely made the choice to have a child, we have been able to adapt to the changes. We none of us have regrets and, despite frustrations, I notice the family all fall into missing Susanna after any absences of longer than a day.

Despite, or is it because of, the hurdles we've tripped and scrambled over so far, I still feel a confidence about the decision. Before we began I had some doubts as to whether Susanna herself would accept the circumstances surrounding her conception. These days I feel that we are creating a secure environment for her and this, plus the knowledge that she was wanted, will give her the tools necessary to handle the situation. The donors were all prepared to accept some long-term responsibility regarding talking with Susanna about her beginnings, and there has been nothing to suggest that this will not happen. Susanna herself may have resolved some of the doubts in her very physical appearance. She so resembles one donor that we suspect we know which one is her father. Rather than create a problem, however, my partner and I, and the donor and his partner, have accepted this.

It may seem strange but I don't find this area a big worry these days; I am far more involved with the same daily concerns as any mother – what she eats, how well she responds to other children and, more recently, the joys of toilet training. Watching her at play, on the pot, asleep in bed, I feel more conscious of a shared continuum with women everywhere, rather than of an awareness of the individuality of my situation.

Vaughan Melzer

'I had grown up believing that I would be a mum and can never remember a time when I didn't have some longing to have a child. This longing grew steadily more and more into a yearning and a fear, as the years passed, that I might never have one . . . I felt terribly stuck – I couldn't find the right man and that absolutely seemed to preclude my having a baby. Becoming a lesbian at thirty-three dramatically changed my entire outlook.'

Dear Arthur,

Although you hardly knew me, I want to tell you that you have a baby grandson, probably your youngest. Fifteen years have passed since we first met as father and daughter. Then I was twenty, hungry and lost, looking for a fairy-tale father but finding only an ordinary old man who disappointed me. What had I expected? You and my mother made me – a true love child – but world events separated us from you before I was born. You remained for her a dream of what might have been, the ideal, and a well of pain for me. It seemed that, had we had you with us, my life would have been untroubled and good, and so I ached for you and was determined to make amends for my own children and to give them a loving and ever-present father, and a secure home.

It is thirty-six years later and I have not fulfilled that dream in the way I had planned. This is how Billy came to be and why it took so long . . .

The first seventeen years were tough for my mother and me. She breastfed me until I was ten months old when she had to leave her friends and come to a job in London. She became a full-time teacher and I went to day nursery five-and-half days a week. From then on we lived alone until I was twelve, when she married an African. She had my sister when I was fifteen. The three of them went to live in Africa a few years later but the marriage was not a happy one and my mother was divorced in 1967, some ten years later.

My childhood was a rich one. On the plus side, I had a book-loving parent who was imaginative in giving me toys, visiting beautiful places like Kew Gardens with other kids, taking me to unusual films and concerts, and who had both our friends visit often. On the minus side, my mother was unable to protect me, as she may have done with a loving partner, from her own personal and practical problems and unhappiness, and I was frequently very depressed, overburdened and insecure.

During the holidays I would stay with my Gran and Grandad in the suburbs. With them I received a much more structured life: warm, predictable days with the occasional surprises and treats (Gran was very good at doing these!) and I loved my time there and especially I loved my Gran.

Although socially disapproved of, my mother was never in any doubt about having me, nor ever ashamed. As a Marxist and non-believer she gave me no comfortable and conventional beliefs, but forced me to question what so many schoolmates and teachers took for granted then. It did not make life easy for me with others.

Her socialism made important to her what to others was taboo or shocking. It was the manner in which people related to and loved each other that mattered, not the conventional form it took. And so she was more concerned that I knew about reciprocal love and sex than about marriage. Unconsciously, she refused to repress her spirit, her intelligence and her energy in order to win a man. She believed in an international world and thought, naïvely as it turned out, that it should be possible to create a happy mixed marriage. So much of her was liberated, yet she still pinned all her hopes of deeper happiness and alleviation of loneliness on meeting a man whom she could love reciprocally. Nonetheless, my experiences of fathers was not turning out too hopeful.

Despite the snobbery and disapproval of comprehensive education that existed in the fifties and which was levelled directly at me in my primary school, my mother actually sought out a coeducational, comprehensive school for me. It never occurred to me to distrust her choice and I willingly made the somewhat arduous journey from Chelsea to Roehampton daily. Overall, I loved and was proud of my school which was often visited as a show piece. Being comprehensive was in itself progressive then, but, in retrospect, I can now see how intellectually rigid and sexist it was too. Although it failed in many ways to give me confidence in my abilities, it allowed me to be the lively and somewhat eccentric person I was without the repressive and disapproving judgements meted out by the grammar schools various friends of mine had gone to. Socially, too, there was a relaxed and happy feel to relationships between adults and children, males and females, where interaction was normally spontaneous and free of guilt.

At university, I felt intellectually inadequate and, to deal with my sense of inferiority, I retreated from my fellow students and mixed with people in the city, so as not to need to compete. I scraped through with a degree and returned to London, having obtained a mediocre teaching job. Soon after, I broke down, and I now consider myself very fortunate to have gone to a psychiatric day hospital run as a therapeutic community. This was a major turning point: a haven from the 'normal' world where I no longer felt odd or different, somewhere where I could spew out my pain and understand myself better, and somewhere where I also discovered my creativity in art. I became hooked on psychotherapy and 'took it' in one form or another for about six years. With each year, I felt better and stronger and more able to enjoy life without the prop of one of my endless boyfriends. I also found my way into social work and became committed and fulfilled professionally.

I had, for years, relegated all my intellectual, professional and creative development as secondary to that of finding a husband. I think I was, in this, mirroring my mother's – and most women's – sense of not being good enough without being reflected in a wonderful man. As a result, I had been involved, to one degree or another, with numerous men since the age of fourteen, ever searching in traumatic cycles of elation, hope, followed by an affair, then collapse and despair. Some of these relationships were obviously more important than others but, by the time I was thirty-three, I was feeling hopeless, both about my ability to relate to men and their limitations for me. Was it my failure, or theirs?

Throughout my life I had held in my imagination and private yearnings a picture of my father, who was strong and gentle, forceful and loving – who, in short, was nearly perfect. My mother had described him to me only in admiring ways; she never criticized him at all, though normally she is slow to praise and tends to be critical. I thus grew up with unreal expectations and hopes of men, perhaps even a fundamental distrust because of their failure to be strong, loving and available to me.

And yet, I assumed I needed a man to make me happy, both as a partner and as a father to my children. The sexism of this society reinforced these ideas and feelings and, despite falling in love repeatedly, I was invariably disappointed and hurt. My generation of men had been reared in a culture which made no demands on them to be emotionally giving or sensitive towards women.

What I should have placed much greater significance on than I did all those years were my friendships with women. Alongside all the trauma and discomfort with my boyfriends I was invariably involved in a deep, warm and much more comfortable relationship with a woman. Nevertheless, it wasn't until 1973 that I met Carole who, though married with teenage children, seemed to place me first in her emotions and reciprocated my affection. Our friendship was always relaxed, happy and, intellectually, very stimulating, yet it still took nearly eight years for us to become lovers. Until then, it had not occurred to us, probably because the taboo is so strong. Once we were, our lives altered radically: Carole broke away from a marriage of twenty-five years' standing and I decided to have a baby!

To reflect a little: I had grown up believing I would be a mum and can never remember a time when I didn't have some longing to have a child. This longing grew steadily more and more into a yearning and a fear, as the years passed, that I might never have one. In more recent years as I felt desperate about it, I deliberated having a child alone. I agonized over this but told myself that as I had been so unhappy without a father I should never impose this situation on a child of mine. I felt terribly stuck – I couldn't find the right man and that seemed absolutely to preclude my having a baby.

Becoming a lesbian at the age of thirty-three dramatically changed my entire outlook. Suddenly my world became bright and hopeful. With Carole, as with other lesbians, I was myself. I could be assertive, powerful, and take the lead if I wished and I felt none of the discomfort that I often felt with my boyfriends. At school, I had experienced such hurt when the boys laughed at me and joked about me being manly because I would not play the game of being a weak, tittering female. Ironically, since being a lesbian I have felt profoundly womanly and also very strong. In my new relationship with Carole, I became relaxed, free and very happy. She and I spent some lovely holidays together and, for a while, she lived in a bedsit and enjoyed for the first time leading the life of a single adult.

My longing for a child did not abate and I continued to fret. Both before and during these momentous changes, I had been very close to the man who was to be my baby's father. We had an affectionate and honest relationship. He knew of my longing to have a child and wished to give me one though he knew all about Carole. The actual decision to go ahead appeared to come very suddenly one day when I put the suggestion to Carole and she wholeheartedly gave me all her support and encouragement to go ahead.

Becoming pregnant took about four months of somewhat chancy timing and, in the event, it happened when I least expected it to.

I had a fairly straightforward pregnancy, but I did have some symptoms in the early months that no one I met seemed to share. One was terribly itchy skin, especially on my breasts, presumably where the skin is being stretched. The other was agonisingly stinging nipples in low temperatures and British breezes!

At seven months I had a minuscule blood show and the hospital took me in immediately for nearly a week while they investigated. This was irrationally depressing; I felt demoralized and unhealthy. The hospital doctors denied me a feeling of confidence in my basically normal pregnancy because I was an elderly primigravida I was asked to come into hospital to be induced if my labour was more than three days 'late'. I was also pressed to consider having an epidural which had the effect of undermining my trust in myself to cope with the labour to come.

After a lot of physical jerks I had to resign myself to the likelihood of being induced. Carole and I had a huge Indian meal before my admission and that seemed to do the trick! I could barely hobble up the hospital steps! I felt tremendously excited, like a child whose special treat had at last arrived. Three hours after fluctuating contractions, I was persuaded to have an oxytocin drip. In retrospect, I can see no valid reason for this except to speed up the labour. After nine hours I had pethidine and then another after four more hours. I dilated fully very suddenly and unexpectedly and again experienced another surge of intense excitement as I knew the last stage should be active and short.

Carole had been with me throughout, bearing the labour pains with me. Labour was, for me, like an out-of-this-world, strange and painfully beautiful dream. I felt intensely emotional and deeply close to Carole; she had been through all this herself. I experienced something akin to love from the midwives who assisted me (why have male doctors got to take over?). They were all so gentle and considerate, so involved with my body; their ministrations made me feel very important and cared for. In the delivery room they became eager and warmly aggressive. They, Carole and I were a team, excitedly trying to push my baby into the world and we all felt intense disappointment when, after an hour of no movement, they had to call the doctor. Roughly, he examined me and pronounced a 'deep transverse arrest' and the need for forceps. I was suddenly demoralized but, almost with a sense of relief, I allowed myself to have a general anaesthetic for the final delivery and Carole found herself excluded and pacing outside with some anxious fathers. Without either of us to see, my son was delivered without blemish and, an hour later, I was holding him.

My immediate impression was of being given something very precious that I should feel overjoyed at and couldn't. Yes, here was my baby at last, but he wasn't yet real to me. In contrast, Carole thought he was beautiful and was very thrilled. It took a few days for me and then, suddenly, I was pervaded and filled by an indescribable tenderness for my new-born child. I have never felt such vulnerable and all-pervading love as I felt then for him. I knew then that I would never again be free of fearing for him at some level.

Breastfeeding was not straightforward, as I had tender and sensitive skin and one inverted nipple. When he couldn't easily latch on to this nipple I would get the hot sweats of panic and would make great efforts to control this so as not to set up a vicious circle of reaction in him. I found a very helpful device was to use the Kynastone breast pump initially to draw the nipple out.

I don't distinguish the breastfeeding experience from the total early nurturing of my new born child. It was utterly absorbing, sensually satisfying and blissful. Billy was amenable to bottles as well as to breast and if we wished to go out I could put milk into a bottle for a baby-sitter. He weaned himself at six months and though, in retrospect, I can see how useful this was, I did not relinquish the breastfeeding without a strong sense of loss.

I had nearly ten months maternity leave and had to plan to return to work when Billy would be about seven months old. Child-minding loomed as a large problem. But, in the meantime, I had asked the council to transfer me from my one-bedroomed flat to a larger one in the same block and to include Carole in the tenancy. To my astonishment, we were offered a magnificent, spacious flat a few weeks later only a few doors along from my old home. The move couldn't have been simpler and Carole and I thoroughly enjoyed planning and making our new home together. Then, like pieces of a jigsaw falling into place, a neighbour with a happy family and a baby of her own, offered to care for Billy. Not only is it wonderfully convenient, but it provides Billy with lots of male company: teenage sons and a warm, voluble father.

Ironically, when the time came to return to work it was myself I was anxious about. While feeling confident that he would be in good hands, I felt quite panicky at the thought of missing out on seeing him all day. Despite my wanting a child for so long, I never realized just how much I would love him and how emotionally full I would feel. The sense of wanting to experience every minute of my child's life made me doubt, for a while, that I wanted to share parenting with a professional job.

I was to be surprised. On returning, I fell back into the work without too much difficulty or conflict. My staff seemed to be pleased to have me back, and I found myself quickly absorbed in my work again.

As a manager at work, I did not have the choice of becoming part-time. I wondered whether this would have been preferable but, observing my part-time colleagues, I gain the impression of them having a greater conflict than I in giving wholly to the parenting or to the work. On the other hand, I always feel horribly pressured and this causes me real distress at times and has perhaps been harder to cope with just because I was my own mistress for so long. However, I need my full-time job because I need the emotional, social and intellectual stimulus it gives me. I need the money and, very important, I need the status of being a worker and of being part of the world outside of the home. I think it is because I gain such satisfaction at work that I feel able to commit myself so emotionally to my child when we are together.

When I set out to have my baby, I saw myself as a single parent with the loving and emotional support of my friend and lover and, to some extent, the baby's father. How these relationships were to be in practice was not initially clear. Carole came to live with me and, in this, I am not a single parent though, in the eyes of the conventional world, I am. This results in some social discomfort at times but also in practical benefits (for example, if Carole were my husband I would not be eligible for a nursery place).

Billy's father visits about once a month, viewing his relationship with Billy as an avuncular one. This relationship, though warm and affectionate, does have its problems. I could not have made a baby with just anyone: the father had to be someone I respected and admired and for whom I felt affection. He reciprocates these feelings, and inevitably there is some pain that for our individual reasons we have not got a conventional marriage together.

I have few relatives and my mother and sister live in towns elsewhere. They know about and accept my situation and our relationships are good ones. My mother, in her early sixties, still works full-time and therefore we do not get to see each other very often. I think all three of us feel that our somewhat truncated, all-female family is enriched by this new little male person.

In an unconventional way I have, paradoxically, a quite conventional set-up. Billy benefits from all the warmth and security that is normally expected from a loving heterosexual couple. Carole treats him as her own, getting up to see to him in the night, buying him things, and lovingly and proudly exclaiming with delight at his new achievements. Indeed, Billy's cup seems entirely full when he is out walking with both of us. This is while he is still a baby. One day he is going to have to cope with prejudice and conventional standards. Children hate to be different and it is likely to be a painful time when he has to present his mother and Carole to his friends. It was painful to me to admit that my mother was unmarried but rarely did I lie and say she was a widow, though she had given me full permission to do so. Even as a child I could accept that there was nothing to be ashamed of though I knew it was thought to be shameful by most people. Tough though it was for me, I think it made me into a more sensitive person and one to whom others feel able to talk to about painful things.

Billy will one day be a man and I often wonder how my being a lesbian will affect his view of himself. Already, he appears to make a strong distinction between the sexes and adores men who are responsive to him. Since having him and living with Carole and not needing to demand of men what they could not give me, I have not felt angry or frustrated by them. I believe I relate warmly and comfortably to men I like. I dislike the strong, anti-man separatism among many feminists and some lesbians, though I share a lot of their views about men. Although there must be inherent differences between men and women, the similarities are far more important. I will help Billy to value his feeling self as much as I will help him to value his intellectual and creative selves. I hope he will value other people for their whole selves irrespective of their sex.

Looking back, it is as if I was over-ready, that the yearning and combined frustration of that longing for motherhood has enabled me to give my all to Billy. I suspect that human beings reach a better maturity in their thirties, needing their twenties to work out who they are and what they want. Although I see my inner growth as a continuing process, I believe I reached a level of really knowing myself around thirty-three and, in so doing, I was better equipped to deal with the compromises and frustrations that parenting entails.

Afterword

Well, over a year has passed and my situation has changed a lot. Some months ago, by mutual but painful consent, Carole and I separated. Despite the pleasure I experienced in the constant sharing and companionship, I did not feel ready to share my life and I felt a great sense of relief to be living independently once again. At the same time, Billy's father decided he could not cope with the situation and we now have no contact with him. So the two people who influenced and assisted me so significantly in having my child are both uninvolved at the moment.

I have a lover who I had known for several years previously. She, too, has children and she takes her relationship with Billy very seriously, and he appears to have adapted to the change of circumstances fairly easily.

He is two-and-a-half now. He is talking, he is full of imagination and ideas, and he has a warm, sunny and interesting personality. Never a day goes past without, at some point, my entire self being flooded with love for him, the same feeling as in those first days of his life. He reciprocates my love with a touching matter-of-fact companionship and slightly protective air. This is embodied for me in his encouraging injunction, 'Come on, Mum!' said very much in the tone of a man who says to his wife, 'Come on, Ducks!' In fact, there is a lovely children's book by Ivor Cutler (*Meal One*, Heinemann) which conveys this relationship beautifully between the son and his mother.

So am I repeating the pattern of my mother's life? Superficially, yes, but in the last year I found an excellent 'alternative' therapy, Bioenergetics, and although I did not plan to go on in the long-term, it has now become an almost integral part of my life. I value it as a means to change and to live with greater strength and confidence. I tried to live 'conventionally' with Carole and I felt myself become gradually drained of vitality, even though I was economically and socially secure. It was risky separating and, though there has been considerable love and excitement with Jean, this relationship has not been comfortable as it has confronted me with various life problems in myself. One immediate effect of it was that I felt able to be much more openly gay.

My hopes for the future are that I do eventually share my life, but it doesn't fill me with dread that I may not. I would also like to have another child. I feel immense curiosity at what a second experience would be like. It would be good for Billy who would then not feel the loneliness of the 'only child' syndrome as I did, nor the burdensome responsibility towards me as my only child. More than this I cannot say, as I am still on my journey.

Glossary of Terms

Amniocentesis
A prenatal test for Down's Syndrome and certain other handicapping conditions, which may be performed at about sixteen weeks of pregnancy. Its purpose is to obtain cells from the amniotic fluid surrounding the foetus and then to check the chromosomes. A syringe is inserted into the uterus through the abdominal wall, and fluid extracted. This is then cultured for two to three weeks, at which time the chromosomes can be stained and counted.

Breech Presentation
A baby positioned in the uterus so that it presents buttocks first.

Caesarian Section
An operation to remove the baby through the abdominal wall, instead of it being delivered through the vagina. This operation used only to be performed under a general anaesthetic, but it is increasingly possible for it to be performed under an epidural anaesthetic. This is usually the case when a woman has an 'elective' Caesarian, when she knows in advance that a vaginal delivery is unlikely to be possible. There is then time for the epidural to take effect before the Caesarian Section is performed. In the case of a Caesarian performed as an emergency, a general anaesthetic is more likely to be given, since there is not enough time for an epidural to take effect.

Down's Syndrome

A genetic disorder caused by the presence of an extra chromosome —forty-seven instead of forty-six — in each cell. Although the risk has generally been associated with older mothers, increasing in the thirties, recent research seems to point to an increase in Down's Syndrome babies born to younger mothers. The condition cannot be cured, but much can be done to minimize the effects.

Ectopic Pregnancy

A pregnancy outside the uterus, often in one of the Fallopian tubes. The foetus cannot survive and the pregnancy must be terminated.

Episiotomy

An incision into the perineum (the area between anus and vagina) to enlarge the opening for the baby's head to emerge.

Epidural Anaesthetic

An anaesthetic given in the epidural space round the spinal cord.

Forceps Delivery

A delivery where forceps are inserted into the vagina, the blades fitted round the baby's head and the baby delivered.

Induction

The artificial starting of labour, done by giving drugs – either intravenously or with vaginal pessaries – to make the uterus contract.

Miscarriage

A natural abortion; an inevitable termination of pregnancy occurring at any time up to twenty-fifth week.

Multigravida

A woman having her second or subsequent pregnancy.

Postnatal Depression

'Postnatal' covers the period between the birth itself and adjustment to motherhood. Contributing factors to depression may be hormonal imbalance and the shock of labour, and one's background and current environment.

Pre-eclampsia
A condition in pregnancy where the blood pressure is raised, protein is present in the urine and fingers or ankles are swollen. It is generally treated with bed-rest in hospital.

Premature Delivery
Delivery between the twenty-fifth and thirty-eighth week of pregnancy.

Primigravida
A woman in her first pregnancy. The term 'elderly primigravida' is currently applied by the medical profession in this country to women having their first baby at thirty-five or older.

Rubella
German measles. A mild viral disease which if caught in the first three months of pregnancy can affect the growth of the early foetal organs and cause such abnormalities as deafness, blindness and heart disease. You can have a blood test before getting pregnant to determine whether or not you are immune; if not, you can then be vaccinated, but must not get pregnant for three months afterwards.

Ultrasound
High-frequency sound waves, inaudible to the human ear, can detect movement and are used to render the foetus visible on a screen rather like a television screen. Ultrasound tests ('having a scan') can be used to diagnose pregnancy very early on, and later to measure growth of the foetus, to diagnose twins, and to see to which part of the uterus the placenta is attached.

PROMPT SHEET FOR CONTRIBUTORS

WHAT THE BOOK'S ABOUT AND WHY WE'RE DOING IT

We're collecting and editing autobiographical accounts of what it's like to become a mother after thirty to dispel the general haze and easy generalities with which our society views it, and so that we, and other readers, might share and learn from these life stories.

The book is intended for women because the change-of-life experience at the centre is motherhood; yet it should interest the reader at large because the experience of absolute change, from one life phase to another, is a universal one.

We're limiting our collection to women over thirty because for you the change will be sharper in that you will have been a childless adult for at least a decade and bring experience from that stage to bear on your experience of motherhood.

. . . . .

We'd like you to consider the following three areas:
(1) Pre-pregnancy, (2) Maternity, (3) Childcare.

. . . . .

Some of these questions may not be applicable. Also, you may have other questions you want asked.

In your reply, feel free to expand in any direction you find suits
yourself.

PRE-PREGNANCY

Childhood Expectations:
> Did you always want to have a child? When did you decide you
> wanted to have a child? Perhaps you never decided. If not, what
> happened?

Parents' Attitude(s):
> What was your mother's/father's attitude towards you and
> motherhood? What kind of influence did their marriage, parenting,
> and home have on you? Perhaps you'll recall a particular incident
> which made it clear for you.

Women Friends:
> In your pre-pregnancy phase, were you close to women who had
> small children? How did this influence your attitude and feelings
> as you approached your own motherhood?

Decision-making:
> Did you ever consider not ever having a child? If so, under what
> circumstances and why? Once you made a decision (if you made a
> decision) what kind of complications did you face? Were there
> career, financial, health, or other factors involved?

Fertility/Infertility:
> Talk about any biological factors or medical procedures. If you
> discovered you were infertile, were you immediately ready to start
> adoption procedures? You might enlarge upon this.

Living Circumstance:
> At the time of your pregnancy or adoption, were you married,
> cohabiting, single, lesbian, separated, living on your own, a
> member of a communal household, or other?

Expectations:
> Did you have a picture of what you imagined motherhood would be
> like? Describe in detail. Were there any recurring anxieties at this
> stage?

MATERNITY

Planning and Preparation:

In which ways did you organize your life? If it was long-planned and you made use of temperature charts and/or other medical aids, you might describe that.

Medical Treatment:

Did you find you were treated differently than younger women by your GP/midwife/consultant? If possible, make this clear by reporting particular incidents. In labour did any difficulties arise which were ascribed to your being an older mother?

Your Body and Sex Life:

How did your feelings about your body change during pregnancy? How did your feelings about sex change?

The Birth:

What was it like? Had you been prepared for it as an event? Mention any complications. What were your feelings during labour and immediately after giving birth?

After-effects:

Do you think your pregnancy and/or birth experience had any effect on your relationship with your newborn in the first few weeks? If so, what kind?

CHILDCARE

Practical Changes:

Did you stop work? Take a leave of absence? What kind of help did you have? mother, friends, neighbours, an employed nurse or nanny? In what ways did your husband/partner contribute?

Changes in Relationships:

What kind of changes occurred? with the father of the child, other women, your mother, family, friends, other men, the community? Did you make new friends? Did you stop going out?

Effect on Yourself:

What aspects of motherhood came as a surprise? What kinds of things did becoming a mother help you to learn about yourself,

others, and/or the society in which we live? What do you see as
essential changes in your feelings or attitudes? Include those
related to your body and sexuality. Do you view men and women,
and their relationship, differently than before? If so, how?

If you have any general points you want to make about your experience
of coming late to motherhood, feel free to do so.

Further Reading

Ann Oakley, *From Here to Maternity: Becoming a Mother* (Pelican Books, 1981). This deals with experiences of pregnancy, birth, and early motherhood during the 1970s. Theoretical statements are fully supported by selections from tape-recorded interviews with first-time mothers and others.

Bonnie Friedland and Carol Kort, *The Mother's Book: Shared Experiences* (Houghton Mifflin Company, 1981). This is an extremely readable cross-section of autobiographical essays from fifty or more American mothers. Each focuses on a single aspect of the experience of motherhood.*

Stephanie Dowrick and Sibyl Grundberg, *Why Children?* (The Women's Press, 1980). Eighteen women, British, American and Australian, write in depth about the pros and cons of having children.

Carole Spearin McCauley, *Pregnancy After 35* (Pocket Books, New York, 1976). This is a well-organized, comprehensive guidebook. Its value, however, is somewhat restricted as it is aimed at an American readership.*

Jane Price, *You're Not Too Old To Have A Baby* (Penguin Books, New York, 1978). This looks at delayed parenthood by surveying the medical, psychological and social issues raised by having children later in life. An American publication.*

Elisabeth Bing and Libby Colman, *Having a Baby After 30* (Bantam Books, 1980). In addition to serving as a useful guidebook, this contains autobiographical accounts about late motherhood by both Elisabeth Bing, the renowned authority on the Lamaze Method of delivery, and by her son Peter. An American publication.*

Dana Breen, *Talking With Mothers: About Pregnancy, Childbirth and Early Motherhood* (Norman and Hobhouse, 1981). This is a very full account of the progress of one woman, amplified with comments from the experiences of others. It is not a manual nor a reference book but a book about being a mother in Britain.

Ann Dally, *Inventing Motherhood: The Consequences of an Ideal* (Hutchinson, 1982). This is a very absorbing and readable social history of motherhood which particularly illuminates how conveniently the ideal fits in with social and political trends.

Sheila Kitzinger, *Birth Over Thirty* (Sheldon Press, 1982). This is an easy-to-follow guide to, and commentary on, the birth experience for women over thirty. Many of the aspects are described in the mothers' own words.

Sheila Kitzinger, *The Good Birth Guide* (revised edition, Penguin, 1983). A guide to current practices in many different hospitals.

Pamela Daniels and Kathie Weingarten, *Sooner or Later: The Timing of Parenthood in Adult Lives* (W. W. Norton, 1982). This is a thick and fascinating text. Supported by the Wellesley College Center for Research on Women, the co-authors have written a comprehensive work, a product of many years of field research on the timing of parenthood and its consequences in the lives of women and families.

Additional Books for Readers Interested in Particular Aspects:

Jo Campling, *Images of Ourselves: Women with Disabilities Talking* (Routledge and Kegan Paul Ltd, 1981).

Rochelle Friedman and Bonnie Gradstein, *Surviving Pregnancy Loss* (Little Brown & Company, 1982).*

Ruth Hall, *Marie Stopes* (Virago, 1978 – out of print). A biography of the great pioneer of contraception in Britain.

Eliot Philipp, *Childlessness, Its Causes and What to Do About Them* (Arrow Books, 1975 – out of print).

Hank Pizer and Christine O'Brien Palinski, *Coping With a Miscarriage* (Jill Norman, 1981).

Gillian E. Hanscombe and Jackie Forster, *Rocking the Cradle: Lesbian Mothers. A Challenge in Family Living* (Sheba Feminist Publishers, 1982). In the summer of 1978 the co-authors toured England and Wales to meet and talk to lesbian mothers and their families, to see how they live and to hear what they had to say. Through detailed reports from the mothers themselves and the authors' descriptions of what they met, they introduce important issues to the general reader.

*Not available in Great Britain.

Useful Addresses

AIMS
Association for Improvements in the Maternity Services
Elizabeth Cockerell
21 Franklin Gardens
Hitchin, Herts SG4 UNE
0462.2179

Association for Postnatal Illness
(A specialist organization offering a counselling service)
7 Gowan Avenue
London SW6

A Woman's Place
Hungerford House
Victoria Embankment
London WC2
(A resource centre for the women's movement)

Down's Children's Association
4 Oxford Street
London W1N 9FL
01-580-0511

Foresight
The Secretary
The Old Vicarage
Church Lane
Witley
Godalming, Surrey GU8 5PN
(Information about planning ahead for pregnancy and birth)

The Maternity Alliance
59-61 Camden High Street
London NW1 7JL
01.388.6337

Gingerbread
Association for One-Parent Families
35 Wellington Street
London WC2
01.240.0953

National Childbirth Trust
9 Queensborough Terrace
London W2 3TE

National Children's Bureau
8 Wakeley Street
London EC1V 7QE

C000053274

NEW HEART ENGLISH BIBLE

HOLY BIBLE | NEW TESTAMENT

The New Heart English Bible: New Testament
ISBN: 978-1947935068

VERIFIED COPY
Although the NHEB is public domain, we believe the meaning of God's Word should not be altered. TheBiblePeople verify that this copy has been presented without change from the translator's intent.

Proceeds from the sales of books go toward the further development of resources that help people read, engage, and apply the Bible.

Learn more at http://thebiblepeople.com/book/new-heart-english-bible

Contact: NHEB@TheBiblePeople.com

TABLE OF CONTENTS

The Books of
The New Testament

ABBREVIATIONS

Cf.	Compare
Hb	Hebrew
DSS	Dead Sea Scroll
Lit.	A literal translation
LXX	Septuagint; Greek Old Testament
Ms, Mss	manuscript, manuscripts
MT	Masoretic Hebrew Old Testament text
OL	Old Latin
Syr	Syriac Peshitta
SP	Samaritan Pentateuch
Vg	Latin Vulgate of Jerome (Hieronymus), ca. 400 AD

PREFACE

What is the New Heart English Bible?
The New Heart English Bible is a new, easy-to-read version of God's Word in modern English. Featuring the most up-to-date biblical scholarship, the NHEB was developed by a translation team led by Wayne A. Mitchell. While the team based their work on the popular World English Bible (WEB), this new translation has been updated for accuracy, clarity, and readability.

The *Biblia Hebraica Stuttgartensia* was the primary Hebrew text utilized for the Old Testament, while the *United Bible Societies Greek New Testament, Fourth Edition* was the basic text for the New Testament.

The New Heart English Bible is in the public domain.

What are the benefits of a public domain Bible?
Copyright laws are important to guard the works of those who produce new content. Since most modern Bible translations are copyrighted, this can be a mixed blessing. While a copyright protects the interests and property of the publisher, it limits how a translation can be used, since a copyright naturally restricts the translation, publication, and distribution of God's Word. Thus it becomes more costly to share the gospel (especially in printed form) across the globe unless an individual or organization uses a public domain translation such as the King James Version, which may be difficult to understand and may not be based on the most accurate biblical scholarship.

The New Heart English Bible is a new, updated public domain version that allows anyone to read, quote, copy, and translate Scripture for personal or commercial purposes. While other translations limit the number of verses that can be copied or reprinted, the NHEB encourages such distribution. It can be used freely, without securing permission from or paying royalties to any publisher.

Though the New Heart English Bible is public domain, this printed edition is copyrighted. Permission is granted to the reader to copy, scan, and distribute pages from this edition. Reproductions of this printed edition may not be sold without permission.

Doesn't public domain mean that it can be changed by anyone?
While public domain indicates that content can be modified, where the Bible is concerned we believe the message should not be altered. No human should change the meaning of the words of God. Thus our organization has worked to ensure that this Bible has been presented just as the translation team has intended. Our verified seal on the copright page underscores that every copy of the New Heart English Bible published by TheBiblePeople (the publisher) has not been altered.

If this edition is public domain, why isn't it free?
There are many places where an electronic version of the New Heart English Bible can be downloaded for free. (Find a link on page 275 of this Bible.) Creating a quality book, however, requires a greater investment of resources (paper, people's time, printing, warehousing, and more).

Because God's Word is worthy of our best efforts, TheBiblePeople have made this investment. We have thus paid our staff (and others) to develop this quality book in the spirit of 1 Timothy 5:18, "For the Scripture says, 'Do not muzzle the ox when it treads out the grain.' And, 'The laborer is worthy of his wages.'" We charge for this edition of the NHEB because we believe in compensating those involved in the book's publishing and distribution—they deserve it.

How readable is the NHEB?

The New Heart English Bible is a very good translation. It generally provides a more literal (word-for-word) translation from Hebrew or Greek into English. While a literal translation can sound more stiff and formal, the NHEB is more readable and understandable than some other versions that use the same translation method.

Look at the chart below to compare how the NHEB compares to that of other popular English Bible translations.

John 3:16	
NHEB For God so loved the world that he gave his only Son, so that whoever believes in him will not perish, but have everlasting life.	**KJV** For God so loved the world, that he gave his only begotten Son, that whosoever believeth in him should not perish, but have everlasting life.
NIV For God so loved the world that he gave his one and only Son, that whoever believes in him shall not perish but have eternal life.	**ESV** For God so loved the world, that he gave his only Son, that whoever believes in him should not perish but have eternal life.

Romans 8:28	
NHEB We know that all things work together for good for those who love God, to those who are called according to his purpose.	**KJV** And we know that all things work together for good to them that love God, to them who are the called according to his purpose.
NIV And we know that in all things God works for the good of those who love him, who have been called according to his purpose.	**ESV** And we know that for those who love God all things work together for good, for those who are called according to his purpose.

Philippians 4:8

NHEB	KJV
Finally, brothers, whatever things are true, whatever things are honest, whatever things are just, whatever things are pure, whatever things are lovely, whatever things are of good report; if there is any virtue, and if there is any praise, think on these things.	Finally, brethren, whatsoever things are true, whatsoever things *are* honest, whatsoever things *are* just, whatsoever things *are* pure, whatsoever things *are* lovely, whatsoever things *are* of good report; if *there be* any virtue, and if *there be* any praise, think on these things.

NIV	ESV
Finally, brothers and sisters, whatever is true, whatever is noble, whatever is right, whatever is pure, whatever is lovely, whatever is admirable--if anything is excellent or praiseworthy--think about such things.	Finally, brothers, whatever is true, whatever is honorable, whatever is just, whatever is pure, whatever is lovely, whatever is commendable, if there is any excellence, if there is anything worthy of praise, think about these things.

1 John 1:9

NHEB	KJV
If we confess our sins, he is faithful and righteous to forgive us the sins, and to cleanse us from all unrighteousness.	If we confess our sins, he is faithful and just to forgive us our sins, and to cleanse us from all unrighteousness.

NIV	ESV
If we confess our sins, he is faithful and just and will forgive us our sins and purify us from all unrighteousness.	If we confess our sins, he is faithful and just to forgive us *our* sins and to cleanse us from all unrighteousness.

What is unique about the NHEB footnotes?

Before the invention of the printing press, Scripture manuscripts had to be copied by hand. Through the centuries, researchers have discovered some modifications in different manuscripts, including those in Hebrew, Greek, Aramaic, and Latin. These changes often occurred because of a scribal error (such as accidentally omitting a word or copying a wrong word), and many times the error was never noticed as the later manuscripts were being copied, thus perpetuating something other than the original word or sentence penned by the biblical writer. As the earlier English translations of the Bible were developed, many of these alterations were not even recognized.

Archaeologists in the last century, however, have discovered ancient manuscripts (such as the Dead Sea Scrolls) that were not available to earlier translators and have often shed new light on where some original words or phrases were changed through the centuries. As modern-day scholars undertake the task of Bible translation, they consider all of the available manuscripts (including the variants) and often must make judgments about the best way to translate a particular word or phrase. This means the text from one manuscript may be favored over that from a different manuscript. In cases where there are differences, often the alternate reading is mentioned in a footnote.

The translation of the New Heart English Bible uses the most updated scholorship and best manuscripts in an effort to present the Word of God with complete accuracy. Where texts may vary slighlty, alternate words or phrases are cited in a footnote, which is why the NHEB has more footnotes than the average translation. While these footnotes don't interfere with the normal reading of a verse or passage, the alternate reading is available at a quick glance for anyone wanting to know the difference. In addition, footnotes in the NHEB provide cross-references to related verses as well as brief explanations of certain words and phrases.

What are some additional benefits of using the NHEB?
Each edition comes with a link to a free PDF download access of the full Bible. This allows God's Word to be used and distributed in a variety of ways and places, reaching more and more people with the Good News of Jesus Christ and further expanding the kingdom of God. In addition, every purchase of the New Heart English Bible contributes to the printing of additional Bibles and Bible-related resources for those who need them. The New Heart English Bible is printed on recycled paper.

Matthew

1 A record of the genealogy of Jesus Christ, the son of David, the son of Abraham. ²Abraham was the father of Isaac, and Isaac the father of Jacob, and Jacob the father of Judah and his brothers, ³and Judah was the father of Perez and Zerah by Tamar, and Perez was the father of Hezron, and Hezron the father of Ram, ⁴and Ram the father of Amminadab, and Amminadab the father of Nahshon, and Nahshon the father of Salmon, ⁵and Salmon the father of Boaz by Rahab, and Boaz was the father of Obed by Ruth, and Obed[a] was the father of Jesse, ⁶and Jesse the father of David the king. And David[b] was the father of Solomon by her who had been the wife of Uriah; ⁷and Solomon was the father of Rehoboam, and Rehoboam the father of Abijah, and Abijah the father of Asa;[c] ⁸and Asa the father of Jehoshaphat, and Jehoshaphat the father of Joram, and Joram the father of Uzziah, ⁹and Uzziah the father of Jotham, and Jotham the father of Ahaz, and Ahaz the father of Hezekiah; ¹⁰and Hezekiah the father of Manasseh, and Manasseh the father of Amon,[d] and Amon the father of Josiah, ¹¹and Josiah the father of Jechoniah and his brothers, at the time of the exile to Babylon. ¹²And after the exile to Babylon, Jechoniah was the father of Shealtiel, and Shealtiel the father of Zerubbabel, ¹³and Zerubbabel the father of Abihud, and Abihud the father of Eliakim, and Eliakim the father of Azzur, ¹⁴and Azzur the father of Zadok, and Zadok the father of Ahiam, and Ahiam the father of Elihud, ¹⁵and Elihud the father of Eleazar, and Eleazar the father of Matthan, and Matthan the father of Jacob, ¹⁶and Jacob the father of Joseph, the husband of Mary, from whom was born Jesus, who is called the Messiah. ¹⁷So all the generations from Abraham to David are fourteen generations; and from David to the exile to Babylon fourteen generations; and from the exile to Babylon to the Messiah, fourteen generations.

¹⁸Now the birth of Jesus Christ happened like this. His mother Mary had been engaged to Joseph, and before they came together, she was found to be with child from the Holy Spirit. ¹⁹And Joseph, her husband, being a righteous man, and not willing to make her a public example, intended to put her away secretly. ²⁰But when he thought about these things, look, an angel of the Lord appeared to him in a dream, saying, "Joseph, son of David, do not be afraid to take to yourself Mary, your wife, for that which is conceived in her is of the Holy Spirit. ²¹And she will bring forth a son, and you are to name him Jesus,[e] for he will save his people from their sins."

²²Now all this has happened, that it might be fulfilled which was spoken by the Lord through the prophet, saying,

²³"Look, the virgin will conceive
    and bear a son,
and they will call his name Immanuel;"
    which is translated, "God with us."[f]

²⁴And Joseph arose from his sleep, and did as the angel of the Lord commanded him, and took his wife to himself; ²⁵and had no marital relations with her until she had brought forth a son[g]; and he named him Jesus.

2 Now when Jesus was born in Bethlehem of Judea in the days of Herod the king, look, wise men[h] from the east came to Jerusalem, saying, ²"Where is he who is born King of the Jews? For we saw his star in the east, and have come to worship him." ³And when King Herod heard it, he was troubled, and all Jerusalem with him. ⁴And gathering together all the chief priests and

---

a   1:5 Some Mss read "Jobed." See 1 Chronicles 2:12
b   1:6 Some Mss add "the king"
c   1:7 Some Mss read "Asaph." See 1 Chronicles 3:10
d   1:10 Some Mss read "Amos." See 1 Chronicles 3:14
e   1:21 Gk. "Iesous" for Hebrew "Yeshua," meaning "salvation"
f   1:23 Isaiah 7:14
g   1:25 Some Mss add "her firstborn"
h   2:1 Or, "Magi"

scribes of the people, he asked them where the Messiah would be born. [5]And they said to him, "In Bethlehem of Judea, for thus it is written through the prophet,

[6]'And you, Bethlehem, land of Judah,
   are in no way least among the rulers
     of Judah;
for out of you will come forth a ruler
   who will shepherd my people,
     Israel.' "[a]

[7]Then Herod secretly called the wise men, and learned from them exactly what time the star appeared. [8]And he sent them to Bethlehem, and said, "Go and search diligently for the young child, and when you have found him, bring me word, so that I also may come and worship him."

[9]And they, having heard the king, went their way; and look, the star which they saw in the east went before them, until it came and stood over where the young child was. [10]And when they saw the star, they rejoiced with exceedingly great joy. [11]And they came into the house and saw the young child with Mary, his mother, and they fell down and worshiped him. Then, opening their treasures, they offered to him gifts: gold, frankincense, and myrrh. [12]Being warned in a dream that they should not return to Herod, they went back to their own country another way.

[13]Now when they had departed, look, an angel of the Lord appeared to Joseph in a dream, saying, "Arise and take the young child and his mother, and flee into Egypt, and stay there until I tell you, for Herod will seek the young child to destroy him."

[14]And he arose and took the young child and his mother by night, and departed into Egypt, [15]and was there until the death of Herod; that it might be fulfilled which was spoken by the Lord through the prophet, saying, "Out of Egypt I called my son."[b]

[16]Then Herod, when he saw that he was mocked by the wise men, was exceedingly angry, and sent out, and killed all the male children who were in Bethlehem and in all the surrounding countryside, from two years old and under, according to the exact time which he had learned from the wise men. [17]Then that which was spoken by Jeremiah the prophet was fulfilled, saying,

[18]"A voice was heard in Ramah,
   lamentation and[c] weeping and great
     mourning,
Rachel weeping for her children;
   and she would not be comforted,
     because they are no more."[d]

[19]But when Herod was dead, look, an angel of the Lord appeared in a dream to Joseph in Egypt, saying, [20]"Arise and take the young child and his mother, and go into the land of Israel, for those who sought the young child's life are dead."

[21]And he arose and took the young child and his mother, and went to the land of Israel. [22]But when he heard that Archelaus was reigning over Judea in the place of his father, Herod, he was afraid to go there. Being warned in a dream, he withdrew into the region of Galilee, [23]and came and lived in a city called Nazareth; that it might be fulfilled which was spoken through the prophets, that he will be called a Nazorean.[e]

3 And in those days John the Baptist came, preaching in the wilderness of Judea, saying, [2]"Repent, for the kingdom of heaven is near." [3]For this is he who was spoken of by Isaiah the prophet, saying,

"The voice of one who calls out in the
   wilderness,
'Prepare the way of the Lord.
Make his roads straight.' "[f]

[4]Now John himself wore clothing made of camel's hair and with a leather belt around his waist, and his food was locusts and wild honey. [5]Then people from Jerusalem, all of Judea, and all the region around the Jordan went out to him, [6]and they were baptized by him in the Jordan river[g],

---

a   2:6 Micah 5:2
b   2:15 Hosea 11:1
c   2:18 Some Mss lack "lamentation and"
d   2:18 Jeremiah 31:15
e   2:23 A word play on Heb netzer "shoot, branch," i.e.
     from king David. Isaiah 11:1
f   3:3 Isaiah 40:3
g   3:6 Some Mss lack "river"

confessing their sins. [7]But when he saw many of the Pharisees and Sadducees coming for his baptism he said to them, "You offspring of vipers, who warned you to flee from the wrath to come? [8]Therefore bring forth fruit worthy of repentance, [9]and do not think to yourselves, 'We have Abraham for our father,' for I tell you that God is able to raise up children to Abraham from these stones.

[10]"Even now the axe lies at the root of the trees. Therefore, every tree that does not bring forth good fruit is cut down, and cast into the fire. [11]I indeed baptize you in water for repentance, but the one who comes after me is mightier than I, whose shoes I am not worthy to carry. He will baptize you in the Holy Spirit and with fire[a]. [12]His winnowing fork is in his hand, and he will thoroughly cleanse his threshing floor. He will gather his wheat into the barn, but the chaff he will burn up with unquenchable fire."

[13]Then Jesus came from Galilee to the Jordan to John, to be baptized by him. [14]But John[b] would have hindered him, saying, "I need to be baptized by you, and you come to me?"

[15]But Jesus, answering, said to him, "Allow it for now, for this is the fitting way for us to fulfill all righteousness." Then he allowed him. [16]And Jesus, when he was baptized, went up directly from the water; and look, the heavens were opened to him, and he saw the Spirit of God descending as a dove, and coming on him. [17]And look, a voice out of the heavens said, "This is my beloved Son, with whom I am well pleased."

4 Then Jesus was led up by the Spirit into the wilderness to be tempted by the devil. [2]And when he had fasted forty days and forty nights, he was hungry afterward. [3]And the tempter came and said to him, "If you are the Son of God, command that these stones become bread."

[4]But he answered and said, "It is written, 'Man does not live by bread alone, but by every word that proceeds out of the mouth of God.'[c]"

[5]Then the devil took him into the holy city. He set him on the pinnacle of the temple, [6]and said to him, "If you are the Son of God, throw yourself down, for it is written, 'He will put his angels in charge of you.' and,

'In their hands they will lift you up,
    so that you will not strike your foot
        against a stone.'"[d]

[7]Jesus said to him, "Again, it is written, 'Do not test the Lord, your God.'"[e]

[8]Again, the devil took him to a very high mountain, and showed him all the kingdoms of the world, and their glory. [9]And he said to him, "I will give you all of these things, if you will fall down and worship me."

[10]Then Jesus said to him, "Go away[f], Satan. For it is written, 'You are to worship the Lord your God, and serve him only.'"[g]

[11]Then the devil left him, and look, angels came and served him. [12]Now when he[h] heard that John was delivered up, he withdrew into Galilee. [13]And leaving Nazareth, he came and lived in Capernaum, which is by the sea, in the region of Zebulun and Naphtali, [14]that it might be fulfilled which was spoken through Isaiah the prophet, saying,

[15]"The land of Zebulun and the land of
        Naphtali,
    toward the sea, beyond the Jordan,
    Galilee of the nations,
[16]the people who sat in darkness saw a
        great light, and
    to those who sat in the region and
        shadow of death,
    to them light has dawned."[i]

[17]From that time, Jesus began to proclaim, and to say, "Repent. For the kingdom of heaven is near."

[18]And walking by the sea of Galilee, he saw two brothers: Simon, who is called

---

a   3:11 Some Mss lack "and with fire"
b   3:14 Gk. "he"
c   4:4 Deuteronomy 8:3
d   4:6 Psalm 91:11-12
e   4:7 Deuteronomy 6:16
f   4:10 Some Mss read "Get behind me"
g   4:10 Deuteronomy 6:13
h   4:12 Some Mss read "Jesus"
i   4:16 Isaiah 9:1-2

Peter, and Andrew, his brother, casting a net into the sea; for they were fishermen. [19]And he said to them, "Come after me, and I will make you fishers of people."

[20]And they immediately left their nets and followed him. [21]Going on from there, he saw two other brothers, James the son of Zebedee, and John his brother, in the boat with Zebedee their father, mending their nets, and he called them. [22]And they immediately left the boat and their father, and followed him.

[23]And he[a] went about in all Galilee, teaching in their synagogues, and preaching the Good News of the kingdom, and healing every disease and every sickness among the people. [24]And the report about him went out into all Syria, and they brought to him all who were sick, afflicted with various diseases and torments, possessed with demons, and epileptics, and paralytics; and he healed them. [25]And large crowds from Galilee, and Decapolis, and Jerusalem, and Judea, and from beyond the Jordan followed him.

5 And seeing the multitudes, he went up onto the mountain, and when he had sat down, his disciples came to him. [2]Then he opened his mouth and taught them, saying,

[3]"Blessed are the poor in spirit,
    for theirs is the kingdom of heaven.
[4]Blessed are those who mourn,
    for they will be comforted.
[5]Blessed are the gentle,
    for they will inherit the earth.
[6]Blessed are those who hunger and
      thirst after righteousness,
    for they will be filled.
[7]Blessed are the merciful,
    for they will obtain mercy.
[8]Blessed are the pure in heart,
    for they will see God.
[9]Blessed are the peacemakers,
    for they will be called sons of God.
[10]Blessed are those who have been
      persecuted for righteousness'
      sake,
    for theirs is the kingdom of heaven.

[11]"Blessed are you when they insult you, persecute you, and say all kinds of evil against you falsely, for my sake. [12]Rejoice, and be exceedingly glad, for great is your reward in heaven. For that is how they persecuted the prophets who were before you.

[13]"You are the salt of the earth, but if the salt has lost its flavor, with what will it be salted? It is then good for nothing, but to be cast out and trampled under people's feet. [14]You are the light of the world. A city located on a hill cannot be hidden. [15]Neither do you light a lamp, and put it under a measuring basket, but on a stand; and it shines to all who are in the house. [16]Even so, let your light shine before people; that they may see your good works, and glorify your Father who is in heaven.

[17]"Do not think that I came to destroy the Law or the Prophets. I did not come to destroy, but to fulfill. [18]For truly, I tell you, until heaven and earth pass away, not the smallest letter[b] or part of a letter will disappear from the Law, until all things are accomplished. [19]Therefore, whoever will break one of these least commandments, and teach others to do so, will be called least in the kingdom of heaven; but whoever will do and teach them will be called great in the kingdom of heaven. [20]For I tell you that unless your righteousness exceeds that of the scribes and Pharisees, there is no way you will enter into the kingdom of heaven.

[21]"You have heard that it was said to the ancient ones, 'Do not murder;'[c] and whoever murders will be liable to judgment.[d] [22]But I tell you, that everyone who is angry with his brother without a cause[e] will be liable to judgment; and whoever will say to his brother, 'Raqa,'[f] will be in danger of the council; and whoever will say, 'You fool,' will be in danger of the fire of hell.

[23]"If therefore you are offering your gift at the altar, and there remember that your

---

a 4:23 Some Mss read "Jesus"
b 5:18 Lit. iota, the smallest letter of the Greek alphabet
c 5:21 Exodus 20:13
d 5:21 Deuteronomy 16:18
e 5:22 Some Mss lack "without a cause"
f 5:22 Meaning "good for nothing"

brother has anything against you, [24]leave your gift there before the altar, and go your way. First be reconciled to your brother, and then come and offer your gift. [25]Agree with your adversary quickly, while you are with him in the way; lest perhaps the prosecutor deliver you to the judge, and the judge[a] to the officer, and you be cast into prison. [26]Truly I tell you, you will never get out of there until you have paid the last penny.

[27]"You have heard that it was said,[b] 'Do not commit adultery;'[c] [28]but I tell you that everyone who looks at a woman to lust after her has committed adultery with her already in his heart. [29]And if your right eye causes you to stumble, pluck it out and throw it away from you. For it is more profitable for you that one of your members should perish, than for your whole body to be thrown into hell.[d,e] [30]And if your right hand causes you to stumble, cut it off, and throw it away from you. For it is more profitable for you that one of your members should perish, than for your whole body to go[f] into hell.[g]

[31]"And it was said, 'Whoever divorces his wife, let him give her a certificate of divorce,'[h] [32]but I tell you that everyone[i] who divorces his wife, except for the cause of sexual immorality, makes her an adulteress; and whoever marries her when she is divorced commits adultery.

[33]"Again you have heard that it was said to them of old time, 'Do not make false vows, but fulfill your vows to the Lord.' [34]But I tell you, do not swear at all: neither by heaven, for it is the throne of God; [35]nor by the earth, for it is the footstool of his feet; nor by Jerusalem, for it is the city of the great King. [36]Neither should you swear by your head, for you cannot make one hair white or black. [37]But let your 'Yes' be 'Yes' and your 'No' be 'No.' Whatever is more than these is of the evil one.

[38]"You have heard that it was said, 'An eye for an eye, and a tooth for a tooth.'[j] [39]But I tell you, do not set yourself against the one who is evil. But whoever strikes you on your[k] right cheek, turn to him the other also. [40]And if anyone sues you to take away your coat, let him have your cloak also. [41]And whoever compels you to go one mile, go with him two. [42]Give to him who asks you, and do not turn away him who desires to borrow from you.

[43]"You have heard that it was said, 'Love your neighbor,[l] and hate your enemy.' [44]But I tell you, love your enemies,[m] and pray for those who[n] persecute you, [45]that you may be children of your Father who is in heaven. For he makes his sun to rise on the evil and the good, and sends rain on the just and the unjust. [46]For if you love those who love you, what reward do you have? Do not even the tax collectors do the same? [47]And if you only greet your brothers[o], what more do you do than others? Do not even the non-Jews[p] do the same? [48]You therefore are to be perfect, as your heavenly Father is perfect.

6 "Be careful that you do not do your righteousness[q] before people, to be seen by them, or else you have no reward from your Father who is in heaven. [2]Therefore when you do merciful deeds, do not sound a trumpet before yourself, as the hypocrites do in the synagogues and in the streets, that they may get glory from people. Truly I tell you, they have received their reward. [3]But when you do merciful deeds, do not let your left hand know what your right hand does, [4]so that your merciful

---

a 5:25 Some Mss add "deliver you"
b 5:27 Some Mss add "to the ancients"
c 5:27 Exodus 20:13
d 5:29 Gk. "Gehenna"
e 5:29 Probable Semitic idiom, e.g., "If you lust or envy, stop it…"
f 5:30 Some Mss read "be cast"
g 5:30 Probable Semitic idiom, e.g., "If you steal, stop it…"
h 5:31 Deuteronomy 24:1
i 5:32 Some Mss read "whoever"
j 5:38 Exodus 21:24; Leviticus 24:20; Deuteronomy 19:21
k 5:39 Some Mss lack "your"
l 5:43 Leviticus 19:18
m 5:44 Some Mss add "bless those who curse you, do good to those who hate you"
n 5:44 Some Mss add "mistreat you and"
o 5:47 Some Mss read "friends"
p 5:47 Some Mss read "tax collectors"
q 6:1 Some Mss read "alms"

deeds may be in secret, then your Father who sees in secret will reward you.

⁵"And when you pray, you are not to be as the hypocrites, for they love to stand and pray in the synagogues and in the corners of the streets, that they may be seen by others. Truly, I tell you, they have received their reward. ⁶But you, when you pray, enter into your inner chamber, and having shut your door, pray to your Father who is in secret, and your Father who sees in secret will reward you.[a] ⁷And in praying, do not use vain repetitions, as the unbelievers do; for they think that they will be heard for their much speaking. ⁸Therefore do not be like them, for your Father knows what things you need, before you ask him. ⁹Therefore, you should pray this way:

'Our Father in heaven, revered be your name. ¹⁰Let your kingdom come. Let your will be done, on earth as it is in heaven. ¹¹Give us today our daily bread. [b]¹²And forgive us our debts, as we also forgive our debtors. ¹³And lead us not into temptation, but deliver us from the evil one.'[c]

¹⁴"For if you forgive people their trespasses, your heavenly Father will also forgive you. ¹⁵But if you do not forgive people,[d] neither will your Father forgive your trespasses.

¹⁶"Moreover when you fast, do not be like the hypocrites, with sad faces. For they disfigure their faces, that they may be seen by people to be fasting. Truly I tell you, they have received their reward. ¹⁷But you, when you fast, anoint your head, and wash your face; ¹⁸so that you are not seen by people to be fasting, but by your Father who is in secret, and your Father, who sees in secret, will reward you.

¹⁹"Do not lay up treasures for yourselves on the earth, where moth and rust consume, and where thieves break through and steal; ²⁰but lay up for yourselves treasures in heaven, where neither moth nor rust consume, and where thieves do not break through and steal; ²¹for where your treasure is, there your heart will be also.

²²"The lamp of the body is the eye. If therefore your eye is sound, your whole body will be full of light. ²³But if your eye is bad, your whole body will be full of darkness. If therefore the light that is in you is darkness, how great is the darkness.

²⁴"No one can serve two masters, for either he will hate the one and love the other; or else he will be devoted to one and despise the other. You cannot serve both God and Mammon. ²⁵Therefore I tell you, do not be anxious about your life, what you will eat or what you will drink;[e] or about your body, what you will wear. Is not life more than food, and the body more than clothing? ²⁶See the birds of the sky, that they do not sow, neither do they reap, nor gather into barns, and your heavenly Father feeds them. Are you not of much more value than they?

²⁷"And which of you, by being anxious, can add one cubit to his height? ²⁸And why are you anxious about clothing? Consider the lilies of the field, how they grow. They do not toil, neither do they spin, ²⁹yet I tell you that even Solomon in all his glory was not dressed like one of these. ³⁰But if God so clothes the grass of the field, which today exists, and tomorrow is thrown into the oven, won't he much more clothe you, you of little faith?

³¹"Therefore do not be anxious, saying, 'What will we eat?', 'What will we drink?' or, 'With what will we be clothed?' ³²For the unbelievers seek after all these things, for your heavenly Father knows that you need all these things. ³³But seek first the kingdom of God and his righteousness, and all these things will be given to you as well. ³⁴Therefore do not be anxious for tomorrow, for tomorrow will be anxious for itself. Each day has enough trouble of its own.

7 "Do not judge, so that you won't be judged. ²For with whatever judgment you judge, you will be judged; and with

---

a　6:6 Some Mss add "openly"
b　6:11 Proverbs 30:8; Isaiah 33:16
c　6:13 Some Mss add "For yours is the kingdom and the power and the glory forever. Amen"
d　6:15 Some Mss add "their transgressions"
e　6:25 Some Mss lack "or what you will drink"

whatever measure you measure, it will be measured to you. [3]And why do you see the speck that is in your brother's eye, but do not notice the log that is in your own eye? [4]Or how will you tell your brother, 'Let me remove the speck from your eye;' and look, the log is in your own eye? [5]You hypocrite. First remove the log out of your own eye, and then you can see clearly to remove the speck out of your brother's eye.

[6]"Do not give that which is holy to the dogs, neither throw your pearls before the pigs, or they will trample them under their feet and turn and tear you to pieces.

[7]"Ask, and it will be given to you. Seek, and you will find. Knock, and it will be opened for you. [8]For everyone who asks receives. He who seeks finds. To him who knocks it will be opened. [9]Or who is there among you, who, if his son will ask him for bread, will give him a stone? [10]Or if he will ask for a fish, who will give him a serpent? [11]If you then, being evil, know how to give good gifts to your children, how much more will your Father who is in heaven give good things to those who ask him. [12]Therefore whatever you desire for people to do to you, do also to them; for this is the Law and the Prophets.

[13]"Enter in by the narrow gate; for wide is the gate and broad is the way that leads to destruction, and many are those who enter in by it. [14]How [a]narrow is the gate, and difficult is the way that leads to life. Few are those who find it.

[15]"Beware[b] of false prophets, who come to you in sheep's clothing, but inwardly are ravening wolves. [16]By their fruits you will know them. Do you gather grapes from thorns, or figs from thistles? [17]Even so, every good tree produces good fruit; but the corrupt tree produces evil fruit. [18]A good tree cannot produce evil fruit, neither can a corrupt tree produce good fruit. [19]Every tree that does not grow good fruit is cut down, and thrown into the fire. [20]Therefore, by their fruits you will know them. [21]Not everyone who says to me, 'Lord, Lord,' will enter into the kingdom of heaven; but he who does the will of my Father who is in heaven.

[22]Many will tell me in that day, 'Lord, Lord, did not we prophesy in your name, in your name cast out demons, and in your name do many mighty works?' [23]And then I will tell them, 'I never knew you. Depart from me, you who practice lawlessness.'[c]

[24]"Everyone therefore who hears these words of mine, and does them, will be compared to[d] a wise man, who built his house on a rock. [25]And the rain came down, the floods came, and the winds blew, and beat on that house; and it did not fall, for it was founded on the rock. [26]And everyone who hears these words of mine, and does not do them will be like a foolish man, who built his house on the sand. [27]And the rain came down, the floods came, and the winds blew, and beat on that house; and it fell—and great was its fall."

[28]And it happened, when Jesus had finished saying these things, that the crowds were astonished at his teaching, [29]for he taught them with authority, and not like their[e] scribes.

8 And when he came down from the mountain, large crowds followed him. [2]And look, a leper came to him and worshiped him, saying, "Lord, if you want to, you can make me clean."

[3]And he stretched out his hand, and touched him, saying, "I am willing. Be cleansed." And immediately his leprosy was cleansed. [4]And Jesus said to him, "See that you tell nobody, but go, show yourself to the priest, and offer the gift that Moses commanded, as a testimony to them."

[5]And when he[f] came into Capernaum, a centurion came to him, asking him, [6]and saying, "Lord, my servant lies in the house paralyzed, grievously tormented."

[7]And he[g] said to him, "I will come and heal him."

---

a   7:14 Some Mss read "Because"
b   7:15 Some Mss read "But beware"
c   7:23 Psalm 6:8
d   7:24 Some Mss read "I will compare him"
e   7:29 Some Mss read "the"
f   8:5 Some Mss read "Jesus"
g   8:7 Some Mss read "Jesus"

⁸And the centurion answered, "Lord, I'm not worthy for you to come under my roof. Just say the word, and my servant will be healed. ⁹For I am also a man under authority, having under myself soldiers. I tell this one, 'Go,' and he goes; and tell another, 'Come,' and he comes; and tell my servant, 'Do this,' and he does it."

¹⁰And when Jesus heard it, he marveled, and said to those who followed, "Truly I tell you, I have not found so great a faith with anyone in Israel. ¹¹And I tell you that many will come from the east and the west, and will sit down with Abraham, and Isaac, and Jacob in the kingdom of heaven, ¹²but the sons of the kingdom will be thrown out into the outer darkness. There will be weeping and gnashing of teeth." ¹³And Jesus said to the centurion, "Go your way. Let it be done for you as you have believed." And theᵃ servant was healed in that hour.

¹⁴And when Jesus came into Peter's house, he saw his wife's mother lying sick with a fever. ¹⁵So he touched her hand, and the fever left her. She got up and served himᵇ. ¹⁶And when evening came, they brought to him many possessed with demons. He cast out the spirits with a word, and healed all who were sick; ¹⁷that it might be fulfilled which was spoken through Isaiah the prophet, saying, "He took our infirmities, and bore our diseases."ᶜ ¹⁸Now when Jesus saw a crowd around him, he gave the order to depart to the other side.

¹⁹Then a scribe came, and said to him, "Teacher, I will follow you wherever you go." ²⁰And Jesus said to him, "The foxes have holes, and the birds of the sky have nests, but the Son of Man has nowhere to lay his head."

²¹And another of theᵈ disciples said to him, "Lord, allow me first to go and bury my father."

²²But Jesus said to him, "Follow me, and leave the dead to bury their own dead."

²³And when he got into a boat, his disciples followed him. ²⁴And look, a violent storm came up on the sea, so much that the boat was covered with the waves, but he was asleep. ²⁵Theyᵉ came to him, and woke him up, saying, "Save us, Lord. We are dying."

²⁶And he said to them, "Why are you fearful, O you of little faith?" Then he got up, rebuked the wind and the sea, and there was a great calm.ᶠ

²⁷And the men marveled, saying, "What kind of man is this, that even the wind and the sea obey him?"

²⁸And when he came to the other side, into the country of the Gadarenes,ᵍ two people possessed by demons met him there, coming out of the tombs, exceedingly fierce, so that nobody could pass that way. ²⁹And look, they shouted, saying, "What do we have to do with you,ʰ Son of God? Have you come here to torment us before the time?" ³⁰Now there was a herd of many pigs feeding far away from them. ³¹And the demons begged him, saying, "If you cast us out, permit us to go away into the herd of pigs."

³²And he said to them, "Go."

And they came out, and went into the pigs, and look, the whole herdⁱ rushed down the cliff into the sea, and died in the water. ³³And those who fed them fled, and went away into the city, and told everything, including what happened to those who were possessed with demons. ³⁴And look, all the city came out to meet Jesus. When they saw him, they begged that he would depart from their borders.

9 And he entered into a boat, and crossed over, and came into his own city. ²And look, they brought to him a man who was paralyzed, lying on a bed. And Jesus, seeing their faith, said to the paralytic, "Son, cheer up. Your sins are forgiven.ʲ"

---

a   8:13 Some Mss read "his"
b   8:15 Some Mss read "them"
c   8:17 Isaiah 53:4
d   8:21 Some Mss read "his"
e   8:25 Some Mss read "The disciples"
f   8:26 Psalm 65:7; 89:9; 107:29
g   8:28 Some Mss read "Gergesenes"
h   8:29 Some Mss add "Jesus"
i   8:32 Some Mss read "herd of pigs, and look, the whole herd of pigs"
j   9:2 Some Mss add "you"

[3]And look, some of the scribes said to themselves, "This man blasphemes."

[4]But Jesus, knowing their thoughts, said, "Why do you think evil in your hearts? [5]For which is easier, to say, 'Your sins are forgiven;' or to say, 'Get up, and walk?' [6]But that you may know that the Son of Man has authority on earth to forgive sins..." (then he said to the paralytic), "Get up, and take up your mat, and go up to your house."

[7]And he arose and departed to his house. [8]Now when the crowds saw it, they were afraid[a] and glorified God who had given such authority to men.

[9]And as Jesus passed by from there, he saw a man called Matthew sitting at the tax collection office. He said to him, "Follow me." And he got up and followed him. [10]And it happened as he sat in the house, look, many tax collectors and sinners came and were reclining with Jesus and his disciples. [11]And when the Pharisees saw it, they said to his disciples, "Why does your Teacher eat with tax collectors and sinners?"

[12]When he[b] heard it, he said to them, "Those who are healthy have no need for a physician, but those who are sick do. [13]But you go and learn what this means: 'I desire mercy, and not sacrifice,'[c] for I came not to call the righteous, but sinners.[d]"

[14]Then John's disciples came to him, saying, "Why do we and the Pharisees fast often, but your disciples do not fast?"

[15]And Jesus said to them, "Can the friends of the bridegroom mourn, as long as the bridegroom is with them? But the days will come when the bridegroom will be taken away from them, and then they will fast. [16]And no one puts a piece of unshrunk cloth on an old garment; for the patch would tear away from the garment, and a worse hole is made. [17]Neither do people put new wine into old wineskins, or else the skins would burst, and the wine be spilled, and the skins ruined. No, they put new wine into fresh wineskins, and both are preserved."

[18]While he told these things to them, look, a ruler came and worshiped him, saying, "My daughter has just died, but come and lay your hand on her, and she will live."

[19]And Jesus got up and followed him, as did his disciples. [20]And look, a woman who had an issue of blood for twelve years came behind him, and touched the fringe of his garment; [21]for she said within herself, "If I just touch his garment, I will be made well."

[22]But Jesus, turning around and seeing her, said, "Daughter, cheer up. Your faith has made you well." And the woman was made well from that hour.

[23]And when Jesus came into the ruler's house, and saw the flute players, and the crowd in noisy disorder, [24]he said[e], "Go away, for the girl is not dead, but asleep." And they laughed at him.

[25]But when the crowd was put out, he entered in, took her by the hand, and the girl arose. [26]And the report of this went out into all that land. [27]And as Jesus passed by from there, two blind men followed him, calling out and saying, "Have mercy on us, son of David."

[28]And when he had come into the house, the blind men came to him, and Jesus said to them, "Do you believe that I am able to do this?"

They told him, "Yes, Lord."

[29]Then he touched their eyes, saying, "According to your faith be it done to you." [30]And their eyes were opened. And Jesus strictly commanded them, saying, "See that no one knows about this." [31]But they went out and spread abroad his fame in all that land.

[32]And as they went out, look, a mute man who was demon possessed was brought to him. [33]And when the demon was cast out, the mute man spoke. And the crowds marveled, saying, "Nothing like this has ever been seen in Israel."

[34]But the Pharisees said, "By the prince of the demons, he casts out demons."

---

a 9:8 Some Mss read "amazed"
b 9:12 Some Mss read "Jesus" instead of "he"
c 9:13 Hosea 6:6
d 9:13 Some Mss add "to repentance"
e 9:24 Some Mss add "to them"

[35]And Jesus went about all the cities and the villages, teaching in their synagogues, and preaching the Good News of the kingdom, and healing every disease and every sickness[a]. [36]But when he saw the crowds, he was moved with compassion for them, because they were harassed and scattered, like sheep without a shepherd. [37]Then he said to his disciples, "The harvest indeed is plentiful, but the laborers are few. [38]Pray therefore that the Lord of the harvest will send out laborers into his harvest."

10 And he called to himself his twelve disciples, and gave them authority over unclean spirits, to cast them out, and to heal every disease and every sickness. [2]Now the names of the twelve apostles are these. The first, Simon, who is called Peter; and Andrew his brother; and James the son of Zebedee, and John his brother; [3]Philip and Bartholomew;[b] Thomas and Matthew the tax collector; James the son of Alphaeus,[c] and Thaddaeus; [4]Simon the Zealot, and Judas Iscariot,[d] who also betrayed him.

[5]Jesus sent these twelve out, and commanded them, saying, "Do not go among the non-Jews, and do not enter into any city of the Samaritans. [6]Rather, go to the lost sheep of the house of Israel. [7]And as you go, proclaim, saying, 'The kingdom of heaven is near.' [8]Heal the sick, raise the dead,[e] cleanse the lepers, cast out demons. Freely you received, freely give. [9]Do not take any gold, nor silver, nor bronze in your money belts. [10]Take no bag for your journey, neither two coats, nor shoes, nor staff: for the laborer is worthy of his food. [11]And into whatever city or village you enter, find out who in it is worthy; and stay there until you go on. [12]And as you enter into the household, greet it. [13]And if the household is worthy, let your peace come on it, but if it is not worthy, let your peace return to you. [14]And whoever does not receive you, nor hear your words, as you leave that house or that city, shake off the dust from your feet. [15]Truly I tell you, it will be more tolerable for the land of Sodom and Gomorrah in the day of judgment than for that city.

[16]"Look, I send you out as sheep in the midst of wolves. Therefore be wise as serpents, and harmless as doves. [17]But beware of people: for they will deliver you up to councils, and in their synagogues they will scourge you. [18]Yes, and you will be brought before governors and kings for my sake, for a testimony to them and to the nations. [19]But when they deliver you over, do not be anxious how or what you will say, for it will be given you in that hour what you will say. [20]For it is not you who speak, but the Spirit of your Father who speaks in you.

[21]"And brother will deliver up brother to death, and the father his child. Children will rise up against parents, and cause them to be put to death. [22]And you will be hated by all for my name's sake, but he who endures to the end will be saved. [23]But when they persecute you in this city, flee into the next, for truly I tell you, you will not have gone through the cities of Israel before the Son of Man comes.

[24]"A disciple is not above his teacher, nor a servant above his lord. [25]It is enough for the disciple that he be like his teacher, and the servant like his lord. If they have called the master of the house Beelzebul, how much more those of his household. [26]Therefore do not be afraid of them, for there is nothing covered that will not be revealed; and hidden that will not be known. [27]What I tell you in the darkness, speak in the light; and what you hear whispered in the ear, proclaim on the housetops. [28]And do not be afraid of those who kill the body, but are not able to kill the soul. Rather, fear him who is able to destroy both soul and body in hell[f].

[29]"Are not two sparrows sold for an assarion coin? Not one of them falls on the ground apart from your Father's will, [30]but

---

a   9:35 Some Mss add "among the people"
b   10:3 Or, son of Tolmai, who is apparently the Nathanael of John 1:45
c   10:3 Some Mss add read "Lebbaeus, whose surname was Thaddaeus"
d   10:4 The village of Kraiyot is 12 miles south of Hebron in Judea
e   10:8 Some Mss lack "raise the dead"
f   10:28 Gk. "Gehenna"

the very hairs of your head are all numbered. ³¹Therefore do not be afraid. You are of more value than many sparrows. ³²Everyone therefore who confesses me before people, him I will also confess before my Father who is in heaven. ³³But whoever denies me before people, him I will also deny before my Father who is in heaven.

³⁴"Do not think that I came to send peace on the earth. I did not come to send peace, but a sword. ³⁵For I came to set a man at odds against his father, and a daughter against her mother, and a daughter-in-law against her mother-in-law. ³⁶And a person's foes will be those of his own household.ᵃ ³⁷Whoever loves father or mother more than me is not worthy of me; and whoever loves son or daughter more than me is not worthy of me. ³⁸And whoever does not take his cross and follow after me, is not worthy of me. ³⁹Whoever seeks his life will lose it; and whoever loses his life for my sake will find it. ⁴⁰Whoever receives you receives me, and whoever receives me receives him who sent me. ⁴¹The one who receives a prophet in the name of a prophet will receive a prophet's reward. The one who receives a righteous person in the name of a righteous person will receive a righteous person's reward. ⁴²And whoever gives one of these little ones just a cup of cold water to drink because he is a disciple, truly I tell you he will in no way lose his reward."

11 And it happened that when Jesus had finished directing his twelve disciples, he departed from there to teach and proclaim in their cities. ²Now when John heard in the prison the works of the Messiah, he sent a messageᵇ byᶜ his disciples ³and said to him, "Are you the one who is to come, or should we look for another?"

⁴And Jesus answered them, "Go and tell John the things which you hear and see: ⁵the blind receive their sight, the lame walk, the lepers are cleansed, the deaf hear, the dead are raised up, and the poor have good news preached to them.ᵈ ⁶And blessed is he who is not offended by me."

⁷And as these went their way, Jesus began to say to the crowds concerning John, "What did you go out into the wilderness to see? A reed shaken by the wind? ⁸But what did you go out to see? A man clothed in soft garments?ᵉ Look, those who wear soft things are in kings'ᶠ houses. ⁹But what did you go out to see? A prophet? Yes, I tell you, and much more than a prophet. ¹⁰This is the one of whom it is written, 'Look, I send my messenger ahead of you, who will prepare your way before you.'ᵍ¹¹Truly I tell you, among those who are born of women there has not arisen anyone greater than John the Baptist; yet he who is least in the kingdom of heaven is greater than he. ¹²And from the days of John the Baptist until now, the kingdom of heaven suffers violence, and the violent take it by force.ʰ ¹³For all the Prophets and the Law prophesied until John. ¹⁴And if you are willing to receive it, this is Elijah, who is to come. ¹⁵He who has ears,ⁱ let him hear.

¹⁶"But to what should I compare this generation? It is like children sitting in the marketplaces, who call to their companions ¹⁷and say, 'We played the flute for you, and you did not dance. We wailed in mourning,ʲ and you did not mourn.' ¹⁸For John came neither eating nor drinking, and they say, 'He has a demon.' ¹⁹The Son of Man came eating and drinking, and they say, 'Look, a gluttonous man and a drunkard, a friend of tax collectors and sinners.' But wisdom is justified by her actions.ᵏ"

²⁰Then he began to denounce the cities in which most of his mighty works had been done, because they did not repent. ²¹"Woe to you, Chorazin. Woe to you, Beth-

---

a   10:36 Micah 7:6
b   11:2 The words "a message" are not in the Greek text, but are implied
c   11:2 Some Mss read "two" instead of "by"
d   11:5 Isaiah 35:5-6, 26:19, 61:1
e   11:8 Some Mss lack "garments"
f   11:8 Some Mss read "royal"
g   11:10 Malachi 3:1
h   11:12 Or, "plunder it"
i   11:15 Some Mss add "to hear"
j   11:17 Some Mss add "you"
k   11:19 Some Mss read "children"

saida. For if the mighty works had been done in Tyre and Sidon which were done in you, they would have repented long ago in sackcloth and ashes. ²²But I tell you, it will be more tolerable for Tyre and Sidon on the day of judgment than for you. ²³And you, Capernaum, who are exalted to heaven, you will be brought^a down to hell.^b For if the mighty works had been done in Sodom which were done in you, it would have remained until this day. ²⁴But I tell you that it will be more tolerable for the land of Sodom, on the day of judgment, than for you."

²⁵At that time, Jesus answered, "I thank you, Father, Lord of heaven and earth, that you hid these things from the wise and intelligent, and revealed them to little children. ²⁶Yes, Father, for so it was well-pleasing in your sight. ²⁷All things have been delivered to me by my Father. No one knows the Son, except the Father; neither does anyone know the Father, except the Son, and he to whom the Son desires to reveal him.

²⁸"Come to me, all you who labor and are heavily burdened, and I will give you rest. ²⁹Take my yoke upon you, and learn from me, for I am gentle and humble in heart; and you will find rest for your souls. ³⁰For my yoke is easy, and my burden is light."

12 At that time, Jesus went on the Sabbath day through the grain fields. His disciples were hungry and began to pluck heads of grain and to eat. ²But the Pharisees, when they saw it, said to him, "Look, your disciples do what is not lawful to do on the Sabbath."

³But he said to them, "Have you not read what David did, when he and his companions were hungry; ⁴how he entered into the house of God, and they^c ate the show bread, which was not lawful for him to eat, neither for those who were with him, but only for the priests?^d ⁵Or have you not read in the Law, that on the Sabbath day the priests in the temple profane the Sabbath and are blameless? ⁶But I tell you that something greater than the temple is here. ⁷But if you had known what this means, 'I

desire mercy, and not sacrifice,'^e you would not have condemned the innocent. ⁸For the Son of Man is Lord of the Sabbath."

⁹And he departed from there and went into their synagogue. ¹⁰And look, there was a man with a withered hand. They asked him, "Is it lawful to heal on the Sabbath day?" that they might accuse him.

¹¹And he said to them, "What man is there among you, who has one sheep, and if this one falls into a pit on the Sabbath day, won't he grab on to it, and lift it out? ¹²Of how much more value then is a person than a sheep. Therefore it is lawful to do good on the Sabbath." ¹³Then he told the man, "Stretch out your hand." And he stretched it out, and it was restored whole, just like the other. ¹⁴But the Pharisees went out, and conspired against him, how they might destroy him. ¹⁵But Jesus, perceiving that, withdrew from there. Large crowds followed him, and he healed them all, ¹⁶and commanded them that they should not make him known. ¹⁷This was to fulfill what had been spoken through Isaiah the prophet, saying,

¹⁸"Look, my servant whom I have chosen;
    my beloved in whom my soul is well pleased.
I will put my Spirit on him;
    and he will proclaim justice to the nations.
¹⁹He will not quarrel, nor shout;
    nor will anyone hear his voice in the streets.
²⁰He won't break a bruised reed,
    and he won't extinguish a smoldering wick,
until he leads justice to victory.
    ²¹And in his name the coastlands will hope."^f

²²Then one possessed by a demon, blind and mute, was brought to him and he

---

a   11:23 Some Mss read "be driven"
b   11:23 Gk. Hades, for Heb. Sheol
c   12:4 Some Mss read "he"
d   12:4 1 Samuel 21:3-6
e   12:7 Hosea 6:6
f   12:21 Isaiah 42:1-4

healed him, so that the[a] mute man spoke and saw. [23]And all the crowds were amazed, and said, "Can this be the son of David?" [24]But when the Pharisees heard it, they said, "This man does not cast out demons, except by Beelzebul, the prince of the demons."

[25]And knowing their thoughts, he[b] said to them, "Every kingdom divided against itself is brought to desolation, and every city or house divided against itself will not stand. [26]And if Satan casts out Satan, he is divided against himself. How then will his kingdom stand? [27]If I by Beelzebul cast out demons, by whom do your children cast them out? Therefore they will be your judges. [28]But if I by the Spirit of God cast out demons, then the kingdom of God has come upon you. [29]Or how can one enter into the house of the strong man, and carry off[c] his possessions, unless he first bind the strong man? And then he will plunder his house.

[30]"He who is not with me is against me, and he who does not gather with me, scatters. [31]Therefore I tell you, every sin and blasphemy will be forgiven people, but the blasphemy against the Spirit will not be forgiven[d]. [32]And whoever speaks a word against the Son of Man, it will be forgiven him; but whoever speaks against the Holy Spirit, it will not be forgiven him, neither in this age, nor in that which is to come.

[33]"Either make the tree good, and its fruit good, or make the tree corrupt, and its fruit corrupt; for the tree is known by its fruit. [34]You offspring of vipers, how can you, being evil, speak good things? For out of the abundance of the heart, the mouth speaks. [35]The good person out of his good treasure brings out good things, and the evil person out of his evil treasure brings out evil things. [36]But I tell you that every careless word that people speak, they will give account of it in the day of judgment. [37]For by your words you will be justified, and by your words you will be condemned."

[38]Then certain of the scribes and Pharisees said to him, "Teacher, we want to see a sign from you."

[39]But he answered and said to them, "An evil and adulterous generation seeks after a sign, but no sign will be given it but the sign of Jonah the prophet. [40]For as Jonah was three days and three nights in the belly of the great fish, so will the Son of Man be three days and three nights in the heart of the earth. [41]The people of Nineveh will stand up in the judgment with this generation, and will condemn it, for they repented at the preaching of Jonah; and look, something greater than Jonah is here. [42]The queen of the south will rise up in the judgment with this generation, and will condemn it, for she came from a distant land[e] to hear the wisdom of Solomon; and look, someone greater than Solomon is here. [43]But the unclean spirit, when he is gone out of the person, passes through waterless places, seeking rest, and does not find it. [44]Then he says, 'I will return into my house from which I came out,' and when he has come back, he finds it empty, swept, and put in order. [45]Then he goes, and takes with himself seven other spirits more evil than he is, and they enter in and dwell there. The last state of that person becomes worse than the first. Even so will it be also to this evil generation."

[46]While[f] he was yet speaking to the crowds, look, his mother and his brothers stood outside, seeking to speak to him. [47]Then one said to him, "Look, your mother and your brothers stand outside, seeking to speak to you."[g]

[48]But he answered him who spoke to him, "Who is my mother? Who are my brothers?" [49]And he stretched out his hand towards his disciples, and said, "Look, my mother and my brothers. [50]For whoever does the will of my Father who is in heaven, he is my brother, and sister, and mother."

---

a   12:22 Some Mss add "blind and."
b   12:25 Some Mss read "Jesus"
c   12:29 Some Mss read "plunder"
d   12:31 Some Mss add "men"
e   12:31 Lit. "ends of the earth," which can be an idiomatic expression when speaking of people in remote places, e.g., Psalm 67:7; 98:3; Isaiah 45:22
f   12:46 Some Mss read "And while"
g   12:47 Some Mss lack this verse

13 On that day Jesus went out of the house, and sat by the seaside. ²And large crowds gathered to him, so that he entered into a boat, and sat, and all the crowd stood on the beach. ³And he spoke to them many things in parables, saying, "Look, a farmer went out to sow. ⁴And as he sowed, some seeds fell by the roadside, and the birds came and devoured them. ⁵And others fell on rocky ground, where they did not have much soil, and immediately they sprang up, because they had no depth of earth. ⁶But when the sun had risen, they were scorched. Because they had no root, they withered away. ⁷Others fell among thorns, and the thorns grew up and choked them. ⁸Still others fell on good soil, and yielded fruit: some one hundred times as much, some sixty, and some thirty. ⁹He who has ears[a], let him hear."

¹⁰Then the disciples came, and said to him, "Why do you speak to them in parables?"

¹¹And answering, he said to them, "To you it is given to know the mysteries of the kingdom of heaven, but it is not given to them. ¹²For whoever has, to him will be given, and he will have abundance, but whoever does not have, from him will be taken away even that which he has. ¹³Therefore I speak to them in parables, because seeing they do not see, and hearing, they do not hear, neither do they understand. ¹⁴And in them the prophecy of Isaiah is fulfilled, which says,

'In hearing you will hear,
    but will not understand,
and seeing you will see,
    but not perceive.
¹⁵For the heart of this people has grown dull,
    and their ears are sluggish in hearing,
    and they have closed their eyes,
otherwise they might see with their eyes,
    and hear with their ears,
and understand with their heart,
    and turn back,
    and I would heal them.'[b]

¹⁶"But blessed are your eyes, for they see; and your ears, for they hear. ¹⁷For truly I tell you that many prophets and righteous people desired to see the things which you see, and did not see them; and to hear the things which you hear, and did not hear them.

¹⁸"Hear, then, the parable of the farmer. ¹⁹When anyone hears the word of the kingdom, and does not understand it, the evil one comes, and snatches away that which has been sown in his heart. This is what was sown by the roadside. ²⁰And what was sown on the rocky places, this is he who hears the word, and immediately with joy receives it; ²¹yet he has no root in himself, but endures for a while. When oppression or persecution arises because of the word, immediately he stumbles. ²²And what was sown among the thorns, this is he who hears the word, but the cares of the world and the deceitfulness of riches choke the word, and he becomes unfruitful. ²³And what was sown on the good ground, this is he who hears the word, and understands it, who truly bears fruit, and brings forth, some one hundred times as much, some sixty, and some thirty."

²⁴He set another parable before them, saying, "The kingdom of heaven is like a man who sowed good seed in his field, ²⁵but while everyone slept, his enemy came and sowed tares[c] also among the wheat, and went away. ²⁶But when the blade sprang up and brought forth fruit, then the tares appeared also. ²⁷So the servants of the householder came and said to him, 'Sir, did you not sow good seed in your field? Where did these tares come from?'

²⁸"And he said to them, 'An enemy has done this.'

"And the servants asked him, 'Then do you want us to go and gather them up?'

²⁹"But he said, 'No, lest perhaps while you gather up the tares, you root up the wheat with them. ³⁰Let both grow together until the harvest, and in the harvest

---

a   13:9 Some Mss add "to hear"
b   13:15 Isaiah 6:9-10
c   13:25 The darnel tare is a weed that resembles wheat until harvest time, when the difference becomes apparent

time I will tell the reapers, "First, gather up the tares, and bind them in bundles to burn them; but gather the wheat into my barn."'"

³¹He set another parable before them, saying, "The kingdom of heaven is like a mustard seed, which a man took, and sowed in his field; ³²which indeed is smaller than all seeds.ᵃ But when it is grown, it is greater than the herbs, and becomes a tree, so that the birds of the air come and lodge in its branches."

³³He spoke another parable to them. "The kingdom of heaven is like yeast, which a woman took, and hid in three measures ᵇof meal, until it was all leavened."

³⁴Jesus spoke all these things in parables to the crowds; and without a parable, he did not speak to them, ³⁵that it might be fulfilled which was spoken through the prophet, saying,

"I will open my mouth in parables;
    I will utter things hidden since the
        beginningᶜ of the world.ᵈ"

³⁶Then Jesus sent the crowds away, and went into the house. His disciples came to him, saying, "Explain to us the parable of the tares in the field."

³⁷And he answered them, "The one who sows the good seed is the Son of Man, ³⁸and the field is the world; and the good seed, these are the sons of the kingdom; and the tares are the sons of the evil one, ³⁹and the enemy who sowed them is the devil, and the harvest is the end of the age, and the reapers are angels. ⁴⁰As therefore the tares are gathered up and burned with fire; so will it be at the end of the age. ⁴¹The Son of Man will send out his angels, and they will gather out of his kingdom all things that cause stumbling, and those who do iniquity, ⁴²and will cast them into the furnace of fire. There will be weeping and the gnashing of teeth. ⁴³Then the righteous will shine forth like the sun in the kingdom of their Father. He who has ears,ᵉ let him hear.

⁴⁴"Theᶠ kingdom of heaven is like a treasure hidden in the field, which a man found, and hid. In his joy, he goes and sells all that he has, and buys that field.

⁴⁵"Again, the kingdom of heaven is like a man who is a merchant seeking fine pearls, ⁴⁶and having found one pearl of great price, he went and sold all that he had, and bought it.

⁴⁷"Again, the kingdom of heaven is like a dragnet, that was cast into the sea, and gathered some fish of every kind, ⁴⁸which, when it was filled, they drew up on the beach. They sat down, and gathered the good into containers, but the bad they threw away. ⁴⁹So will it be in the end of the world. The angels will come forth, and separate the wicked from among the righteous, ⁵⁰and will cast them into the furnace of fire. There will be the weeping and the gnashing of teeth." ⁵¹ᵍHave you understood all these things?"

They answered him, "Yes, Lord."

⁵²And he said to them, "Therefore, every scribe who has been made a disciple in the kingdom of heaven is like a man who is a householder, who brings out of his treasure new and old things."

⁵³And it happened that when Jesus had finished these parables, he departed from there. ⁵⁴And coming into his own country, he taught them in their synagogue, so that they were astonished, and said, "Where did this man get this wisdom, and these mighty works? ⁵⁵Is not this the carpenter'sʰ son? Is not his mother called Mary, and his brothers, James and Josephⁱ and Simon and Judas? ⁵⁶And are not all of his sisters with us? Where then did this man get all of these things?" ⁵⁷And they were offended by him.

But Jesus said to them, "A prophet is not without honor, except in his own country, and in his own house." ⁵⁸And he did not do many mighty works there because of their unbelief.

---

a   4:31 E.g., concerning vegetables in a garden in that area
b   13:33 Lit. three sata
c   13:35 Psalm 78:2
d   13:35 Some Mss lack "of the world"
e   13:43 Some Mss add "to hear"
f   13:44 Some Mss read "Again, the"
g   13:51 Some Mss add "Jesus said to them"
h   13:55 Or, "craftsman's"
i   13:55 Some Mss read "Josi"

14 At that time, Herod the tetrarch heard the report concerning Jesus, [2]and said to his servants, "This is John the Baptist. He is risen from the dead. That is why these powers work in him." [3]For Herod had arrested John, and bound him, and put him in prison for the sake of Herodias, his brother Philip's wife. [4]For John said to him, "It is not lawful for you to have her." [5]And though he wanted to kill him, he feared the crowd because they regarded him as a prophet. [6]But when Herod's birthday came, the daughter of Herodias danced among them and pleased Herod. [7]Whereupon he promised with an oath to give her whatever she should ask. [8]And she, being prompted by her mother, said, "Give me here on a platter the head of John the Baptist."

[9]And the king was grieved, but for the sake of his oaths, and of those who sat at the table with him, he commanded it to be given, [10]and he sent and beheaded John in the prison. [11]And his head was brought on a platter, and given to the young lady: and she brought it to her mother. [12]Then his disciples came, and took the dead body, and buried him; and they went and told Jesus. [13]Now when Jesus heard this, he withdrew from there in a boat, to a secluded place to be alone. When the crowds heard it, they followed him on foot from the cities.

[14]And he[a] went out, and he saw a large crowd, and he had compassion on them, and healed their sick. [15]Now when evening had come, the[b] disciples came to him, saying, "This place is desolate, and the hour is already late. Send the crowds away, that they may go into the villages, and buy themselves food."

[16]But he[c] said to them, "They do not need to go away. You give them something to eat."

[17]And they told him, "We only have here five loaves and two fish."

[18]So he said, "Bring them here to me." [19]Then he commanded the crowds to sit down on the grass; and he took the five loaves and the two fish, and looking up to heaven, he blessed, broke and gave the loaves to the disciples, and the disciples gave to the crowds. [20]And they all ate and were filled, and they took up twelve baskets full of that which remained left over from the broken pieces. [21]Now those who ate were about five thousand men, besides women and children.

[22]And immediately he[d] made the disciples get into the boat and to go ahead of him to the other side, while he sent the crowds away. [23]And after he had sent the crowds away, he went up into the mountain by himself to pray. When evening had come, he was there alone. [24]But the boat was now hundreds of yards from the land,[e] distressed by the waves, for the wind was against it. [25]And in the watch between three and six in the morning,[f] he[g] came to them, walking on the sea.[h] [26]And when the disciples saw him walking on the sea, they were troubled, saying, "It's a ghost." and they screamed with fear. [27]But immediately he[i] spoke to them, saying "Cheer up. It is I.[j] Do not be afraid."

[28]Peter answered him and said, "Lord, if it is you, command me to come to you on the waters."

[29]He said, "Come."

Peter stepped down from the boat, and walked on the water and went toward Jesus. [30]But when he saw the strong wind, he was afraid, and beginning to sink, he yelled, saying, "Lord, save me."

[31]Immediately Jesus stretched out his hand, took hold of him, and said to him, "You of little faith, why did you doubt?" [32]When they got up into the boat, the wind ceased. [33]Those who were in the boat[k] worshiped him, saying, "You are truly the Son of God."[l]

---

a　14:14 Some Mss read "Jesus"
b　14:15 Some Mss read "his"
c　14:16 Some Mss read "Jesus"
d　14:22 Some Mss read "Jesus"
e　14:24 Some Mss read "in the midst of the sea"
f　14:25 Lit. in the fourth watch of the night
g　14:25 Some Mss read "Jesus"
h　14:25 See Job 9:8, Psalm 89:9, 104:3, 107:29
i　14:27 Some Mss read "Jesus"
j　14:27 Or," I AM."
k　14:33 Some Mss add "came
l　14:33 Psalm 2:7; Proverbs 30:4

³⁴When they had crossed over, they came to the land of Gennesaret. ³⁵When the people of that place recognized him, they sent into all that surrounding region, and brought to him all who were sick, ³⁶and they begged him that they might just touch the fringe of his garment. As many as touched it were made whole.

15 Then the Pharisees and scribes came to Jesus from Jerusalem, saying, ²"Why do your disciples disobey the tradition of the elders? For they do not wash their hands when they eat bread."

³And he answered them, "Why do you also disobey the commandment of God because of your tradition? ⁴For God said,ᵃ 'Honor your father and your mother,'ᵇ and, 'He who speaks evil of father or mother, let him be put to death.'ᶜ ⁵But you say, 'Whoever may tell his father or his mother, "Whatever help you might otherwise have gotten from me is a gift devoted to God," ⁶he is not to honor his father or his mother.'ᵈ You have made the wordᵉ of God void because of your tradition. ⁷You hypocrites. Well did Isaiah prophesy of you, saying,

⁸"These peopleᶠ honor me with their lips;
but their heart is far from me.
⁹And in vain do they worship me,
teaching instructions that are the commandments of humans.'"ᵍ

¹⁰He summoned the crowd, and said to them, "Hear, and understand. ¹¹That which enters into the mouth does not defile the man; but that which proceeds out of the mouth, this defiles the man."

¹²Then theʰ disciples came, and said to him, "Do you know that the Pharisees were offended, when they heard this saying?"

¹³But he answered, "Every plant which my heavenly Father did not plant will be uprooted. ¹⁴Leave them alone. They are blind guides of the blind. If the blind guide the blind, both will fall into a pit."

¹⁵And answering, Peter said to him, "Explain thisⁱ parable to us."

¹⁶So he said, "Do you also still not understand? ¹⁷Do you not understand that whatever goes into the mouth passes into the belly, and then out of the body? ¹⁸But the things which proceed out of the mouth come out of the heart, and they defile the man. ¹⁹For out of the heart come forth evil thoughts, murders, adulteries, sexual sins, thefts, false testimony, and blasphemies. ²⁰These are the things which defile the man; but to eat with unwashed hands does not defile the man."

²¹Jesus went out from there, and withdrew into the region of Tyre and Sidon. ²²And look, a Canaanite woman came out from those borders, and started shouting, saying, "Have mercy on me, Lord, Son of David. My daughter is severely demonized."

²³But he did not answer her a word.

His disciples came and begged him, saying, "Send her away; for she cries after us."

²⁴But he answered, "I was not sent to anyone but the lost sheep of the house of Israel."

²⁵But she came and worshiped him, saying, "Lord, help me."

²⁶But he answered, "It is not appropriate to take the children's bread and throw it to the dogs."

²⁷But she said, "Yes, Lord, but even the dogs eat the crumbs which fall from their masters' table."

²⁸Then Jesus answered her, "Woman, great is your faith. Be it done to you even as you desire." And her daughter was healed from that hour.

²⁹Jesus departed there, and came near to the sea of Galilee; and he went up into the mountain, and sat there. ³⁰Large crowds came to him, having with them the lame, blind, mute, crippled, and many others, and they put them down at his feet; and he

---

a   15:4 Some Mss read "God commanded, saying"
b   15:4 Exodus 20:12; Deuteronomy 5:16
c   15:4 Exodus 21:17; Leviticus 20:9
d   15:6 Some Mss lack "or his mother"
e   15:6 Some Mss read "commandment"
f   15:8 Some Mss add "draw near to me with their mouth, and"
g   15:9 Isaiah 29:13
h   15:12 Some Mss read "his"
i   15:15 Some Mss lack "this"

healed them. ³¹So the crowd was amazed when they saw the mute speaking, injured whole, lame walking, and blind seeing—and they glorified the God of Israel.

³²Jesus summoned his disciples and said, "I have compassion on the crowd, because they continue with me now three days and have nothing to eat. I do not want to send them away fasting, or they might faint on the way."

³³Then the disciples said to him, "Where should we get so many loaves in a deserted place as to satisfy so great a crowd?"

³⁴Jesus said to them, "How many loaves do you have?"

They said, "Seven, and a few small fish."

³⁵He commanded the crowd to sit down on the ground; ³⁶and he took the seven loaves and the fish. He gave thanks and broke them, and gave to the disciples, and the[a] disciples to the crowds. ³⁷They all ate, and were filled. They took up seven baskets full of the broken pieces that were left over. ³⁸Those who ate were four thousand men, besides women and children. ³⁹Then he sent away the crowds, got into the boat, and came into the borders of Magadan[b].

16 The Pharisees and Sadducees came, and testing him, asked him to show them a sign from heaven. ²But he answered and said to them, "When it is evening, you say, 'It will be fair weather, for the sky is red.' ³In the morning, 'It will be foul weather today, for the sky is red and threatening.'[c] You know how to discern the appearance of the sky, but you cannot discern the signs of the times.[d]

⁴An evil and adulterous generation seeks after a sign, and there will be no sign given to it, except the sign of[e] Jonah."

He left them, and departed. ⁵The[f] disciples came to the other side and had forgotten to take bread. ⁶Jesus said to them, "Take heed and beware of the yeast of the Pharisees and Sadducees."

⁷And they discussed it among themselves, saying, "Because we took no bread."

⁸But Jesus, becoming aware of this, said,[g] "You of little faith, why are you discussing among yourselves about having no bread? ⁹Do you still not understand, or remember the five loaves for the five thousand, and how many baskets you took up? ¹⁰Nor the seven loaves for the four thousand, and how many baskets you took up? ¹¹Why is it that you do not understand that I did not speak to you concerning bread? But beware of the yeast of the Pharisees and Sadducees."

¹²Then they understood that he did not tell them to beware of the yeast of bread, but of the teaching of the Pharisees and Sadducees. ¹³Now when Jesus came into the parts of Caesarea Philippi, he asked his disciples, saying, "Who do people say that[h] the Son of Man is?"

¹⁴They said, "Some say John the Baptist, some, Elijah, and others, Jeremiah, or one of the prophets."

¹⁵He said to them, "But who do you say that I am?"

¹⁶Simon Peter answered, "You are the Messiah, the Son of the living God."

¹⁷And Jesus answered him, "Blessed are you, Simon Bar Jonah, for flesh and blood has not revealed this to you, but my Father who is in heaven. ¹⁸I also tell you that you are Peter,[i] and on this Rock[j] I will build my church,[k] and the gates of hell will not prevail against it. ¹⁹I will give to you the keys of the kingdom of heaven, and whatever you bind on earth will be bound in heaven, and whatever you loose on earth will be loosed in heaven."[l] ²⁰Then he commanded the[m] disciples that they

---

a   15:16 Some Mss read "Jesus"
b   15:39 Some Mss read "Magdala"
c   16:3 Some Mss add "Hypocrites"
d   16:2-3 Some Mss lack "When it is …of the times"
e   16:4 Some Mss add "the prophet"
f   16:5 Some Mss read "His" instead of "The"
g   16:8 Some Mss add "to them"
h   16:13 Some Mss add "I"
i   16:18 Gk. Petros, meaning a specific rock or stone
j   16:18 Gk. petra, a rock mass or bedrock. See also
    1 Corinthians 3:11, 10:4
k   16:18 Gk. ekklesia means "assembly" or "congregation,"
    usually translated in English as "church," from Gk.
    kuriakee, meaning "house of the Lord"
l   16:19 Isaiah 22:22
m   16:20 Some Mss read "his"

should tell no one that he is[a] the Messiah. [21]From that time, Jesus[b] began to show his disciples that he must go to Jerusalem and suffer many things from the elders, chief priests, and scribes, and be killed, and the third day be raised up.

[22]Peter took him aside, and began to rebuke him, saying, "Far be it from you, Lord. This will never be done to you."

[23]But he turned, and said to Peter, "Get behind me, Satan. You are a stumbling block to me, for you are not setting your mind on the things of God, but on the things of man." [24]Then Jesus said to his disciples, "If anyone desires to come after me, let him deny himself, and take up his cross, and follow me. [25]For whoever desires to save his life will lose it, and whoever will lose his life for my sake will find it. [26]For what will it profit a person, if he gains the whole world, and forfeits his life? Or what will a person give in exchange for his life? [27]For the Son of Man will come in the glory of his Father with his angels, and then he will render to everyone according to his deeds. [28]Truly I tell you, there are some standing here who will in no way taste of death, until they see the Son of Man coming in his kingdom."

17 After six days, Jesus took with him Peter, James, and John his brother, and brought them up into a high mountain by themselves. [2]He was transfigured before them. His face shone like the sun, and his garments became as white as the light. [3]And look, Moses and Elijah appeared to them talking with him.

[4]Peter answered, and said to Jesus, "Lord, it is good for us to be here. If you want, let us make three tents here: one for you, one for Moses, and one for Elijah."

[5]While he was still speaking, look, a bright cloud overshadowed them. And look, a voice came out of the cloud, saying, "This is my beloved Son, in whom I am well pleased. Listen to him."

[6]When the disciples heard it, they fell on their faces, and were very afraid. [7]Jesus came and touched them and said, "Get up,

and do not be afraid." [8]And when they lifted up their eyes, they saw no one except Jesus himself[c] alone. [9]As they were coming down from the mountain, Jesus commanded them, saying, "Do not tell anyone what you saw, until the Son of Man has risen from the dead."

[10]The[d] disciples asked him, saying, "Then why do the scribes say that Elijah must come first?"

[11]And he answered and said[e], "Elijah indeed comes first, [f]and will restore all things, [12]but I tell you that Elijah has come already, and they did not recognize him, but did to him whatever they wanted to. Even so the Son of Man will also suffer by them." [13]Then the disciples understood that he spoke to them of John the Baptist.

[14]And when they came to the crowd, a man came to him, knelt before him, [15]and said, "Lord, have mercy on my son, for he is epileptic, and suffers severely; for he often falls into the fire, and often into the water. [16]So I brought him to your disciples, and they could not cure him."

[17]Jesus answered, "Faithless and perverse generation. How long will I be with you? How long will I bear with you? Bring him here to me." [18]Jesus rebuked him, the demon went out of him, and the boy was cured from that hour.

[19]Then the disciples came to Jesus privately, and said, "Why weren't we able to cast it out?"

[20]So he[g] said to them, "Because of your little faith. For truly I tell you, if you have faith as a grain of mustard seed, you will tell this mountain, 'Move from here to there,' and it will move; and nothing will be impossible for you." [21h]

---

a   16:20 Some Mss add "Jesus"
b   16:21 Some Mss add "Christ"
c   17:8 Some Mss lack "himself"
d   17:10 Some Mss read "His"
e   17:11 Some Mss read "And Jesus answered and said to them"
f   17:11 Some Mss lack "first"
g   17:20 Some Mss read "Jesus"
h   17:21 Some Mss add "But this kind does not go out except by prayer and fasting"

²²While they were gathering together[a] in Galilee, Jesus said to them, "The Son of Man is about to be delivered up into the hands of men, ²³and they will kill him, and the third day he will be raised up."

They were exceedingly sorry. ²⁴When they had come to Capernaum, those who collected the didrachma coins came to Peter, and said, "Does not your teacher pay the didrachma?" ²⁵He said, "Yes."

When he came into the house, Jesus anticipated him, saying, "What do you think, Simon? From whom do the kings of the earth receive toll or tribute? From their children, or from strangers?"

²⁶And when he said,[b] "From strangers." Jesus said to him, "Therefore the sons are exempt. ²⁷But, lest we cause them to stumble, go to the sea, cast a hook, and take up the first fish that comes up. When you have opened its mouth, you will find a stater coin. Take that, and give it to them for me and you."

18 In that hour the disciples came to Jesus, saying, "Who then is greatest in the kingdom of heaven?"

²He[c] called a little child to himself, and set him in the midst of them, ³and said, "Truly I tell you, unless you turn, and become as little children, you will in no way enter into the kingdom of heaven. ⁴Whoever therefore humbles himself as this little child, the same is the greatest in the kingdom of heaven. ⁵Whoever receives one such little child in my name receives me, ⁶but whoever causes one of these little ones who believe in me to stumble, it would be better for him that a huge millstone should be hung around his neck, and that he should be sunk in the depths of the sea.

⁷"Woe to the world because of stumbling blocks. For there will always be something to cause people to stumble, but woe to the person through whom the stumbling block comes. ⁸If your hand or your foot causes you to stumble, cut it off, and cast it from you. It is better for you to enter into life crippled or maimed, rather than having two hands or two feet to be cast into the everlasting fire.[d] ⁹If your eye causes you to stumble, pluck it out, and cast it from you. It is better for you to enter into life with one eye, rather than having two eyes to be cast into the fire of hell.[e]

¹⁰See that you do not despise one of these little ones, for I tell you that in heaven their angels always see the face of my Father who is in heaven. ¹¹[f]

¹²"What do you think? If someone has one hundred sheep, and one of them goes astray, does he not leave the ninety-nine, go to the mountains, and seek that which has gone astray? ¹³If he finds it, truly I tell you, he rejoices over it more than over the ninety-nine which have not gone astray. ¹⁴Even so it is not the will of my[g] Father who is in heaven that one of these little ones should perish.

¹⁵"If your brother sins against you,[h] go, show him his fault between you and him alone. If he listens to you, you have gained back your brother. ¹⁶But if he does not listen, take one or two more with you, that at the mouth of two or three witnesses every word may be established.[i] ¹⁷If he refuses to listen to them, tell it to the church. If he refuses to hear the church also, let him be to you as an unbeliever or a tax collector. ¹⁸Truly I tell you, whatever you bind on earth will be bound in heaven, and whatever you loose on earth will be loosed in heaven. ¹⁹Again, truly I tell you, that if two of you agree on earth concerning anything that they will ask, it will be done for them by my Father who is in heaven. ²⁰For where two or three are gathered together in my name, there I am in the midst of them."

---

a   17:22 Some Mss read "staying"
b   17:26 Some Mss read "Peter said to him"
c   18:2 Some Mss read "Jesus"
d   18:8 Probable Semitic idiom, "If with your hand you steal, and with your feet you trespass, stop it…"
e   18:9 Probable Semitic idiom, "If with your eye you have a habit of lust or envying others, stop it…"
f   18:11 Some Mss add "For the Son of Man came to save what was lost"
g   18:14 Some Mss read "your"
h   18:15 Some Mss lack "against you"
i   18:16 Deuteronomy 19:15

²¹Then Peter came to him and said, "Lord, how often can my brother sin against me, and I forgive him? Up to seven times?"

²²Jesus said to him, "I do not tell you up to seven times, but up to seventy times seven. ²³Therefore the kingdom of heaven is like a certain king, who wanted to reconcile accounts with his servants. ²⁴When he had begun to reconcile, one was brought to him who owed him ten thousand talents.ᵃ ²⁵But because he could not pay, his lord commanded him to be sold, with his wife, his children, and all that he had, and payment to be made. ²⁶The servant therefore fell down and kneeled before him, saying, 'Lord,ᵇ have patience with me, and I will repay you all.' ²⁷The lord of that servant, being moved with compassion, released him, and forgave him the debt.

²⁸"But that servant went out, and found one of his fellow servants, who owed him one hundred denarii,ᶜ and he grabbed him, and took him by the throat, saying, 'Payᵈ what you owe.'

²⁹"So his fellow servant fell down at his feetᵉ and begged him, saying, 'Have patience with me, and I will repay you all.' ³⁰He would not, but went and cast him into prison, until he should pay back that which was due. ³¹So when his fellow servants saw what was done, they were exceedingly sorry, and came and told to their lord all that was done. ³²Then his lord called him in, and said to him, 'You wicked servant. I forgave you all that debt, because you begged me. ³³Should you not also have had mercy on your fellow servant, even as I had mercy on you?' ³⁴His lord was angry, and delivered him to the tormentors, until he should pay all that was due.ᶠ ³⁵So my heavenly Father will also do to you, if you do not each forgive your brother from your heart."ᵍ

19 It happened when Jesus had finished these words, he departed from Galilee, and came into the borders of Judea beyond the Jordan. ²Great crowds followed him, and he healed them there. ³And Pharisees came to him, testing him,

and saying to him, "Is it lawful for a manʰ to divorce a wife for any reason?"

⁴He answered, and said,ⁱ "Have you not read that he who createdʲ them from the beginning made them male and female,ᵏ ⁵and said, 'For this reason a man will leave his father and mother, and be joined to his wife; and the two will become one flesh?'ˡ ⁶So that they are no more two, but one flesh. What therefore God has joined together, do not let man tear apart."

⁷They asked him, "Why then did Moses command us to give her a certificate of divorce, and divorce her?"

⁸He said to them, "Moses, because of the hardness of your hearts, allowed you to divorce your wives, but from the beginning it has not been so. ⁹I tell you that whoever divorces his wife, except for sexual immorality, and marries another, commits adultery. And he who marries her when she is divorced commits adultery."ᵐ

¹⁰Theⁿ disciples said to him, "If this is the case of a husband with a wife, it is not expedient to marry."

¹¹But he said to them, "Not everyone can receive this saying, but those to whom it is given. ¹²For there are eunuchs who were born that way from their mother's womb, and there are eunuchs who were made eunuchs by men; and there are eunuchs who made themselves eunuchs for the kingdom of heaven's sake. He who is able to receive it, let him receive it."

¹³Then little children were brought to him, that he should lay his hands on them

---

a   18:24 Ten thousand talents is equivalent to about 60,000,000 denarii, where one denarius was typical of one day's wages for agricultural labor
b   18:26 Some Mss lack "Lord"
c   18:28 100 denarii was about one sixtieth of a talent
d   18:28 Some Mss add "me"
e   18:29 Some Mss lack "at his feet"
f   18:34 Some Mss add "to him"
g   18:35 Some Mss add "for his misdeeds"
h   19:3 Some Mss lack "a man"
i   19:4 Some Mss add "to them"
j   19:4 Some Mss read "made"
k   19:4 Genesis 1:27
l   19:5 Genesis 2:24
m   19:9 Some Mss lack "And he who...adultery"
n   19:10 Some Mss read "His"

and pray; and the disciples rebuked them. ¹⁴But Jesus said, "Allow the little children, and do not forbid them to come to me; for the kingdom of heaven belongs to ones like these." ¹⁵He placed his hands on them, and departed from there.

¹⁶And look, someone came to him and said, "ᵃTeacher, what good thing must I do, that I may have everlasting life?"

¹⁷He said to him, "Why do you ask me about what is good? ᵇNo one is good but one.ᶜ But if you want to enter into life, keep the commandments."

¹⁸He said to him, "Which ones?" And Jesus said, "'Do not murder.' 'Do not commit adultery.' 'Do not steal.' 'Do not offer false testimony.' ¹⁹'Honor your father and mother.'ᵈ And, 'Love your neighbor as yourself.'"ᵉ

²⁰The young man said to him, "All these things I have kept.ᶠ What do I still lack?"

²¹Jesus said to him, "If you want to be perfect, go, sell what you have and give to theᵍ poor, and you will have treasure in heaven; and come, follow me." ²²But when the young man heard the saying, he went away sad, for he was one who had great possessions. ²³Jesus said to his disciples, "Truly I say to you, it is difficult for a rich person to enter the kingdom of heaven. ²⁴Again I tell you, it is easier for a camelʰ to go through a needle's eye, than for a rich person to enter into the kingdom of God."

²⁵When theⁱ disciples heard it, they were exceedingly astonished, saying, "Who then can be saved?"

²⁶Looking at them, Jesus said, "With humans this is impossible, but with God all things are possible."

²⁷Then Peter answered, "Look, we have left everything, and followed you. What then will we have?"

²⁸Jesus said to them, "Truly I tell you that you who have followed me, in the regeneration when the Son of Man will sit on the throne of his glory, you also will sit on twelve thrones, judging the twelve tribes of Israel. ²⁹Everyone who has left houses, or brothers, or sisters, or father, or mother, or wife,ʲ or children, or lands, for my name's sake, will receive one hundred times, and will inherit everlasting life. ³⁰But many will be last who are first; and first who are last.

20 "For the kingdom of heaven is like a landowner who went out early in the morning to hire laborers for his vineyard. ²When he had agreed with the laborers for a denarius a day, he sent them into his vineyard. ³He went out about the nine in the morningᵏ, and saw others standing idle in the marketplace. ⁴To them he said, 'You also go into the vineyard, and whatever is right I will give you.' So they went their way. ⁵Again he went out about noon and at three in the afternoonˡ and did likewise. ⁶About five that afternoonᵐ he went out, and found others standingⁿ. He said to them, 'Why do you stand here all day idle?'

⁷"They said to him, 'Because no one has hired us.'

"He said to them, 'You also go into the vineyard.'ᵒ ⁸When evening had come, the lord of the vineyard said to his manager, 'Call the laborers and pay them their wages, beginning from the last to the first.'

⁹"When those who were hired at about five that afternoon came, they each received a denarius. ¹⁰When the first came, they supposed that they would receive more; and they likewise each received a denarius. ¹¹When they received it, they murmured against the master of the household, ¹²saying, 'These last have spent one hour, and you have made them equal to us, who have borne the burden of the day and the scorching heat.'

---

a　19:16 Some Mss add "Good"
b　19:17 Some Mss read "call me good"
c　19:17 Some Mss add "[that is,] God"
d　19:19 Exodus 20:12-16; Deuteronomy 5:16-20
e　19:19 Leviticus 19:18
f　19:20 Some Mss add "from my youth"
g　19:21 Some Mss lack "the"
h　19:24 Use of hyperbole
i　19:25 Some Mss read "his"
j　19:29 Some Mss lack "or wife"
k　20:3 Lit. the third hour
l　20:5 Lit. the sixth and ninth hour
m　20:6 Lit. the eleventh hour
n　20:6 Some Mss add "idle"
o　20:7 Some Mss add "and you will receive whatever is right"

¹³"But he answered one of them, 'Friend, I am doing you no wrong. Did you not agree with me for a denarius? ¹⁴Take that which is yours, and go your way. It is my desire to give to this last just as much as to you. ¹⁵Is it not lawful for me to do what I want to with what I own? Or is your eye evil, because I am good?' ¹⁶So the last will be first, and the first last; for many are called, but few are chosen.ᵃ"

¹⁷As Jesus was going up to Jerusalem, he took the Twelve ᵇaside, and on the way he said to them, ¹⁸"Look, we are going up to Jerusalem, and the Son of Man will be delivered to the chief priests and scribes, and they will condemn him to death, ¹⁹and will hand him over to the non-Jews to mock, to scourge, and to crucify; and the third day he will be raised up."

²⁰Then the mother of the sons of Zebedee came to him with her sons, kneeling and asking a certain thing of him. ²¹He said to her, "What do you want?"

She said to him, "Command that these, my two sons, may sit, one on your right hand, and one on your left hand, in your kingdom."

²²But Jesus answered and said, "You do not know what you are asking. Are you able to drink the cup that I am about to drinkᶜ?"

They said to him, "We are able."

²³He said to them, "You will indeed drink my cup, but to sit on my right hand and on my left hand is not mine to give; but it is for whom it has been prepared by my Father."

²⁴When the ten heard it, they were indignant with the two brothers.

²⁵But Jesus summoned them, and said, "You know that the rulers of the nations lord it over them, and their great ones exercise authority over them. ²⁶It will not be so among you, but whoever desires to become great among you must be your servant. ²⁷And whoever desires to be first among you must be your slave, ²⁸even as the Son of Man came not to be served, but to serve, and to give his life as a ransom for many."

²⁹As they went out from Jericho, a large crowd followed him. ³⁰And look, two blind men sitting by the road, when they heard that Jesus was passing by, shouted, "Have mercy on us, Lord, son of David." ³¹The crowd rebuked them, telling them that they should be quiet, but they shouted even more, "Lord, have mercy on us, son of David."

³²Jesus stood still, and called them, and asked, "What do you want me to do for you?"

³³They told him, "Lord, that our eyes may be opened."

³⁴Jesus, being moved with compassion, touched their eyes; and immediately their eyes received their sight, and they followed him.

21 When they drew near to Jerusalem, and came to Bethphage,ᵈ to the Mount of Olives, then Jesus sent two disciples, ²saying to them, "Go into the village that is opposite you, and immediately you will find a donkey tied, and a colt with her. Untie them, and bring them to me. ³And if anyone says anything to you, you are to say, 'The Lord needs them,' and immediately he will send them."

⁴Thisᵉ took place that it might be fulfilled which was spoken through the prophet, saying,

⁵Say to the daughter of Zion,ᶠ

"Look, your King comes to you,
humble, and riding on a donkey,
on a colt, the foal of a donkey."ᵍ

⁶The disciples went, and did just as Jesus directed them, ⁷and brought the donkey and the colt, and placed their clothes on them; and he sat on them.ʰ ⁸A very large crowd spread their clothes on the road. Others cut branches from the trees, and spread them on the road. ⁹The crowds who

a   20:16 Some Mss lack "for many are called, but few are chosen"
b   20:17 Some Mss add "disciples"
c   20:22 Some Mss add "and be baptized with the baptism that I am baptized with"
d   21:1 Some Mss read "Bethsphage"
e   21:4 Some Mss read "All this"
f   21:5 Isaiah 62:11
g   21:5 Zechariah 9:9
h   21:7 I.e., on the garments

went before him, and who followed kept shouting, "Hosanna[a] to the son of David. Blessed is he who comes in the name of the Lord. Hosanna in the highest."[b]

¹⁰When he had come into Jerusalem, all the city was stirred up, saying, "Who is this?" ¹¹The crowds said, "This is the prophet Jesus, from Nazareth of Galilee."

¹²Jesus entered into the temple,[c] and drove out all of those who sold and bought in the temple, and overthrew the money changers' tables and the seats of those who sold the doves. ¹³He said to them, "It is written, 'My house will be called a house of prayer,'[d] but you have made it a den of robbers."[e]

¹⁴The blind and the lame came to him in the temple, and he healed them. ¹⁵But when the chief priests and the scribes saw the wonderful things that he did, and the children crying out in the temple and saying, "Hosanna to the son of David." they were indignant, ¹⁶and said to him, "Do you hear what these are saying?"

Jesus said to them, "Yes. Did you never read, 'Out of the mouth of children and infants you have prepared praise?'"[f]

¹⁷He left them, and went out of the city to Bethany, and lodged there. ¹⁸Now in the morning, as he returned to the city, he was hungry. ¹⁹Seeing a fig tree by the road, he came to it, and found nothing on it but leaves. He said to it, "Let there be no fruit from you forever."

Immediately the fig tree withered away. ²⁰When the disciples saw it, they marveled, saying, "How did the fig tree immediately wither away?"

²¹Jesus answered them, "Truly I tell you, if you have faith, and do not doubt[g], you will not only do what was done to the fig tree, but even if you told this mountain, 'Be taken up and cast into the sea,' it would be done. ²²All things, whatever you ask in prayer, believing, you will receive."

²³When he had come into the temple, the chief priests and the elders of the people came to him as he was teaching, and said, "By what authority do you do these things? Who gave you this authority?"

²⁴Jesus answered them, "I also will ask you one question, which if you tell me, I likewise will tell you by what authority I do these things. ²⁵The baptism of John, where was it from? From heaven or from people?"

They reasoned with themselves, saying, "If we say, 'From heaven,' he will ask us, 'Why then did you not believe him?' ²⁶But if we say, 'From people,' we fear the crowd, for all hold John as a prophet." ²⁷They answered Jesus, and said, "We do not know."

He also said to them, "Neither will I tell you by what authority I do these things. ²⁸But what do you think? A man had two sons, and he came to the first, and said, 'Son, go work today in the[h] vineyard.' ²⁹He answered, 'I will not,' but afterward he changed his mind, and went. ³⁰And he came to the other,[i] and said the same thing. And he answered and said, 'I go, sir,' but he did not go. ³¹Which of the two did the will of his father?"

They said[j], "The first."

Jesus said to them, "Truly I tell you that the tax collectors and the prostitutes are entering into the kingdom of God before you. ³²For John came to you in the way of righteousness, and you did not believe him, but the tax collectors and the prostitutes believed him. When you saw it, you did not even repent afterward, that you might believe him.

³³"Hear another parable. There was a landowner who planted a vineyard, set a hedge about it, dug a winepress in it, built a tower, leased it out to tenant farmers, and went on a journey. ³⁴When the season for the fruit drew near, he sent his servants to the tenants, to receive his fruit. ³⁵The tenants took his servants, beat one, killed

---

a   21:9 Gk. "Hosanna" for Hebrew "Hoshiana," meaning "save us" or "help us, we pray"

b   21:9 Psalm 118:26

c   21:12 Some Mss add "of God"

d   21:13 Isaiah 56:7

e   21:13 Jeremiah 7:11

f   21:16 Psalm 8:2

g   21:21 Or, "draw distinctions", "judge"

h   21:21 Or, "draw distinctions", "judge"

i   21:30 Some Mss read "second"

j   21:31 Some Mss add "to him"

another, and stoned another. [36]Again, he sent other servants more than the first: and they treated them the same way. [37]But afterward he sent to them his son, saying, 'They will respect my son.' [38]But the tenants, when they saw the son, said among themselves, 'This is the heir. Come, let us kill him, and have[a] his inheritance.' [39]So they took him, and threw him out of the vineyard, and killed him. [40]When therefore the lord of the vineyard comes, what will he do to those tenants?"

[41]They told him, "He will utterly destroy those evil men, and will lease out the vineyard to other tenants, who will give him the fruit in its season."

[42]Jesus said to them, "Did you never read in the Scriptures,

'The stone which the builders rejected,
    the same was made the head of the corner.

This was from the Lord.

It is marvelous in our eyes?'[b]

[43]"Therefore I tell you, the kingdom of God will be taken away from you, and will be given to a nation bringing forth its fruit. [44]He who falls on this stone will be broken to pieces; but on whomever it will fall, it will crush him.[c]"

[45]When the chief priests and the Pharisees heard his parables, they perceived that he spoke about them. [46]When they sought to seize him, they feared the crowds, because they considered him to be a prophet.

22 Jesus answered and spoke again in parables to them, saying, [2]"The kingdom of heaven is like a certain king, who made a marriage feast for his son, [3]and sent out his servants to call those who were invited to the marriage feast, but they would not come. [4]Again he sent out other servants, saying, 'Tell those who are invited, "Look, I have made ready my dinner. My cattle and my fatlings are killed, and all things are ready. Come to the marriage feast."' [5]But they made light of it, and went their ways, one to his own farm, another to his merchandise, [6]and the rest grabbed his servants, and treated them shamefully, and killed them. [7]The king[d] was enraged, and sent his armies, destroyed those murderers, and burned their city.

[8]"Then he said to his servants, 'The wedding is ready, but those who were invited weren't worthy. [9]Go therefore to the intersections of the highways, and as many as you may find, invite to the marriage feast.' [10]And those servants went out into the highways, and gathered together all they found, both bad and good, and the wedding was filled with those reclining.[e] [11]But when the king came in to see the guests, he saw there a man who did not have on wedding clothing, [12]and he said to him, 'Friend, how did you come in here not wearing wedding clothing?' He was speechless. [13]Then the king said to the servants, 'Bind him hand and foot,[f] and throw him into the outer darkness; there is where the weeping and grinding of teeth will be.' [14]For many are called, but few chosen."

[15]Then the Pharisees went and took counsel how they might entrap him in his talk. [16]They sent their disciples to him, along with the Herodians, saying, "Teacher, we know that you are honest, and teach the way of God in truth, no matter whom you teach, for you are not partial to anyone. [17]Tell us therefore, what do you think? Is it lawful to pay taxes to Caesar, or not?"

[18]But Jesus perceived their wickedness, and said, "Why do you test me, you hypocrites? [19]Show me the tax money."

They brought to him a denarius.

[20]He asked them, "Whose is this image and inscription?"

[21]They said to him, "Caesar's."

Then he said to them, "Give therefore to Caesar the things that are Caesar's, and to God the things that are God's."

---

a   21:38 Some Mss read "take possession of"
b   21:42 Psalm 118:22-23
c   21:44 Isaiah 8:14-15; Daniel 2:34-35, 44-45; Romans 9:32-33; 1 Peter 2:8
d   22:7 Some Mss add "having heard"
e   22:10 Or, "with guests"
f   22:13 Some Mss add "take him away"

²²When they heard it, they marveled, and left him, and went away.

²³On that day Sadducees came to him, the ones saying that there is no resurrection. And they asked him, ²⁴saying, "Teacher, Moses said, 'If a man dies, having no children, his brother is to marry his wife, and raise up offspring for his brother.'ᵃ ²⁵Now there were with us seven brothers. The first married and died, and having no offspring, left his wife to his brother. ²⁶In like manner the second also, and the third, to the seventh. ²⁷After them all, the woman diedᵇ. ²⁸In the resurrection therefore, whose wife will she be of the seven? For they all had her."

²⁹But Jesus answered them, "You are mistaken, not knowing the Scriptures, nor the power of God. ³⁰For in the resurrection they neither marry, nor are given in marriage, but are like the angelsᶜ in heaven. ³¹But concerning the resurrection of the dead, Have you not read that which was spoken to you by God, saying, ³²'I am the God of Abraham, and the God of Isaac, and the God of Jacob?'ᵈ God is not the God of the dead, but of the living."

³³When the crowds heard it, they were astonished at his teaching. ³⁴But the Pharisees, when they heard that he had silenced the Sadducees, gathered themselves together. ³⁵One of them, a Law scholar, asked him a question, testing himᵉ. ³⁶"Teacher, which is the greatest commandment in the law?"

³⁷Heᶠ said to him, "'You are to love the Lord your God with all your heart, with all your soul, and with all your mind.'ᵍ ³⁸This is the great and first commandment. ³⁹A second likewise is this, 'You are to love your neighbor as yourself.'ʰ ⁴⁰The whole Law and the Prophets depend on these two commandments."

⁴¹Now while the Pharisees were gathered together, Jesus asked them a question, ⁴²saying, "What do you think of the Messiah? Whose son is he?"

They said to him, "Of David."

⁴³He said to them, "How then does David in the Spirit call him Lord, saying,

⁴⁴'The Lord said to my Lord,
    sit on my right hand,
    until I make your enemies the
       footstoolⁱ of your feet'?ʲ

⁴⁵"If then David calls him Lord, how is he his son?"

⁴⁶No one was able to answer him a word, neither did anyone dare ask him any more questions from that day forth.

23 Then Jesus spoke to the crowds and to his disciples, ²saying, "Upon the seat of Moses the Pharisees and scribes sit. ³All which they will say unto you, observe and do; but their works do not do, because they say, and do not do. ⁴For they bind heavy and hard to bearᵏ burdens, and lay them on men's shoulders; but they themselves will not lift a finger to help them. ⁵But all their works they do to be seen by others. They make their tefillin broad and enlarge the fringe of their garments, ⁶and love the place of honor at feasts, the best seats in the synagogues, ⁷the salutations in the marketplaces, and to be called 'Rabbi' by people. ⁸But you are not to be called 'Rabbi,' for one is your Teacher, ˡand all of you are brothers. ⁹Call no man on the earth your father, for one is your Father, he who is in heaven. ¹⁰Neither be called masters, for one is your master, the Messiah. ¹¹But he who is greatest among you will be your servant. ¹²Whoever exalts himself will be humbled, and whoever humbles himself will be exalted.ᵐ

¹³"Woe to you, scribes and Pharisees, hypocrites. For you devour the houses of widows, and for show make long prayers.

---

a   22:24 Deuteronomy 25:5,6
b   22:27 Some Mss add "also"
c   22:30 Some Mss add "of God"
d   22:32 Exodus 3:6
e   22:35 Some Mss add "and saying"
f   22:37 Some Mss read "Jesus"
g   22:37 Deuteronomy 6:5
h   22:39 Leviticus 19:18
i   22:44 Some Mss read "beneath" 20:43; Acts 2:35;
       Hebrews 1:13
j   22:44 Psalm 110:1
k   23:4 Some Mss lack "and hard to bear"
l   23:8 Some Mss add "the Christ"
m   23:12 Proverbs 29:23; Ezekiel 21:26

Therefore you will receive greater condemnation.[a]

[14]"Woe to you, scribes and Pharisees, hypocrites. For you shut up the Kingdom of Heaven in front of people; for you do not enter in yourselves, neither do you allow those who are entering in to enter."

[15]Woe to you, scribes and Pharisees, hypocrites. For you travel around by sea and land to make one proselyte; and when he becomes one, you make him twice as much of a son of hell[b] as yourselves.

[16]"Woe to you, you blind guides, who say, 'Whoever swears by the temple, it is nothing; but whoever swears by the gold of the temple, he is obligated.' [17]You blind fools. For which is greater, the gold, or the temple that sanctified[c] the gold? [18]"Whoever swears by the altar, it is nothing; but whoever swears by the gift that is on it, he is obligated?' [19]You blind people.[d] For which is greater, the gift, or the altar that sanctifies the gift? [20]He therefore who swears by the altar, swears by it, and by everything on it. [21]He who swears by the temple, swears by it, and by him who dwells[e] in it. [22]He who swears by heaven, swears by the throne of God, and by him who sits on it.

[23]"Woe to you, scribes and Pharisees, hypocrites. For you tithe mint, dill, and cumin, and have left undone the weightier matters of the Law: justice, mercy, and faith. But you ought to have done these, and not to have left the other undone. [24]You blind guides, who strain out a gnat, and swallow a camel.

[25]"Woe to you, scribes and Pharisees, hypocrites. For you clean the outside of the cup and of the plate, but within they are full of extortion and self-indulgence.[f] [26]You blind Pharisee, first clean the inside of the cup,[g] that its outside may become clean also.

[27]"Woe to you, scribes and Pharisees, hypocrites. For you are like whitened tombs, which outwardly appear beautiful, but inwardly are full of dead men's bones, and of all uncleanness. [28]Even so you also outwardly appear righteous to people, but inwardly you are full of hypocrisy and iniquity.

[29]"Woe to you, scribes and Pharisees, hypocrites. For you build the tombs of the prophets, and decorate the tombs of the righteous, [30]and say, 'If we had lived in the days of our fathers, we would not have been partakers with them in the blood of the prophets.' [31]Therefore you testify to yourselves that you are children of those who killed the prophets. [32]Fill up, then, the measure of your fathers. [33]You serpents, you offspring of vipers, how will you escape the judgment of hell[h]? [34]Therefore look, I send to you prophets, wise men, and scribes. Some of them you will kill and crucify; and some of them you will scourge in your synagogues, and persecute from city to city; [35]that on you may come all the righteous blood shed on the earth, from the blood of righteous Abel to the blood of Zechariah son of Berekiah, whom you killed between the sanctuary and the altar. [36]Truly I tell you,[i] all these things will come upon this generation.

[37]"Jerusalem, Jerusalem, who kills the prophets, and stones those who are sent to her. How often I would have gathered your children together, even as a hen gathers her chicks under her wings, and you would not. [38]Look, your house is left to you desolate.[j] [39]For I tell you, you will not see me from now on, until you say, 'Blessed is he who comes in the name of the Lord.'"[k]

24 Jesus went out from the temple, and was going on his way. His disciples came to him to show him the buildings of the temple. [2]But answering, he[l] said to

---

a   23:13 Some Mss lack this verse, which is sometimes numbered as 14
b   23:19 Gk "Gehenna"
c   23:17 Some Mss read "sanctifies"
d   23:19 Some Mss add "fools"
e   23:21 Some Mss read "who was dwelling"
f   23:25 Some Mss read "unrighteousness"
g   23:26 Some Mss add "and of the plate"
h   23:33 Gk. "Gehenna"
i   23:36 Some Mss add "that"
j   23:38 Jeremiah 22:5
k   23:39 Psalm 118:26
l   24:2 Some Mss read "Jesus"

them, "Do you not see all of these things? Truly I tell you, there will not be left here one stone on another, that will not be thrown down."

³As he sat on the Mount of Olives, the disciples came to him privately, saying, "Tell us, when will these things be? And what will be the sign of your coming, and of the end of the age?"

⁴Jesus answered them, "Be careful that no one leads you astray. ⁵For many will come in my name, saying, 'I am the Messiah,' and will lead many astray. ⁶You will hear of wars and rumors of wars. See that you are not troubled, forᵃ this must happen, but the end is not yet. ⁷For nation will rise against nation, and kingdom against kingdom; and there will be famines and plaguesᵇ and earthquakes in various places. ⁸But all these things are the beginning of birth pains. ⁹Then they will deliver you up to oppression, and will kill you. You will be hated by all of the nations for my name's sake. ¹⁰Then many will stumble, and will deliver up one another, and will hate one another. ¹¹Many false prophets will arise, and will lead many astray. ¹²And because lawlessness is multiplied, the love of many will grow cold. ¹³But he who endures to the end, the same will be saved. ¹⁴This Good News of the kingdom will be preached in the whole world for a testimony to all the nations, and then the end will come.

¹⁵"When, therefore, you see the abomination of desolation,ᶜ which was spoken of through Daniel the prophet, standing in the holy place (let the reader understand), ¹⁶then let those who are in Judea flee to the mountains. ¹⁷Let him who is on the housetop not go down to take out things that are in his house. ¹⁸Let him who is in the field not return back to take his coat. ᵈ¹⁹But woe to those who are with child and to nursing mothers in those days. ²⁰Pray that your flight will not be in the winter, nor on a Sabbath, ²¹for then there will be great oppression, such as has not been from the beginning of the world until now, no, nor ever will be. ²²Unless those days had been shortened, no flesh would have been saved.

But for the sake of the chosen ones, those days will be shortened.

²³"Then if anyone tells you, 'Look, here is the Messiah,' or, 'There,' do not believe it. ²⁴For there will arise false messiahs, and false prophets, and they will show great signs and wonders, so as to lead astray, if possible, even the chosen ones.

²⁵"See, I have told you beforehand. ²⁶If therefore they tell you, 'Look, he is in the wilderness,' do not go out; 'Look, he is in the inner chambers,' do not believe it. ²⁷For as the lightning flashes from the east, and is seen even to the west, so will be the coming of the Son of Man. ²⁸Whereverᵉ the carcass is, there is where the vulturesᶠ gather together. ²⁹But immediately after the oppression of those days, the sun will be darkened, the moon will not give its light, the stars will fall from heaven, and the powers of the heavens will be shaken;ᵍ ³⁰and then the sign of the Son of Man will appear in the sky. Then all the tribes of the earth will mourn,ʰ and they will see the Son of Man coming on the clouds of the skyⁱ with power and great glory. ³¹He will send out his angels with aʲ loud trumpet blast,ᵏ and they will gather together his chosen ones from the four winds, from one end of the sky to theˡ other.

³²"Now from the fig tree learn this parable. When its branch has now become tender, and puts forth its leaves, you know that the summer is near. ³³Even so you also, when you see all these things, know that it is near, even at the doors. ³⁴Truly I tell you, this generation will not pass away, until all these things are accomplished. ³⁵Heaven and earth will pass away, but my words

---

a   24:6 Some Mss add "all"
b   24:7 Some Mss lack "and plagues"
c   24:15 Daniel 9:27; 11:31; 12:11
d   24:18 Some Mss read "clothes"
e   24:27 Some Mss read "For wherever"
f   24:28 Or, "eagles"
g   24:29 Isaiah 13:10; 34:4; Ezekiel 32:7; Joel 2:10
h   24:30 Zechariah 12:10, 14
i   24:30 Daniel 7:13
j   24:31 Some Mss add "sound of a"
k   24:31 Isaiah 27:13
l   24:31 Some Mss lack "the"

will not pass away. ³⁶But no one knows of that day and hour, not even the angels of heaven, nor the Son,ᵃ but my Father only.

³⁷"As the days of Noah were, so will be the coming of the Son of Man. ³⁸For as in thoseᵇ days before the flood they were eating and drinking, marrying and giving in marriage, until the day that Noah entered into the box-shaped vesselᶜ, ³⁹and they did not know until the flood came, and took them all away, soᵈ will be the coming of the Son of Man. ⁴⁰Then two men will be in the field: one will be taken and one will be left; ⁴¹two women grinding at the mill, one will be taken and one will be left. ⁴²Watch therefore, for you do not know on what dayᵉ your Lord comes. ⁴³But know this, that if the master of the house had known in what watch of the night the thief was coming, he would have watched, and would not have allowed his house to be broken into. ⁴⁴Therefore also be ready, for in an hour that you do not expect, the Son of Man will come.

⁴⁵"Who then is the faithful and wise servant, whom his lord has set over his household, to give them their food in due season? ⁴⁶Blessed is that servant whom his lord finds doing so when he comes. ⁴⁷Truly I tell you that he will set him over all that he has. ⁴⁸But if that evil servant should say in his heart, 'My lord is delayed,'ᶠ ⁴⁹and begins to beat his fellow servants, and eat and drink with the drunkards, ⁵⁰the lord of that servant will come in a day when he does not expect it, and in an hour when he does not know it, ⁵¹and will cut him in pieces, and appoint his portion with the hypocrites. There is where the weeping and grinding of teeth will be.

25 "Then the kingdom of heaven will be like ten virgins, who took their lamps, and went out to meet the bridegroom. ²Five of them were foolish, and five were wise. ³For the foolish, when they took their lamps, took no oil with them, ⁴but the wise took oil in their vessels with their lamps. ⁵Now while the bridegroom delayed, they all slumbered and slept. ⁶But at midnight there was a cry, 'Look. The bridegroom.ᵍ Come out to

meet him.' ⁷Then all those virgins arose, and trimmed their lamps. ⁸The foolish said to the wise, 'Give us some of your oil, for our lamps are going out.' ⁹But the wise answered, saying, 'No,ʰ there will not be enough for us and you. Go rather to those who sell, and buy for yourselves.' ¹⁰While they went away to buy, the bridegroom came, and those who were ready went in with him to the marriage feast, and the door was shut. ¹¹Afterward the other virgins also came, saying, 'Lord, Lord, open to us.' ¹²But he answered, 'Truly I tell you, I do not know you.' ¹³Watch therefore, for you do not know the day nor the hour.ⁱ

¹⁴"For it is like a man, going on a journey, who called his own servants, and entrusted his goods to them. ¹⁵To one he gave five talents, to another two, to another one; to each according to his own ability. Then he went on his journey. ¹⁶Immediatelyʲ the one who received the five talents went and traded with them, and made another five talents. ¹⁷In like mannerᵏ he who got the two gained another two. ¹⁸But he who received the one went away and dug in the earth, and hid his lord's money.

¹⁹"Now after a long time the lord of those servants came, and reconciled accounts with them. ²⁰And he who received the five talents came and brought another five talents, saying, 'Lord, you delivered to me five talents. See, I have gained another five talents.'ˡ ²¹"His lord said to him, 'Well done, good and faithful servant. You have been faithful

---

a   24:36 Some Mss lack "nor the Son"

b   24:38 Some Mss lack "those"

c   24:38 Or, "ship." Gk. kibotos "box-shaped." Traditionally "ark," from Latin arca "box, chest." The vessel, according to the Hebrew royal cubit of 52.5 centimeters, was 517 feet in length x 86 feet in width x 52 feet in height, or 157.5 meters x 26.3 meters x 15.8 meters. See Genesis 6:15

d   24:39 Some Mss lack "so"

e   24:42 Some Mss read "hour"

f   24:48 Some Mss add "in his coming"

g   25:6 Some Mss add "is coming"

h   25:9 Some Mss lack "No"

i   25:13 Some Mss add "in which the Son of Man is coming"

j   25:16 Some Mss read "Then immediately"

k   25:17 Some Mss add "also"

l   25:20 Some Mss add "besides them"

over a few things, I will set you over many things. Enter into the joy of your lord.'

²²"And he also who had the two talents came and said, 'Lord, you delivered to me two talents. See, I have gained another two talents.ᵃ'

²³"His lord said to him, 'Well done, good and faithful servant. You have been faithful over a few things, I will set you over many things. Enter into the joy of your lord.'

²⁴"He also who had received the one talent came and said, 'Lord, I knew you that you are a hard man, reaping where you did not sow, and gathering where you did not scatter. ²⁵I was afraid, and went away and hid your talent in the earth. See, you have what is yours.'

²⁶"But his lord answered him, 'You wicked and slothful servant. You knew that I reap where I did not sow, and gather where I did not scatter. ²⁷You ought therefore to have deposited my money with the bankers, and at my coming I should have received back my own with interest. ²⁸Take away therefore the talent from him, and give it to him who has the ten talents. ²⁹For to everyone who has will be given, and he will have abundance, but from him who does not have, even that which he has will be taken away. ³⁰Throw out the unprofitable servant into the outer darkness, where there will be weeping and gnashing of teeth.'

³¹"But when the Son of Man comes in his glory, and all theᵇ angels with him, then he will sit on the throne of his glory. ³²Before him all the nations will be gathered, and he will separate them one from another, as a shepherd separates the sheep from the goats. ³³He will set the sheep on his right hand, but the goats on the left. ³⁴Then the King will tell those on his right hand, 'Come, blessed of my Father, inherit the kingdom prepared for you from the foundation of the world; ³⁵for I was hungry, and you gave me food to eat. I was thirsty, and you gave me drink. I was a stranger, and you took me in. ³⁶I was naked, and you clothed me. I was sick, and you visited me. I was in prison, and you came to me.'

³⁷"Then the righteous will answer him, saying, 'Lord, when did we see you hungry, and feed you; or thirsty, and give you a drink? ³⁸When did we see you as a stranger, and take you in; or naked, and clothe you? ³⁹When did we see you sick, or in prison, and come to you?'

⁴⁰"The King will answer them, 'Truly I tell you, inasmuch as you did it to one of the least of these my brothers,ᶜ you did it to me.' ⁴¹Then he will say also to those on the left hand, 'Depart from me, you cursed, into the everlasting fire which is prepared for the devil and his angels; ⁴²for I was hungry, and you did not give me food to eat; I was thirsty, and you gave me no drink; ⁴³I was a stranger, and you did not take me in; naked, and you did not clothe me; sick, and in prison, and you did not visit me.'

⁴⁴"Then they will also answer, saying, 'Lord, when did we see you hungry, or thirsty, or a stranger, or naked, or sick, or in prison, and did not help you?'

⁴⁵"Then he will answer them, saying, 'Truly I tell you, inasmuch as you did not do it to one of the least of these, you did not do it to me.' ⁴⁶These will go away into everlasting punishment, but the righteous into everlasting life."

26 And it happened, when Jesus had finished all these words, that he said to his disciples, ²"You know that after two days the Passover is coming, and the Son of Man will be delivered up to be crucified."

³Then the chief priests and the scribesᵈ and the elders of the people gathered together in the court of the high priest, who was called Caiaphas. ⁴They took counsel together that they might take Jesus by deceit, and kill him. ⁵But they said, "Not during the feast, lest a riot occur among the people."

⁶Now when Jesus was in Bethany, in the house of Simon the leper, ⁷a woman came to him having an alabaster jar of very expensive ointment, and she poured it on his

---

a 25:22 Some Mss add "besides them"

b 25:31 Some Mss add "holy"

c 25:40 Some Mss lack "my brothers"

d 26:3 Some Mss lack "and the scribes"

head as he sat at the table. [8]But when the[a] disciples saw this, they were indignant, saying, "Why this waste? [9]For this ointment might have been sold for much, and given to the poor."

[10]However, knowing this, Jesus said to them, "Why do you trouble the woman? Because she has done a good work for me. [11]For you always have the poor with you; but you do not always have me. [12]For in pouring this ointment on my body, she did it to prepare me for burial. [13]Truly I tell you, wherever this Good News is preached in the whole world, what this woman has done will also be spoken of as a memorial of her."

[14]Then one of the twelve, who was called Judas Iscariot, went to the chief priests, [15]and said, "What are you willing to give me, that I should deliver him to you?" They weighed out for him thirty pieces of silver.[b] [16]From that time he sought opportunity to betray him.

[17]Now on the first day of unleavened bread, the disciples came to Jesus, saying[c], "Where do you want us to prepare for you to eat the Passover?"

[18]He said, "Go into the city to a certain person, and tell him, 'The Teacher says, "My time is near. I will keep the Passover at your house with my disciples."'"

[19]The disciples did as Jesus commanded them, and they prepared the Passover. [20]Now when evening had come, he was reclining at the table with the twelve.[d] [21]As they were eating, he said, "Truly I tell you that one of you will betray me."

[22]And they were greatly distressed, and each one began to ask him, "It is not me, is it, Lord?"

[23]He answered, "He who dipped his hand with me in the dish, the same will betray me. [24]The Son of Man goes, even as it is written of him, but woe to that man through whom the Son of Man is betrayed. It would be better for that man if he had not been born."

[25]Judas, who betrayed him, answered, "It is not me, is it, Rabbi?"

He said to him, "You said it."

[26]As they were eating, Jesus took bread, gave thanks for it, and broke it. He gave to the disciples, and said, "Take, eat; this is my body." [27]He took a[e] cup, gave thanks, and gave to them, saying, "All of you drink it, [28]for this is my blood of the new[f] covenant, which is poured out for many for the remission of sins. [29]But I tell you that I will not drink of this fruit of the vine from now on, until that day when I drink it anew with you in my Father's kingdom." [30]When they had sung the hymn, they went out to the Mount of Olives.

[31]Then Jesus said to them, "All of you will be made to stumble because of me tonight, for it is written, 'I will strike the shepherd, and the sheep of the flock will be scattered.'[g] [32]But after I am raised up, I will go before you into Galilee."

[33]But Peter answered him, "Even if all will be made to stumble because of you, I will never be made to stumble."

[34]Jesus said to him, "Truly I tell you that tonight, before the rooster crows, you will deny me three times."

[35]Peter said to him, "Even if I must die with you, I will not deny you." All of the disciples also said likewise.

[36]Then Jesus came with them to a place called Gethsemane, and said to his disciples, "Sit here, while I go there and pray." [37]He took with him Peter and the two sons of Zebedee, and began to be sorrowful and severely troubled. [38]Then he[h] said to them, "My soul is exceedingly sorrowful, even to death. Stay here, and watch with me."

[39]He went forward a little, fell on his face, and prayed, saying, "My Father, if it is possible, let this cup pass away from me; nevertheless, not what I desire, but what you desire."

---

a   26:8 Some Mss read "his"
b   26:15 Zechariah 11:12
c   26:17 Some Mss add "to him"
d   26:20 Some Mss add "disciples"
e   26:27 Some Mss read "the"
f   26:28 Some Mss lack "new"
g   26:31 Zechariah 13:7
h   26:38 Some Mss read "Jesus"

[40]He came to the disciples, and found them sleeping, and said to Peter, "What, could you not watch with me for one hour? [41]Watch and pray, that you do not enter into temptation. The spirit indeed is willing, but the flesh is weak."

[42]Again, a second time he went away, and prayed, saying, "My Father, if this[a] cannot pass away[b] unless I drink it, your desire be done." [43]He came again and found them sleeping, for their eyes were heavy. [44]He left them again, went away, and prayed a third time, saying the same words. [45]Then he came to the[c] disciples, and said to them, "Sleep on now, and take your rest. Look, the hour is near, and the Son of Man is betrayed into the hands of sinners. [46]Arise, let us be going. Look, he who betrays me is near."

[47]While he was still speaking, look, Judas, one of the twelve, came, and with him a large crowd with swords and clubs, from the chief priests and elders of the people. [48]Now he who betrayed him gave them a sign, saying, "Whoever I kiss, he is the one. Seize him." [49]Immediately he came to Jesus, and said, "Hail, Rabbi." and kissed him.

[50]Jesus said to him, "Friend, why are you here?" Then they came and laid hands on Jesus, and took him. [51]And look, one of those who were with Jesus stretched out his hand, and drew his sword, and struck the servant of the high priest, and struck off his ear. [52]Then Jesus said to him, "Put your sword back into its place, for all those who take the sword will die by the sword. [53]Or do you think that I could not ask my Father, and he would even now send me more than twelve legions of angels? [54]How then would the Scriptures be fulfilled that it must be so?"

[55]In that hour Jesus said to the crowds, "Have you come out as against a robber with swords and clubs to seize me? I sat daily in the temple teaching, and you did not arrest me. [56]But all this has happened, that the Scriptures of the prophets might be fulfilled."

Then all the disciples left him, and fled. [57]Those who had taken Jesus led him away to Caiaphas the high priest, where the scribes and the elders were gathered together. [58]But Peter followed him from a distance, to the court of the high priest, and entered in and sat with the officers, to see the end. [59]Now the chief priests[d] and the whole council sought false testimony against Jesus so they could put him to death; [60]and they found none, even though many false witnesses came forward.[e] But afterward two[f] came forward, [61]and said, "This man said, 'I am able to destroy the temple of God, and to build it in three days.'"

[62]The high priest stood up, and said to him, "Have you no answer? What is this that these testify against you?" [63]But Jesus held his peace. The high priest answered him, "I adjure you by the living God, that you tell us whether you are the Messiah, the Son of God."

[64]Jesus said to him, "You have said it. Nevertheless, I tell you, after this you will see the Son of Man sitting at the right hand of Power, and coming on the clouds of the sky."[g]

[65]Then the high priest tore his clothing, saying, "He has spoken blasphemy. Why do we need any more witnesses? Look, now you have heard his blasphemy. [66]What do you think?"

They answered, "He is worthy of death." [67]Then they spit in his face[h] and beat him with their fists, and some slapped him, [68]saying, "Prophesy to us, you Messiah. Who hit you?"

[69]Now Peter was sitting outside in the courtyard, and a servant girl came to him, saying, "You were also with Jesus, the Galilean."

[70]But he denied it before them all, saying, "I do not know what you are talking about."

---

a   26:42 Some Mss add "cup"
b   26:42 Some Mss add "from me"
c   26:45 Some Mss read "his"
d   26:59 Some Mss add "and the elders"
e   26:60 Some Mss add "they found none"
f   26:60 Some Mss add "false witnesses"
g   26:64 Daniel 7:13
h   26:67 Isaiah 50:6

[71]And when he had gone out onto the porch, another girl saw him, and said to those who were there, "This man also was with Jesus the Nazorean."

[72]Again he denied it with an oath, "I do not know the man."

[73]After a little while those who stood by came and said to Peter, "Surely you are also one of them, for your accent makes you known."

[74]Then he began to curse and to swear, "I do not know the man."

Immediately the rooster crowed. [75]Peter remembered the word which Jesus had said[a], "Before the rooster crows, you will deny me three times." He went out and wept bitterly.

27

Now when morning had come, all the chief priests and the elders of the people took counsel against Jesus to put him to death: [2]and they bound him, and led him away, and delivered him up to[b] Pilate, the governor. [3]Then Judas, who betrayed him, when he saw that Jesus was condemned, felt remorse, and returned the thirty pieces of silver to the chief priests and elders, [4]saying, "I have sinned in that I betrayed innocent blood."

But they said, "What is that to us? You see to it."

[5]He threw down the pieces of silver in the sanctuary, and departed. He went away and hanged himself. [6]The chief priests took the pieces of silver, and said, "It's not lawful to put them into the treasury, since it is the price of blood." [7]They took counsel, and bought the potter's field with them, to bury strangers in. [8]Therefore that field was called "The Field of Blood" to this day. [9]Then that which was spoken through Jeremiah the prophet was fulfilled, saying,

> "They took the thirty pieces of silver,
>> the price of him upon whom a price
>>> had been set,
>> whom some of the sons of Israel
>>> priced,
> [10]and they gave them for the potter's field,
>> as the Lord commanded me."[c]

[11]Now Jesus stood before the governor: and the governor asked him, saying, "Are you the King of the Jews?"

Jesus said to him, "You say so."

[12]When he was accused by the chief priests and elders, he answered nothing. [13]Then Pilate said to him, "Do you not hear how many things they testify against you?"

[14]He gave him no answer, not even one word, so that the governor marveled greatly. [15]Now at the feast the governor was accustomed to release to the crowd one prisoner, whom they desired. [16]They had then a notable prisoner, called Barabbas. [17]When therefore they were gathered together, Pilate said to them, "Whom do you want me to release to you? Barabbas, or Jesus, who is called Messiah?" [18]For he knew that because of envy they had delivered him up.

[19]While he was sitting on the judgment seat, his wife sent to him, saying, "Have nothing to do with that righteous man, for I have suffered many things this day in a dream because of him." [20]Now the chief priests and the elders persuaded the crowds to ask for Barabbas, and destroy Jesus. [21]But the governor answered them, "Which of the two do you want me to release to you?"

They said, "Barabbas."

[22]Pilate said to them, "What then should I do with Jesus, who is called Messiah?" They all said,[d] "Let him be crucified."

[23]But he[e] said, "Why? What evil has he done?"

But they shouted all the louder, saying, "Let him be crucified."

[24]So Pilate, seeing that nothing was being gained, but rather that a disturbance

---

a   26:75 Some Mss add "to him"

b   27:2 Some Mss add "Pontius"

c   27:10 A composite quotation where two or more scriptures are combined because of common vocabulary, a Jewish exegetical technique known as gezera shawa, here involving words and themes from the book of Jeremiah, as well as Zechariah, which represent a prefiguring of Judas's actions. For the naming of the major prophet in a composite quotation see Mark 1:2 and Romans 9:27-28

d   27:22 Some Mss add "to him"

e   27:23 Some Mss read "the governor"

was starting, took water and he washed his hands before the crowd, saying, "I am innocent of the blood of this righteous[a] man. You see to it."

[25]All the people answered, "May his blood be on us, and on our children."

[26]Then he released to them Barabbas, but Jesus he flogged[b] and delivered to be crucified. [27]Then the governor's soldiers took Jesus into the Praetorium, and gathered the whole garrison together against him. [28]They stripped him, and put a scarlet robe on him. [29]They braided a crown of thorns and put it on his head, and a reed in his right hand; and they kneeled down before him, and mocked him, saying, "Hail, King of the Jews."[d] [30]They spat on him,[e] and took the reed and struck him on the head. [31]When they had mocked him, they took the robe off of him, and put his clothes on him, and led him away to crucify him.

[32]As they came out, they found a man of Cyrene, Simon by name, and they compelled him to go with them, that he might carry his cross. [33]They came to a place called "Golgotha," that is to say, "The place of a skull."[f] [34]They gave him wine[g] to drink mixed with gall. When he had tasted it, he would not drink. [35]When they had crucified him, they divided his clothing among themselves, casting a lot, that it might be fulfilled which was spoken by the prophet: 'They divided my clothes among themselves, and for my clothing they cast a lot.'[h] [36]And they sat and watched him there. [37]They set up over his head the accusation written against him: "THIS IS JESUS, THE KING OF THE JEWS."

[38]Then there were two robbers crucified with him, one on his right hand and one on the left.[i] [39]Those who passed by blasphemed him, wagging their heads,[j] [40]and saying, "You who destroy the temple, and build it in three days, save yourself. If you are the Son of God,[k] come down from the cross."

[41]Likewise the chief priests also mocking, with the scribes, [l]and the elders, said, [42]"He saved others, but he cannot save himself. He[m] is the King of Israel; let him come down from the cross now, and we will believe in him. [43]He trusts in God. Let God deliver him now, if he wants him; for he said, 'I am the Son of God.'" [44]The robbers also who were crucified with him cast on him the same reproach.

[45]Now from noon until three in the afternoon[n] there was darkness over all the land.[o] [46]Then at about three in the afternoon[p] Jesus called out with a loud voice, saying, "Eli, Eli, lema sabachthani?" That is, "My God, my God, why have you forsaken me?"[q]

[47]Some of them who stood there, when they heard it, said, "This man is calling Elijah."

[48]Immediately one of them ran, and took a sponge, and filled it with vinegar, and put it on a reed, and gave him a drink.[r] [49]The rest said, "Let him be. Let us see whether Elijah comes to save him."

[50]And Jesus cried out again with a loud voice, and yielded up his spirit. [51]And look, the veil of the temple was torn in two from the top to the bottom. The earth quaked and the rocks were split. [52]The tombs were opened, and many bodies of the saints who had fallen asleep were raised; [53]and coming out of the tombs after his resurrection, they entered into the holy city and appeared to many. [54]Now the centurion, and those who were with him watching Jesus, when they saw the earthquake, and the things that were done,

---

a   27:24 Some Mss lack "righteous"
b   27:26 Isaiah 53:5
c   27:26 Isaiah 53:8
d   27:29 Isaiah 53:3; Psalm 69:19
e   27:30 Isaiah 50:6
f   27:33 Known as "Calvary" in Latin
g   27:34 Some Mss read "wine vinegar"
h   27:35 Some Mss lack "that it might...lot"
i   27:38 Isaiah 53:12
j   27:39 Psalm 22:7
k   27:40 Some Mss add "and"
l   27:41 Some Mss add "the Pharisees"
m   27:42 Some Mss read "If he"
n   27:45 Lit. the sixth hour until the ninth hour
o   27:45 Amos 8:9
p   27:46 Lit. the ninth hour
q   27:46 Psalm 22:1
r   27:48 Psalm 69:21

feared exceedingly, saying, "Truly this was the Son of God."

⁵⁵Many women were there watching from afar, who had followed Jesus from Galilee, serving him. ⁵⁶Among them were Mary Magdalene, Mary the mother of James and Joseph,^a and the mother of the sons of Zebedee. ⁵⁷When evening had come, a rich man from Arimathaea, named Joseph, who himself was also Jesus' disciple came. ⁵⁸This man went to Pilate, and asked for the body of Jesus. Then Pilate commanded that it^b be released. ⁵⁹Joseph took the body, and wrapped it in a clean linen cloth, ⁶⁰and placed it in his own new tomb,^c which he had cut out in the rock, and he rolled a great stone to the door of the tomb, and departed. ⁶¹Mary Magdalene was there, and the other Mary, sitting opposite the tomb. ⁶²Now on the next day, which was the day after the Preparation Day, the chief priests and the Pharisees were gathered together to Pilate, ⁶³saying, "Sir, we remember what that deceiver said while he was still alive: 'After three days I will rise again.' ⁶⁴Command therefore that the tomb be made secure until the third day, lest perhaps his disciples come^d and steal him away, and tell the people, 'He is risen from the dead;' and the last deception will be worse than the first."

⁶⁵Pilate said to them, "You have a guard. Go, make it as secure as you can." ⁶⁶So they went with the guard and made the tomb secure, sealing the stone.

28 Now after the Sabbath, as it began to dawn on the first day of the week, Mary Magdalene and the other Mary came to see the tomb. ²And look, there was a great earthquake, for an angel of the Lord descended from the sky, and came and rolled away the stone,^e and sat on it. ³His appearance was like lightning, and his clothing white as snow. ⁴For fear of him, the guards shook, and became like dead men. ⁵The angel answered the women, "Do not be afraid, for I know that you seek Jesus, who has been crucified. ⁶He is not here, for

he has risen,^f just like he said. Come, see the place where he ^gwas lying. ⁷Go quickly and tell his disciples, 'He has risen from the dead, and look, he goes before you into Galilee; there you will see him.' See, I have told you."

⁸They departed quickly from the tomb with fear and great joy, and ran to bring his disciples word. ⁹And^h look, Jesus met them, saying, "Rejoice!" And they came and took hold of his feet, and worshiped him.

¹⁰Then Jesus said to them, "Do not be afraid. Go tell my brothers that they should go into Galilee, and there they will see me."

¹¹Now while they were going, look, some of the guards came into the city, and told the chief priests all the things that had happened. ¹²When they were assembled with the elders, and had taken counsel, they gave a large amount of silver to the soldiers, ¹³saying, "Say that his disciples came by night, and stole him away while we slept. ¹⁴If this comes to the governor's ears, we will persuade him and make you free of worry." ¹⁵So they took the money and did as they were told. This saying was spread abroad among the Jewish people, and continues until this day.

¹⁶But the eleven disciples went into Galilee, to the mountain where Jesus had sent them. ¹⁷When they saw him, they bowed down to him, but some doubted. ¹⁸Jesus came to them and spoke to them, saying, "All authority has been given to me in heaven and on earth.ⁱ ¹⁹Therefore go, and make disciples of all nations, baptizing them in the name of the Father and of the Son and of the Holy Spirit, ²⁰teaching them to obey all things that I commanded you. And look, I am with you every day, even to the end of the age."^j

---

a   27:56 Some Mss read "Josi"
b   27:58 Some Mss read "the body"
c   27:60 Isaiah 53:9
d   27:64 Some Mss add "at night"
e   28:2 Some Mss add "from the door"
f   28:6 Psalm 16:10; Isaiah 53:11 DSS LXX
g   28:6 Some Mss read "the Lord"
h   28:9 Some Mss add "As they went to tell his disciples"
i   28:18 Daniel 7:14
j   28:20 Some Mss add "Amen."

Mark

1 The beginning of the Good News of Jesus Christ,[a] the Son of God.[b] [2]As it is written in Isaiah the prophet,[c]

"Look, I send my messenger ahead
  of you,
 who will prepare your way before
  you.[d]
[3]The voice of one crying in the
  wilderness,
 'Prepare the way of the Lord.
 Make his roads straight.'"[e]

[4]John came baptizing in the wilderness and preaching a baptism of repentance for forgiveness of sins. [5]And all the country of Judea went out to him and all those from Jerusalem, and they were baptized by him in the Jordan river, confessing their sins. [6]And John was clothed with camel's hair and a leather belt around his waist. He ate locusts and wild honey. [7]And he preached, saying, "After me comes he who is mightier than I, the strap of whose sandals I am not worthy to stoop down and loosen. [8]I[f] baptized you in water, but he will baptize you in the Holy Spirit."

[9]And it happened in those days, that Jesus came from Nazareth of Galilee, and was baptized by John in the Jordan. [10]Immediately coming up from the water, he saw the heavens parting, and the Spirit descending on him like a dove. [11]And a voice came out of the sky, "You are my beloved Son, with you[g] I am well pleased."

[12]And immediately the Spirit drove him out into the wilderness. [13]And he was in the wilderness forty days tempted by Satan. He was[h] with the wild animals; and the angels were serving him.

[14]Now after John was taken into custody, Jesus came into Galilee, proclaiming the Good News[i] of God, [15]and saying, "The time is fulfilled, and the kingdom of God is near. Repent, and believe in the Good News."

[16]And passing along by the sea of Galilee, he saw Simon and Andrew the brother of Simon casting a net into the sea, for they were fishermen. [17]And Jesus said to them, "Come after me, and I will make you into fishers of people."

[18]And immediately they left the nets, and followed him. [19]And going on a little further, [j]he saw James the son of Zebedee, and John, his brother, who were also in the boat mending the nets. [20]And immediately he called them, and they left their father, Zebedee, in the boat with the hired servants, and went after him. [21]And they went into Capernaum, and immediately on the Sabbath day he entered into the synagogue and taught. [22]And they were astonished at his teaching, for he taught them as having authority, and not as the scribes. [23]And just then there was in their synagogue a man with an unclean spirit, and he shouted, [24]saying, "[k]What do we have to do with you, Jesus, Nazarene? Have you come to destroy us? I know you who you are: the Holy One of God."

[25]And Jesus rebuked him, saying, "Be quiet, and come out of him."

[26]And the unclean spirit, convulsing him and crying with a loud voice, came out of him. [27]And they were all amazed, so that they questioned among themselves, saying, "What is this? A new teaching? For with authority he commands even the unclean spirits, and they obey him." [28]And at once the news of him went out everywhere[l] into all the region of Galilee and its surrounding area.

[29]And immediately, when they had come out of the synagogue, they came into the house of Simon and Andrew,

---

a 1:1 Or, "Messiah"
b 1:1 Some Mss lack "the Son of God"
c 1:2 Some Mss read "in the prophets"
d 1:2 Some Mss lack "before you." See Malachi 3:1; Exodus 23:20; Matthew 11:10; Luke 7:27
e 1:3 Isaiah 40:3
f 1:8 Some Mss add "indeed"
g 1:11 Some Mss read "in whom"
h 1:13 Some Mss add "there"
i 1:14 Some Mss add "of the kingdom"
j 1:19 Some Mss add "from there"
k 1:24 Some Mss add "Ah!"
l 1:28 Some Mss lack "And" and "everywhere"

with James and John. ³⁰Now Simon's wife's mother lay sick with a fever, and immediately they told him about her. ³¹And he came and took her by the hand, and raised her up. The fever left her, and she served them. ³²At evening, when the sun had set, they brought to him all who were sick, and those who were possessed by demons. ³³And all the city was gathered together at the door. ³⁴And he healed many who were sick with various diseases, and cast out many demons. He did not allow the demons to speak, because they knew him.

³⁵And early in the morning, while it was still dark, he rose up and went out, and departed into a deserted place, and prayed there. ³⁶And Simon and those who were with him followed after him; ³⁷and they found him, and told him, "Everyone is looking for you."

³⁸And he said to them, "Let us go somewhere else[a] into the next towns, that I may preach there also, because I came out for this reason." ³⁹And he went into their synagogues throughout all Galilee, preaching and casting out demons.

⁴⁰And a leper came to him, begging him, and knelt down[b] and said to him, "If you want to, you can make me clean."

⁴¹And being moved with compassion, he[c] stretched out his hand, and touched him, and said to him, "I am willing. Be cleansed." ⁴²[d]And immediately the leprosy departed from him, and he was made clean. ⁴³And he strictly warned him, and immediately sent him out, ⁴⁴and said to him, "See you say nothing to anyone, but go show yourself to the priest, and offer for your cleansing the things which Moses commanded, for a testimony to them."

⁴⁵But he went out, and began to proclaim it freely, and to spread about the matter, so that Jesus could no more openly enter into a city, but was outside in desert places: and they came to him from everywhere.

2 And when he entered again into Capernaum after some days, it was heard that he was in the house. ²And[e] many were gathered together, so that there was no more room, not even around the door; and he spoke the word to them. ³And four people came, carrying a paralytic to him. ⁴And when they could not bring[f] him because of the crowd, they removed the roof above him. When they had broken it up, they let down the mat that the paralytic was lying on. ⁵And Jesus, seeing their faith, said to the paralytic, "Son, your sins are forgiven you."

⁶But there were some of the scribes sitting there, and reasoning in their hearts, ⁷"Why does this man speak like that? He is blaspheming; who can forgive sins but God alone?"

⁸And immediately Jesus, perceiving in his spirit that they so reasoned within themselves, said to them, "Why do you reason these things in your hearts? ⁹Which is easier, to tell the paralytic, 'Your sins are forgiven;' or to say, 'Arise, and take up your bed, and walk?' ¹⁰But that you may know that the Son of Man has authority on earth to forgive sins", he said to the paralytic, ¹¹"I tell you, arise, take up your mat, and go to your house."

¹²And he arose immediately, and took up the mat, and went out in front of them all; so that they were all amazed, and glorified God, saying, "We never saw anything like this."

¹³And he went out again by the seaside. All the crowd came to him, and he taught them. ¹⁴And as he passed by, he saw Levi, the son of Alphaeus, sitting at the tax office, and he said to him, "Follow me." And he arose and followed him.

¹⁵And it happened that he was reclining at the table in his house, and many tax collectors and sinners sat down with Jesus and his disciples, for there were many, and they followed him. ¹⁶And the scribes of[g] the Pharisees, when they saw him eating with the tax collectors and sinners,

---

a   1:38 Some Mss lack "somewhere else"
b   1:40 Some Mss lack "and knelt down"
c   1:41 Some Mss read "Jesus"
d   1:42 Some Mss add "When he had said this"
e   2:2 Some Mss add "immediately"
f   2:4 Some Mss read "not get near"
g   2:16 Some Mss read "and"

said to his disciples, "Why is it that he eats and drinks[a] with tax collectors and sinners?"

[17]And when Jesus heard it, he said to them, "Those who are healthy have no need for a physician, but those who are sick. I came not to call the righteous, but sinners.[b]"

[18]And John's disciples and the Pharisees were fasting, and they came and asked him, "Why do the disciples of John and those of the Pharisees fast, but your disciples do not fast?"

[19]And Jesus said to them, "Can the groomsmen fast while the bridegroom is with them? As long as they have the bridegroom with them, they cannot fast. [20]But the days will come when the bridegroom will be taken away from them, and then will they fast in that day.[c] [21]No one sews a piece of unshrunk cloth on an old garment, or else the patch shrinks and the new tears away from the old, and a worse hole is made. [22]And no one puts new wine into old wineskins, or else the[d] wine will burst the skins, and the wine is lost,[e] and the skins will be destroyed; but they put new wine into fresh wineskins."

[23]And it happened that he was going on the Sabbath day through the grain fields, and his disciples began, as they went, to pluck the ears of grain. [24]And the Pharisees said to him, "Look, why do they do that which is not lawful on the Sabbath day?"

[25]And he said to them, "Did you never read what David did, when he had need, and was hungry—he, and those who were with him? [26]How he entered into the house of God in the time of Abiathar the high priest, and ate the show bread,[f] which is not lawful to eat except for the priests, and gave also to those who were with him?" [27]And he said to them, "The Sabbath was made for people, not people for the Sabbath. [28]Therefore the Son of Man is lord even of the Sabbath."

3 And he entered again into the synagogue, and there was a man there who had his hand withered. [2]And they watched him, whether he would heal him on the Sabbath day, that they might accuse him. [3]And he said to the man with the withered hand[g], "Stand up in the middle." [4]And he said to them, "Is it lawful on the Sabbath day to do good, or to do harm? To save a life, or to kill?" But they were silent. [5]And when he had looked around at them with anger, being grieved at the hardening of their hearts, he said to the man, "Stretch out your hand." He stretched it out, and his hand was restored.[h] [6]And the Pharisees went out, and immediately conspired with the Herodians against him, how they might destroy him.

[7]And Jesus withdrew to the sea with his disciples, and a large crowd followed[i] from Galilee, from Judea, [8]and from Jerusalem, and from Idumea, and beyond the Jordan, and those from around Tyre and Sidon. A large crowd, when they heard what great things he did, came to him. [9]And he told his disciples that a small boat should stay near him because of the crowd, so that they would not press on him. [10]For he had healed many, so that as many as had diseases pressed on him that they might touch him. [11]And the unclean spirits, whenever they saw him, fell down before him, and shouted, saying, "You are the Son of God." [12]And he sternly warned them that they should not make him known.

[13]And he went up into the mountain, and called to himself those whom he wanted, and they went to him. [14]And he appointed twelve,[j] that they might be with him, and that he might send them out to preach, [15]and to have authority to heal sicknesses and to[k] cast out demons. [16]And he appointed the twelve.[l] And to Simon he

---

a   2:16 Some Mss lack "and drinks"
b   2:17 Some Mss add "to repentance"
c   2:20 Some Mss read "in those days"
d   2:22 Some Mss add "new"
e   2:22 Some Mss read "is poured out"
f   2:26 1Samuel 21:1-7; 2Samuel 8:17; 1Chronicles 24:6
g   3:3 Some Mss read "who had a withered hand"
h   3:5 Some Mss add "as healthy as the other"
i   3:7 Some Mss add "him"
j   3:14 Some Mss add "designating them apostles"
k   3:15 Some Mss lack "heal sicknesses and to"
l   3:16 Some Mss lack "And he appointed the Twelve"

gave the name Peter; [17]and James the son of Zebedee; and John the brother of James (and he surnamed them Boanerges which means, Sons of Thunder); [18]and Andrew, and Philip, and Bartholomew, and Matthew, and Thomas, and James the son of Alphaeus, and Thaddaeus, and Simon the Zealot; [19]and Judas Iscariot, who also betrayed him.

[20]And he came into a house,[a] and the crowd came together again, so that they could not so much as eat bread. [21]And when his family heard it, they went out to take charge of him, for they said, "He is out of his mind." [22]And the scribes who came down from Jerusalem said, "He has Beelzebul," and, "By the prince of the demons he casts out the demons."

[23]And so he summoned them, and said to them in parables, "How can Satan cast out Satan? [24]And if a kingdom is divided against itself, that kingdom cannot stand. [25]And if a house is divided against itself, that house will not be able to stand. [26]And if Satan has risen up against himself, and is divided, he is not able to[b] stand, but has an end. [27]But no one can enter into the house of the strong man to plunder, unless he first binds the strong man; and then he will plunder his house. [28]Truly I tell you, all human[c] sins will be forgiven, including their blasphemies with which they may blaspheme; [29]but whoever may blaspheme against the Holy Spirit never has forgiveness, but is guilty of an everlasting sin" [30]—because they said, "He has an unclean spirit."

[31]And his mother and his brothers came, and standing outside, they sent to him, calling him. [32]And a crowd was sitting around him, and they told him, "Look, your mother and your brothers[d] are outside looking for you."

[33]And he answered them, saying, "Who are my mother and my brothers?" [34]And looking around at those who sat around him, he said, "Look, my mother and my brothers. [35]For whoever does the will of God, the same is my brother, and my sister, and mother."

[4] And again he began to teach by the seaside. And a large crowd was gathered to him, so that he entered into a boat in the sea, and sat down. And the whole crowd was on the land by the sea. [2]And then he taught them many things in parables, and told them in his teaching, [3]"Listen. Look, the sower who went out to sow. [4]And it happened, as he sowed, some seed fell by the road, and the birds[e] came and devoured it. [5]And others fell on the rocky ground, where it had little soil, and immediately it sprang up, because it had no depth of soil. [6]And when the sun came up, it was scorched; and because it had no root, it withered away. [7]And others fell among the thorns, and the thorns grew up, and choked it, and it yielded no fruit. [8]And others fell into the good ground, and yielded fruit, growing up and increasing; and brought forth thirty times, and sixty times, and one hundred times." [9]And he said, "Whoever has ears to hear, let him hear.[f]"

[10]And when he was alone, those who were around him with the twelve asked him about the parables. [11]And he said to them, "To you has been given[g] the mystery of the kingdom of God, but to those who are outside, all things are done in parables, [12]that 'seeing they may see, and not perceive; and hearing they may hear, and not understand; lest perhaps they should turn and be forgiven.[h]'"[i]

[13]And he said to them, "Do you not understand this parable? And how will you understand all of the parables? [14]The farmer sows the word. [15]And these are the ones by the road where the word is sown; and when they have heard, immediately Satan comes, and takes away the word which has been sown in them.[j] [16]And these in a

a   3:20 Some Mss move the sentence to end of 3:19
b   3:26 Some Mss read "he cannot"
c   3:28 Lit. "sons/children of humankind"
d   3:32 Some Mss add "and your sisters"
e   4:4 Some Mss add "of the air"
f   4:9 Some Mss add "and understand"
g   4:11 Some Mss add "to know"
h   4:12 Some Mss read "and their sins be forgiven them"
i   4:12 Isaiah 6:9-10
j   4:15 Some Mss read "in their hearts"

similar way[a] are those who are sown on the rocky places, who, when they have heard the word, immediately receive it with joy. [17]And they have no root in themselves, but are short-lived. Then, when oppression or persecution arises because of the word, immediately they stumble. [18]And others[b] are those who are sown among the thorns; these are the ones who have heard the word, [19]and the cares of the[c] age, and the deceitfulness of riches, and the lusts of other things entering in choke the word, and it becomes unfruitful. [20]And those which were sown on the good ground are those who hear the word, and accept it, and bear fruit, some thirty times, some sixty times, and some one hundred times."

[21]And he said to them, "Is the lamp brought to be put under a basket[d] or under a bed? Is it not put on a stand? [22]For there is nothing hidden, except that it should be made known; neither was anything made secret, but that it should come to light. [23]If anyone has ears to hear, let him hear."

[24]And he said to them, "Take heed what you hear. With whatever measure you measure, it will be measured to you, and more will be given to you.[e] [25]For whoever has, more will be given, and he who does not have, even that which he has will be taken away from him."

[26]And he said, "The kingdom of God is like someone who scatters seed on the earth, [27]and he sleeps and rises night and day, and the seed springs up and grows; he doesn't know how. [28]The[f] earth bears fruit, first the blade, then the ear, then the full grain in the ear. [29]But when the fruit is ripe, immediately he puts forth the sickle, because the harvest has come."

[30]And he said, "To what will we liken the kingdom of God? Or with what parable will we use for it? [31]It's like a mustard seed, which, when it is sown upon the soil, though it is less than all the seeds that are upon the soil, [32]yet when it is sown, grows up, and becomes greater than all the herbs, and puts out great branches, so that the birds of the sky can lodge under its shadow."

[33]And with many[g] such parables he spoke the word to them, as they were able to hear it. [34]And he did not speak to them without a parable; but privately to his own[h] disciples he explained everything.

[35]And on that day, when evening had come, he said to them, "Let us go over to the other side." [36]And leaving the crowd, they took him with them, even as he was, in the boat. And other[i] boats were[j] with him. [37]And a big wind storm arose, and the waves beat into the boat, so much that the boat[k] was already filled. [38]And he himself was in the stern, asleep on the cushion, and they woke him up, and told him, "Teacher, do you not care that we are dying?"

[39]And he awoke, and rebuked the wind, and said to the sea, "Peace. Be still." And the wind ceased, and there was a great calm.[l] [40]And he said to them, "Why are you so afraid? Do[m] you still have no faith?"

[41]And they were greatly afraid, and said to one another, "Who then is this, that even the wind and the sea obey him?"

5 And they came to the other side of the sea, into the territory of the Gerasenes[n]. [2]And when he had come out of the boat, immediately a man with an unclean spirit met him out of the tombs. [3]He lived in the tombs, and no one could bind him any more, not even with a chain.[o] [4]For he had been often bound with fetters and chains, and the chains had been torn apart by him, and the fetters broken in

---

a   4:16 Some Mss have a different word order. Others lack "in a similar way"

b   4:18 Some Mss read "These"

c   4:19 Some Mss read "this"

d   4:21 Lit. a modion, a dry measuring basket containing about a peck (about 9 liters)

e   4:24 Some Mss add "who hear"

f   4:28 Some Mss read "For the"

g   4:33 Some Mss omit "many"

h   4:34 Some Mss lack "own"

i   4:36 Some Mss add "small"

j   4:36 Some Mss add "also"

k   4:37 Some Mss read "that it"

l   4:39 Psalm 65:7; 89:9; 107:29

m   4:40 Some Mss read "How"

n   5:1 Some Mss read "Gadarenes"

o   5:3 Some Mss read "with chains"

pieces. No one had the strength to tame him. [5]And always, night and day, in the tombs and in the mountains, he was crying out, and cutting himself with stones. [6]And when he saw Jesus from afar, he ran and bowed down to him, [7]and crying out with a loud voice, he said, "What have I to do with you, Jesus, you Son of the Most High God? I adjure you by God, do not torment me." [8]For he said to him, "Come out of the man, you unclean spirit."

[9]And then he asked him, "What is your name?"

And he replied, "My name is Legion, for we are many." [10]And he begged him much that he would not send them away out of the region. [11]Now on the mountainside there was a great herd of pigs feeding. [12]And they[a] begged him, saying, "Send us into the pigs, that we may enter into them."

[13]And he[b] gave them permission. The unclean spirits came out and entered into the pigs; and the herd of about two thousand rushed down the steep bank into the sea, and they were drowned in the sea. [14]And those who fed them[c] fled, and told it in the city and in the country. And the people went[d] to see what it was that had happened. [15]And they came to Jesus, and saw him who had been possessed by demons sitting, clothed and in his right mind, even him who had the legion; and they were afraid. [16]And those who saw it declared to them how it happened to him who was possessed by demons, and about the pigs. [17]And then they began to beg him to depart from their region.

[18]And as he was entering into the boat, he who had been possessed by demons begged him that he might be with him. [19]And he[e] did not allow him, but said to him, "Go to your house, to your own, and tell them what great things the Lord has done for you, and how he had mercy on you."

[20]And so he went his way, and began to proclaim in Decapolis how Jesus had done great things for him, and everyone marveled.

[21]And when Jesus had crossed back over in the boat to the other side, a large crowd was gathered to him; and he was by the sea. [22f]And one of the rulers of the synagogue, Jairus by name, came; and seeing him, he fell at his feet, [23]and pleaded with him repeatedly, saying, "My little daughter is at the point of death. Please come and lay your hands on her, that she may be made healthy, and live."

[24]And he went with him, and a large crowd followed him, and they pressed upon him on all sides. [25]And a[g] woman, who had an issue of blood for twelve years, [26]and had suffered many things by many physicians, and had spent all that she had, and was no better, but rather grew worse, [27]having heard the things concerning Jesus, came up behind him in the crowd, and touched his clothes. [28]For she said, "If I just touch his clothes, I will be made well." [29]And immediately the flow of her blood was dried up, and she felt in her body that she was healed of her affliction.

[30]And immediately Jesus, perceiving in himself that the power had gone out from him, turned around in the crowd, and asked, "Who touched my clothes?"

[31]And his disciples said to him, "You see the crowd pressing against you, and you say, 'Who touched me?'"

[32]And he looked around to see her who had done this thing. [33]But the woman, fearing and trembling, knowing what had been done to her, came and fell down before him, and told him all the truth.

[34]And he said to her, "Daughter, your faith has made you well. Go in peace, and be cured of your disease."

[35]While he was still speaking, people came from the synagogue ruler's house saying, "Your daughter is dead. Why bother the Teacher any more?"

---

a   5:12 Some Mss read "All the demons"
b   5:13 Some Mss read "At once Jesus"
c   5:14 Some Mss add "the pigs"
d   5:14 Some Mss add "out"
e   5:19 Some Mss read "Jesus"
f   5:22 Some Mss add "Look"
g   5:25 Some Mss add "certain"

³⁶But Jesus, overhearing the message spoken, ªsaid to the ruler of the synagogue, "Do not be afraid, only believe." ³⁷And he allowed no one to follow him, except Peter, James, and John the brother of James. ³⁸And theyᵇ came to the synagogue ruler's house, and he saw an uproar, weeping, and great wailing. ³⁹And when he had entered in, he said to them, "Why do you make an uproar and weep? The child is not dead, but is asleep."

⁴⁰And they ridiculed him. But he, having put them all out, took the father of the child, her mother, and those who were with him, and went in where the child was.ᶜ ⁴¹And taking the child by the hand, he said to her, "Talitha koum," which translated means, "Little girl, I tell you, get up." ⁴²And immediately ᵈthe girl rose up and walked, for she was twelve years old. And immediately they were overcome with amazement. ⁴³And he strictly ordered them that no one should know this, and commanded that something should be given to her to eat.

6 And he went out from there and came into his own country, and his disciples followed him. ²And when the Sabbath had come, he began to teach in the synagogue, and many hearing him were astonished, saying, "Where did this man get these things?" and, "What is the wisdom that is given to this man, that such mighty works come about by his hands? ³Is not this the carpenter,ᵉ the son of Mary, and brother of James, Josi, Judas, and Simon? Are not his sisters here with us?" They were offended at him.

⁴Jesus said to them, "A prophet is not without honor, except in his own country, and among his own relatives, and in his own house." ⁵And he could do no mighty work there, except that he laid his hands on a few sick people, and healed them. ⁶And He marveled because of their unbelief.

And he went around the villages teaching. ⁷And he called to himself the twelve, and began to send them out two by two; and he gave them authority over the unclean spirits. ⁸And he commanded them

that they should take nothing for their journey, except a staff only: no bread, no pack, no money in their belts, ⁹but to wear sandals, and not to put on two tunics. ¹⁰And he said to them, "Wherever you enter into a house, stay there until you depart from there. ¹¹And if any place will not receive you or listen to you, as you depart from there, shake off the dust that is under your feet for a testimony against them.'"

¹²So they went out and proclaimed that all should repent. ¹³They cast out many demons, and anointed many with oil who were sick, and healed them. ¹⁴King Herod heard this, for his name had become known, and he said, "John the Baptist has risen from the dead, and therefore these powers are at work in him." ¹⁵But others said, "He is Elijah." Others said, "He is a prophet, like one of the prophets." ¹⁶But Herod, when he heard this, said, "This is John, whom I beheaded. He has risen.ᵍ" ¹⁷For Herod himself had sent out and arrested John, and bound him in prison for the sake of Herodias, his brother Philip's wife, for he had married her. ¹⁸For John said to Herod, "It is not lawful for you to have your brother's wife." ¹⁹So Herodias set herself against him, and desired to kill him, but she could not, ²⁰for Herod feared John, knowing that he was a righteous and holy man, and kept him safe. And when he heard him, he was very perplexed,ʰ but he heard him gladly.

²¹And then a convenient day came, that Herod on his birthday gaveⁱ a supper for his nobles, the high officers, and the chief men of Galilee. ²²And when the daughter of Herodias herselfʲ came in and danced,

---

a   5:36 Some Mss add "immediately"
b   5:38 Some Mss read "He"
c   5:40 Some Mss add "lying"
d   5:42 Some Mss lack "Immediately"
e   6:3 Or, "craftsman." Gk. tekton
f   6:11 Some Mss add "Assuredly, I tell you, it will be more tolerable for Sodom and Gomorrah in the day of judgment than for that city"
g   6:16 Some Mss add "from the dead"
h   6:20 Some Mss read "did many things"
i   6:21 Some Mss read "made"
j   6:22 Some Mss read "And when his daughter Herodias"

she pleased Herod and those sitting with him. The king said to the young lady, "Ask me whatever you want, and I will give it to you." [23]And he swore to her, "Whatever you ask me, I will give you, up to half of my kingdom."

[24]So she went out, and said to her mother, "What should I ask?"

And she said, "The head of John the baptizer."

[25]And she came in immediately with haste to the king, and asked, "I want you to give me right now the head of John the Baptist on a platter."

[26]And the king was exceedingly sorry, but for the sake of his oaths, and those reclining, he did not wish to refuse her. [27]So immediately the king sent out a soldier of his guard, and commanded to bring John's head, and he went and beheaded him in the prison, [28]and brought his head on a platter, and gave it to the young lady; and the young lady gave it to her mother.

[29]And when his disciples heard this, they came and took up his corpse, and placed it in a tomb.

[30]Then the apostles gathered themselves together to Jesus, and they told him all things, whatever they had done, and whatever they had taught. [31]And he said to them, "Come away by yourselves to an isolated place, and rest awhile." For there were many coming and going, and they had no leisure so much as to eat. [32]So they went away in the boat to an isolated place by themselves. [33]But they[a] saw them going, and many recognized him and ran there on foot from all the cities and they arrived before them.[b] [34]And he[c] came out, saw a large crowd, and he had compassion on them, because they were like sheep without a shepherd, and he began to teach them many things. [35]And when it was late in the day, his disciples came to him, and said, "This place is desolate, and it is late in the day. [36]Send them away, that they may go into the surrounding country and villages, and buy themselves something[d] to eat."

[37]But he answered them, "You give them something to eat."

And they said to him, "Are we to go and buy two hundred denarii[e] worth of bread, and give them something to eat?"

[38]He said to them, "How many loaves do you have? Go see."

When they knew, they said, "Five, and two fish."

[39]He commanded them that everyone should sit down in groups on the green grass. [40]They sat down in ranks, by hundreds and by fifties. [41]He took the five loaves and the two fish, and looking up to heaven, he blessed and broke the loaves, and he gave to his disciples to set before them, and he divided the two fish among them all. [42]They all ate, and were filled. [43]They took up twelve baskets full of broken pieces and also of the fish. [44]Those who ate the loaves were[f] five thousand men.

[45]And immediately he made his disciples get into the boat, and to go ahead to the other side, to Bethsaida, while he himself was sending the crowd away. [46]After he had taken leave of them, he went up the mountain to pray.

[47]When evening had come, the boat was in the midst of the sea, and he was alone on the land. [48]He saw them distressed in rowing, for the wind was against them. In the watch between three and six in the morning[g] he came to them, walking on the sea,[h] and he would have passed by them, [49]but they, when they saw him walking on the sea, supposed that it was a ghost, and began to scream; [50]for they all saw him, and were troubled. But he immediately spoke with them, and said to them, "Cheer up. It is I.[i] Do not be afraid." [51]And he got into the boat with them, and the wind ceased.[j] And they were completely profusely[k] aston-

---

a　6:33 Some Mss read "the crowds"
b　6:33 Some Mss add "and came together to him"
c　6:34 Some Mss read "Jesus"
d　6:36 Some Mss read "bread, for they have nothing"
e　6:37 200 denarii was about 7 or 8 months wages for an agricultural laborer
f　6:44 Some Mss add "about"
g　6:48 Lit. the fourth watch of the night
h　6:48 See Job 9:8
i　6:50 Or, "I AM."
j　6:51 See Psalm 107:29
k　6:51 Some Mss lack "profusely"

ished among themselves;[a] [52]for they had not understood about the loaves, but their hearts were hardened.

[53]When they had crossed over, they came to land at Gennesaret, and moored to the shore. [54]When they had come out of the boat, immediately the people recognized him, [55]and ran around that whole[b] region, and began to bring those who were sick, on their mats, to where they heard he was. [56]Wherever he entered, into villages, or into cities, or into the country, they placed the sick in the marketplaces, and begged him that they might touch just the fringe of his garment; and as many as touched him were made well.

7 Then the Pharisees, and some of the scribes gathered together to him, having come from Jerusalem. [2]Now when they saw that some of his disciples ate bread with defiled, that is, unwashed, hands, they found fault. [3](For the Pharisees, and all the Jews, do not eat unless they wash their hands and forearms, holding to the tradition of the elders. [4]They do not eat when they come from the marketplace unless they wash. And there are many other things which they have received and hold to, the washing of cups and pitchers and copper vessels and dining couches.[c]) [5]The Pharisees and the scribes asked him, "Why do your disciples not walk according to the tradition of the elders, but eat their bread with unwashed hands?"

[6]He[d] said to them, "Well did Isaiah prophesy of you hypocrites, as it is written,
'This people honors me with their lips,
    but their heart is far from me.
[7]But in vain do they worship me,
    teaching instructions that are the
        commandments of humans.'[e]

[8]"For you set aside the commandment of God, and hold tightly to human tradition."[f] [9]He said to them, "Full well do you reject the commandment of God, that you may keep[g] your tradition. [10]For Moses said, 'Honor your father and your mother;'[h] and, 'Anyone who speaks evil of father or mother, let him be put to death.'[i] [11]But you

say, 'If anyone tells his father or mother, "Whatever profit you might have received from me is Corban[j], that is to say, given to God;"' [12]then you no longer allow him to do anything for his father or his mother, [13]making void the word of God by your tradition, which you have handed down. You do many things like this."

[14]And he called the crowd to himself again,[k] and said to them, "Hear me, all of you, and understand. [15]There is nothing from outside of the person, that going into him can defile him; but the things which proceed out of the person are[l] what defile the person."[16m]

[17]When he had entered into a house away from the crowd, his disciples asked him about the parable. [18]He said to them, "Are you thus without understanding also? Do you not perceive that whatever goes into the person from outside cannot defile him, [19]because it does not go into his heart, but into his stomach, then into the latrine, cleansing all the foods?" [20]He said, "That which proceeds out of the person, that defiles the person. [21]For from within, out of a person's heart, proceed evil thoughts, adulteries, sexual sins, murders, thefts, [22]covetings, wickedness, deceit, lustful desires, an evil eye, blasphemy, pride, and foolishness. [23]All these evil things come from within, and defile the person."

[24]From there he arose, and went away into the region[n] of Tyre and Sidon. He entered into a house, and did not want

---

a   6:51 Some Mss add "and marveled"
b   6:55 Some Mss add "surrounding"
c   7:4 Some Mss lack "and dining couches"
d   7:6 Some Mss add "answered and"
e   7:7 Isaiah 29:13
f   7:8 Some Mss add "the washing of pitchers and cups, and you do many other such things"
g   7:9 Some Mss read establish/set up
h   7:10 Exodus 20:12; Deuteronomy 5:16
i   7:10 Exodus 21:17; Leviticus 20:9
j   7:11 Corban is a Hebrew word for an offering devoted to God
k   7:14 Some Mss read "all"
l   7:15 Some Mss add "those"
m   7:16 Some Mss add "If anyone has ears to hear, let him hear"
n   7:24 Some Mss read "border"

anyone to know it, but he could not escape notice. [25]But immediately[a] a woman whose young daughter had an unclean spirit heard of him and came and fell at his feet. [26]Now the woman was a Greek, a Syrophoenician by race. She begged him that he would cast the demon out of her daughter. [27]But he[b] said to her, "Let the children be filled first, for it is not appropriate to take the children's bread and throw it to the dogs."

[28]But she answered him, "Yes,[c] Lord, but even the dogs under the table eat the children's crumbs."

[29]He said to her, "For this saying, go your way. The demon has gone out of your daughter."

[30]And when she went away to her house, she found the child lying on the bed, the demon having left[d].

[31]Again he departed from the borders of Tyre, and came through Sidon[e] to the sea of Galilee, through the midst of the region of Decapolis. [32]They brought to him one who was deaf and had an impediment in his speech. They begged him to lay his hand on him. [33]He took him aside from the crowd, privately, and put his fingers into his ears, and he spat, and touched his tongue. [34]Looking up to heaven, he sighed, and said to him, "Ephphatha" that is, "Be opened." [35]And[f] his ears were opened, and the impediment of his tongue was released, and he spoke clearly. [36]He commanded them that they should tell no one, but the more he commanded them, so much the more widely they proclaimed it. [37]They were astonished beyond measure, saying, "He has done all things well. He makes even the deaf hear, and the[g] mute speak."

8 In those days, when there was a[h] large crowd, and they had nothing to eat, he[i] called his disciples to himself, and said to them, [2]"I have compassion on the crowd, because they have stayed with me now three days, and have nothing to eat. [3]If I send them away fasting to their home, they will faint on the way, and[j] some of them have come a long way."

[4]His disciples answered him, "From where could one satisfy these people with bread here in a deserted place?"

[5]He asked them, "How many loaves do you have?"

They said, "Seven."

[6]He commanded the crowd to sit down on the ground, and he took the seven loaves. Having given thanks, he broke them, and gave them to his disciples to serve, and they served the crowd. [7]They had a few small fish. Having blessed them, he said to serve these also. [8]They ate, and were filled. They took up seven baskets of broken pieces that were left over. [9]Now they[k] were about four thousand. Then he sent them away.

[10]Immediately he entered into the boat with his disciples, and came into the region of Dalmanutha. [11]The Pharisees came out and began to question him, seeking from him a sign from heaven, and testing him. [12]He sighed deeply in his spirit, and said, "Why does this generation seek a sign? Truly I tell you, no sign will be given to this generation."

[13]And he left them, and got into the boat again[l], and went to the other side. [14]Now they[m] forgot to take bread; and they did not have more than one loaf in the boat with them. [15]He warned them, saying, "Take heed: beware of the yeast of the Pharisees and the yeast of Herod."

[16]And they began discussing among themselves[n] that they had no bread.[o]

---

a   7:25 Some Mss lack "immediately," and add "For"
b   7:27 Some Mss read "Jesus"
c   7:28 Some Mss add "yet. Others lack "Yes"
d   7:30 Some Mss read "found the demon gone out, and the child lying on the bed"
e   7:31 Some Mss read "borders of Tyre and Sidon, and came through"
f   7:35 Some Mss add "immediately"
g   7:37 Some Mss omit "the"
h   8:1 Some Mss add "very"
i   8:1 Some Mss read "Jesus"
j   8:3 Some Mss read "for"
k   8:9 Some Mss add "who had eaten"
l   8:13 Some Mss lack "into a boat"
m   8:14 Some Mss read "the disciples"
n   8:16 Some Mss add "saying"
o   8:16 Some Mss read "we have"

[17]He,[a] perceiving it, said to them, "Why do you reason that it's because you have no bread? Do you not perceive yet, neither understand? Are your hearts [b]hardened? [18]Having eyes, do you not see? Having ears, do you not hear? Do you not remember? [19]When I broke the five loaves among the five thousand, how many baskets full of broken pieces did you take up?"

They told him, "Twelve."

[20]"When the seven loaves fed the four thousand, how many baskets full of broken pieces did you take up?"

They told him, "Seven."

[21]He asked them, "Do you not yet[c] understand?"

[22]He came to Bethsaida. They brought a blind man to him, and begged him to touch him. [23]He took hold of the blind man by the hand, and brought him out of the village. When he had spit on his eyes, and laid his hands on him, he asked him if he saw anything.

[24]He looked up, and said, "I see people; they look like trees walking."

[25]Then again he laid his hands on his eyes. He made him look up, and was restored, and saw everything clearly. [26]He sent him away to his house, saying, "Do not enter into the village.[d]"

[27]Jesus went out, with his disciples, into the villages of Caesarea Philippi. On the way he asked his disciples, "Who do people say that I am?"

[28]And they said to him, saying,[e] "John the Baptist, and others say Elijah, but others: one of the prophets."

[29]He said to them, "But who do you say that I am?"

Peter answered and said to him, "You are the Messiah."

[30]He commanded them that they should tell no one about him. [31]He began to teach them that the Son of Man must suffer many things, and be rejected by the elders, the chief priests, and the scribes, and be killed, and after three days rise again. [32]He spoke to them openly. Peter took him, and began to rebuke him. [33]But he, turning around, and seeing his disciples, rebuked Peter, and said, "Get behind me, Satan. For you have in mind not the things of God, but the things of man."

[34]He called the crowd to himself with his disciples, and said to them, "If anyone[f] wants to come after me, let him deny himself, and take up his cross, and follow me. [35]For whoever wants to save his life will lose it; and whoever will lose his life for my sake and the sake of the Good News will save it. [36]For what does it profit a person to gain the whole world, and forfeit his soul? [37]For[g] what will a person give in exchange for his soul? [38]For whoever will be ashamed of me and of my words[h] in this adulterous and sinful generation, the Son of Man also will be ashamed of him, when he comes in the glory of his Father with the holy angels."

9 He said to them, "Truly I tell you, there are some standing here who will in no way taste death until they see the kingdom of God come with power."

[2]After six days Jesus took with him Peter, James, and John, and brought them up onto a high mountain privately by themselves, and he was changed into another form in front of them. [3]His clothing became glistening, exceedingly white,[i] such as no launderer on earth can whiten them. [4]Elijah and Moses appeared to them, and they were talking with Jesus.

[5]Peter said to Jesus, "Rabbi, it is good for us to be here. Let us make three tents: one for you, one for Moses, and one for Elijah." [6]For he did not know what to answer, for they became[j] very afraid.

[7]A cloud came, overshadowing them, and a voice came out of the cloud, "This is my beloved Son. Listen to him."

---

a   8:17 Some Mss read "Jesus"
b   8:17 Some Mss add "still"
c   8:21 Some Mss read "How do you not"
d   8:26 Some Mss add "nor tell anyone in the village"
e   8:28 Some Mss lack "him"
f   8:34 Some Mss read "Whoever"
g   8:37 Some Mss read "Or"
h   8:38 Some Mss lack "my words"
i   9:3 Some Mss add "like snow"
j   9:6 Some Mss read "were"

⁸Suddenly looking around, they saw no one with them any more, except Jesus only.

⁹As they were coming down from the mountain, he commanded them that they should tell no one what things they had seen, until after the Son of Man had risen from the dead. ¹⁰They kept this saying to themselves, questioning what the "rising from the dead" meant.

¹¹They asked him, saying, "Why do the scribes say that Elijah must come first?"

¹²And he[a] said to them, "Elijah indeed comes first, and restores all things. And why is it written of the Son of Man that he should suffer many things and be rejected? ¹³But I tell you that Elijah has come, and they have also done to him whatever they wanted to, even as it is written about him."

¹⁴And when they came to the disciples, they saw a large crowd around them, and scribes questioning them. ¹⁵Immediately all the crowd, when they saw him, were greatly amazed, and running to him greeted him. ¹⁶He asked them,[b] "What are you arguing about with them?"

¹⁷And one out of the crowd answered him,[c] "Teacher, I brought to you my son, who has a mute spirit; ¹⁸and wherever it seizes him, it throws him down, and he foams at the mouth, and grinds his teeth, and wastes away. I asked your disciples to cast it out, and they weren't able."

¹⁹And answering, he said to them, "You unbelieving generation, how long must I be with you? How long must I put up with you? Bring him to me."

²⁰They brought him to him, and when he saw him, immediately the spirit convulsed him, and he fell on the ground, wallowing and foaming at the mouth.

²¹He asked his father, "How long has it been since this has come to him?"

He said, "From childhood. ²²And it has often cast him both into fire and into water, to destroy him. But if you can do anything, have compassion on us, and help us."

²³Jesus said to him, "'If you can?'[d] All things are possible to him who believes."

²⁴Immediately the father of the child cried out and said,[e] "I believe. Help my unbelief."

²⁵When Jesus saw that a crowd came running together, he rebuked the unclean spirit, saying to him, "You deaf and mute[f] spirit, I command you, come out of him, and never enter him again."

²⁶Having screamed, and convulsed greatly, it came out of him. The boy became like one dead; so much that most of them said, "He is dead." ²⁷But Jesus took him by the hand, and raised him up; and he arose.

²⁸And when he had come into the house, his disciples asked him privately, "Why could we not cast it out?" ²⁹And he said to them, "This kind can come out by nothing, except by prayer and fasting."[g]

³⁰They went out from there, and passed through Galilee. He did not want anyone to know it. ³¹For he was teaching his disciples, and said to them, "The Son of Man is being handed over to the hands of men, and they will kill him; and when he is killed, after three days[h] he will rise again."

³²But they did not understand the saying, and were afraid to ask him.

³³He came to Capernaum, and when he was in the house he asked them, "What were you arguing[i] on the way?"

³⁴But they were silent, for they had disputed one with another on the way about who was the greatest.

³⁵And he sat down, and called the twelve; and he said to them, "If anyone wants to be first, he must be last of all, and servant of all." ³⁶He took a little child, and set him in the midst of them. Taking him in his arms, he said to them, ³⁷"Whoever receives one such little child in my name, receives me, and whoever receives me, does not receive me, but him who sent me."

---

a   9:12 Some Mss add "answered"
b   9:16 Some Mss read "the scribes"
c   9:17 Some Mss lack "him" and add "and said"
d   9:23 Some Mss add "believe"
e   9:24 Some Mss add "with tears. Lord"
f   9:25 Some Mss read "mute and deaf"
g   9:29 Some Mss lack "and fasting"
h   9:31 Some Mss read "on the third day"
i   9:33 Some Mss add "among yourselves"

[38]John said to him,[a] "Teacher, we saw someone casting out demons in your name; and we forbade him, because he was not following[b] us."

[39]But Jesus said, "Do not forbid him, for there is no one who will do a mighty work in my name, and be able quickly to speak evil of me. [40]For whoever is not against us is for us[c]. [41]For whoever will give you a cup of water to drink in my name, because you belong to the Messiah, truly I tell you, he will in no way lose his reward. [42]Whoever will cause one of these little ones who believe in me to stumble, it would be better for him if he was thrown into the sea with a millstone hung around his neck. [43]If your hand causes you to stumble, cut it off.[d] It is better for you to enter into life maimed, rather than having your two hands to go into hell[e], into the unquenchable fire.[44f] [45]If your foot causes you to stumble, cut it off.[g] It is better for you to enter into life lame, rather than having your two feet to be cast into hell.[h] [46i] [47]If your eye causes you to stumble, cast it out.[j] It is better for you to enter into the kingdom of God with one eye, rather than having two eyes to be cast into hell[k], [48]"where their worm does not die, and the fire is not quenched."[l] [49]For everyone will be salted with fire,[m] and every sacrifice will be salted with salt.[n] [50]Salt is good, but if the salt has lost its saltiness, how can you make it salty? Have salt in yourselves, and be at peace with one another."

10 He arose from there and came into the borders of Judea and beyond[o] the Jordan. Crowds came together to him again. As he usually did, he was again teaching them. [2]Pharisees came to him testing him, and asked him, "Is it lawful for a man to divorce his wife?"

[3]He answered, "What did Moses command you?"

[4]They said, "Moses allowed a certificate of divorce to be written, and to divorce her."

[5]But Jesus said to them,[p] "Because of your hardness of heart, he wrote you this commandment. [6]But from the beginning of the creation, he[q] made them male and female.[r] [7]For this cause a man will leave his father and mother, and will join to his wife,[s] [8]and the two will become one flesh,[t] so that they are no longer two, but one flesh. [9]What therefore God has joined together, let no one separate."

[10]In the house, the[u] disciples asked him again about the same matter. [11]He said to them, "Whoever divorces his wife, and marries another, commits adultery against her. [12]If she[v] herself divorces her husband, and marries another, she commits adultery."

[13]They were bringing to him little children, that he should touch them, but the disciples rebuked[w] them. [14]But when Jesus saw it, he was moved with indignation, and said to them, "Allow the little children to come to me. Do not forbid them, for the kingdom of God belongs to such as these. [15]Truly I tell you, whoever will not receive the kingdom of God like a little child, he will in no way enter into it." [16]And he took them in his arms, laying his hands on them, and blessed them.

---

a   9:38 Some Mss read "Then John answered him, saying"

b   9:38 Some Mss read "he does not follow"

c   9:40 Some Mss read "you is on our side"

d   9:43 Probable idiom, "If with your hand you have a habit of stealing, stop it…"

e   9:43 Gk. "Gehenna"

f   9:44 Some Mss add "where their worm does not die, and the fire is not quenched."

g   9:45 Probable idiom, e.g., "If you trespass, stop it…"

h   9:45 Some Mss add "into the fire that will never be quenched"

i   9:46 Some Mss add "where their worm does not die, and the fire is not quenched"

j   9:47 Probable idiom, "If with your eye you have a habit of lust or envying others, stop it..."

k   9:47 Gk. "Gehenna". Some Mss add "of the fire"

l   9:48 Isaiah 66:24

m   9:49 See Matthew 3:11

n   9:49 Some Mss lack "and every sacrifice…salt"

o   10:1 Some Mss read "by the other side of"

p   10:5 Some Mss read "Jesus answered, and said to them"

q   10:6 Some Mss read "God"

r   10:6 Genesis 1:27

s   10:7 Some Mss lack "and join to his wife"

t   10:8 Genesis 2:24

u   10:10 Some Mss read "his"

v   10:12 Some Mss read "a woman"

w   10:13 Some Mss add "those who were bringing"

¹⁷As he was going out into the way, one ran to him, knelt before him, and asked him, "Good Teacher, what must I do that I may inherit everlasting life?"

¹⁸Jesus said to him, "Why do you call me good? No one is good except one—God. ¹⁹You know the commandments: 'Do not commit adultery,' 'Do not murder,'ᵃ 'Do not steal,' 'Do not give false testimony,' 'Do not defraud,' 'Honor your father and mother.'"ᵇ

²⁰And heᶜ said to him, "Teacher, I have kept all these things from my youth."

²¹Jesus looking at him loved him, and said to him, "One thing you lack. Go, sell whatever you have, and give to the poor, and you will have treasure in heaven; and come, follow me, taking up the cross."

²²But his face fell at that saying, and he went away sorrowful, for he was one who had great possessions. ²³Jesus looked around, and said to his disciples, "How difficult it is for those who have riches to enter into the kingdom of God."

²⁴The disciples were amazed at his words. But Jesus answered again and said to them, "Children, how hard it is for those who trust in richesᵈ to enter the kingdom of God. ²⁵It is easier for a camelᵉ to go through a needle's eye than for a rich person to enter into the kingdom of God."

²⁶They were exceedingly astonished, saying to him, "Then who can be saved?"

²⁷Jesus, looking at them, said, "With humans it is impossible, but not with God, for all things are possible with God."

²⁸Peter began to tell him, "Look, we have left everything, and have followed you."

²⁹Jesusᶠ said, "Truly I tell you, there is no one who has left house, or brothers, or sisters, or mother, or father,ᵍ or children, or land, for my sake, and for the sake of the Good News, ³⁰but he will receive one hundred times more now in this time, houses, brothers, sisters, mothers, children, and land, with persecutions; and in the age to come, everlasting life. ³¹But many who are first will be last; and the last first."

³²They were on the way, going up to Jerusalem; and Jesus was going in front of them, and they were amazed; and those who followed were afraid. He again took the twelve, and began to tell them the things that were going to happen to him. ³³"Look, we are going up to Jerusalem. The Son of Man will be delivered to the chief priests and the scribes. They will condemn him to death, and will deliver him to foreigners. ³⁴They will mock him, spit on him, scourge him, and kill him. After three daysʰ he will rise again."

³⁵James and John, the sons of Zebedee, came near to him, and said to him,ⁱ "Teacher, we want you to do for us whatever we will ask."

³⁶He said to them, "What do you want me to do for you?"

³⁷They said to him, "Grant to us that we may sit, one at your right hand, and one at your left hand, in your glory."

³⁸But Jesus said to them, "You do not know what you are asking. Are you able to drink the cup that I drink, orʲ to be baptized with the baptism that I am baptized with?"

³⁹And they said to him, "We are able." And Jesus said to them, "You will drink the cup I drink, and you will be baptized with the baptism that I am baptized with; ⁴⁰but to sit at my right hand and at my left hand is not mine to give, but for whom it has been prepared."

⁴¹When the ten heard it, they began to be indignant towards James and John.

⁴²Jesus summoned them, and said to them, "You know that they who are recognized as rulers over the nations lord it over them, and their great ones exercise authority over them. ⁴³But it will not be so among

---

a   10:19 Some Mss have the order "Do not commit
    murder, Do not commit adultery." See Luke 18:20,
    Romans 13:9. Cf. Exodus 20:13 fn and Deuteronomy
    5:17 fn.
b   10:19 Exodus 20:12-16; Deuteronomy 5:16-20
c   10:20 Some Mss add "answered, and"
d   10:24 Some Mss lack "for those who trust in riches"
e   10:25 Use of hyperbole
f   10:29 Some Mss add "answered and"
g   10:29 Some Mss add "or wife"
h   10:34 Some Mss read "On the third day"
i   10:35 Some Mss read "saying"
j   10:38 Some Mss read "and"

you, but whoever wants to become great among you must be your servant. [44]And whoever wants to be first among you[a] must be slave of all. [45]For the Son of Man also came not to be served, but to serve, and to give his life as a ransom for many."

[46]They came to Jericho. As he went out from Jericho, with his disciples and a large crowd, Bartimaeus, the son of Timaeus, a blind beggar,[b] was sitting by the road.[c] [47]When he heard that it was Jesus the Nazarene, he began to cry out, and say, "Jesus, Son of David, have mercy on me." [48]Many rebuked him, that he should be quiet, but he shouted all the louder, "Son of David, have mercy on me."

[49]Jesus stood still, and said, "Call him."

They called the blind man, saying to him, "Cheer up. Get up. He is calling you."

[50]He, casting away his cloak, jumped up,[d] and came to Jesus.

[51]Jesus asked him, "What do you want me to do for you?"

The blind man said to him, "Rabboni, that I may see again."

[52]Jesus said to him, "Go your way. Your faith has made you well." And immediately he received his sight, and followed him[e] on the road.

11 When they drew near to Jerusalem, to Bethphage[f] and Bethany, at the Mount of Olives, he sent two of his disciples, [2]and said to them, "Go your way into the village that is opposite you. Immediately as you enter into it, you will find a young donkey tied, on which no one has yet[g] sat. Untie him, and bring him. [3]If anyone asks you, 'Why are you doing this?' say, 'The Lord needs him;' and immediately he will send him back here."

[4]They went away, and found a colt tied at the door outside in the open street, and they untied him. [5]Some of those who stood there asked them, "What are you doing, untying the young donkey?" [6]They said to them just as Jesus had said, and they let them go.

[7]They brought the young donkey to Jesus, and threw their garments on it, and Je-

sus sat on it. [8]Many spread their garments on the way, and others spread branches which they had cut from the fields.[h] [9]Those who went in front, and those who followed, shouted,[i] "Hosanna.[j] Blessed is he who comes in the name of the Lord.[k] [10]Blessed is the kingdom of our father David.[l] Hosanna in the highest."

[11]And he[m] entered into the temple in Jerusalem. When he had looked around at everything, it being now evening, he went out to Bethany with the twelve.

[12]The next day, when they had come out from Bethany, he was hungry. [13]Seeing a fig tree afar off having leaves, he came to see if perhaps he might find anything on it. When he came to it, he found nothing but leaves, for it was not the season for figs. [14]Jesus told it, "May no one ever eat fruit from you again." and his disciples heard it.

[15]They came to Jerusalem, and he[n] entered into the temple, and began to throw out those who sold and those who bought in the temple, and overthrew the tables of the money changers, and the seats of those who sold the doves. [16]He would not allow anyone to carry a container through the temple. [17]He taught, saying to them, "Is it not written, 'My house will be called a house of prayer for all the nations?'[o] But you have made it a den of robbers."[p]

[18]The chief priests and the scribes[q] heard it, and sought how they might destroy him. For they feared him, because all the crowd was astonished at his teaching.

---

a   10:44 Some Mss lack "among you"
b   10:46 Some Mss read "the blind"
c   10:46 Some Mss add "begging"
d   10:50 Some Mss read "rose"
e   10:52 Some Mss read "Jesus"
f   11:1 Some Mss read "Bethsphage"
g   11:2 Some Mss lack "yet"
h   11:8 Some Mss add "and spread them on the road"
i   11:9 Some Mss add "saying"
j   11:9 "Hosanna" means "save us" or "help us, we pray."
k   11:9 Psalm 118:25-26
l   11:10 Some Mss add "that is coming in the name of the Lord"
m   11:11 Some Mss read "Jesus"
n   11:15 Some Mss read "Jesus"
o   11:17 Isaiah 56:7
p   11:17 Jeremiah 7:11
q   11:18 Some Mss read "scribes and chief priests"

[19]When evening came, they[a] went out of the city. [20]As they passed by in the morning, they saw the fig tree withered away from the roots. [21]Peter, remembering, said to him, "Teacher, look. The fig tree which you cursed has withered away."

[22]Jesus answered them, "Have faith in God. [23]Truly[b] I tell you, whoever may tell this mountain, 'Be taken up and cast into the sea,' and does not doubt in his heart, but believes that what he says will happen, it will be done for him[c]. [24]Therefore I tell you, whatever you ask for in prayer, believe that you have received it, and it will be yours. [25]Whenever you stand praying, forgive, if you have anything against anyone; so that your Father, who is in heaven, may also forgive you your transgressions. [26]But if you do not forgive, neither will your Father in heaven forgive your transgressions."[d]

[27]They came again to Jerusalem, and as he was walking in the temple, the chief priests, and the scribes, and the elders came to him, [28]and they began saying to him, "By what authority do you do these things? And who gave you this authority to do these things?"

[29]Jesus[e] said to them, "I will also ask you one question. Answer me, and I will tell you by what authority I do these things. [30]The baptism of John—was it from heaven, or from people? Answer me."

[31]They reasoned with themselves, saying, "If we should say, 'From heaven;' he will say, 'Why then[f] did you not believe him?' [32]If we should say, 'From people'"— they feared the crowd,[g] for all held John to really be a prophet. [33]They answered and said to Jesus, "We do not know."

Jesus[h] said to them, "Neither do I tell you by what authority I do these things."

12 He began to speak to them in parables. "A man planted a vineyard, put a hedge around it, dug a pit for the winepress, built a tower, rented it out to a farmer, and went on a journey. [2]When it was time, he sent a servant to the farmer to get from the farmer his share of the fruit of the vineyard. [3]They took him, beat him, and sent

him away empty. [4]Again, he sent another servant to them; and they[i] wounded him in the head, and[j] treated him shamefully. [5]And[k] he sent another; and they killed him; and many others, beating some, and killing some. [6]He had one left[l] a beloved son, he sent him last to them, saying, 'They will respect my son.' [7]But those farmers said among themselves, 'This is the heir. Come, let us kill him, and the inheritance will be ours.' [8]They took him, killed him, and cast him out of the vineyard. [9]What therefore will the lord of the vineyard do? He will come and destroy the farmers, and will give the vineyard to others. [10]Haven't you even read this Scripture:

'The stone which the builders rejected,
the same was made the head of the corner.

[11]This was from the Lord.
It is marvelous in our eyes'?"[m]

[12]They tried to seize him, but they feared the crowd; for they perceived that he spoke the parable against them. They left him, and went away. [13]They sent some of the Pharisees and of the Herodians to him, that they might trap him with words. [14]When they had come, they asked him, "Teacher, we know that you are honest, and do not defer to anyone; for you are not partial to anyone, but truly teach the way of God. Is it lawful to pay taxes to Caesar, or not? [15]Should we pay, or should we not pay?"

But he, knowing their hypocrisy, said to them, "Why do you test me? Bring me a denarius, that I may see it."

[16]They brought it.

He said to them, "Whose is this image and inscription?"

a   11:19 Some Mss read "he"
b   11:23 Some Mss read "For truly"
c   11:23 Some Mss add "whatever he says"
d   11:26 Some Mss lack "But if you...transgressions"
e   11:29 Some Mss add "answered and"
f   11:31 Some Mss lack "then"
g   11:32 Some Mss read "people"
h   11:33 Some Mss add "answering"
i   12:4 Some Mss add "threw stones at him"
j   12:4 Some Mss add "sent him away"
k   12:5 Some Mss add "again"
l   12:6 Some Mss read "Therefore still having one"
m   12:11 Psalm 118:22-23

They said to him, "Caesar's."

[17]And Jesus[a] said to them, "Render to Caesar the things that are Caesar's, and to God the things that are God's."

They marveled greatly at him.

[18]There came to him Sadducees, who say that there is no resurrection. They asked him, saying, [19]"Teacher, Moses wrote to us, 'If a man's brother dies, and leaves a wife behind him, and leaves no children, that his brother should take the [b]wife, and raise up offspring for his brother.' [20]There were seven brothers. The first took a wife, and dying left no offspring. [21]The second took her, and died, leaving no[c] children behind him. The third likewise; [22]and the seven[d] left no children. Last of all the woman also died. [23]In the resurrection, when they rise, whose wife will she be of them? For the seven had her as a wife."

[24]Jesus[e] said to them, "Is not this because you are mistaken, not knowing the Scriptures, nor the power of God? [25]For when they will rise from the dead, they neither marry, nor are given in marriage, but are like angels in heaven. [26]But about the dead, that they are raised; have you not read in the book of Moses, about the Bush, how God spoke to him, saying, 'I am the God of Abraham, and the God of Isaac, and the God of Jacob'[f]? [27]He is not the God of the dead, but of the living. You are therefore badly mistaken."

[28]And one of the scribes came, and heard them questioning together. Seeing[g] that he had answered them well, asked him, "Which commandment is the greatest of all?"

[29]Jesus answered,[h] "The first[i] is, 'Hear, Israel, the Lord our God, the Lord is one. [30]And you shall love the Lord your God with all your heart, and with all your soul, and with all your mind, and with all your strength.'[j][k] [31]The second is[l] this, 'You are to love your neighbor as yourself.'[m] There is no other commandment greater than these."

[32]The scribe said to him, "Truly, Teacher, you have said well that he[n] is one, and there is none other but he, [33]and to love him with all the heart, and with all the understanding, and with all the soul,[o] and with all the strength, and to love his neighbor as himself, is more important than all whole burnt offerings and sacrifices."

[34]When Jesus saw that he answered wisely, he said to him, "You are not far from the kingdom of God."

No one dared ask him any question after that. [35]Jesus responded, as he taught in the temple, "How can the scribes say that the Messiah is the son of David? [36]David[p] himself said in the Holy Spirit,

'The Lord said[q] to my Lord,
  "Sit at my right hand,
  until I make your enemies the
    footstool[r] of your feet."'[s]

[37]David[t] himself calls him Lord, so how can he be his son?"

The common people heard him gladly. [38]In his teaching he said to them, "Beware of the scribes, who like to walk in long robes, and to get greetings in the marketplaces, [39]and the best seats in the synagogues, and the best places at feasts: [40]those who devour widows' houses, and for a pretense make long prayers. These will receive greater condemnation."

[41]And he[u] sat down opposite the treasury, and saw how the crowd put money into the treasury. Many who were rich

---

a   12:17 Some Mss add "answered and"
b   12:19 Some Mss read "his"
c   12:21 Some Mss read "and neither did he leave any"
d   12:22 Some Mss add "took her and"
e   12:24 Some Mss add "answered and"
f   12:26 Exodus 3:6
g   12:28 Some Mss read "Knowing"
h   12:29 Some Mss read "Then Jesus answered him"
i   12:29 Some Mss read "The greatest of all the commandments is"
j   12:30 Deuteronomy 6:4-5 and Joshua 22:5 (LXX)
k   12:30 Some Mss add "This is the first commandment"
l   12:31 Some Mss add "like"
m   12:31 Leviticus 19:18
n   12:32 Some Mss read "God"
o   12:33 Some Mss lack "with all the soul"
p   12:36 Some Mss read "For David"
q   12:36 Some Mss read "says"
r   12:36 Some Mss read "beneath"
s   12:36 Psalm 110:1
t   12:37 Some Mss read "Therefore David"
u   12:41 Some Mss read "Jesus"

cast in much. [42]A poor widow came, and she cast in two lepta,[a] which equal a kodrantes.[b] [43]He called his disciples to himself, and said to them, "Truly I tell you, this poor widow gave[c] more than all those who are giving into the treasury, [44]for they all gave out of their abundance, but she, out of her poverty, gave all that she had to live on."

13 As he went out of the temple, one of his disciples said to him, "Teacher, see what kind of stones and what kind of buildings."

[2]And Jesus[d] said to him, "Do you see these great buildings? There will not be left here one stone on another, which will not be thrown down."

[3]As he sat on the Mount of Olives opposite the temple, Peter, James, John, and Andrew asked him privately, [4]"Tell us, when will these things be? What is the sign that these things are all about to be fulfilled?"

[5]And Jesus[e] began to say to them, "Be careful that no one leads you astray. [6]Many[f] will come in my name, saying, 'I am he.'[g] and will lead many astray.

[7]"When you hear of wars and rumors of wars, do not be troubled. Such[h] things must happen, but the end is not yet. [8]For nation will rise against nation, and kingdom against kingdom. There will be earthquakes in various places. There will be famines.[i] These things are the beginning of birth pains. [9]But watch yourselves, for they will deliver you up to councils. You will be beaten in synagogues. You will stand before rulers and kings for my sake, as a testimony to them. [10]The Good News must first be preached to all the nations. [11]When they lead you away and deliver you up, do not be anxious beforehand, or premeditate what you will say, but say whatever will be given you in that hour. For it is not you who speak, but the Holy Spirit.

[12]"Brother will deliver up brother to death, and the father his child. Children will rise up against parents, and cause them to be put to death. [13]You will be hated by all for my name's sake, but he who endures to the end, the same will be saved.

[14]But when you see the abomination of desolation,[j] standing where it ought not (let the reader understand), then let those who are in Judea flee to the mountains, [15]and let him who is on the housetop not go down,[k] nor enter in, to take anything out of his house. [16]Let him who is in the field not return back to take his cloak. [17]But woe to those who are with child and to those who nurse babies in those days. [18]And pray that it[l] won't be in the winter. [19]For in those days there will be oppression, such as there has not been the like from the beginning of the creation which God created until now, and never will be. [20]Unless the Lord had shortened the days, no flesh would have been saved; but for the sake of the chosen ones, whom he picked out, he shortened the days. [21]Then if anyone tells you, 'Look, here is the Messiah.' or, 'Look, there.' do not believe[m] it. [22]For there will arise false messiahs and false prophets, and will show signs and wonders, that they may lead astray, if possible,[n] the chosen ones. [23]But you watch. "I[o] have told you all things beforehand. [24]But in those days, after that oppression, the sun will be darkened, the moon will not give its light, [25]the stars will be falling from heaven, and the powers that are in the heavens will be shaken.[p] [26]Then they will see the Son of Man coming in clouds with great power and glory. [27]Then he will send out his angels, and will gather together his chosen ones from the

a   12:42 The lepton was the least valuable Greek coin
b   12:42 A kodrantes is a coin worth about 1/64 of a denarius. A denarius is about one day's wages for an agricultural laborer.
c   12:43 Some Mss read "having put"
d   13:2 Some Mss add "answered and"
e   13:5 Some Mss add "answering them"
f   13:6 Some Mss read "For many"
g   13:6 Or, "I AM."
h   13:7 Some Mss read "For such"
i   13:8 Some Mss add "and troubles"
j   13:14 Daniel 9:17; 11:31; 12:11. Some Mss add "spoken of by Daniel the prophet"
k   13:15 Some Mss add "into the house"
l   13:18 Some Mss read "your flight"
m   13:21 Some Mss read "stop believing it"
n   13:22 Some Mss add "even"
o   13:23 Some Mss read "Look, I"
p   13:25 Isaiah 13:10; 34:4

four winds, from the farthest part of the earth to the farthest part of the sky.

²⁸"Now from the fig tree, learn this parable. When the branch has now become tender, and puts forth its leaves, you know that the summer is near; ²⁹even so you also, when you see these things coming to pass, know that it is near, at the doors. ³⁰Truly I say to you, this generation will not pass away until all these things happen. ³¹Heaven and earth will pass away, but my words will not pass away. ³²But of that day or the[a] hour no one knows, not even the angels in heaven, nor the Son, but only the Father. ³³Watch, keep alert;[b] for you do not know when the time is.

³⁴"It is like a man, traveling to another country, having left his house, and given authority to his servants, and to each one his work, and also commanded the doorkeeper to keep watch. ³⁵Watch therefore, for you do not know when the lord of the house is coming -- at evening, or at midnight, or when the rooster crows, or in the morning; ³⁶lest coming suddenly he might find you sleeping. ³⁷What I tell you, I tell all: Watch."

14 It was now two days before the feast of the Passover and the unleavened bread, and the chief priests and the scribes sought how they might seize him by deception, and kill him. ²For they said, "Not during the feast, because there might be a riot of the people."

³While he was at Bethany, in the house of Simon the leper, as he was reclining, a woman came having an alabaster jar of ointment of pure nard—very costly. She broke the jar, and poured it over his head. ⁴But there were some who were indignant among themselves, and saying,[c] "Why has this ointment[d] been wasted? ⁵For this ointment might have been sold for more than three hundred denarii,[e] and given to the poor." They grumbled against her.

⁶But Jesus said, "Leave her alone. Why do you trouble her? She has done a good work for me. ⁷For you always have the poor with you, and whenever you want to, you

can do them good; but you will not always have me. ⁸She has done what she could. She has anointed my body beforehand for the burying. ⁹Truly I tell you, wherever this Good News may be preached throughout the whole world, that which this woman has done will also be spoken of for a memorial of her."

¹⁰Judas Iscariot, who was one of the twelve, went away to the chief priests, that he might deliver him to them. ¹¹They, when they heard it, were glad, and promised to give him money. He sought how he might conveniently deliver him. ¹²On the first day of unleavened bread, when they sacrificed the Passover, his disciples asked him, "Where do you want us to go and make ready that you may eat the Passover?"

¹³He sent two of his disciples, and said to them, "Go into the city, and there you will meet a man carrying a pitcher of water. Follow him, ¹⁴and wherever he enters in, tell the master of the house, 'The Teacher says, "Where is my[f] guest room, where I may eat the Passover with my disciples?"' ¹⁵He will himself show you a large upper room furnished and ready. Make ready for us there."

¹⁶The[g] disciples went out, and came into the city, and found things as he had said to them, and they prepared the Passover.

¹⁷When it was evening he came with the twelve. ¹⁸And as they were reclining and eating, Jesus said, "Truly I tell you, one of you will betray me—he who eats with me."

¹⁹And they began to be sorrowful, and to say to him one by one, "Surely not I?" And another said, "Surely not I?"[h]

²⁰He[i] said to them, "It is one of the twelve, he who dips with me in the dish. ²¹For the Son of Man goes, even as it is written about

---

a   13:32 Some Mss lack "the"
b   13:33 Some Mss add "and pray"
c   14:4 Some Mss lack "and saying"
d   14:5 Some Mss lack "ointment"
e   14:5 300 denarii was about a years wages for an agricultural laborer
f   14:14 Some Mss read "the"
g   14:16 Some Mss read "His"
h   14:19 Some Mss lack "And another said, 'Surely not I?,'"
i   14:20 Some Mss add "answered and"

him, but woe to that man by whom the Son of Man is betrayed. It would be better for that man if he had not been born."

²²As they were eating, he[a] took bread, and when he had blessed, he broke it, and gave to them, and said, "Take[b]; this is my body."

²³He took a[c] cup, and when he had given thanks, he gave to them. They all drank of it. ²⁴He said to them, "This is my blood of the new[d] covenant, which is poured out for many. ²⁵Truly I tell you, I will no more drink of the fruit of the vine, until that day when I drink it anew in the kingdom of God." ²⁶When they had sung the hymn, they went out to the Mount of Olives.

²⁷Jesus said to them, "All of you will fall away,[e] for it is written, 'I will strike the shepherd, and the sheep will be scattered.'[f] ²⁸However, after I am raised up, I will go before you into Galilee."

²⁹But Peter said to him, "Although all will be offended, yet I will not."

³⁰Jesus said to him, "Truly I tell you, that today, even this night, before the rooster crows twice, you will deny me three times."

³¹But he insisted,[g] "If I must die with you, I will not deny you." They all said the same thing.

³²They came to a place which was named Gethsemane. He said to his disciples, "Sit here, while I pray." ³³He took with him Peter, James, and John, and began to be greatly troubled and distressed. ³⁴He said to them, "My soul is exceedingly sorrowful, even to death. Stay here, and watch."

³⁵He went forward a little, and fell on the ground, and prayed that, if it were possible, the hour might pass away from him. ³⁶He said, "Abba, Father, all things are possible to you. Please remove this cup from me. However, not what I desire, but what you desire."

³⁷He came and found them sleeping, and said to Peter, "Simon, are you sleeping? Could you not watch one hour? ³⁸Watch and pray, that you may not enter into temptation. The spirit indeed is willing, but the flesh is weak."

³⁹Again he went away, and prayed, saying the same words. ⁴⁰Again he came[h] and found them sleeping again, for their eyes were very heavy, and they did not know what to answer him. ⁴¹He came the third time, and said to them, "Sleep on now, and take your rest. It is enough. The hour has come. Look, the Son of Man is betrayed into the hands of sinners. ⁴²Arise, let us be going. Look, he who betrays me is near."

⁴³Immediately, while he was still speaking, Judas, one of the twelve, came—and with him a[i] crowd with swords and clubs, from the chief priests, the scribes, and the elders. ⁴⁴Now he who betrayed him had given them a sign, saying, "Whomever I will kiss, that is he. Seize him, and lead him away safely." ⁴⁵When he had come, immediately he came to him, and said, "Rabbi."[j] and kissed him. ⁴⁶They laid[k] hands on him, and seized him. ⁴⁷But a certain one of those who stood by drew his sword, and struck the servant of the high priest, and cut off his ear.

⁴⁸Jesus answered them, "Have you come out, as against a robber, with swords and clubs to seize me? ⁴⁹I was daily with you in the temple teaching, and you did not arrest me. But this is so that the Scriptures might be fulfilled."

⁵⁰They all left him, and fled. ⁵¹And a certain young man followed him, having a linen cloth thrown around himself, over his naked body. And they[l] grabbed him, ⁵²but he left the linen cloth, and fled[m] naked. ⁵³They led Jesus away to the high priest. All the chief priests, the elders, and the scribes came together.[n]

⁵⁴Peter had followed him from a distance, until he came into the court of the

---

a   14:22 Some Mss read "Jesus"
b   14:22 Some Mss add "eat"
c   14:23 Some Mss read "the"
d   14:24 Some Mss lack "new"
e   14:27 Some Mss add "because of me tonight"
f   14:27 Zechariah 13:7
g   14:31 Some Mss add "all the more"
h   14:40 Some Mss read "returned"
i   14:43 Some Mss add "great"
j   14:45 Some Mss add "Rabbi"
k   14:46 Some Mss read "their"
l   14:51 Some Mss read "the young men"
m   14:52 Some Mss add "from them"
n   14:53 Some Mss add "with him"

high priest. He was sitting with the officers, and warming himself in the light of the fire. ⁵⁵Now the chief priests and the whole council sought witnesses against Jesus to put him to death, and found none. ⁵⁶For many gave false testimony against him, and their testimony did not agree with each other. ⁵⁷Some stood up, and gave false testimony against him, saying, ⁵⁸"We heard him say, 'I will destroy this temple that is made with hands, and in three days I will build another made without hands.'" ⁵⁹Even so, their testimony did not agree.

⁶⁰The high priest stood up in the midst, and asked Jesus, "Have you no answer? What is it which these testify against you?" ⁶¹But he stayed quiet, and answered nothing. Again the high priest asked him, "Are you the Messiah, the Son of the Blessed One?"

⁶²And Jesus said, "I am, and you will see the Son of Man sitting at the right hand of Power, and coming with the clouds of the sky."

⁶³The high priest tore his clothes, and said, "What further need have we of witnesses? ⁶⁴You have heard the blasphemy. What do you think?" They all condemned him to be worthy of death. ⁶⁵Some began to spit on him, and to cover his face, and to beat him with fists, and to tell him, "Prophesy." And the officers took[a] him and beat him.

⁶⁶Now as Peter was in the courtyard below, one of the servant girls of the high priest came, ⁶⁷and seeing Peter warming himself, she looked at him, and said, "You were also with the Nazarene, Jesus."

⁶⁸But he denied it, saying, "I neither know nor understand what you are saying." And he went out into the forecourt, and a rooster crowed.[b]

⁶⁹And the servant girl saw him, and began again to tell those who stood by, "This is one of them." ⁷⁰But he again denied it. After a little while again those who stood by said to Peter, "You truly are one of them, for you are a Galilean, and your accent shows it."[c] ⁷¹But he began to curse, and to swear, "I do not know this man of whom you speak." ⁷²And immediately[d] the rooster crowed

the second time. Peter remembered the word, how that Jesus said to him, "Before the rooster crows twice, you will deny me three times." When he thought about that, he wept.

15 Immediately in the morning the chief priests, with the elders and scribes, and the whole council, held a consultation, and bound Jesus, and carried him away, and delivered him to Pilate. ²Pilate asked him, "Are you the King of the Jews?"

He answered, "You say so."

³The chief priests accused him of many things. ⁴Pilate again asked him, "Have you no answer? See how many things they testify against you."

⁵But Jesus made no further answer, so that Pilate marveled.

⁶Now at the feast he used to release to them one prisoner, whom they requested. ⁷There was one called Barabbas, bound with those who had made insurrection, who in the insurrection had committed murder. ⁸And the crowd went up[e] and began to ask him to do as he always did for them. ⁹Pilate answered them, saying, "Do you want me to release to you the King of the Jews?" ¹⁰For he perceived that for envy the chief priests had delivered him up. ¹¹But the chief priests stirred up the crowd, that he should release Barabbas to them instead. ¹²Pilate again asked them, "What then should I do to him whom you call the King of the Jews?"

¹³They shouted again, "Crucify him."

¹⁴Pilate said to them, "Why, what evil has he done?"

But they shouted all the louder, "Crucify him."

¹⁵Pilate, wishing to please the crowd, released Barabbas to them, and handed over Jesus, when he had flogged him, to be crucified. ¹⁶The soldiers led him away within the court, which is the Praetorium;

---

a 14:65 Gk. elabon "took." Some Mss read "struck"
b 14:68 Some Mss omit "and a rooster crowed"
c 14:70 Some Mss lack "and your accent shows it"
d 14:72 Some Mss lack "immediately"
e 15:8 Some Mss read "crying aloud"

and they called together the whole cohort. [17]They clothed him with purple, and weaving a crown of thorns, they put it on him. [18]They began to salute him, "Hail, King of the Jews." [19]They struck his head with a reed, and spat on him, and bowing their knees, did homage to him. [20]When they had mocked him, they took the purple off of him, and put his own garments on him. They led him out to crucify him. [21]And they forced one passing by, Simon of Cyrene, coming from the country,[a] the father of Alexander and Rufus, to go with them, that he might carry his cross. [22]And they brought him to the place called Golgotha, which is translated, "The place of a skull.[b]" [23]They offered him[c] wine mixed with myrrh to drink, but he did not take it.

[24]Crucifying him, they parted his garments among them, casting lots on them, what each should take. [25]It was nine in the morning,[d] and they crucified him. [26]The superscription of his accusation was written over him, "THE KING OF THE JEWS." [27]With him they crucified two robbers; one on his right hand, and one on his left. [28]And the Scripture was fulfilled which says, "And he was numbered with transgressors."[e] [29]Those who passed by blasphemed him, wagging their heads, and saying, "Ha. You who destroy the temple, and build it in three days, [30]save yourself.[f] Come down from the cross."

[31]Likewise, also the chief priests mocking among themselves with the scribes said, "He saved others. He cannot save himself. [32]Let the Messiah, the King of Israel, now come down from the cross, that we may see and believe him." Those who were crucified with him insulted him.

[33]Now when it was noon[h], there was darkness over the whole land until three in the afternoon.[i]

[34]Then at three in the afternoon[j] Jesus called out with a loud voice, saying, "Eloi, Eloi, lema sabachthani?" which is translated, "My God, my God, why have you forsaken me?"[k]

[35]Some of those who stood by, when they heard it, said, "Look, he is calling for Elijah."

[36]One ran, and filling a sponge full of vinegar, put it on a reed, and gave it to him to drink, saying, "Let him be. Let us see whether Elijah comes to take him down."

[37]Jesus gave a loud cry, and gave up the spirit. [38]The veil of the temple was torn in two from the top to the bottom. [39]And when the centurion, who stood by opposite him, saw that he cried out[l] like this and breathed his last, he said, "Truly this man was the Son of God."

[40]There were also women watching from afar, among whom were both Mary Magdalene, and Mary the mother of James the younger and of Josi, and Salome; [41]who, when he was in Galilee, followed him, and served him; and many other women who came up with him to Jerusalem.

[42]When evening had now come, because it was the Preparation Day, that is, the day before the Sabbath, [43]Joseph of Arimathaea, a prominent council member who also himself was looking for the kingdom of God, came. He boldly went in to Pilate, and asked for the body of Jesus. [44]Pilate marveled if he were already dead; and summoning the centurion, he asked him whether he had been dead long. [45]When he found out from the centurion, he granted the body to Joseph. [46]He bought a linen cloth, and taking him down, wound him in the linen cloth, and placed him in a tomb which had been cut out of a rock. He rolled a stone against the door of the tomb. [47]Mary Magdalene and Mary, the mother of Josi, saw where he was placed.

16 When the Sabbath was past, Mary Magdalene, and Mary the[m] mother

a   15:21 Or, "from a field"
b   15:22 Known in Latin translations as "Calvary"
c   15:23 Some Mss add "to drink"
d   15:25 Lit. the third hour
e   15:28 Some Mss lack "The Scripture was… transgressors." Isaiah 53:12; Luke 22:37
f   15:30 Some Mss add "and"
g   15:33 Or, "noon"
h   15:33 Amos 8:9
i   15:33 Lit. the sixth hour
j   15:34 Lit. the ninth hour
k   15:34 Psalm 22:1
l   15:39 Some Mss lack "cried out"
m   16:1 Some Mss lack "the"

of James, and Salome, bought spices, that they might come and anoint him. [2]Very early on the first day of the week, they came to the tomb when the sun had risen. [3]They were saying among themselves, "Who will roll away the stone from the door of the tomb for us?" [4]for it was very big. Looking up, they saw that the stone was rolled back.

[5]Entering into the tomb, they saw a young man sitting on the right side, dressed in a white robe, and they were amazed. [6]He said to them, "Do not be amazed. You seek Jesus, the Nazarene, who has been crucified. He has risen. He is not here. Look, the place where they put him. [7]But go, tell his disciples and Peter, 'He goes before you into Galilee. There you will see him, as he said to you.'" [8]They went out, and fled from the tomb, for trembling and astonishment had come on them. They said nothing to anyone; for they were afraid.

[9]Now when he had risen early on the first day of the week, he appeared first to Mary Magdalene,[a] from whom he had cast out seven demons. [10]She went and told those who had been with him,[b] as they mourned and wept. [11]When they heard that he was alive, and had been seen by her, they disbelieved.[c] [12]And after these things he appeared in another form to two of them, as they walked on their way into the country.[d] [13]And they went away and told it to the rest.[e] They did not believe them, either.

[14]Afterward he was revealed to the eleven themselves as they were reclining,[f] and he rebuked them for their unbelief and hardness of heart, because they did not believe those who had seen him after he had risen. [15]And he said to them, "Go into all the world, and proclaim the Good News to the whole creation.[g] [16]He who believes and is baptized will be saved[h]; but he who disbelieves will be condemned. [17]And these signs will accompany those who believe: In my name they will cast out demons;[i] they will speak with new tongues;[j] [18]they will pick up[k] serpents;[l] and if they drink any deadly thing, it will not harm them; they will lay hands on the sick, and they will recover."[m]

[19]So then the Lord Jesus,[n] after he had spoken to them, was taken up into heaven,[o] and sat down at the right hand of God.[p] [20]And they went out and preached everywhere, the Lord working with them and confirming the message by the signs that followed.[q]

Luke

1 Since many have undertaken to set in order a narrative concerning those matters which have been fulfilled among us, [2]even as those who from the beginning were eyewitnesses and servants of the word delivered them to us, [3]it seemed good to me also, having traced the course of all things accurately from the first, to write to you in order, most excellent Theophilus; [4]that you might know the certainty concerning the things in which you were instructed.

[5]There was in the days of Herod, the king of Judea, a certain priest named Zechariah, of the division of Abijah. He had a wife of the daughters of Aaron, and her name was Elizabeth. [6]They were both righteous before God, walking blamelessly in all the commandments and ordinances of the Lord.

[7]But they had no child, because Elizabeth was barren, and they both were well advanced in years. [8]Now it happened, while

a   16:9 John 20:14
b   16:10 John 20:18
c   16:11 Luke 24:11
d   16:12 Luke 24:13-32
e   16:13 Luke 24:33-35
f   16:14 Luke 24:36; John 20:19
g   16:15 Colossians 1:23
h   16:16 1 Peter 3:21
i   16:17 Matthew 10:8; Mark 3:15; Luke 10:17
j   16:17 Acts 2:4; 1Co 12:10-30, 14:5-39
k   16:18 Some Mss add "with their hands"
l   16:18 Luke 10:19; Acts 28:3-5
m   16:18 Matthew 10:8; Mark 3:15; Luke 10:9
n   16:19 Some Mss lack "Jesus"
o   16:19 Luke 24:51; Acts 1:9
p   16:19 Colossians 3:1; Hebrews 10:12, 12:2
q   16:20 Acts 2:43, 4:30, 6:8, 8:6, 14:3; Hebrews 2:4.
     Some Mss add "Amen." A few Mss lack vv. 9-20

he was performing the priest's office before God in the order of his division, [9]according to the custom of the priest's office, his lot was to enter into the temple of the Lord and burn incense. [10]And the whole crowd of people were praying outside at the hour of incense.

[11]An angel of the Lord appeared to him, standing on the right side of the altar of incense. [12]Zechariah was troubled when he saw him, and fear fell upon him. [13]But the angel said to him, "Do not be afraid, Zechariah, because your request has been heard, and your wife, Elizabeth, will bear you a son, and you are to name him John.[a] [14]You will have joy and gladness; and many will rejoice at his birth. [15]For he will be great in the sight of the[b] Lord, and he will drink no wine nor strong drink. He will be filled with the Holy Spirit, even from his mother's womb. [16]He will turn many of the sons of Israel to the Lord, their God. [17]He will go before him in the spirit and power of Elijah, 'to turn the hearts of the fathers to the children,' and the disobedient to the wisdom of the just; to make ready a people prepared for the Lord."

[18]Zechariah said to the angel, "How can I be sure of this? For I am an old man, and my wife is well advanced in years."

[19]The angel answered him, "I am Gabriel, who stands in the presence of God. I was sent to speak to you, and to bring you this good news. [20]And look, you will be silent and not able to speak, until the day that these things will happen, because you did not believe my words, which will be fulfilled in their proper time."

[21]The people were waiting for Zechariah, and they marveled that he delayed in the temple. [22]When he came out, he could not speak to them, and they perceived that he had seen a vision in the temple. He continued making signs to them, and remained mute. [23]It happened, when the days of his service were fulfilled, he departed to his house. [24]After these days Elizabeth, his wife, conceived, and she hid herself five months, saying, [25]"Thus has the Lord done to me in the days in which

he looked at me, to take away my reproach among people."

[26]Now in the sixth month, the angel Gabriel was sent from God to a city of Galilee, named Nazareth, [27]to a virgin pledged to be married to a man whose name was Joseph, of the house of David. The virgin's name was Mary. [28]Having come in, the angel said to her, "Greetings, favored one. The Lord is with you.[c]"

[29]But when she saw him, she was greatly troubled at the saying, and considered what kind of salutation this might be. [30]The angel said to her, "Do not be afraid, Mary, for you have found favor with God. [31]And look, you will conceive in your womb, and bring forth a son, and will call his name 'Jesus.' [32]He will be great, and will be called the Son of the Most High. The Lord God will give him the throne of his father, David, [33]and he will reign over the house of Jacob forever.[d] There will be no end to his kingdom."

[34]Mary said to the angel, "How can this be, seeing I am a virgin?"

[35]The angel answered her, "The Holy Spirit will come on you, and the power of the Most High will overshadow you. Therefore also the holy one who is born will be called the Son of God. [36]And look, Elizabeth, your relative, also has conceived a son in her old age; and this is the sixth month with her who was called barren. [37]For with God nothing will be impossible."

[38]And Mary said, "See, the handmaid of the Lord; be it to me according to your word."

The angel departed from her. [39]Mary arose in those days and went into the hill country with haste, into a city of Judah, [40]and entered into the house of Zechariah and greeted Elizabeth. [41]It happened, when Elizabeth heard Mary's greeting, that the baby leaped in her womb, and Elizabeth

---

a   1:13 Meaning "God gives grace"
b   1:15 Some Mss lack "the"
c   1:28 Some Mss add "Blessed are you among women"
d   1:33 Daniel 2:44; 7:14, 18, 27; Hebrews 1:8; Revelation 11:15

was filled with the Holy Spirit. [42]She called out with a loud voice, and said, "Blessed are you among women, and blessed is the fruit of your womb. [43]Why am I so favored, that the mother of my Lord should come to me? [44]For look, when the voice of your greeting came into my ears, the baby leaped in my womb for joy. [45]Blessed is she who believed, for there will be a fulfillment of the things which have been spoken to her from the Lord."

[46]Mary said,

"My soul magnifies the Lord.
[47]And my spirit rejoices in God my
    Savior,
[48]for he has looked at the humble
    state of his servant girl.[a]
For look, from now on all generations
    will call me blessed.
[49]For he who is mighty has done
    great[b] things for me,
and holy is his name.
[50]His mercy is for generations of
    generations on those who fear
    him.[c]
[51]He has shown strength with his arm.
He has scattered the proud in the
    imagination of their hearts.
[52]He has put down princes from their
    thrones.
And has exalted the lowly.
[53]He has filled the hungry with good
    things.[d]
He has sent the rich away empty.
[54]He has given help to Israel, his
    servant, that he might
    remember mercy,
[55]As he spoke to our fathers,
to Abraham and his offspring
    forever."

[56]Mary stayed with her about three months, and then returned to her house. [57]Now the time that Elizabeth should give birth was fulfilled, and she brought forth a son. [58]Her neighbors and her relatives heard that the Lord had magnified his mercy towards her, and they rejoiced with her. [59]It happened on the eighth day, that they came to circumcise the child; and they would have called him Zechariah,

after the name of the father. [60]His mother answered, "Not so; but he will be called John."

[61]They said to her, "There is no one among your relatives who is called by this name." [62]They made signs to his father, what he would have him called.

[63]And he asked for a writing tablet, and wrote, "His name is John."

And they were all amazed. [64]His mouth was opened immediately, and his tongue freed, and he spoke, blessing God. [65]Fear came on all who lived around them, and all these sayings were talked about throughout all the hill country of Judea. [66]All who heard them laid them up in their heart, saying, "What then will this child be?" The hand of the Lord was with him. [67]His father, Zechariah, was filled with the Holy Spirit, and prophesied, saying,

[68]"Blessed be the Lord, the God of
    Israel,
for he has visited and worked
    redemption for his people;
[69]and has raised up a horn of salvation
    for us in the house of his
    servant David
[70](as he spoke by the mouth of his
    holy prophets who have been
    from of old),
[71]salvation from our enemies, and
    from the hand of all who hate
    us;
[72]to show mercy towards our fathers,
to remember his holy covenant,
[73]the oath which he spoke to Abraham,
    our father,
[74]to grant to us that we, being
    delivered out of the hand of our
    enemies,
should serve him without fear,
[75]In holiness and righteousness
    before him all our days.[e]
[76]And you, child, will be called a
    prophet of the Most High,

---

a   1:48 1 Samuel 2:1, 1:11
b   1:49 Some Mss read "marvelous"
c   1:50 Psalm 103:17
d   1:53 Psalm 107:9
e   1:75 Some Mss read "all the days of our life"

for you will go before[a] the Lord to
   make ready his ways,[b]
[77]to give knowledge of salvation to
   his people by the remission of
   their sins,
[78]because of the tender mercy of our
   God,
   whereby the dawn from on high will[c]
   visit us,
[79]to shine on those who sit in
   darkness and the shadow of
   death;[d]
   to guide our feet into the way of
   peace."

[80]The child was growing, and becoming strong in spirit, and was in the desert until the day of his public appearance to Israel.

2 Now it happened in those days, that a decree went out from Caesar Augustus that all the world should be enrolled. [2]This was the first enrollment made when Quirinius was governor of Syria. [3]All went to enroll themselves, everyone to his own city. [4]Joseph also went up from Galilee, out of the city of Nazareth, into Judea, to the city of David, which is called Bethlehem, because he was of the house and family of David; [5]to enroll himself with Mary, who was pledged to be married to him,[e] being pregnant.

[6]It happened, while they were there, that the day had come that she should give birth. [7]She brought forth her firstborn son, and she wrapped him in bands of cloth, and placed him in a feeding trough, because there was no room for them in the inn. [8]There were shepherds in the same country staying in the field, and keeping watch by night over their flock. [9]And look, an angel of the Lord stood by them, and the glory of the Lord shone around them, and they were terrified. [10]The angel said to them, "Do not be afraid, for see, I bring you good news of great joy which will be to all the people. [11]For there is born to you, this day, in the city of David, a Savior, who is Messiah, the Lord. [12]This is the sign to you: you will find a baby wrapped in strips of cloth, lying in a feeding trough." [13]Sudden-

ly, there was with the angel a multitude of the heavenly host praising God, and saying,
[14]"Glory to God in the highest,
   and on earth peace,
   good will toward humanity."[f]

[15]And it happened that when the angels went away from them into the sky,[g] the shepherds said one to another, "Let us go to Bethlehem, now, and see this thing that has happened, which the Lord has made known to us." [16]They came with haste, and found both Mary and Joseph, and the baby was lying in the feeding trough. [17]When they saw it, they made known[h] the saying which was spoken to them about this child. [18]All who heard it wondered at the things which were spoken to them by the shepherds. [19]But Mary kept all these sayings, pondering them in her heart. [20]The shepherds returned, glorifying and praising God for all the things that they had heard and seen, just as it was told them.

[21]When eight days were fulfilled to circumcise him,[i] his name was called Jesus, which was given by the angel before he was conceived in the womb.

[22]When the days of their[j] purification according to the Law of Moses were fulfilled, they brought him up to Jerusalem, to present him to the Lord [23](as it is written in the Law of the Lord, "Every male who opens the womb will be called holy to the Lord"),[k] [24]and to offer a sacrifice according to that which is said in the Law of the Lord, "A pair of turtledoves, or two young pigeons."[l]

[25]And look, there was a man in Jerusalem whose name was Simeon. This man

---

a 1:76 Some Mss add "the face of"
b 1:76 Malachi 3:1; Isaiah 40:3-5
c 1:78 Some Mss read "has"
d 1:79 Isaiah 9:1-2; 42:7; 49:9-10
e 2:5 Some Mss add "as wife"
f 2:14 Some Mss read "among humanity with whom he is pleased"
g 2:15 Some Mss add "that the men"
h 2:17 Some Mss read "publicized"
i 2:21 Some Mss read "the child." Leviticus 12:3
j 2:22 Some Mss read "her"
k 2:23 Exodus 13:2,12
l 2:24 Leviticus 12:8

was righteous and devout, looking for the consolation of Israel,[a] and the Holy Spirit was on him. [26]It had been revealed to him by the Holy Spirit that he should not see death before he had seen the Lord's Messiah. [27]He came in the Spirit into the temple. When the parents brought in the child, Jesus, that they might do concerning him according to the requirement of the Law, [28]then he received him into his arms, and blessed God, and said,

[29]"Now you are releasing your servant, Lord,

according to your word, in peace;
[30]for my eyes have seen your salvation,
[31]which you have prepared before the face of all peoples;
[32]a light for revelation to the nations, and the glory of your people Israel."

[33]And his father[b] and his mother were marveling at the things which were spoken concerning him, [34]and Simeon blessed them, and said to Mary, his mother, "Look, this child is set for the falling and the rising of many in Israel, and for a sign which is spoken against. [35]Yes, a sword will pierce through your own soul, that the thoughts of many hearts may be revealed."

[36]There was one Anna, a prophetess, the daughter of Penuel, of the tribe of Asher (she was of a great age, having lived with a husband seven years from her virginity, [37]and she had been a widow for about eighty-four years), who did not depart from the temple, worshipping with fastings and petitions night and day. [38]Coming up at that very hour, she gave thanks to God,[c] and spoke of him to all those who were looking for the redemption of[d] Jerusalem.

[39]When they had accomplished all things that were according to the Law of the Lord, they returned into Galilee, to their own city, Nazareth. [40]The child was growing, and was becoming strong,[e] being filled with wisdom, and the grace of God was upon him. [41]His parents went every year to Jerusalem at the feast of the Passover.

[42]When he was twelve years old, they went up[f] according to the custom of the feast, [43]and when they had fulfilled the days, as they were returning, the boy Jesus stayed behind in Jerusalem. His parents[g] did not know it, [44]but supposing him to be in the company, they went a day's journey, and they looked for him among their relatives and acquaintances. [45]When they did not find him, they returned to Jerusalem, looking for him. [46]It happened after three days they found him in the temple, sitting in the midst of the teachers, both listening to them, and asking them questions. [47]All who heard him were amazed at his understanding and his answers. [48]When they saw him, they were astonished, and his mother said to him, "Son, why have you treated us this way? Look, your father and I were anxiously looking for you."

[49]He said to them, "Why were you looking for me? Did you not know that I must be doing the works of my Father?" [50]They did not understand the saying which he spoke to them. [51]And he went down with them, and came to Nazareth. He was subject to them, and his mother kept all these sayings in her heart. [52]And Jesus increased in wisdom and stature, and in favor with God and people.

3 Now in the fifteenth year of the reign of Tiberius Caesar, Pontius Pilate being governor of Judea, and Herod being tetrarch of Galilee, and his brother Philip tetrarch of the region of Ituraea and Trachonitis, and Lysanias tetrarch of Abilene, [2]in the high priesthood of Annas and Caiaphas, the word of God came to John, the son of Zechariah, in the wilderness. [3]He came into all the region around the[h] Jordan, preaching a baptism of repentance for remission of sins. [4]As it is written in the scroll of the words of Isaiah the prophet,

---

a 2:25 Isaiah 40:1; 49: 13; 51:3; 57:18; 61:2
b 2:33 Some Mss read "Joseph"
c 2:38 Some Mss read "the Lord"
d 2:38 Some Mss read "in"
e 2:40 Some Mss add "in spirit"
f 2:42 Some Mss add "to Jerusalem"
g 2:43 Some Mss read "Joseph and his mother"
h 3:3 Some Mss lack "the"

"The voice of one crying in the
    wilderness,
'Prepare the way of the Lord.
Make his roads straight.
[5]Every valley will be filled,
and every mountain and hill will be
    made low;
    and the crooked will be made
        straight,
    and the rough ways smooth.
[6]And all flesh will see the salvation of
    God.'"[a]

[7]He said therefore to the crowds who
went out to be baptized by him, "You offspring of vipers, who warned you to flee
from the wrath to come? [8]Bring forth
therefore fruits worthy of repentance, and
do not begin to say among yourselves, 'We
have Abraham for our father;' for I tell you
that God is able to raise up children to
Abraham from these stones. [9]Even now the
axe also lies at the root of the trees. Every
tree therefore that does not bring forth
good fruit is cut down, and thrown into
the fire."

[10]The crowds asked him, "What then
must we do?"

[11]He answered them, "He who has two
coats, let him give to him who has none.
He who has food, let him do likewise."

[12]Tax collectors also came to be baptized, and they said to him, "Teacher, what
must we do?"

[13]He said to them, "Collect no more than
that which is appointed to you."

[14]Soldiers also asked him, saying, "What
about us? What must we do?"

He said to them, "Extort from no one by
violence, neither accuse anyone wrongfully. Be content with your wages."

[15]As the people were in expectation,
and all were wondering in their hearts
concerning John, whether perhaps he was
the Messiah, [16]John answered them all,
"I indeed baptize you with water, but he
comes who is mightier than I, the strap of
whose sandals I am not worthy to loosen.
He will baptize you with the Holy Spirit
and with fire, [17]whose winnowing fork is
in his hand, to[b] clear his threshing floor,

and to[c] gather the wheat into his barn; but
he will burn up the chaff with unquenchable fire."

[18]Then with many other exhortations
he preached good news to the people, [19]but
Herod the tetrarch, being reproved by him
for Herodias, his brother's[d] wife, and for
all the evil things which Herod had done,
[20]added this also to them all, that[e] he shut
up John in prison. [21]Now it happened,
when all the people were baptized, Jesus
also had been baptized, and was praying.
The sky was opened, [22]and the Holy Spirit
descended in a bodily form as a dove on
him; and a voice came out of the sky, saying "You are my beloved Son. In you I am
well pleased."

[23]When he began, Jesus was about thirty
years old, being the son, as was supposed,
of Joseph, of Eli, [24]of Matthat,[f] of Levi, of
Melchi, of Janna,[g] of Joseph, [25]of Mattithiah, of Amos, of Nahum, of Hesli, of Naggai,
[26]of Mahath, of Mattithiah, of Shimei,[h] of
Joseph,[i] of Judah,[j] [27]of Johanan, of Rhesa,
of Zerubbabel, of Shealtiel, of Neri, [28]of
Melchi, of Addi, of Cosam, of Elmodam,[k]
of Er, [29]of Josi,[l] of Eliezer, of Jorim, of Matthat, of Levi, [30]of Simeon, of Judah, of Joseph, of Jonan,[m] of Eliakim, [31]of Maleah,
of Menan,[n] of Mattathah, of Nathan,[o] of
David, [32]of Jesse, of Obed,[p] of Boaz,[q] of
Salmon,[r] of Nahshon, [33]of Amminadab, of
Ram,[s] of Hezron, of Perez, of Judah, [34]of
Jacob, of Isaac, of Abraham, of Terah, of

a   3:6 Isaiah 40:3-5
b   3:17 Some Mss read "and he will"
c   3:17 Some Mss read "will"
d   3:19 Some Mss read "brother Philip's"
e   3:20 Some Mss lack "that"
f   3:24 Some Mss read "Maththat"
g   3:24 Some Mss read "Jannai"
h   3:26 Some Mss read "Semein"
i   3:26 Some Mss read "Josech"
j   3:26 Some Mss read "Jodah"
k   3:28 Some Mss read "Elmadam"
l   3:29 Some Mss read "Jesus"
m 3:30 Some Mss read "Jonam"
n   3:31 Some Mss read "Menna"
o   3:31 Some Mss read "Natham"
p   3:32 Some Mss read "Jobed." 1Chronicles 2:12
q   3:32 Gk. Booz. Some Mss read Boos
r   3:32 Some Mss read "Sala." 1 Chronicles 2:11
s   3:33 Some Mss read "Admin of Arni." Ruth 4:19

Nahor, [35]of Serug, of Reu, of Peleg,[a] of Eber, of Shelah, [36]of Kenan,[b] of Arpachshad,[c] of Shem, of Noah, of Lamech, [37]of Methuselah, of Enoch, of Jared,[d] of Mahalalel, of Kenan, [38]of Enosh, of Seth, of Adam, of God.

4 Jesus, full of the Holy Spirit, returned from the Jordan, and was led by the Spirit into the wilderness [2]for forty days, being tempted by the devil. He ate nothing in those days.[e] When they were completed, he was hungry. [3]The devil said to him, "If you are the Son of God, command this stone to become bread."

[4]Jesus answered him, saying, "It is written, 'Man does not live by bread alone.'[f] "[g]

[5]And the devil, taking him up to a high mountain,[h] showed him all the kingdoms of the world in a moment of time. [6]The devil said to him, "I will give you all this authority, and their glory, for it has been delivered to me; and I give it to whomever I want. [7]If you therefore will worship before me, it will all be yours."

[8]Jesus answered and said to him,[i] "It is written, 'You are to worship the Lord your God, and serve him only.'"[j]

[9]He led him to Jerusalem, and set him on the pinnacle of the temple, and said to him, "If you are the Son of God, cast yourself down from here, [10]for it is written,

'He will put his angels in charge
    of you, to guard you;'

[11]and,

'On their hands they will bear you up,
    lest perhaps you dash your foot
        against a stone.'"[k]

[12]And Jesus, answering, said to him, "It is said, 'Do not test the Lord your God.'"[l]

[13]When the devil had completed every temptation, he departed from him until another time.

[14]Jesus returned in the power of the Spirit into Galilee, and news about him spread through all the surrounding area. [15]He taught in their synagogues, being praised by all.

[16]He came to Nazareth, where he had been brought up. He entered, as was his custom, into the synagogue on the Sabbath day, and stood up to read. [17]The scroll of the prophet Isaiah was handed to him. He opened the scroll, and found the place where it was written,

[18]"The Spirit of the Lord is upon me, because he has anointed me to preach good news to the poor. He has sent me to heal the brokenhearted,[m] to proclaim liberty to the captives, recovering of sight to the blind, to deliver those who are crushed, [19]and to proclaim the acceptable year of the Lord."[n]

[20]He closed the scroll, gave it back to the attendant, and sat down. The eyes of all in the synagogue were fastened on him. [21]He began to tell them, "Today, this Scripture has been fulfilled in your hearing."

[22]All testified about him, and wondered at the gracious words which proceeded out of his mouth, and they said, "Is not this Joseph's son?"

[23]He said to them, "Doubtless you will tell me this parable, 'Physician, heal yourself. Whatever we have heard done at Capernaum, do also here in your hometown.'" [24]He said, "Truly I tell you, no prophet is acceptable in his hometown. [25]But truly I tell you, there were many widows in Israel in the days of Elijah, when the sky was shut up three years and six months, when a great famine came over all the land. [26]Elijah was sent to none of them, except to Zarephath, in the land of Sidon, to a woman who was a widow. [27]There

---

a   3:35 Gk. Phaleg. Some Mss read "Phalek."
    1 Chronicles 1:25
b   3:36 Gk. Cainan (here and in v. 37), a spelling used
    in the Greek LXX for Hebrew Kenan. Some Mss read
    Cainam
c   3:36 Gk. Arphaxad, a spelling used in the Greek LXX
    for Hebrew Arpachshad
d   3:37 Some Mss read "Jaret." Genesis 5:15
e   4:2 Some Mss add "Afterward"
f   4:4 Some Mss add "but by every word of God"
g   4:4 Deuteronomy 8:3
h   4:5 Some Mss lack "the devil... up to a high
    mountain"
i   4:8 Some Mss add "Get behind me Satan"
j   4:8 Deuteronomy 6:13
k   4:11 Psalm 91:11-12
l   4:12 Deuteronomy 6:16
m   4:18 Some Mss lack "to heal the brokenhearted"
n   4:19 Isaiah 61:1-2

were many lepers in Israel in the time of Elisha the prophet, yet not one of them was cleansed, except Naaman, the Syrian."

²⁸They were all filled with wrath in the synagogue, as they heard these things. ²⁹They rose up, threw him out of the city, and led him to the brow of the hill that their city was built on, that they might throw him off the cliff. ³⁰But he, passing through the midst of them, went his way.

³¹He came down to Capernaum, a city of Galilee. He was teaching them on the Sabbath day, ³²and they were astonished at his teaching, for his word was with authority. ³³In the synagogue there was a man who had a spirit of an unclean demon, and he shouted with a loud voice, ³⁴saying, "Ah, what have we to do with you, Jesus, Nazarene? Have you come to destroy us? I know you who you are: the Holy One of God."

³⁵Jesus rebuked him, saying, "Be silent, and come out of him." When the demon had thrown him down in their midst, he came out of him, having done him no harm.

³⁶Amazement came on all, and they spoke together, one with another, saying, "What is this word? For with authority and power he commands the unclean spirits, and they come out." ³⁷News about him went out into every place of the surrounding region.

³⁸He rose up from the synagogue, and entered into Simon's house. Simon's mother-in-law was afflicted with a great fever, and they begged him for her. ³⁹He stood over her, and rebuked the fever; and it left her. Immediately she rose up and served them. ⁴⁰When the sun was setting, all those who had any sick with various diseases brought them to him; and he laid his hands on every one of them, and healed them. ⁴¹Demons also came out from many, crying out, and saying, "You are the[a] Son of God." But he rebuked them and did not allow them to speak, because they knew that he was the Messiah.

⁴²When it was day, he departed and went into an uninhabited place, and the crowds looked for him, and came to him, and held on to him, so that he would not go away from them. ⁴³But he said to them, "I must proclaim the good news of the kingdom of God to the other cities also. For this reason I have been sent." ⁴⁴And he was preaching in the synagogues of Galilee.[b]

5 Now it happened, while the crowd pressed on him and heard the word of God, that he was standing by the lake of Gennesaret.[c] ²He saw two boats standing by the lake, but the fishermen had gone out of them, and were washing their nets. ³He entered into one of the boats, which was Simon's, and asked him to put out a little from the land. He sat down and taught the crowds from the boat. ⁴When he had finished speaking, he said to Simon, "Put out into the deep, and let down your nets for a catch."

⁵Simon answered him, "Master, we worked all night, and took nothing; but at your word I will let down the nets.[d]" ⁶When they had done this, they caught a great multitude of fish, and their net was breaking. ⁷They beckoned to their partners in the other boat, that they should come and help them. They came, and filled both boats, so that they began to sink. ⁸But Simon Peter, when he saw it, fell down at Jesus' knees, saying, "Depart from me, for I am a sinful man, Lord." ⁹For he was amazed, and all who were with him, at the catch of fish which they had caught; ¹⁰and so also were James and John, sons of Zebedee, who were partners with Simon.

Jesus said to Simon, "Do not be afraid. From now on you will be catching people."

¹¹When they had brought their boats to land, they left everything, and followed him. ¹²It happened, while he was in one of the cities, look, there was a man full of leprosy. When he saw Jesus, he fell on his face, and begged him, saying, "Lord, if you want to, you can make me clean."

---

a   4:41 Some Mss add "Christ, the"
b   4:44 Some Mss read "Judea"
c   5:1 Meaning, "garden of the prince"
d   5:5 Some Mss read "net"

¹³And he stretched out his hand, and touched him, saying, "I am willing. Be cleansed."

Immediately the leprosy left him. ¹⁴He commanded him to tell no one, "But go your way, and show yourself to the priest, and offer for your cleansing according to what Moses commanded, for a testimony to them." ¹⁵But the report concerning him spread much more, and large crowds came together to hear, and to be healed[a] of their infirmities. ¹⁶But he withdrew himself into the desert, and prayed.

¹⁷It happened on one of those days, that he was teaching; and there were Pharisees and teachers of the Law sitting by, who had come out of every village of Galilee, Judea, and Jerusalem. The power of the Lord was with him to heal.[b] ¹⁸And look, men brought a paralyzed man on a cot, and they sought to bring him[c] in to lay before him. ¹⁹Not finding a way to bring him in because of the crowd, they went up to the housetop, and let him down through the tiles with his cot into the midst before Jesus. ²⁰Seeing their faith, he said,[d] "Man, your sins are forgiven you."

²¹The scribes and the Pharisees began to reason, saying, "Who is this that speaks blasphemies? Who can forgive sins, but God alone?"

²²But Jesus, perceiving their thoughts, answered them, "Why are you reasoning so in your hearts? ²³Which is easier to say, 'Your sins are forgiven you;' or to say, 'Arise and walk?' ²⁴But that you may know that the Son of Man has authority on earth to forgive sins" (he said to the paralyzed man), "I tell you, arise, and take up your cot, and go to your house."

²⁵Immediately he rose up before them, and took up that which he was laying on, and departed to his house, glorifying God. ²⁶Amazement took hold on all, and they glorified God. They were filled with fear, saying, "We have seen remarkable things today."

²⁷After these things he went out, and saw a tax collector named Levi sitting at the tax office, and said to him, "Follow me."

²⁸He left everything, and rose up and followed him. ²⁹Levi made a great feast for him in his house. There was a large crowd of tax collectors and others who were reclining with them. ³⁰The Pharisees and their scribes[e] grumbled at his disciples, saying, "Why do you eat and drink with the tax collectors and sinners?" ³¹Jesus answered them, "Those who are healthy have no need for a physician, but those who are sick do. ³²I have not come to call the righteous, but sinners to repentance."

³³They said to him, "The disciples of John[f] often fast and pray, likewise also the disciples of the Pharisees, but yours eat and drink."

³⁴He said to them, "Can you make the friends of the bridegroom fast, while the bridegroom is with them? ³⁵But the days will come when the bridegroom will be taken away from them. Then they will fast in those days." ³⁶He also told a parable to them. "No one having torn[g] a piece from a new garment puts it on an old garment, or else he will tear the new, and also the piece from the new will not match the old. ³⁷And no one puts new wine into old wineskins, or else the new wine will burst the skins, and it will be spilled, and the skins will be destroyed. ³⁸But new wine must be put into fresh wineskins.[h] ³⁹And[i] no one having drunk old wine[j] desires new, for he says, 'The old is good.[k]'"

6 Now it happened on the second chief[l] Sabbath that he was going through the grain fields. His disciples plucked the heads of grain, and ate, rubbing them in

---

a   5:15 Some Mss add "by him"
b   5:17 Some Mss read "was present to heal them"
c   5:18 Some Mss lack "him"
d   5:20 Some Mss add "to him"
e   5:30 Some Mss read "Their scribes and the Pharisees"
f   5:33 Some Mss read "Why do John's disciples"
g   5:36 Some Mss read "puts"
h   5:38 Some Mss add "and both are preserved"
i   5:39 Some Mss lack "And"
j   5:39 Some Mss add "immediately"
k   5:39 Some Mss read "better"
l   6:1 Possibly the second first-fruits offering, on the Feast of Weeks. Some Mss lack "second chief"

their hands. ²But some of the Pharisees said,ᵃ "Why do you do that which is not lawfulᵇ on the Sabbath day?"

³Jesus, answering them, said, "Have you not read what David did when he was hungry, he, and those who were with him; ⁴how he entered into the house of God, and took and ate the show bread, and gave also to those who were with him, which is not lawful to eat except for the priests alone?" ⁵He said to them, "The Son of Man is lord of the Sabbath."

⁶It also happened on another Sabbath that he entered into the synagogue and taught. There was a man there, and his right hand was withered. ⁷The scribes and the Pharisees watched himᶜ, to see whether he would heal on the Sabbath, that they might find an accusation against him. ⁸But he knew their thoughts; and he said to the man who had the withered hand, "Rise up, and stand in the middle." He arose and stood. ⁹Then Jesus said to them, "I ask youᵈ, is it lawful on the Sabbath to do good, or to do harm? To save a life, or to destroy itᵉ?" ¹⁰He looked around at them all, and said to the man,ᶠ "Stretch out your hand." He did, and his hand was restored.ᵍ ¹¹But they were filled with rage, and talked with one another about what they might do to Jesus.

¹²It happened in these days, that he went out to the mountain to pray, and he continued all night in prayer to God. ¹³When it was day, he called his disciples, and from them he chose twelve, whom he also named apostles: ¹⁴Simon, whom he also named Peter, and Andrew his brother; James; John; Philip; Bartholomew; ¹⁵Matthew; Thomas; James, the son of Alphaeus; Simon, who was called the Zealot; ¹⁶Judas the son of James; and Judas Iscariot, who also became a traitor. ¹⁷He came down with them, and stood on a level place, with a largeʰ crowd of his disciples, and a great number of the people from all Judea and Jerusalem, and the sea coast of Tyre and Sidon, ¹⁸who came to hear him and to be healed of their diseases; who came to hear him and to be healed of their diseases; and those who were troubled with unclean

spirits were cured. ¹⁹All the crowd sought to touch him, for power came out from him and healed them all.

²⁰He lifted up his eyes to his disciples, and said,

"Blessed are you who are poor,
for yours is the kingdom of God.
²¹Blessed are you who hunger now,
for you will be filled.
Blessed are you who weep now,
for you will laugh.
²²Blessed are you when people hate you,
and when they exclude you and
insult you, and throw out your
name as evil, for the Son of
Man's sake.
²³Rejoice in that day, and leap for joy,
for look, your reward is great
in heaven, for their fathers
did the same thing to the
prophets.

²⁴"But woe to you who are rich.
For you have received your
consolation.
²⁵Woe to you, you who are full now,ⁱ
for you will be hungry.
Woe to you who laugh now,
for you will mourn and weep.
²⁶Woe to youʲ when allᵏ people speak
well of you,
for their fathers did the same thingˡ
to the false prophets.

²⁷"But I tell you who hear: love your enemies, do good to those who hate you, ²⁸bless those who curse you, and pray for those who mistreat you. ²⁹To him who strikes you on the cheek, offer also the other; and from him who takes away your cloak, do not

a 6:2 Some Mss add "to them"
b 6:2 Some Mss add "to do"
c 6:7 Some Mss lack "him"
d 6:9 Some Mss read "I will ask you something"
e 6:9 Some Mss read "or to kill"
f 6:10 Some Mss read "to the man"
g 6:10 Some Mss add "as sound as the other"
h 6:17 Some Mss lack "large"
i 6:25 Some Mss lack "now"
j 6:26 The words "to you" are supplied because of English requirements
k 6:26 Some Mss lack "all"
l 6:26 Some Mss lack "fathers did the same thing"

withhold your coat also. ³⁰Give to everyone who asks you, and do not ask him who takes away your goods to give them back again.

³¹"And as you would like people to do to you,[a] do the same to them. ³²If you love those who love you, what credit is that to you? For even sinners love those who love them. ³³If you do good to those who do good to you, what credit is that to you? For even sinners do the same. ³⁴If you lend to those from whom you hope to receive, what credit is that to you? Even sinners lend to sinners, to receive back as much. ³⁵But love your enemies, and do good, and lend, expecting nothing back; and your reward will be great, and you will be children of the Most High; for he is kind toward the unthankful and evil.

³⁶Therefore be merciful, even as your Father is also merciful. ³⁷Do not judge, and you won't be judged. Do not condemn, and you won't be condemned. Forgive, and you will be forgiven.[b]

³⁸"Give, and it will be given to you: good measure, pressed down, shaken together, and running over, will be poured into your lap. For with the same measure you measure it will be measured back to you."

³⁹He spoke a parable to them. "Can the blind guide the blind? Won't they both fall into a pit? ⁴⁰A disciple is not above his teacher, but everyone when he is fully trained will be like his teacher. ⁴¹And why do you see the speck of chaff that is in your brother's eye, but do not notice the log that is in your own eye? ⁴²Or how can you tell your brother, 'Brother, let me remove the speck of chaff that is in your eye,' when you yourself do not see the log that is in your own eye? You hypocrite. First remove the log from your own eye, and then you can see clearly to remove the speck of chaff that is in your brother's eye. ⁴³For there is no good tree that brings forth rotten fruit; nor again[c] a rotten tree that brings forth good fruit. ⁴⁴For each tree is known by its own fruit. For people do not gather figs from thorns, nor do they gather grapes from a bramble bush. ⁴⁵The good person[d]

out of the good treasure of his heart brings out that which is good, and the evil person out of the evil treasure[e] brings out that which is evil, for out of the abundance of the heart, his mouth speaks.

⁴⁶"Why do you call me, 'Lord, Lord,' and do not do the things which I say? ⁴⁷Everyone who comes to me, and hears my words, and does them, I will show you who he is like. ⁴⁸He is like someone building a house, who dug and went deep, and laid a foundation on the rock. When a flood arose, the stream broke against that house, and could not shake it, because it had been well built.[f] ⁴⁹But he who hears, and does not do, is like someone who built a house on the earth without a foundation, against which the stream broke, and immediately it fell, and the ruin of that house was great."

7 After he had finished speaking in the hearing of the people, he entered into Capernaum. ²A certain centurion's servant, who was dear to him, was sick and at the point of death. ³When he heard about Jesus, he sent to him Jewish elders, asking him to come and save his servant. ⁴When they came to Jesus, they begged him earnestly, saying, "He is worthy for you to do this for him, ⁵for he loves our nation, and he built our synagogue for us." ⁶Jesus went with them. When he was now not far from the house, the centurion sent friends,[g] saying to him, "Lord, do not trouble yourself, for I am not worthy for you to come under my roof. ⁷Therefore I did not even think myself worthy to come to you; but say the word, and my servant will be healed. ⁸For I also am a man placed under authority, having under myself soldiers. I tell this one, 'Go.' and he goes; and to another, 'Come.' and he comes; and to my servant, 'Do this,' and he does it."

---

a   6:31 Some Mss add "also"
b   6:37 Or, "Set free, and you will be set free"
c   6:43 Some Mss lack "again"
d   6:45 Some Mss add "man"
e   6:45 Lit., "and the evil, out of the evil." Some Mss add "of his heart"
f   6:48 Some Mss read "was founded on the rock"
g   7:6 Some Mss add "to him"

[9]When Jesus heard these things, he marveled at him, and turned and said to the crowd who followed him, "I tell you, I have not found such great faith, no, not in Israel." [10]And when those who had been sent returned to the house, they found the servant[a] in good health.

[11]It happened soon afterwards, that he went to a city called Nain; and many[b] of his disciples, along with a large crowd, went with him. [12]And when he drew near to the gate of the city, then look, a man who was dead was carried out, the only son of his mother, and she was a widow; and a large crowd from the city was with her. [13]When the Lord saw her, he had compassion on her, and said to her, "Do not cry." [14]He came near and touched the coffin, and the bearers stood still. He said, "Young man, I tell you, arise." [15]He who was dead sat up, and began to speak. And he gave him to his mother.

[16]Fear took hold of all, and they glorified God, saying, "A great prophet has arisen among us." and, "God has visited his people." [17]This report went out concerning him in the whole of Judea, and in all the surrounding region.

[18]The disciples of John told him about all these things. [19]John, calling to himself two of his disciples, sent them to the Lord,[c] saying, "Are you the one who is to come, or should we look for another?" [20]When the men had come to him, they said, "John the Baptist has sent us to you, saying, 'Are you the one who is to come, or should we look for another?'"

[21]In that hour he cured many of diseases and plagues and evil spirits; and to many who were blind he gave sight. [22]Jesus answered them, "Go and tell John the things which you have seen and heard: that the blind receive their sight, the lame walk, the lepers are cleansed, the deaf hear, the dead are raised up, and the poor have good news preached to them.[d] [23]Blessed is he who is not offended by me."

[24]When John's messengers had departed, he began to tell the crowds about John, "What did you go out into the wilderness to see? A reed shaken by the wind? [25]But what did you go out to see? A man clothed in soft clothing? Look, those who are gorgeously dressed, and live delicately, are in kings' courts. [26]But what did you go out to see? A prophet? Yes, I tell you, and much more than a prophet. [27]This is he of whom it is written,

'Look, I send my messenger ahead of you,

who will prepare your way before you.'[e]

[28]"I[f] tell you, among those who are born of women there is none greater[g] than John,[h] yet he who is least in the kingdom of God is greater than he."

[29]When all the people and the tax collectors heard this, they declared God to be just, having been baptized with John's baptism. [30]But the Pharisees and the Law scholars rejected the counsel of God, not being baptized by him themselves.

[31]"To what then will I liken the people of this generation? What are they like? [32]They are like children who sit in the marketplace, and call one to another, saying, 'We played the flute for you, and you did not dance. We mourned,[j] and you did not weep.' [33]For John the Baptist came neither eating bread nor drinking wine, and you say, 'He has a demon.' [34]The Son of Man has come eating and drinking, and you say, 'Look, a gluttonous man, and a drunkard; a friend of tax collectors and sinners.' [35]Wisdom is justified by all her children."

[36]One of the Pharisees invited him to eat with him. He entered into the Pharisee's house, and sat at the table. [37]And look, a woman in the city who was a sinner, when she knew that he was reclining in the Pharisee's house, she brought an alabaster jar of ointment. [38]Standing behind at his feet

---

a   7:10 Some Mss add "who had been sick"
b   7:11 Mss read instead lack "many"
c   7:19 Some Mss read "Jesus"
d   7:22 Isaiah 35:5-6, 26:19, 61:1
e   7:27 Malachi 3:1
f   7:27 Some Mss add "For"
g   7:28 Some Mss add "a prophet"
h   7:28 Some Mss add "the Baptist"
i   7:31 Some Mss add "And the Lord said,"
j   7:32 Some Mss add "for you"

weeping, she began to wet his feet with her tears, and she wiped them with the hair of her head, kissed his feet, and anointed them with the ointment. [39]Now when the Pharisee who had invited him saw it, he said to himself, "This man, if he were a prophet, would have perceived who and what kind of woman this is who touches him, that she is a sinner."

[40]Jesus answered him, "Simon, I have something to tell you." He said, "Teacher, say on."

[41]"A certain lender had two debtors. The one owed five hundred denarii, and the other fifty. [42]When they could not pay, he forgave them both. Which of them therefore will love him most?" [43]Simon answered, "He, I suppose, to whom he forgave the most." He said to him, "You have judged correctly." [44]Turning to the woman, he said to Simon, "Do you see this woman? I entered into your house, and you gave me no water for my feet, but she has wet my feet with her tears, and wiped them with her hair.[a] [45]You gave me no kiss, but she, since the time I came in, has not ceased to kiss my feet. [46]You did not anoint my head with oil, but she has anointed my feet with ointment. [47]Therefore I tell you, her sins, which are many, are forgiven, for she loved much. But to whom little is forgiven, the same loves little." [48]He said to her, "Your sins are forgiven."

[49]And those who were reclining with him began to say to themselves, "Who is this who even forgives sins?"

[50]He said to the woman, "Your faith has saved you. Go in peace."

8 It happened soon afterwards, that he went about through cities and villages, proclaiming and bringing the good news of the kingdom of God. With him were the twelve, [2]and certain women who had been healed of evil spirits and infirmities: Mary who was called Magdalene, from whom seven demons had gone out; [3]and Joanna, the wife of Chuza, Herod's steward; Susanna; and many others; who provided for them from their possessions. [4]When a large crowd came together, and people from every city were coming to him, he spoke by a parable. [5]"The farmer went out to sow his seed. As he sowed, some fell along the road, and it was trampled under foot, and the birds of the sky devoured it. [6]Other seed fell on the rock, and as soon as it grew, it withered away, because it had no moisture. [7]Other fell amid the thorns, and the thorns grew with it, and choked it. [8]Other fell into the good ground, and grew, and brought forth fruit one hundred times." As he said these things, he called out, "He who has ears to hear, let him hear."

[9]Then his disciples asked him, "What does this parable mean?"

[10]He said, "To you it is given to know the mysteries of the kingdom of God, but to the rest in parables; that 'seeing they may not see, and hearing they may not understand.'[b] [11]Now the parable is this: The seed is the word of God. [12]Those along the road are those who hear, then the devil comes, and takes away the word from their heart, that they may not believe and be saved. [13]Those on the rock are they who, when they hear, receive the word with joy; but these have no root, who believe for a while, then fall away in time of temptation. [14]That which fell among the thorns, these are those who have heard, and as they go on their way they are choked with cares, riches, and pleasures of life, and bring no fruit to maturity. [15]That in the good ground, these are such as in an honest and good heart, having heard the word, hold it tightly, and bring forth fruit with patience.

[16]"No one, when he has lit a lamp, covers it with a container, or puts it under a bed; but puts it on a stand, that those who enter in may see the light. [17]For nothing is hidden, that will not be revealed; nor anything secret, that will not be known and come to light. [18]Be careful therefore how you hear. For whoever has, to him will be given; and whoever does not have, from him will be

---

a   7:44 Some Mss read "the hair of her head"

b   8:10 Isaiah 6:9

taken away even that which he thinks he has."

¹⁹His mother and brothers came to him, and they could not come near him for the crowd. ²⁰It was told him by some saying, "Your mother and your brothers stand outside, desiring to see you."

²¹But he answered them, "My mother and my brothers are these who hear the word of God, and do it."

²²Now it happened on one of those days, that he entered into a boat, himself and his disciples, and he said to them, "Let us go over to the other side of the lake." So they launched out. ²³But as they sailed, he fell asleep. A wind storm came down on the lake, and they were taking on dangerous amounts of water. ²⁴So they came to him, and awoke him, saying, "Master, master, we are dying." And he awoke, and rebuked the wind and the raging of the water, and they ceased, and it was calm.ᵃ ²⁵He said to them, "Where is your faith?" Being afraid they marveled, saying one to another, "Who is this, then, that he commands even the winds and the water, and they obey him?"

²⁶They arrived at the country of the Gerasenes,ᵇ which is opposite Galilee.

²⁷When Jesus stepped ashore, a certain man out of the city who had demons for a long time met him. He wore no clothes, and did not live in a house, but in the tombs. ²⁸When he saw Jesus, he shouted, and fell down before him, and with a loud voice said, "What do I have to do with you, Jesus, you Son of the Most High God? I beg you, do not torment me." ²⁹For Jesus was commanding the unclean spirit to come out of the man. For the unclean spirit had often seized the man. He was kept under guard, and bound with chains and fetters. Breaking the bands apart, he was driven by the demon into the desert.

³⁰Jesus asked him, "What is your name?"

He said, "Legion," for many demons had entered into him. ³¹Theyᶜ begged him that he would not command them to go into the abyss.ᵈ ³²Now there was there a herd of many pigs feeding on the mountain, and they begged him that he would allow

them to enter into those. He allowed them. ³³The demons came out from the man, and entered into the pigs, and the herd rushed down the steep bank into the lake, and were drowned. ³⁴When those who fed them saw what had happened, they fled, and told it in the city and in the country.

³⁵Then people went out to see what had happened. They came to Jesus, and found the man from whom the demons had gone out, sitting at Jesus' feet, clothed and in his right mind; and they were afraid. ³⁶Those who saw it told them how he who had been possessed by demons was healed. ³⁷All the people of the surrounding country of the Geresenesᵉ asked him to depart from them, for they were very much afraid; and he entered into the boat and returned. ³⁸But the man from whom the demons had gone out begged him that he might go with him, but Jesus sent him away, saying, ³⁹"Return to your house, and declare what great things God has done for you." He went his way, proclaiming throughout the whole city what great things Jesus had done for him.

⁴⁰Whenᶠ Jesus returned, the crowd welcomed him, for they were all waiting for him. ⁴¹And look, there came a man named Jairus, and he was a ruler of the synagogue. He fell down at Jesus' feet, and pleaded with him to come into his house, ⁴²for he had an only daughter, about twelve years of age, and she was dying. But as he went, the crowds pressed against him. ⁴³A woman who had a flow of blood for twelve years (who had spent all her living on physicians)ᵍ and could not be healed by any, ⁴⁴came behind him, and touched the fringe of his cloak, and immediately the flow of her blood stopped. ⁴⁵Jesus said, "Who touched me?"

---

a   8:24 Psalm 65:7; 89:9; 107:29
b   8:26 Some Mss read "Gadarenes"
c   8:31 Some Mss read "He"
d   8:31 Gk. abussos, used in the LXX for Heb. tehom
e   8:37 Some Mss read "Gadarenes"
f   8:40 Some Mss read "It happened when"
g   8:43 Some Mss lack "who had spent… physicians"
    The skillful condensation of Mark 5:26 and
    substitution with a hapax legomenon (prosanalisko
    for dapanao) suggests Lukan authorship

When all denied it, Peter[a] said, "Master, the crowds press and jostle you.[b]"

[46]But Jesus said, "Someone did touch me, for I perceived that power has gone out of me." [47]When the woman saw that she was not hidden, she came trembling, and falling down before him declared to him in the presence of all the people the reason why she had touched him, and how she was healed immediately. [48]He said to her, "Daughter,[c] your faith has made you well. Go in peace."

[49]While he still spoke, one from the ruler of the synagogue's house came, saying to him, "Your daughter is dead. Do not trouble the Teacher."

[50]But Jesus hearing it, answered him, "Do not be afraid. Only believe, and she will be healed."

[51]When he came to the house, he did not allow anyone to enter in with him,[d] except Peter, John, James, the father of the child, and her mother. [52]All were weeping and mourning her, but he said, "Do not weep. She is not dead, but sleeping."

[53]They were ridiculing him, knowing that she was dead. [54]But he,[e] taking her by the hand, called, saying, "Child, arise." [55]Her spirit returned, and she rose up immediately. He commanded that something be given to her to eat. [56]Her parents were amazed, but he commanded them to tell no one what had been done.

9 He called the twelve[f] together, and gave them power and authority over all demons, and to cure diseases. [2]He sent them forth to proclaim the kingdom of God, and to heal the sick.[g] [3]And he said to them, "Take nothing for your journey—neither staff,[h] nor pack, nor bread, nor money; neither have two coats apiece. [4]Into whatever house you enter, stay there, and depart from there. [5]As many as do not receive you, when you depart from that city, shake off even the dust from your feet for a testimony against them."

[6]They departed, and went throughout the villages, preaching the Good News, and healing everywhere. [7]Now Herod the tetrarch heard of all that was done;[i] and he was very perplexed, because it was said by some that John had risen from the dead, [8]and by some that Elijah had appeared, and by others that one of the old prophets had risen again. [9]Herod said, "John I beheaded, but who is this, about whom I hear such things?" He sought to see him. [10]The apostles, when they had returned, told him what things they had done.

He took them, and withdrew apart to[j] a city called Bethsaida. [11]But the crowds, perceiving it, followed him. He welcomed them, and spoke to them of the kingdom of God, and he cured those who needed healing. [12]The day began to wear away; and the twelve came, and said to him, "Send the crowd away, that they may go into the surrounding villages and farms, and lodge, and get food, for we are here in a deserted place."

[13]But he said to them, "You give them something to eat."

They said, "We have no more than five loaves and two fish, unless we should go and buy food for all these people." [14]For they were about five thousand men.

He said to his disciples, "Make them sit down in groups of about fifty each." [15]They did so, and made them all sit down. [16]He took the five loaves and the two fish, and looking up to the sky, he blessed them, and broke them, and gave them to the disciples to set before the crowd. [17]They ate, and were all filled. They gathered up twelve baskets of broken pieces that were left over.

[18]It happened, as he was praying alone, that the disciples were with him, and he asked them, "Who do the crowds say that I am?"

---

a   8:45 Some Mss add "and those with him"

b   8:45 Some Mss add "and you say, 'Who touched me?'"

c   8:48 Some Mss add "take courage,"

d   8:51 Some Mss lack "with him"

e   8:54 Some Mss add "put them all outside"

f   9:1 Some Mss read "his twelve disciples." Other Mss read "apostles"

g   9:2 Some Mss lack "the sick"

h   9:3 Some Mss read "staffs"

i   9:7 Some Mss add "by him"

j   9:10 Some Mss add "a deserted place of a"

[19]They answered, "'John the Baptist,' but others say, 'Elijah,' and others, that one of the old prophets is risen again."

[20]He said to them, "But who do you say that I am?"

Peter answered, "The Messiah of God."

[21]But he warned them, and commanded them to tell this to no one, [22]saying, "The Son of Man must suffer many things, and be rejected by the elders, chief priests, and scribes, and be killed, and the third day be raised up."

[23]He said to all, "If anyone desires to come after me, let him deny himself, take up his cross daily[a], and follow me. [24]For whoever desires to save his life will lose it, but whoever will lose his life for my sake, the same will save it. [25]For what does it profit a person if he gains the whole world, and loses or forfeits his own self? [26]For whoever will be ashamed of me and of my words, of him will the Son of Man be ashamed, when he comes in his glory, and the glory of the Father, and of the holy angels. [27]But I tell you the truth: There are some of those who stand here, who will in no way taste of death, until they see the kingdom of God."

[28]It happened about eight days after these sayings, that he took with him Peter, John, and James, and went up onto the mountain to pray. [29]As he was praying, the appearance of his face was altered, and his clothing became white and dazzling. [30]And look, two men were talking with him, who were Moses and Elijah, [31]who appeared in glory, and spoke of his departure,[b] which he was about to accomplish at Jerusalem.

[32]Now Peter and those who were with him were heavy with sleep, but when they were fully awake, they saw his glory, and the two men who stood with him. [33]It happened, as they were parting from him, that Peter said to Jesus, "Master, it is good for us to be here. Let us make three tents: one for you, and one for Moses, and one for Elijah," not knowing what he said.

[34]While he said these things, a cloud came and overshadowed them, and they were afraid as they entered into the cloud. [35]A voice came out of the cloud, saying, "This is my Son, my Chosen One.[c] Listen to him." [36]When the voice came, Jesus was found alone. They were silent, and told no one in those days any of the things which they had seen.

[37]It happened on the next day, when they had come down from the mountain, that a large crowd met him. [38]And look, a man from the crowd called out, saying, "Teacher, I beg you to look at my son, for he is my only child. [39]And look, a spirit seizes him, and all at once he cries out, and it convulses him so that he foams, and it hardly departs from him, bruising him severely. [40]I begged your disciples to cast it out, and they could not."

[41]Jesus answered, "Faithless and perverse generation, how long must I be with you and put up with you? Bring your son here."

[42]While he was still coming, the demon threw him down and convulsed him violently. But Jesus rebuked the unclean spirit, and healed the boy, and gave him back to his father. [43]They were all astonished at the majesty of God.

But while all were marveling at all the things which Jesus did, he said to his disciples, [44]"Let these words sink into your ears, for the Son of Man will be delivered up into the hands of men." [45]But they did not understand this saying. It was concealed from them, that they should not perceive it, and they were afraid to ask him about this saying.

[46]There arose an argument among them about which of them was the greatest. [47]Jesus, knowing[d] the reasoning of their hearts, took a little child, and set him by his side, [48]and said to them, "Whoever receives this little child in my name receives me. Whoever receives me receives him who sent me. For whoever is least among you all, this one is great."

---

a   9:23 Some Mss lack "daily"

b   9:31 Lit., "exodus"

c   9:35 Some Mss read "my beloved son"

d   9:47 Some Mss read "perceiving"

⁴⁹John answered, "Master, we saw someone casting out demons in your name, and we forbade him, because he does not follow with us."

⁵⁰Jesus said to him, "Do not forbid him, for he who is not against you is for you.ᵃ"

⁵¹It came to pass, when the days were near that he should be taken up, he intently set his face to go to Jerusalem, ⁵²and sent messengers before his face. They went, and entered into a village of the Samaritans, so as to prepare for him. ⁵³But they did not receive him, because he was traveling with his face set towards Jerusalem. ⁵⁴And when his disciples James and John saw this, they said, "Lord, do you want us to command fire to come down from the sky, and consume themᵇ?"

⁵⁵And he turned and rebuked them, and said, "You do not realize what kind of Spirit you belong to. ⁵⁶For the Son of Man did not come to destroy people's lives, but to save them."ᶜ And they went to another village.

⁵⁷As they went on the way, a certain man said to him, "I want to follow you wherever you go. ᵈ"

⁵⁸And Jesus said to him, "The foxes have holes, and the birds of the sky have nests, but the Son of Man has no place to lay his head."

⁵⁹He said to another, "Follow me."

But he said, "Lord,ᵉ allow me first to go and bury my father."

⁶⁰But Jesus said to him, "Leave the dead to bury their own dead, but you go and announce the kingdom of God."

⁶¹Another also said, "I want to follow you, Lord, but first allow me to bid farewell to those who are at my house."

⁶²But Jesus said to him, "No one, having put his hand to the plow, and looking back, is fit for the kingdom of God."

10 Now after these things, the Lord also appointed seventy-twoᶠ others, and sent them two by two ahead of himᵍ into every city and place, where he was about to come. ²Then he said to them, "The harvest is indeed plentiful, but the laborers are few. Pray therefore to the Lord of the harvest, that he may send out laborers into his harvest. ³Go your way. Look, I send you out as lambs among wolves. ⁴Carry no money bag, nor pack, nor sandals; and greet no one on the way. ⁵Into whatever house you enter, first say, 'Peace be to this house.' ⁶If a peaceful person is there, your peace will rest on him; but if not, it will return to you. ⁷Remain in that same house, eating and drinking the things they give, for the laborer is worthy of his wages. Do not go from house to house. ⁸Into whatever city you enter, and they receive you, eat the things that are set before you. ⁹And heal the sick who are there, and tell them, 'The kingdom of God has come near to you.' ¹⁰But into whatever city you enter, and they do not receive you, go out into its streets and say, ¹¹"Even the dust from your city that clings to our feet,ʰ we wipe off against you. Nevertheless know this, that the kingdom of God is near.'' ¹²I tell you, it will be more tolerable in that day for Sodom than for that city.

¹³"Woe to you, Chorazin. Woe to you, Bethsaida. For if the mighty works had been done in Tyre and Sidon which were done in you, they would have repented long ago, sitting in sackcloth and ashes. ¹⁴But it will be more tolerable for Tyre and Sidon in the judgment than for you. ¹⁵And you, Capernaum, will you beʲ exalted to heaven? You will be brought down to hellᵏ.

¹⁶Whoever listens to you listens to me, and whoever rejects you rejects me. Whoever rejects me rejects him who sent me."

¹⁷The seventy-twoˡ returned with joy, saying, "Lord, even the demons are subject to us in your name."

---

a 9:50 Some Mss read "us" twice
b 9:54 Some Mss add "just as Elijah did"
c 9:55b-56a Some Mss lack "and said, You…them" from haplography
d 9:57 Some Mss add "Lord"
e 9:59 A few Mss lack "Lord"
f 10:1 Some Mss read "seventy"
g 10:1 Lit., "before his face"
h 10:11 Some Mss read "us"
i 10:11 Some Mss add "to you"
j 10:15 Some Mss read "who are"
k 10:15 Gk. Hades, for Heb. Sheol
l 10:17 Some Mss read "seventy"

[18]He said to them, "I saw Satan having fallen like lightning from heaven. [19]Look, I have given[a] you authority to tread on serpents and scorpions, and over all the power of the enemy, and nothing will in any way hurt you. [20]Nevertheless, do not rejoice in this, that the spirits are subject to you, but rejoice that your names are written in heaven."

[21]In that same hour he[b] rejoiced in the Holy[c] Spirit, and said, "I thank[d] you, Father, Lord of heaven and earth, that you have hidden these things from the wise and understanding, and revealed them to little children. Yes, Father, for so it was well-pleasing in your sight."

[22e]"All things have been delivered to me by my Father. No one knows who the Son is, except the Father, and who the Father is, except the Son, and he to whomever the Son desires to reveal him."

[23]Turning to the disciples, he said privately, "Blessed are the eyes which see the things that you see, [24]for I tell you that many prophets and kings desired to see the things which you see, and did not see them, and to hear the things which you hear, and did not hear them."

[25]And look, a certain Law scholar stood up and tested him, saying, "Teacher, what must I do to inherit everlasting life?"

[26]He said to him, "What is written in the Law? How do you read it?"

[27]He answered, "You are to love the Lord your God with all[f] your heart, with all your soul, with all your strength, and with all your mind;[g] and your neighbor as yourself."[h]

[28]He said to him, "You have answered correctly. Do this, and you will live."

[29]But he, desiring to justify himself, asked Jesus, "Who is my neighbor?"

[30]Jesus answered, "A certain man was going down from Jerusalem to Jericho, and he fell among robbers, who both stripped him and beat him, and departed, leaving him half dead. [31]By chance a certain priest was going down that way. When he saw him, he passed by on the other side. [32]In the same way a Levite also, when he came[i]

to the place, and saw him, passed by on the other side. [33]But a certain Samaritan, as he traveled, came where he was. When he saw him, he was moved with compassion, [34]came to him, and bound up his wounds, pouring on oil and wine. He set him on his own animal, and brought him to an inn, and took care of him. [35]On the next day,[j] he took out two denarii, and gave them to the host, and said to him, 'Take care of him. Whatever you spend beyond that, I will repay you when I return.' [36]Now which of these three do you think seemed to be a neighbor to him who fell among the robbers?"

[37]He said, "He who showed mercy on him."

Then Jesus said to him, "Go and do likewise."

[38]It happened as they went on their way, he entered into a certain village, and a certain woman named Martha received him into her house.[k] [39]She had a sister called Mary, who also sat at the Lord's[l] feet, and heard his word. [40]But Martha was distracted with much serving, and she came up to him, and said, "Lord, do you not care that my sister left me to serve alone? Ask her therefore to help me."

[41]But the Lord[m] answered and said to her, "Martha, Martha, you are anxious and troubled about many things, [42]but one thing is needed. Mary has chosen the good part, which will not be taken away from her."

11 It happened, that when he finished praying in a certain place, one of his disciples said to him, "Lord, teach us

---

a 10:19 Some Mss read "I give" instead of "I have given"
b 10:21 Some Mss read "Jesus"
c 10:21 Some Mss lack "Holy"
d 10:21 Or, "praise"
e 10:22 Some Mss add "And turning to the disciples, he said"
f 10:27 Some Mss lack "the"
g 10:27 Deuteronomy 6:5
h 10:27 Leviticus 19:18
i 10:32 Some Mss lack "when he came"
j 10:35 Some Mss add "when he departed"
k 10:38 Some Mss lack "into her house"
l 10:39 Some Mss read "Jesus
m 10:41 Some Mss read "Jesus"

to pray, just as John also taught his disciples."

²He said to them, "When you pray, say,
'Father,ª revered be your name.
May your kingdom come.ᵇ
³Give us day by day our daily bread.
⁴Forgive us our sins,
    for we ourselves also forgive
        everyone who is indebted to us.
And lead us not into temptation.ᶜ'"

⁵He said to them, "Which of you, if you go to a friend at midnight, and tell him, 'Friend, lend me three loaves of bread, ⁶for a friend of mine has come to me from a journey, and I have nothing to set before him,' ⁷and he from within will answer and say, 'Do not bother me. The door is now shut, and my children are with me in bed. I cannot get up and give it to you'? ⁸I tell you, although he will not rise and give it to him because he is his friend, yet because of his persistence, he will get up and give him as many as he needs.

⁹"I tell you, ask, and it will be given to you. Seek, and you will find. Knock, and it will be opened to you. ¹⁰For everyone who asks receives. He who seeks finds. To him who knocks it will be opened.

¹¹"Which of you fathers, if your son asks forᵈ a fish, he won't give him a snake instead of a fish, will he? ¹²Or if he asks for an egg, will give him a scorpion? ¹³If you then, being evil, know how to give good gifts to your children, how much more will your heavenly Father give the Holy Spirit to those who ask him?"

¹⁴He was casting out a demon, and it wasᵉ mute. It happened, when the demon had gone out, the mute man spoke; and the crowds marveled. ¹⁵But some of them said, "He casts out demons by Beelzebul, the prince of the demons." ¹⁶Others, testing him, sought from him a sign from heaven. ¹⁷But he, knowing their thoughts, said to them, "Every kingdom divided against itself is brought to desolation. A house divided against itself falls. ¹⁸If Satan also is divided against himself, how will his kingdom stand? For you say that I cast out demons by Beelzebul. ¹⁹But if I cast out demons by Beelzebul, by whom do your children cast them out? Therefore will they be your judges. ²⁰But if Iᶠ by the finger of God cast out demons, then the kingdom of God has come to you.

²¹"When the strong man, fully armed, guards his own dwelling, his goods are safe. ²²But when someone stronger attacks him and overcomes him, he takes from him his whole armor in which he trusted, and divides up his plunder.

²³"He that is not with me is against me. He who does not gather with me scatters. ²⁴The unclean spirit, when he has gone out of the person, passes through dry places, seeking rest, and finding none, he says, 'I will turn back to my house from which I came out.' ²⁵When he returns, he finds it swept and put in order. ²⁶Then he goes, and takes seven other spirits more evil than himself, and they enter in and dwell there. The last state of that person becomes worse than the first."

²⁷It came to pass, as he said these things, a certain woman out of the crowd lifted up her voice, and said to him, "Blessed is the womb that bore you, and the breasts which nursed you."

²⁸But he said, "On the contrary, blessed are those who hear the word of God, and keep it."

²⁹When the crowds were gathering together to him, he began to say, "This generationᵍ is an evil generation. It seeks after a sign. No sign will be given to it but the sign of Jonah.ʰ ³⁰For even as Jonah became a sign to the Ninevites, so will also the Son of Man be to this generation. ³¹The Queen of the South will rise up in the judgment with the people of this generation, and will condemn them: for she came from a dis-

---

a   11:2 Some Mss add "in heaven"
b   11:2 Some Mss add "May your will be done on earth, as it is in heaven"
c   11:4 Some Mss add "but deliver us from the evil one"
d   11:11 Some Mss add "bread, will give him a stone? Or if he asks for"
e   11:14 Some Mss lack "and it was"
f   11:20 Some Mss lack "I"
g   11:29 Some Mss lack "generation"
h   11:29 Some Mss add "the prophet"

tant land[a] to hear the wisdom of Solomon; and look, one greater than Solomon is here. [32]The people of Nineveh will stand up in the judgment with this generation, and will condemn it: for they repented at the preaching of Jonah, and look, one greater than Jonah is here.

[33]"No one, when he has lit a lamp, puts it in a cellar or under a basket,[b] but on a stand, that those who come in may see the light. [34]The lamp of the body is the eye. Therefore when your eye is good, your whole body is also full of light; but when it is bad, your body also is full of darkness. [35]Therefore see whether the light that is in you is not darkness. [36]If therefore your whole body is full of light, having no part dark, it will be wholly full of light, as when the lamp with its bright shining gives you light."

[37]Now as he spoke, a[c] Pharisee asked him to dine with him. He went in, and sat at the table. [38]When the Pharisee saw it, he marveled that he had not first washed himself before dinner. [39]The Lord said to him, "Now you Pharisees cleanse the outside of the cup and of the platter, but your inward part is full of extortion and wickedness. [40]You foolish ones, did not he who made the outside make the inside also? [41]But give for gifts to the needy those things which are within, and see, all things will be clean to you. [42]But woe to you Pharisees. For you tithe mint and rue and every herb, but you bypass justice and the love of God. You ought to have done these, and not to have left the other undone. [43]Woe to you Pharisees. For you love the best seats in the synagogues, and the greetings in the marketplaces. [44]Woe to you.[d] For you are like hidden graves, and the people who walk over them do not know it."

[45]One of the Law scholars answered him, "Teacher, in saying this you insult us also."

[46]He said, "Woe to you Law scholars also. For you load people with burdens that are difficult to carry, and you yourselves won't even lift one finger to help carry those burdens. [47]Woe to you. For you build the tombs of the prophets, and your fathers killed them. [48]So you are witnesses and consent to the works of your fathers. For they killed them, and you build their tombs. [49]Therefore also the wisdom of God said, 'I will send to them prophets and apostles; and some of them they will kill and persecute, [50]that the blood of all the prophets, which was shed from the foundation of the world, may be required of this generation; [51]from the blood of Abel to the blood of Zechariah, who perished between the altar and the sanctuary.' Yes, I tell you, it will be required of this generation. [52]Woe to you Law scholars. For you took away the key of knowledge. You did not enter in yourselves, and those who were entering in, you hindered."

[53]And when he left there,[e] the scribes and the Pharisees began to be terribly angry, and to draw many things out of him; [54]lying in wait for him,[f] to catch him in something he might say.[g]

12 Meanwhile, when a crowd of many thousands had gathered together, so much so that they trampled on each other, he began to tell his disciples first of all, "Beware of the yeast of the Pharisees, which is hypocrisy. [2]But there is nothing covered up, that will not be revealed, nor hidden, that will not be known. [3]Therefore whatever you have said in the darkness will be heard in the light. What you have spoken in the ear in the inner chambers will be proclaimed on the housetops.

[4]"I tell you, my friends, do not be afraid of those who kill the body, and after that

---

a   11:31 Lit. "borders of the earth," which can be an idiomatic expression when speaking of people in remote places, e.g., Psalm 67:7; 98:3; Isaiah 45:22

b   11:33 Some Mss lack "or under a basket"

c   11:37 Some Mss add "certain"

d   11:44 Some Mss add "scribes and Pharisees, hypocrites"

e   11:53 Some Mss read "As he was speaking these things to them"

f   11:54 Some Mss add "seeking"

g   11:54 Some Mss add "that they might accuse him"

have no more that they can do. [5]But I will warn you whom you should fear. Fear him, who after he has killed, has power to cast into hell[a]. Yes, I tell you, fear him.

[6]"Are not five sparrows sold for two assaria coins[b]? Not one of them is forgotten by God. [7]But the very hairs of your head are all numbered. Therefore do not be afraid. You are of more value than many sparrows.

[8]"I tell you, everyone who confesses me before people, him will the Son of Man also confess before the angels of God; [9]but the one who denies me in the presence of people will be denied in the presence of the angels of God. [10]Everyone who speaks a word against the Son of Man will be forgiven, but those who blaspheme against the Holy Spirit will not be forgiven. [11]When they bring you before the synagogues, the rulers, and the authorities, do not be anxious how or what you will answer, or what you will say; [12]for the Holy Spirit will teach you in that same hour what you must say."

[13]And someone in the crowd said to him, "Teacher, tell my brother to divide the inheritance with me."

[14]But he said to him, "Man, who made me a judge or an arbitrator over you?" [15]He said to them, "Beware. Keep yourselves from all covetousness, for a man's life does not consist of the abundance of the things which he possesses."

[16]He spoke a parable to them, saying, "The ground of a certain rich man brought forth abundantly. [17]He reasoned within himself, saying, 'What will I do, because I do not have room to store my crops?' [18]He said, 'This is what I will do. I will pull down my barns, and build bigger ones, and there I will store all my grain and my goods. [19]I will tell my soul, "Soul, you have many goods laid up for many years. Take your ease, eat, drink, be merry."'

[20]"But God said to him, 'You foolish one, tonight your soul is required of you. The things which you have prepared—whose will they be?' [21]So is he who lays up treasure for himself, and is not rich toward God."

[22]He said to his disciples, "Therefore I tell you, do not be anxious for your life, what you will eat, nor yet for your body, what you will wear. [23]Life is more than food, and the body is more than clothing. [24]Consider the ravens: they do not sow, they do not reap, they have no warehouse or barn, and God feeds them. How much more valuable are you than birds. [25]Which of you by being anxious can add a cubit to his height? [26]If then you are not able to do even the least things, why are you anxious about the rest? [27]Consider the lilies, how they grow. They do not toil, neither do they spin; yet I tell you, even Solomon in all his glory was not arrayed like one of these. [28]But if this is how God clothes the grass in the field, which today exists, and tomorrow is cast into the oven, how much more will he clothe you, O you of little faith? [29]Do not seek what you will eat or what you will drink; neither be anxious. [30]For the nations of the world seek after all of these things, but your Father knows that you need these things. [31]But seek his[c] kingdom, and[d] these things will be added to you. [32]Do not be afraid, little flock, for it is your Father's good pleasure to give you the kingdom. [33]Sell that which you have, and give gifts to the needy. Make for yourselves purses which do not grow old, a treasure in the heavens that does not fail, where no thief approaches, neither moth destroys. [34]For where your treasure is, there will your heart be also.

[35]"Let your waist be girded and your lamps burning. [36]Be like people watching for their lord, when he returns from the marriage feast; that, when he comes and knocks, they may immediately open to him. [37]Blessed are those servants, whom the lord will find watching when he comes. Truly I tell you, that he will dress

---

a   12:5 Gk. "Gehenna"
b   12:6 An assarion was a small copper coin worth about an hour's wages for an agricultural laborer.
c   12:31 Some Mss read "God's"
d   12:31 Some Mss add "all"

himself, and make them recline, and will come and serve them. [38]And if he comes in the second watch, or even in the third, and finds them so, blessed are they.[a] [39]But know this, that if the master of the house had known in what hour the thief was coming, he would have watched and[b] not have allowed his house to be broken into. [40]Therefore be ready also, for the Son of Man is coming in an hour that you do not expect him."

[41]Peter said to him, "Lord, are you telling this parable to us, or to everybody?"

[42]The Lord said, "Who then is the faithful and wise steward, whom his lord will set over his household, to give them their portion of food at the right times? [43]Blessed is that servant whom his lord will find doing so when he comes. [44]Truly I tell you, that he will set him over all that he has. [45]But if that servant says in his heart, 'My lord delays his coming,' and begins to beat the menservants and the maidservants, and to eat and drink, and to be drunk, [46]then the lord of that servant will come in a day when he is not expecting him, and in an hour that he does not know, and will cut him in two, and place his portion with the unfaithful. [47]That servant, who knew his lord's will, and did not prepare, nor do what he wanted, will be beaten with many stripes, [48]but he who did not know, and did things worthy of stripes, will be beaten with few stripes. To whomever much is given, of him will much be required; and to whom much was entrusted, of him more will be asked.

[49]"I came to throw fire on the earth. I wish it were already kindled. [50]But I have a baptism to be baptized with, and how distressed I am until it is accomplished. [51]Do you think that I have come to give peace in the earth? I tell you, no, but rather division. [52]For from now on, there will be five in one house divided, three against two, and two against three. [53]They will be divided, father against son, and son against father; mother against daughter, and daughter against her mother; mother-in-law against her daughter-in-law, and daughter-in-law against her mother-in-law."

[54]He said to the crowds also, "When you see a cloud rising from the west, immediately you say, 'A shower is coming,' and so it happens. [55]When a south wind blows, you say, 'There will be a scorching heat,' and it happens. [56]Hypocrites. You know how to interpret the appearance of the earth and the sky, but why do you not know[c] how to interpret this time? [57]Why do you not judge for yourselves what is right? [58]For when you are going with your adversary before the magistrate, try diligently on the way to be released from him, lest perhaps he drag you to the judge, and the judge deliver you to the officer, and the officer throw you into prison. [59]I tell you, you will by no means get out of there, until you have paid the very last penny.[d]"

13 Now there were some present at the same time who told him about the Galileans, whose blood Pilate had mixed with their sacrifices. [2]And he[e] answered and said to them, "Do you think that these Galileans were worse sinners than all the other Galileans, because they suffered these[f] things? [3]I tell you, no, but unless you repent, you will all perish in the same way. [4]Or those eighteen, on whom the tower in Siloam fell, and killed them; do you think that they were worse offenders than all the others who dwell in Jerusalem? [5]I tell you, no, but, unless you repent, you will all perish in the same way."

[6]He spoke this parable. "A certain man had a fig tree planted in his vineyard, and he came seeking fruit on it, and found none. [7]He said to the vine dresser, 'Look,

---

a   12:38 Some Mss read "And if he comes in the second watch, or comes in the third watch, and finds them so, blessed are those servants"

b   12:39 Some Mss lack "have watched and"

c   12:56 Some Mss lack "do you know"

d   12:59 Lit. lepton.

e   13:2 Some Mss add "Jesus "

f   13:2 Some Mss read "such"

for these[a] three years I have come looking for fruit on this fig tree, and found none. Cut[b] it down. Why does it waste the soil?' [8]He answered, 'Lord, leave it alone this year also, until I dig around it, and fertilize it. [9]And if it bears fruit next time, fine; but if not, you can cut it down.[c]'"

[10]He was teaching in one of the synagogues on the Sabbath day. [11]And look, a woman who had a spirit of infirmity eighteen years, and she was bent over, and could in no way straighten herself up. [12]When Jesus saw her, he called her, and said to her, "Woman, you are freed from your infirmity." [13]He laid his hands on her, and immediately she stood up straight, and glorified God.

[14]The ruler of the synagogue, being indignant because Jesus had healed on the Sabbath, said to the crowd, "There are six days when work should be done. Therefore come on those days and be healed, and not on the Sabbath day."

[15]Therefore the Lord answered him, "You hypocrites.[d] Does not each one of you free his ox or his donkey from the stall on the Sabbath, and lead him away to water? [16]Ought not this woman, being a daughter of Abraham, whom Satan had bound, look, eighteen years, be freed from this bondage on the Sabbath day?"

[17]As he said these things, all his adversaries were disappointed, and all the crowd rejoiced for all the glorious things that were done by him.

[18]Then he said, "What is the kingdom of God like? And to what can I compare it? [19]It is like a grain of mustard seed, which a man took, and put in his own garden. It grew, and became a[e] tree, and the birds of the sky lodged in its branches."

[20]And again he said, "To what can I compare the kingdom of God? [21]It is like yeast, which a woman took and hid in three measures[f] of flour, until it was all leavened."

[22]He went on his way through cities and villages, teaching, and traveling on to Jerusalem. [23]One said to him, "Lord, are they few who are saved?" He said to them, [24]"Strive to enter in by the narrow door,[g] for many, I tell you, will seek to enter in, and will not be able. [25]When once the master of the house has risen up, and has shut the door, and you begin to stand outside, and to knock at the door, saying, 'Lord,[h] open to us.' then he will answer and tell you, 'I do not know you or where you come from.' [26]Then you will begin to say, 'We ate and drank in your presence, and you taught in our streets.' [27]He will say, 'I tell you, I do not know where you come from. Depart from me, all you workers of iniquity.' [28]There will be weeping and gnashing of teeth, when you see Abraham, Isaac, Jacob, and all the prophets, in the kingdom of God, and yourselves being thrown outside. [29]They will come from the east, west, north, and south, and will sit down in the kingdom of God. [30]And look, there are some who are last who will be first, and there are some who are first who will be last."

[31]In that same hour[i] some Pharisees came, saying to him, "Get out of here, and go away, for Herod wants to kill you."

[32]And he said to them, "Go and tell that fox, 'Look, I cast out demons and perform cures today and tomorrow, and the third day I complete my mission. [33]Nevertheless I must go on my way today and tomorrow and the next day, for it cannot be that a prophet perish outside of Jerusalem.'

[34]"Jerusalem, Jerusalem, that kills the prophets, and stones those who are sent to her. How often I wanted to gather your children together, like a hen gathers her own brood under her wings, and you refused. [35]Look, your house is forsaken.[j] I tell you,[k] you will not see me until you say,

---

a   13:7 Some Mss lack "for these"
b   13:7 Some Mss read "Therefore, cut"
c   13:9 Some Mss read "fruit, fine; but if not, next time, you"
d   13:15 Some Mss read "hypocrite"
e   13:19 Some Mss add "large"
f   13:21 Lit., "three sata," which is about 39 liter or a bit more than a bushel
g   13:24 Some Mss read "gate"
h   13:25 Some Mss add "Lord"
i   13:31 Some Mss read "On that same day"
j   13:35 Some Mss add "desolate"
k   13:35 Some Mss add "assuredly"

'Blessed is he who comes in the name of the Lord.'"[a]

14 And it happened, when he went into the house of one of the rulers of the[b] Pharisees on a Sabbath to eat bread, that they were watching him. [2]And look, a certain man who had dropsy was in front of him. [3]Jesus, answering, spoke to the Law scholars and Pharisees, saying, "Is it lawful to heal on the Sabbath or not[c]?"

[4]But they were silent. He took him, and healed him, and let him go. [5]He answered them, "Which of you, if your son[d] or an ox fell into a well, would not immediately pull him out on a Sabbath day?"

[6]They could not answer him regarding these things.

[7]He spoke a parable to those who were invited, when he noticed how they chose the best seats, and said to them, [8]"When you are invited by anyone to a marriage feast, do not sit in the best seat, since perhaps someone more honorable than you might be invited by him, [9]and he who invited both of you would come and tell you, 'Make room for this person.' Then you would begin, with shame, to take the lowest place. [10]But when you are invited, go and sit in the lowest place, so that when he who invited you comes, he may tell you, 'Friend, move up higher.' Then you will be honored in the presence of all[e] who sit at the table with you. [11]For everyone who exalts himself will be humbled, and whoever humbles himself will be exalted."

[12]He also said to the one who had invited him, "When you make a dinner or a supper, do not call your friends, nor your brothers, nor your kinsmen, nor rich neighbors, or perhaps they might also return the favor, and pay you back. [13]But when you make a feast, ask the poor, the maimed, the lame, or the blind; [14]and you will be blessed, because they do not have the resources to repay you. For you will be repaid in the resurrection of the righteous."

[15]Now when one of those who were reclining with him heard these things, he said to him, "Blessed is he who will eat bread[f] in the kingdom of God."

[16]But he said to him, "A certain man made a great supper, and he invited many people. [17]And he sent his servant at the hour for supper to tell those who were invited, 'Come, for everything is ready now.' [18]They all as one began to make excuses.

"The first said to him, 'I have bought a field, and I must go and see it. Please have me excused.'

[19]"Another said, 'I have bought five yoke of oxen, and I must go try them out. Please have me excused.'

[20]"Another said, 'I have married a wife, and therefore I cannot come.'

[21]"That servant came, and told his lord these things. Then the master of the house, being angry, said to his servant, 'Go out quickly into the streets and lanes of the city, and bring in the poor, maimed, blind, and lame.'

[22]"The servant said, 'Lord, it is done as you commanded, and there is still room.'

[23]"The lord said to the servant, 'Go out into the highways and hedges, and compel them to come in, that my house may be filled. [24]For I tell you that none of those individuals who were invited will taste of my supper.[g]'"

[25]Now large crowds were going with him. He turned and said to them, [26]"If anyone comes to me, and does not hate[h] his own father, mother, wife, children, brothers, and sisters, yes, and his own life also, he cannot be my disciple. [27]Whoever does not bear his own cross, and come after me, cannot be my disciple. [28]For which of you, desiring to build a tower, does not first sit down and count the cost, to see if he has enough to complete it? [29]Or perhaps, when he has

---

a   13:35 Psalm 118:26
b   14:1 Some Mss lack "the"
c   14:3 Some Mss lack "or not"
d   14:5 Some Mss read "donkey"
e   14:10 Some Mss lack "all"
f   14:15 Some Mss read "dinner"
g   14:24 Some Mss add "For many are called, but few are chosen"
h   14:26 Hebraistically, a lower preference, i.e., "prefer less," "love less." Cf. Matthew 10:37, Mark 7:10, 10:19

laid a foundation, and is not able to finish, everyone who sees begins to mock him, ³⁰saying, 'This man began to build, and was not able to finish.' ³¹Or what king, as he goes to encounter another king in war, will not sit down first and consider whether he is able with ten thousand to meet him who comes against him with twenty thousand? ³²Or else, while the other is yet a great way off, he sends an envoy, and asks for conditions of peace. ³³So therefore whoever of you who does not renounce all that he has, he cannot be my disciple. ³⁴Salt is good, but if the salt becomes flat and tasteless, with what do you season it? ³⁵It is fit neither for the soil nor for the manure pile. It is thrown out. He who has ears to hear, let him hear."

15 Now all[a] the tax collectors and sinners were coming close to him to hear him. ²The Pharisees and the scribes murmured, saying, "This man welcomes sinners, and eats with them."

³He told them this parable. ⁴"Which one of you, if you had one hundred sheep, and lost one of them, would not leave the ninety-nine in the wilderness, and go after the one that was lost, until he found it? ⁵When he has found it, he carries it on his shoulders, rejoicing. ⁶When he comes home, he calls together his friends and his neighbors, saying to them, 'Rejoice with me, for I have found my sheep which was lost.' ⁷I tell you that even so there will be more joy in heaven over one sinner who repents, than over ninety-nine righteous people who need no repentance. ⁸Or what woman, if she had ten drachma[b] coins, if she lost one drachma coin, would not light a lamp, sweep the house, and seek diligently until she found it? ⁹When she has found it, she calls together her friends and neighbors, saying, 'Rejoice with me, for I have found the drachma which I had lost.' ¹⁰Even so, I tell you, there is joy in the presence of the angels of God over one sinner repenting."

¹¹He said, "A certain man had two sons. ¹²The younger of them said to his father, 'Father, give me my share of your prop-

erty.' He divided his livelihood between them. ¹³Not many days after, the younger son gathered all of this together and traveled into a far country. There he wasted his property with riotous living. ¹⁴When he had spent all of it, there arose a severe famine in that country, and he began to be in need. ¹⁵He went and joined himself to one of the citizens of that country, and he sent him into his fields to feed pigs. ¹⁶And he wanted to fill himself[c] with the carob pods that the pigs ate, but no one gave him any. ¹⁷But when he came to himself he said, 'How many hired servants of my father's have bread enough to spare, and I'm dying here[d] with hunger. ¹⁸I will get up and go to my father, and will tell him, "Father, I have sinned against heaven, and in your sight. ¹⁹I am no longer worthy to be called your son. Make me like one of your hired servants."'

²⁰"He arose, and came to his father. But while he was still far off, his father saw him, and was moved with compassion, and ran, and fell on his neck, and kissed him. ²¹The son said to him, 'Father, I have sinned against heaven, and in your sight. I am no longer worthy to be called your son.[e]'

²²"But the father said to his servants, 'Quickly,[f] bring out the best robe, and put it on him. Put a ring on his hand, and shoes on his feet. ²³Bring the fattened calf, kill it, and let us eat, and celebrate; ²⁴for this, my son, was dead, and is alive again. He was lost, and is found.' They began to celebrate.

²⁵"Now his elder son was in the field. As he came near to the house, he heard music and dancing. ²⁶He called one of the servants to him, and asked what was going on. ²⁷He said to him, 'Your brother has come, and your father has killed the fattened calf,

---

a   15:1 Some Mss lack "all"
b   15:8 A drachma coin was worth about 2 days wages for an agricultural laborer.
c   15:16 Some Mss read "fill his stomach"
d   15:17 Some Mss lack "here"
e   15:21 Some Mss add "Make me like one of your hired servants"
f   15:22 Some Mss lack "Quickly"

because he has received him back safe and healthy.' ²⁸But he was angry, and would not go in. Therefore his father came out, and begged him. ²⁹But he answered his father, 'Look, these many years I have served you, and I never disobeyed a commandment of yours, but you never gave me a goat, that I might celebrate with my friends. ³⁰But when this, your son, came, who has devoured your living with prostitutes, you killed the fattened calf for him.'

³¹"He said to him, 'Son, you are always with me, and all that is mine is yours. ³²But it was appropriate to celebrate and be glad, for this brother of yours was dead and is alive;ᵃ and he was lost, and is found.'"

16 He also said to his disciples, "There was a certain rich man who had a manager. An accusation was made to him that this man was wasting his possessions. ²He called him, and said to him, 'What is this that I hear about you? Give an accounting of your management, for you can no longer be manager.'

³"The manager said within himself, 'What will I do, seeing that my lord is taking away the management position from me? I do not have strength to dig. I am ashamed to beg. ⁴I know what I will do, so that when I am removed from management, they may receive me into their houses.' ⁵Calling each one of his lord's debtors to him, he said to the first, 'How much do you owe to my lord?' ⁶He said, 'A hundred batosᵇ of oil.' He said to him, 'Take your bill, and sit down quickly and write fifty.' ⁷Then he said to another, 'How much do you owe?' He said, 'A hundred corsᶜ of wheat.' He said to him, 'Take your bill, and write eighty.'

⁸"His lord commended the dishonest manager for his shrewdness, for the sons of this world are, in their own generation, more shrewd than the sons of light. ⁹And I say to you, make friends for yourselves by means of unrighteous mammon, so that when itᵈ fails, they may receive you into the everlasting tents. ¹⁰He who is faithful in a very little is faithful also in much. He who is dishonest in a very little is also dishonest in much. ¹¹If

therefore you have not been faithful in the unrighteous mammon, who will commit to your trust the true riches? ¹²If you have not been faithful in that which is another's, who will give you that which is your own? ¹³No servant can serve two masters, for either he will hate the one, and love the other; or else he will hold to one, and despise the other. You are not able to serve God and wealth.ᵉ"

¹⁴The Pharisees, who were lovers of money, also heard all these things, and they scoffed at him. ¹⁵He said to them, "You are those who justify yourselves in the sight of people, but God knows your hearts. For that which is exalted among men is an abomination in the sight of God. ¹⁶The Law and the Prophets were until John. From that time the Good News of the kingdom of God is preached, and everyone is forcing his way into it. ¹⁷But it is easier for heaven and earth to pass away, than for one tiny stroke of a pen in the Law to become void. ¹⁸Everyone who divorces his wife, and marries another, commits adultery. He who marries one who is divorced from a husband commits adultery.

¹⁹"Now there was a certain rich man, and he was clothed in purple and fine linen, living in luxury every day. ²⁰A certain beggar, named Lazarus, was placed at his gate, full of sores, ²¹and desiring to be fed with the crumbs thatᶠ fell from the rich man's table. Yes, even the dogs came and licked his sores. ²²It happened that the beggar died, and that he was carried away by the angels to Abraham's bosom. The rich man also died, and was buried. ²³In hell, he lifted up his eyes, being in torment, and saw Abraham far off, and Lazarus at his bosom. ²⁴He called out and said, 'Father Abraham, have mercy on me, and send Lazarus, that he may dip the tip of his finger in water, and cool my tongue. For I am in anguish in this flame.'

a   15:32 Some Mss read "alive again"
b   16:6 100 batos is about 395 liters, 104 U. S. gallons, or 87 imperial gallons.
c   16:7 100 cors = about 3,910 liters or 600 bushels.
d   16:9 Some Mss read "you"
e   16:13 Gk "Mammon"
f   16:21 Some Mss lack "with the crumbs that"

²⁵"But Abraham said, 'Son, remember that you, in your lifetime, received your good things, and Lazarus, in like manner, bad things. But now here he is comforted and you are in anguish. ²⁶Besides all this, between us and you there is a great gulf fixed, that those who want to pass from here to you are not able, and that none may cross over from there to us.'

²⁷"He said, 'I ask you therefore, father, that you would send him to my father's house; ²⁸for I have five brothers, that he may testify to them, so they won't also come into this place of torment.'

²⁹"But Abraham said to him, 'They have Moses and the Prophets. Let them listen to them.'

³⁰"He said, 'No, father Abraham, but if one goes to them from the dead, they will repent.'

³¹"He said to him, 'If they do not listen to Moses and the Prophets, neither will they be persuaded if one rises from the dead.'"

17 He said to the disciples, "It is impossible that no occasions of stumbling should come, but woe to him through whom they come. ²It would be better for him if a millstone were hung around his neck, and he were thrown into the sea, rather than that he should cause one of these little ones to stumble. ³Watch yourselves. If your brother sins,ᵃ rebuke him. If he repents, forgive him. ⁴And if he sins against you seven times in the day, and seven timesᵇ returns to youᶜ, saying, 'I repent,' you must forgive him."

⁵The apostles said to the Lord, "Increase our faith."

⁶The Lord said, "If you had faith like a grain of mustard seed, you would tell this mulberry tree, 'Be uprooted, and be planted in the sea,' and it would obey you. ⁷But who is there among you, having a servant plowing or keeping sheep, that will say, when he comes in from the field, 'Come immediately and sit down at the table'? ⁸But will he not say to him, 'Prepare my supper, clothe yourself properly, and serve me, while I eat and drink, and afterward

you can eat and drink'? ⁹Does he thank that servant because he did the things that were commanded?ᵈ ¹⁰Even so you also, when you have done all the things that are commanded you, say, 'We are unworthy servants. We have done our duty.'"

¹¹It happened as he was on his way to Jerusalem, that he was passing along the borders of Samaria and Galilee. ¹²As he entered into a certain village, ten men who were lepers met him, who stoodᵉ at a distance. ¹³They lifted up their voices, saying, "Jesus, Master, have mercy on us."

¹⁴When he saw them, he said to them, "Go and show yourselves to the priests." It happened that as they went, they were cleansed. ¹⁵One of them, when he saw that he was healed, turned back, glorifying God with a loud voice. ¹⁶He fell on his face at Jesus' feet, giving him thanks; and he was a Samaritan. ¹⁷Jesus answered, "Weren't the ten cleansed? But where are the nine? ¹⁸Were there none found who returned to give glory to God, except this stranger?" ¹⁹Then he said to him, "Get up, and go your way. Your faith has healed you."

²⁰Being asked by the Pharisees when the kingdom of God would come, he answered them, "The kingdom of God does not come with observation; ²¹neither will they say, 'Look, here.' or, 'Look, there.' forᶠ the kingdom of God is within you."

²²He said to the disciples, "The days will come, when you will desire to see one of the days of the Son of Man, and you will not see it. ²³And they will tell you, 'Look, there.' or 'Look, here.' Do not go away, nor follow after them, ²⁴for as the lightning, when it flashes out of the one part under the sky, shines to the other part under the sky; so will the Son of Man be in his day.ᵍ ²⁵But first, he must suffer many things and be rejected by this generation. ²⁶As it happened in the days of

---

a　17:3 Some Mss add "against you"
b　17:4 Some Mss add "in the day"
c　17:4 Some Mss lack "to you"
d　17:9 Some Mss add "I think not"
e　17:12 Some Mss read "stood up"
f　17:21 Some Mss add "look"
g　17:24 Some Mss lack "in his day"

Noah, even so will it be also in the days of the Son of Man. ²⁷They ate, they drank, they married, they were given in marriage, until the day that Noah entered into the box-shaped vessel[a] and the flood came, and destroyed them all. ²⁸Likewise, even as it happened in the days of Lot: they ate, they drank, they bought, they sold, they planted, they built; ²⁹but in the day that Lot went out from Sodom, it rained fire and sulfur from the sky, and destroyed them all. ³⁰It will be the same way in the day that the Son of Man is revealed. ³¹In that day, he who will be on the housetop, and his goods in the house, let him not go down to take them away. Let him who is in the field likewise not turn back. ³²Remember Lot's wife.[b] ³³Whoever seeks to keep[c] his life will lose it, but whoever loses it will preserve it. ³⁴I tell you, in that night there will be two people in one bed. The one will be taken, and the other will be left. ³⁵There will be two grinding grain together. One will be taken, and the other will be left. ³⁶[d]

³⁷They, answering, asked him, "Where, Lord?"

He said to them, "Where the body is, there will the vultures also be gathered together."

18 He also spoke a parable to them that they must always pray, and not give up, ²saying, "There was a judge in a certain city who did not fear God, and did not respect people. ³A widow was in that city, and she often came to him, saying, 'Give me justice against my adversary.' ⁴He would not for a while, but afterward he said to himself, 'Though I neither fear God, nor respect people, ⁵yet because this widow bothers me, I will give her justice, or else she will wear me out by her continual coming.'"

⁶The Lord said, "Listen to what the unrighteous judge says. ⁷Won't God avenge his chosen ones, who are crying out to him day and night, and yet he exercises patience with them? ⁸I tell you that he will avenge them quickly. Nevertheless, when the Son of Man comes, will he find faith on the earth?"

⁹He spoke also this parable to certain people who were convinced of their own

righteousness, and who despised all others. ¹⁰"Two men went up into the temple to pray; one was a Pharisee, and the other was a tax collector. ¹¹The Pharisee stood and prayed to himself like this: 'God, I thank you, that I am not like other people, extortioners, unrighteous, adulterers, or even like this tax collector. ¹²I fast twice a week. I give tithes of all that I get.' ¹³But the tax collector, standing far away, would not even lift up his eyes to heaven, but beat his breast, saying, 'God, be merciful to me, a sinner.' ¹⁴I tell you, this man went down to his house justified rather than the other; for everyone who exalts himself will be humbled, but he who humbles himself will be exalted."

¹⁵Now they were also bringing their babies to him, that he might touch them. But when the disciples saw it, they rebuked them. ¹⁶Jesus summoned them, saying, "Allow the little children to come to me, and do not hinder them, for the kingdom of God belongs to such as these. ¹⁷Truly, I tell you, whoever does not receive the kingdom of God like a little child, he will in no way enter into it."

¹⁸A certain ruler asked him, saying, "Good Teacher, what must I do to inherit everlasting life?"

¹⁹Jesus asked him, "Why do you call me good? No one is good, except one—God. ²⁰You know the commandments: 'Do not commit adultery,' 'Do not murder,' 'Do not steal,' 'Do not give false testimony,' 'Honor your father and your mother.'"[e]

²¹And he said, "I have kept all these things from my youth up."

²²When Jesus heard it,[f] he said to him, "You still lack one thing. Sell all that you

---

a   17:27 Or, "ship." Gk. kibotos "box-shaped." Traditionally "ark," from Latin arca "box, chest." The vessel, according to the Hebrew royal cubit of 52.5 centimeters, was 517 feet in length x 86 feet in width x 52 feet in height, or 157.5 meters x 26.3 meters x 15.8 meters. See Genesis 6:15

b   17:32 Genesis 19:26

c   17:33 Some Mss read "save"

d   17:36 Some Mss add "Two will be in the field, the one taken, and the other left"

e   18:20 Exodus 20:12-16; Deuteronomy 5:16-20

f   18:22 Some Mss read " these things"

have, and distribute it to the poor, and you will have treasure in[a] heaven; and come, follow me."

[23]But when he heard these things, he became very sad, for he was very rich.

[24]And Jesus, seeing that he became very sad,[b] said, "How hard it is for those who have riches to enter into the kingdom of God. [25]For it is easier for a camel to enter in through a needle's eye, than for a rich person to enter into the kingdom of God."

[26]Those who heard it said, "Then who can be saved?"

[27]But he said, "The things which are impossible with humans are possible with God."

[28]And Peter said, "Look, we have left our own[c] things and followed you."

[29]He said to them, "Truly I tell you, there is no one who has left house, or wife, or brothers, or parents, or children, for the kingdom of God's sake, [30]who will not receive many times more in this time, and in the world to come, everlasting life."

[31]He took the twelve aside, and said to them, "Look, we are going up to Jerusalem, and all the things that are written through the prophets concerning the Son of Man will be completed. [32]For he will be delivered up to the non-Jews, will be mocked, treated shamefully, and spit on. [33]They will scourge and kill him. On the third day, he will rise again."

[34]They understood none of these things. This saying was hidden from them, and they did not understand the things that were said. [35]It happened, as he came near Jericho, a certain blind man sat by the road, begging. [36]Hearing a crowd going by, he asked what this meant. [37]They told him that Jesus of Nazareth was passing by. [38]He called out, "Jesus, Son of David, have mercy on me." [39]Those who led the way rebuked him, that he should be quiet; but he shouted all the more, "Son of David, have mercy on me."

[40]Standing still, Jesus commanded him to be brought to him. When he had come near, he asked him, [41]"What do you want me to do?"

He said, "Lord, that I may see again."

[42]Jesus said to him, "Receive your sight. Your faith has healed you."

[43]And immediately he received his sight, and followed him, glorifying God. All the people, when they saw it, praised God.

19 He entered and was passing through Jericho. [2]And look, there was a man named Zacchaeus. He was a chief tax collector, and he was rich. [3]He was trying to see who Jesus was, and could not because of the crowd, because he was short. [4]He ran on ahead, and climbed up into a sycamore tree to see him, for he was to pass that way. [5]When Jesus came to the place, he looked up,[d] and said to him, "Zacchaeus, hurry and come down, for today I must stay at your house." [6]He hurried, came down, and received him joyfully. [7]And when they saw it, they all murmured, saying, "He has gone in to lodge with a man who is a sinner."

[8]And Zacchaeus stood and said to the Lord, "Look, Lord, half of my goods I give to the poor. If I have wrongfully exacted anything of anyone, I restore four times as much."

[9]Jesus said to him, "Today, salvation has come to this house, because he also is a son of Abraham. [10]For the Son of Man came to seek and to save that which was lost."

[11]As they heard these things, he went on and told a parable, because he was near Jerusalem, and they supposed that the kingdom of God would be revealed immediately. [12]He said therefore, "A certain nobleman went into a far country to receive for himself a kingdom, and to return. [13]He called ten servants of his, and gave them ten mina coins,[e] and told them, 'Conduct business until I come.' [14]But his citizens hated him, and sent an envoy after him, saying, 'We do not want this man to reign over us.'

---

a   18:22 Gk. "in the heavens." Some Mss lack "the"
b   18:24 Some Mss lack "became very sad"
c   18:28 Some Mss read "all"
d   19:5 Some Mss add "and saw him"
e   19:13 10 minas was more than 3 years' wages for an agricultural laborer.

[15]"It happened when he had come back again, having received the kingdom, that he commanded these servants, to whom he had given the money, to be called to him, that he might know what they[a] had gained by conducting business. [16]The first came before him, saying, 'Lord, your mina has made ten more minas.'

[17]"And he said to him, 'Well done, good servant. Because you were faithful with very little, you will have authority over ten cities.'

[18]"The second came, saying, 'Your mina, Lord, has made five minas.'

[19]"So he said to him, 'And you are to be over five cities.' [20]And another came, saying, 'Lord, look, your mina, which I kept laid away in a handkerchief, [21]for I feared you, because you are an exacting man. You take up that which you did not lay down, and reap that which you did not sow.'

[22]"He said to him, 'Out of your own mouth will I judge you, you wicked servant. You knew that I am an exacting man, taking up that which I did not lay down, and reaping that which I did not sow. [23]Then why did you not deposit my money in the bank, and at my coming, I might have earned interest on it?' [24]He said to those who stood by, 'Take the mina away from him, and give it to him who has the ten minas.'

[25]"They said to him, 'Lord, he has ten minas.' [26]'For I tell you that to everyone who has, will more be given; but from him who does not have, even that which he has will be taken away.[b] [27]But bring those enemies of mine who did not want me to reign over them here, and kill them before me.'" [28]Having said these things, he went on ahead, going up to Jerusalem.

[29]It happened, when he drew near to Bethphage[c] and Bethany, at the mountain that is called Olivet, he sent two of the[d] disciples, [30]saying, "Go your way into the village on the other side, in which, as you enter, you will find a colt tied, whereon no one ever yet sat. Untie it, and bring it. [31]If anyone asks you, 'Why are you untying it?' say to him: 'The Lord needs it.'"

[32]Those who were sent went away, and found things just as he had told them. [33]As they were untying the colt, its owners said to them, "Why are you untying the colt?" [34]They said, "The Lord needs it." [35]They brought it to Jesus. They threw their cloaks on the colt, and set Jesus on them. [36]As he went, they spread their cloaks in the way. [37]As he was now getting near, at the descent of the Mount of Olives, the whole crowd of the disciples began to rejoice and praise God with a loud voice for all the mighty works which they had seen, [38]saying, "Blessed is the King who comes in the name of the Lord.[e] Peace in heaven, and glory in the highest."

[39]Some of the Pharisees from the crowd said to him, "Teacher, rebuke your disciples."

[40]He answered them, "I tell you that if these were silent, the stones would cry out."

[41]When he drew near, he saw the city and wept over it, [42]saying, "If you, even you, had known today the things that make for peace. But now, they are hidden from your eyes. [43]For the days will come on you, when your enemies will throw up a barricade against you, surround you, hem you in on every side, [44]and will dash you and your children within you to the ground. They will not leave in you one stone on another, because you did not know the time of your visitation."

[45]And he entered into the temple, and began to drive out those who were selling and buying in it,[f] [46]saying to them, "It is written, 'And my house will be[g] a house of prayer,'[h] but you have made it a 'den of robbers'."[i]

[47]He was teaching daily in the temple, but the chief priests and the scribes and the leaders among the people sought to

---

a   19:15 Some Mss read "any one"
b   19:26 Some Mss add "from him"
c   19:29 Some Mss read "Bethsphage"
d   19:29 Some Mss read "his"
e   19:38 Psalm 118:26
f   19:45 Some Mss lack "and buying in it"
g   19:46 Some Mss read "My house is"
h   19:46 Isaiah 56:7
i   19:46 Jeremiah 7:11

destroy him. ⁴⁸They could not find what they might do, for all the people hung on to every word that he said.

20 It happened on one of those days, as he was teaching the people in the temple and preaching the Good News, that the chief[a] priests and scribes came to him with the elders. ²They asked him, "Tell us: by what authority do you do these things? Or who is giving you this authority?"

³He answered them, "I also will ask you one question. Tell me: ⁴the baptism of John, was it from heaven, or from people?"

⁵They reasoned with themselves, saying, "If we say, 'From heaven,' he will say, 'Why did you not believe him?' ⁶But if we say, 'From people,' all the people will stone us, for they are persuaded that John was a prophet." ⁷They answered that they did not know where it was from.

⁸Jesus said to them, "Neither will I tell you by what authority I do these things."

⁹He began to tell the people this parable. "A man[b] planted a vineyard, and rented it out to some farmers, and went on a journey for a long time. ¹⁰At the proper season, he sent a servant to the farmers to collect his share of the fruit of the vineyard. But the farmers beat him, and sent him away empty. ¹¹He sent yet another servant, and they also beat him, and treated him shamefully, and sent him away empty. ¹²He sent yet a third, and they also wounded him, and threw him out. ¹³The lord of the vineyard said, 'What am I to do? I will send my beloved son. It may be that[c] they will respect him.'

¹⁴"But when the farmers saw him, they reasoned among themselves, saying, 'This[d] is the heir. [e]Let us kill him, that the inheritance may be ours.' ¹⁵They threw him out of the vineyard, and killed him. What therefore will the lord of the vineyard do to them? ¹⁶He will come and destroy these farmers, and will give the vineyard to others."

When they heard it, they said, "May it never be."

¹⁷But he looked at them, and said, "Then what is this that is written,

'The stone which the builders rejected,
    the same was made the chief
        cornerstone?'[f]
¹⁸Everyone who falls on that stone will
    be broken to pieces;
but on whomever it falls, it will
    crush him."[g]

¹⁹The chief priests and the scribes sought to lay hands on him that very hour, but they feared the people[h]—for they knew he had spoken this parable against them. ²⁰They watched him, and sent out spies, who pretended to be righteous, that they might trap him in something he said, so as to deliver him up to the power and authority of the governor. ²¹They asked him, "Teacher, we know that you say and teach what is right, and are not partial to anyone, but truly teach the way of God. ²²Is it lawful for us to pay taxes to Caesar, or not?"

²³But he perceived their craftiness, and said to them,[i] ²⁴"Show me a denarius. Whose image and inscription are on it?"

They answered, "Caesar's."

²⁵He said to them, "Then give to Caesar the things that are Caesar's, and to God the things that are God's."

²⁶They weren't able to trap him in his words before the people. They marveled at his answer, and were silent. ²⁷Some of the Sadducees came to him, those who deny that there is a resurrection. ²⁸They asked him, "Teacher, Moses wrote to us that if a man's brother dies having a wife, and he is[j] childless, his brother should take the wife, and raise up children for his brother. ²⁹There were therefore seven brothers. The first took a wife, and died childless. ³⁰The second[k] and ³¹the third took her, and like-

---

a   20:1 Some Mss lack "chief"
b   20:9 Some Mss lack "certain"
c   20:13 Some Mss add "seeing him"
d   20:14 Some Mss read "Come, this"
e   20:14 Some Mss read "Come, let us"
f   20:17 Psalm 118:22
g   20:18 Isaiah 8:14-15; Daniel 2:34-35, 44-45; Romans 9:32-33; 1 Peter 2:8
h   20:19 Some Mss lack "the people"
i   20:23 Some Mss add "Why do you test me"
j   20:28 Some Mss read "dies"
k   20:30 Some Mss add "took her as wife, and he died childless"

wise the seven all left no children, and died. ³²Afterward the woman also died. ³³Therefore in the resurrection whose wife of them will she be? For the seven had her as a wife."

³⁴Jesus said to them, "The sons of this age marry, and are given in marriage. ³⁵But those who are considered worthy to attain to that age and the resurrection from the dead, neither marry, nor are given in marriage. ³⁶For they cannot die any more, for they are like the angels, and are sons of God, being sons of the resurrection. ³⁷But that the dead are raised, even Moses showed at the bush, when he called the Lord 'The God of Abraham, and the God of Isaac, and the God of Jacob.'ᵃ ³⁸Now he is not the God of the dead, but of the living, for all are alive to him."

³⁹Some of the scribes answered, "Teacher, you speak well." ⁴⁰They did not dare to ask him any more questions.

⁴¹He said to them, "Why do they say that the Messiah is David's son? ⁴²David himself says in the scroll of Psalms,

'The Lord said to my Lord,
    "Sit at my right hand,
        ⁴³until I make your enemies the
            footstool of your feet." 'ᵇ

⁴⁴"David therefore calls him Lord, so how is he his son?"

⁴⁵In the hearing of all the people, he said to his disciples, ⁴⁶"Beware of the scribes, who like to walk in long robes, and love greetings in the marketplaces, the best seats in the synagogues, and the best places at feasts; ⁴⁷who devour widows' houses, and for a pretense make long prayers: these will receive greater condemnation."

21 He looked up, and saw the rich people who were putting their gifts into the treasury. ²He saw a certain poor widow casting in two lepta.ᶜ ³He said, "Truly I tell you, this poor widow put in more than all of them, ⁴for all these put in giftsᵈ from their abundance, but she, out of her poverty, put in all that she had to live on."

⁵As some were talking about the temple and how it was decorated with beautiful stones and gifts, he said, ⁶"As for these things which you see, the days will come, in which there will not be left here one stone on another that will not be thrown down."

⁷They asked him, "Teacher, so when will these things be? What is the sign that these things are about to happen?"

⁸He said, "Watch out that you do not get led astray, for many will come in my name, saying, 'I am heᵉ,' and, 'The time is near.' Therefore do not follow them. ⁹When you hear of wars and disturbances, do not be terrified, for these things must happen first, but the end won't come immediately."

¹⁰Then he said to them, "Nation will rise against nation, and kingdom against kingdom. ¹¹There will be great earthquakes, famines, and plagues in various places. There will be terrors and great signs from heaven. ¹²But before all these things, they will lay their hands on you and will persecute you, delivering you up to synagogues and prisons, bringing you before kings and governors for my name's sake. ¹³It will turn out as a testimony for you. ¹⁴Settle it therefore in your hearts not to meditate beforehand how to answer, ¹⁵for I will give you a mouth and wisdom which all your adversaries will not be able to withstand or to contradict. ¹⁶You will be handed over even by parents, brothers, relatives, and friends. They will cause some of you to be put to death. ¹⁷You will be hated by all for my name's sake. ¹⁸And not a hair of your head will perish.

¹⁹"By your endurance you will win your lives.

²⁰"But when you see Jerusalem surrounded by armies, then know that its desolation is near. ²¹Then let those who are in Judea flee to the mountains. Let those who are in the midst of her depart. Let those who are in the country not enter it. ²²For these are days of vengeance, that all things which are written may be fulfilled. ²³Woe

---

a   20:37 Exodus 3:6
b   20:43 Psalm 110:1
c   21:2 Lit., "two lepta," which was about 1% of a day's
     wages for an agricultural laborer.
d   21:4 Some Mss add "for God"
e   21:8 Or, "I AM"

to those who are pregnant and to those who nurse infants in those days. For there will be great distress in the land, and wrath to this people. ²⁴They will fall by the edge of the sword, and will be led captive into all the nations. Jerusalem will be trampled down by the nations, until the times of the nations are fulfilled. ²⁵There will be signs in the sun, moon, and stars; and on the earth anxiety of nations, in perplexity for the roaring of the sea and the waves; ²⁶people fainting for fear, and for expectation of the things which are coming on the world: for the powers of the heavens will be shaken. ²⁷Then they will see the Son of Man coming in a cloud with power and great glory. ²⁸But when these things begin to happen, look up, and lift up your heads, because your redemption is near."

²⁹He told them a parable. "See the fig tree, and all the trees. ³⁰When they are already budding, you see it and know by your own selves that the summer is already near. ³¹Even so you also, when you see these things happening, know that the kingdom of God is near. ³²Truly I tell you, this generation will not pass away until all things are accomplished. ³³Heaven and earth will pass away, but my words will by no means pass away.

³⁴"So be careful, or your hearts will be loaded down with carousing, drunkenness, and cares of this life, and that day will come on you suddenly. ³⁵For it will come like a snare on all those who dwell on the surface of all the earth. ³⁶Therefore be watchful all the time, praying that you may be able[a] to escape all these things that will happen, and to stand before the Son of Man."

³⁷Every day Jesus was teaching in the temple, and every night he would go out and spend the night on the mountain that is called Olivet. ³⁸All the people came early in the morning to him in the temple to hear him.

22 Now the feast of unleavened bread, which is called the Passover, drew near. ²The chief priests and the scribes sought how they might kill him, for they feared the people. ³Satan entered into Judas, who was called[b] Iscariot, who was numbered with the twelve. ⁴He went away, and talked with the chief priests and captains about how he might deliver him to them. ⁵They were glad, and agreed to give him money. ⁶He consented, and sought an opportunity to deliver him to them in the absence of the crowd. ⁷The day of unleavened bread came, on which the Passover must be sacrificed. ⁸He sent Peter and John, saying, "Go and prepare the Passover for us, that we may eat."

⁹They said to him, "Where do you want us to prepare?"

¹⁰He said to them, "Look, when you have entered into the city, a man carrying a pitcher of water will meet you. Follow him into the house which he enters. ¹¹Tell the master of the house, 'The Teacher says to you, "Where is the guest room, where I may eat the Passover with my disciples?"' ¹²He will show you a large, furnished upper room. Make preparations there."

¹³They went, found things as he had told them, and they prepared the Passover. ¹⁴When the hour had come, he sat down with the twelve.[c] ¹⁵He said to them, "I have earnestly desired to eat this Passover with you before I suffer, ¹⁶for I say to you, I will not eat of it again[d] until it is fulfilled in the kingdom of God." ¹⁷He received a cup, and when he had given thanks, he said, "Take this, and share it among yourselves, ¹⁸for I tell you, from now on[e] I will not drink of the fruit of the vine until the kingdom of God comes."

¹⁹He took bread, and when he had given thanks, he broke it, and gave to them, saying, "This is my body which is given for you. Do this in remembrance of me." ²⁰Likewise, he took the cup after they had eaten, saying, "This cup is the New Covenant in my blood, which is poured out for you.[f] ²¹But look, the hand of him who betrays me is with me on

---

a   21:36 Some Mss read "counted worthy"
b   22:3 Some Mss read "surnamed"
c   22:14 Some Mss add "apostles"
d   22:16 Some Mss lack "again"
e   22:18 Some Mss lack "from now on"
f   22:20 Jeremiah 31:31; 1Corinthians 11:23-25

the table. ²²The Son of Man indeed goes, as it has been determined, but woe to that man through whom he is betrayed."

²³They began to question among themselves, which of them it was who would do this thing. ²⁴There arose also a contention among them, which of them was considered to be greatest. ²⁵He said to them, "The kings of the nations lord it over them, and those who have authority over them are called 'benefactors.' ²⁶But not so with you. But one who is the greater among you, let him become as the younger, and one who is governing, as one who serves. ²⁷For who is greater, one who sits at the table, or one who serves? Is it not he who sits at the table? But I am in the midst of you as one who serves. ²⁸But you are those who have continued with me in my trials. ²⁹I confer on you a kingdom, even as my Father conferred on me, ³⁰that you may eat and drink at my table in my kingdom,ᵃ and you will sit on thrones judging the twelve tribes of Israel."

³¹ᵇ"Simon, Simon, look, Satan asked to have you, that he might sift you as wheat, ³²but I prayed for you, that your faith would not fail. You, when once you have turned again, establish your brothers."

³³He said to him, "Lord, I am ready to go with you both to prison and to death."

³⁴He said, "I tell you, Peter, the rooster will by no means crow today untilᶜ you deny that you know me three times."

³⁵He said to them, "When I sent you out without money bag, and pack, and shoes, did you lack anything?"

They said, "Nothing."

³⁶Then he said to them, "But now, whoever has a money bag mustᵈ take it, and likewise a pack. Whoever has none, must sell his cloak, and buy a sword. ³⁷For I tell you that this which is written must still be fulfilled in me: 'And he was numbered with transgressors.'ᵉ For that which concerns me has an end."

³⁸They said, "Lord, look, here are two swords."

He said to them, "That is enough."

³⁹He came out, and went, as his custom was, to the Mount of Olives. His disciples also followed him. ⁴⁰When he was at the place, he said to them, "Pray that you do not enter into temptation."

⁴¹He was withdrawn from them about a stone's throw, and he knelt down and prayed, ⁴²saying, "Father, if you are willing, remove this cup from me. Nevertheless, not my will, but yours, be done."

⁴³And an angel from heaven appeared to him, strengthening him. ⁴⁴Being in agony he prayed more earnestly. His sweat became like great drops of blood falling down on the ground.ᶠ

⁴⁵When he rose up from his prayer, he came to the disciples, and found them sleeping because of grief, ⁴⁶and said to them, "Why do you sleep? Rise and pray that you may not enter into temptation."

⁴⁷While he was still speaking, look, a crowd came, and he who was called Judas, one of the twelve, was leading them. He came near to Jesus to kiss him. ⁴⁸But Jesus said to him, "Judas, do you betray the Son of Man with a kiss?"

⁴⁹When those who were around him saw what was about to happen, they said to him, "Lord, should we strike with the sword?" ⁵⁰A certain one of them struck the servant of the high priest, and cut off his right ear.

⁵¹But Jesus answered and said, "No more of this." Then he touched his ear and healed him. ⁵²Jesus said to the chief priests, captains of the temple, and elders, who had come against him, "Have you come out as against a robber, with swords and clubs? ⁵³When I was with you in the temple daily, you did not stretch out your hands against me. But this is your hour, and the power of darkness."

⁵⁴They seized him, and led him away, and brought him into the high priest's house. But Peter followed from a distance.

---

a 22:30 Some Mss lack "in my kingdom"
b 22:31 Some Mss add "And the Lord said"
c 22:34 Some Mss read "before"
d 22:36 Some Mss read "let him"
e 22:37 Isaiah 53:12
f 22:43-44 Some Mss lack vv. 43-44. Possibly edited out for doctrinal reasons. The very early patristic support and typically Lukan wording support the originality of the words

[55]When they had kindled a fire in the middle of the courtyard, and had sat down together, Peter sat among them. [56]A certain servant girl saw him as he sat in the light, and looking intently at him, said, "This man also was with him."

[57]But he denied it,[a] saying, "Woman, I do not know him."

[58]After a little while someone else saw him, and said, "You also are one of them."

But Peter answered, "Man, I am not."

[59]After about one hour passed, another confidently affirmed, saying, "Truly this man also was with him, for he is a Galilean."

[60]But Peter said, "Man, I do not know what you are talking about." Immediately, while he was still speaking, a rooster crowed. [61]The Lord turned, and looked at Peter. Then Peter remembered the Lord's word, how he said to him, "Before the rooster crows today[b] you will deny me three times." [62]And he[c] went out, and wept bitterly.

[63]The men who held Jesus mocked him and beat him. [64]And they blindfolded him[d] and kept asking him, "Prophesy. Who is the one who struck you?" [65]They spoke many other things against him, insulting him.

[66]As soon as it was day, the council of the elders of the people gathered together, both[e] chief priests and scribes, and they led him away into their council, saying, [67]"If you are the Messiah, tell us."

But he said to them, "If I tell you, you won't believe, [68]and if I ask, you will not answer me, or let me go.[f] [69]From now on, the Son of Man will be seated at the right hand of the power of God."

[70]They all said, "Are you then the Son of God?"

He said to them, "You say that I am."

[71]They said, "Why do we need any more witness? For we ourselves have heard from his own mouth."

23 The whole company of them rose up and brought him before Pilate. [2]They began to accuse him, saying, "We found this man subverting our[g] nation, forbidding paying taxes to Caesar, and saying that he himself is the Messiah, a king."

[3]Pilate asked him, "Are you the King of the Jews?"

He answered him, "You say so."

[4]Pilate said to the chief priests and the crowds, "I find no basis for a charge against this man."

[5]But they insisted, saying, "He stirs up the people, teaching throughout all Judea, beginning from Galilee even to this place."

[6]But when Pilate heard it[h], he asked if the man was a Galilean. [7]When he found out that he was in Herod's jurisdiction, he sent him to Herod, who was also in Jerusalem during those days.

[8]Now when Herod saw Jesus, he was exceedingly glad, for he had wanted to see him for a long time, because he had heard[i] about him. He hoped to see some miracle done by him. [9]He questioned him with many words, but he gave no answers. [10]The chief priests and the scribes stood, vehemently accusing him. [11]Herod with his soldiers treated him with contempt and mocked him. Dressing him in luxurious clothing, they sent him back to Pilate. [12]Herod and Pilate became friends with each other that very day, for before that they were enemies with each other.

[13]Pilate called together the chief priests and the rulers and the people, [14]and said to them, "You brought this man to me as one that subverts the people, and see, I have examined him before you, and found no basis for a charge against this man concerning those things of which you accuse him. [15]Neither has Herod, for he sent him back to us[j], and see, nothing worthy of death has been done by him. [16]I will therefore chastise him and release him." [17](Now he had to release one prisoner to them at the feast.)[k]

a 22:57 Some Mss read "him"
b 22:61 Some Mss lack "today"
c 22:62 Some Mss read "Peter"
d 22:64 Some Mss add "they struck him on the face"
e 22:65 Some Mss lack "both"
f 22:68 Some Mss lack "me, or let me go"
g 23:2 Some Mss read "the"
h 23:6 Some Mss read "Galilee"
i 23:8 Some Mss add "many things"
j 23:15 Some Mss read "I sent him to you"
k 23:17 Some Mss lack "Now he had...feast"

¹⁸But they all shouted out together, saying, "Away with this man. Release to us Barabbas."—¹⁹(one who was thrown into prison for a certain revolt in the city, and for murder.)

²⁰Then Pilate spoke to them again, wanting to release Jesus, ²¹but they shouted, saying, "Crucify. Crucify him."

²²He said to them the third time, "Why? What evil has this man done? I have found no capital crime in him. I will therefore chastise him and release him." ²³But they were urgent with loud voices, asking that he might be crucified. And their voices, and those of the chief priests,ᵃ prevailed. ²⁴Pilate decreed that what they asked for should be done. ²⁵He releasedᵇ him who had been thrown into prison for insurrection and murder, for whom they asked, but he delivered Jesus up to their will.

²⁶When they led him away, they grabbed one Simon of Cyrene, coming from the country, and placed on him the cross, to carry it after Jesus. ²⁷A large crowd of the people followed him, including women who also mourned and lamented him. ²⁸But Jesus, turning to them, said, "Daughters of Jerusalem, do not weep for me, but weep for yourselves and for your children. ²⁹For look, the days are coming in which they will say, 'Blessed are the barren, the wombs that never bore, and the breasts that never nursed.' ³⁰Then they will begin to say to the mountains, 'Fall on us,' and to the hills, 'Cover us.'ᶜ ³¹For if they do these things in the green tree, what will be done in the dry?"

³²There were also others, two criminals, led with him to be put to death. ³³When they came to the place that is called The Skull,ᵈ they crucified him there with the criminals, one on the right and the other on the left.

³⁴And Jesus said, "Father, forgive them, for they do not know what they are doing."ᵉ

Dividing his garments among them, they cast lots. ³⁵The people stood watching. The rulersᶠ also scoffed at him, saying, "He saved others. Let him save himself, if this is the Messiah of God, his Chosen One."

³⁶The soldiers also mocked him, coming to him and offering him vinegar, ³⁷and saying, "If you are the King of the Jews, save yourself."

³⁸An inscription was also written above himᵍ: "THIS IS THE KING OF THE JEWS."

³⁹One of the criminals who hung there insulted him, saying, "Are you notʰ the Messiah? Save yourself and us."

⁴⁰But the other answered, and rebuking him said, "Do you not even fear God, seeing you are under the same condemnation? ⁴¹And we indeed justly, for we receive the due reward for our deeds; but this man has done nothing wrong." ⁴²And he said, "Jesus,ⁱ remember me when you come into your kingdom."

⁴³And heʲ said to him, "Assuredly I tell you, today you will be with me in Paradise."

⁴⁴It was now about noonᵏ, and darkness came over the whole landˡ until three in the afternoonᵐ, ⁴⁵for the sun's light failedⁿ. And the veil of the temple was torn in two. ⁴⁶And Jesus, crying with a loud voice, said, "Father, into your hands I commit my spirit." Having said this, he breathed his last.

⁴⁷When the centurion saw what was done, he glorified God, saying, "Certainly this was a righteous man." ⁴⁸All the crowds that came together to see this, when they saw the things that were done, returned home beating their breasts. ⁴⁹All his acquaintances, and the women who followed

---

a   23:23 Some Mss lack "and those of the chief priests"
b   23:25 Some Mss add "to them"
c   23:30 Hosea 10:8
d   23:33 Latin "Calvary"
e   23:34 Some Mss lack "Father, forgive…doing." The words may have been omitted for doctrinal reasons. The very early external support and typically Lukan vocabulary support the originality of the words
f   23:35 Some Mss add "with them"
g   23:38 Some Mss add "in letters of Greek, Latin, and Hebrew"
h   23:39 Some Mss read "If you are"
i   23:42 Some Mss read "And he said to Jesus, "Lord,"
j   23:42 Some Mss read "Jesus"
k   23:44 Lit. the sixth hour
l   23:44 Amos 8:9
m   23:44 Lit. the ninth hour
n   23:45 Some Mss read "The sun was darkened"

with him from Galilee, stood at a distance, watching these things.

⁵⁰And look, a man named Joseph, who was a member of the council, a good and righteous man ⁵¹(he had not consented to their counsel and deed), from Arimathaea, a city of the Judeans, who was also waiting for the kingdom of God: ⁵²this man went to Pilate, and asked for the body of Jesus. ⁵³He took it down, and wrapped it in a linen cloth, and placed him in a tomb that was cut in stone, where no one had ever been placed. ⁵⁴It was the day of the Preparation, and the Sabbath was drawing near. ⁵⁵The women, who had come with him out of Galilee, followed after, and saw the tomb, and how his body was placed. ⁵⁶They returned, and prepared spices and ointments. On the Sabbath they rested according to the commandment.

24 But on the first day of the week, at early dawn, they[a] came to the tomb, bringing the spices which they had prepared. ²They found the stone rolled away from the tomb. ³They entered in, and did not find the body of the Lord Jesus. ⁴It happened, while they were greatly perplexed about this, look, two men stood by them in dazzling clothing. ⁵Becoming terrified, they bowed their faces down to the earth.

They said to them, "Why do you seek the living among the dead? ⁶He is not here, but is risen. Remember what he told you when he was still in Galilee, ⁷saying that the Son of Man must be delivered up into the hands of sinful men, and be crucified, and the third day rise again?"

⁸They remembered his words, ⁹returned from the tomb, and told all these things to the eleven, and to all the rest. ¹⁰Now they were Mary Magdalene and Joanna and Mary the mother of James and the other women with them who told these things to the apostles. ¹¹These words seemed to them to be nonsense, and they did not believe them. ¹²But Peter got up and ran to the tomb. Stooping and looking in, he saw the strips of linen[b] by themselves, and he departed to his home, wondering what had happened.

¹³And look, two of them were going that very day to a village named Emmaus, which was about seven miles[c] from Jerusalem. ¹⁴They talked with each other about all of these things which had happened. ¹⁵It happened, while they talked and questioned together, that Jesus himself came near, and went with them. ¹⁶But their eyes were kept from recognizing him. ¹⁷And he said to them, "What are these words that you are exchanging with each other as you walk?" And they stood still, looking sad.[d]

¹⁸One of them, named Cleopas, answered him, "Are you the only stranger in Jerusalem who does not know the things which have happened there in these days?"

¹⁹He said to them, "What things?"

They said to him, "The things concerning Jesus, the Nazarene, a man who was a prophet mighty in deed and word before God and all the people; ²⁰and how the chief priests and our rulers delivered him up to be condemned to death, and crucified him. ²¹But we were hoping that it was he who would redeem Israel. Yes, and besides all this, it is now the third day since these things happened. ²²Also, certain women of our company amazed us, having arrived early at the tomb; ²³and when they did not find his body, they came saying that they had also seen a vision of angels, who said that he was alive. ²⁴Some of us went to the tomb, and found it just like the women had said, but they did not see him."

²⁵Then he said to them, "O foolish ones, and slow of heart to believe in all that the prophets have spoken. ²⁶Did not the Messiah have to suffer these things and to enter into his glory?" ²⁷Beginning from Moses and from all the prophets, he explained to them in all the Scriptures the things concerning himself. ²⁸They drew near to the village, where they were going, and he acted like he would go further.

---

a   24:1 Some Mss add "and some others"
b   24:12 Some Mss add "lying"
c   24:13 Or, 11 about kilometers. Lit. 60 stadia
d   24:17 Some Mss read "walk, and are sad?"

²⁹They urged him, saying, "Stay with us, for it is almost evening, and the day is almost over."

He went in to stay with them. ³⁰It happened, that when he had sat down at the table with them, he took the bread and gave thanks. Breaking it, he gave to them. ³¹Their eyes were opened, and they recognized him, and he vanished out of their sight. ³²They said one to another, "Weren't our hearts burning within us, while he spoke to us along the way, and while he opened the Scriptures to us?" ³³They rose up that very hour, returned to Jerusalem, and found the eleven gathered together, and those who were with them, ³⁴saying, "The Lord is risen indeed, and has appeared to Simon." ³⁵They related the things that happened along the way, and how he was recognized by them in the breaking of the bread.

³⁶As they said these things, Jesus himself stood among them, and said to them, "Peace be to you."

³⁷But they were terrified and filled with fear, and supposed that they had seen a spirit.

³⁸He said to them, "Why are you troubled? Why do doubts arise in your hearts? ³⁹See my hands and my feet, that it is truly me. Touch me and see, for a spirit does not have flesh and bones, as you see that I have." ⁴⁰When he had said this, he showed them his hands and his feet. ⁴¹While they still did not believe for joy, and wondered, he said to them, "Do you have anything here to eat?"

⁴²And they gave him a piece of a broiled fish.ᵃ ⁴³And he took it and ate in front of them. ⁴⁴And he said to them, "This is what I told you, while I was still with you, that all things which are written in the Law of Moses, the Prophets, and the Psalms, concerning me must be fulfilled."

⁴⁵Then he opened their minds, that they might understand the Scriptures. ⁴⁶He said to them, "Thus it is written,ᵇ for the Messiah to suffer and to rise from the dead the third day, ⁴⁷and that repentance leading toᶜ forgiveness of sins should be preached in his name to all the nations, beginning at Jerusalem. ⁴⁸You are witnesses of these things. ⁴⁹And look, I send forth the promise of my Father on you. But wait in the cityᵈ until you are clothed with power from on high."

⁵⁰He led them outᵉ as far as Bethany, and he lifted up his hands, and blessed them. ⁵¹It happened, while he blessed them, that he departed from them, and was carried up into heaven.ᶠ ⁵²They worshiped him, and returned to Jerusalem with great joy, ⁵³and were continually in the temple, praising andᵍ blessing God.ʰ

John

1 In the beginning was the Word, and the Word was with God, and the Word was God. ²He was in the beginning with God. ³All things were made through him, and apart from him nothing was made that has been made. ⁴In him was life, and the life was the light of humanity. ⁵The light shines in the darkness, and the darkness hasn't overcome it. ⁶There came a man, sent from God, whose name was John. ⁷He came as a witness to testify about the light, that all might believe through him. ⁸He was not the light, but was sent that he might testify about the light. ⁹The true light that enlightens everyone was coming into the world.

¹⁰He was in the world, and the world was made through him, but the world did not recognize him. ¹¹He came to his own, and those who were his own did not re-

a   24:42 Some Mss add "and some honeycomb"
b   24:46 Some Mss add "and thus it was necessary"
c   24:47 Or, "repentance for." Some Mss read "and"
d   24:49 Some Mss add "of Jerusalem"
e   24:50 Some Mss lack "out"
f   24:51 Some Mss lack "and was carried up into heaven" from haplography: n kai a-n kai a
g   24:53 Some Mss lack "praising and"
h   24:53 Some Mss add "Amen"

ceive him. [12]But as many as received him, to them he gave the right to become God's children, to those who believe in his name, [13]who were born not of blood, nor of the will of the flesh, nor of the will of man, but of God. [14]And the Word became flesh and lived among us, and we saw his glory, such glory as of the one and only of the Father, full of grace and truth. [15]John testified about him and shouted out, saying, "This was the one of whom I said, 'He who comes after me has surpassed me, for he was before me.'" [16]For of his fullness we all received, and grace upon grace. [17]For the Law was given through Moses, grace and truth came through Jesus Christ. [18]No one has seen God at any time. The only Son,[a] who is at the Father's side,[b] has made him known.

[19]And this is John's testimony, when the Jewish leaders[c] sent priests and Levites to him[d] from Jerusalem to ask him, "Who are you?"

[20]And he confessed, and did not deny, but he confessed, "I am not the Messiah."

[21]And they asked him, "What then? Are you Elijah?"[e] And he said, "I am not." "Are you the Prophet?"[f] And he answered, "No."

[22]They said therefore to him, "Who are you? Give us an answer to take back to those who sent us. What do you say about yourself?"

[23]He said, "I am the voice of one crying in the wilderness, 'Make straight the way of the Lord,'[g] as Isaiah the prophet said."

[24](Now they had been sent from the Pharisees.) [25]And they asked him, "Why then do you baptize, if you are not the Messiah, nor Elijah, nor the Prophet?"

[26]John answered them, saying, "I baptize in water, but among you stands one whom you do not know. [27]He is the one who comes after me,[h] whose sandal strap I'm not worthy to loosen." [28]These things were done in Bethany[i] across the Jordan, where John was baptizing.

[29]The next day, he saw Jesus coming to him, and said, "Look, the Lamb of God, who takes away the sin of the world. [30]This is he of whom I said, 'After me comes a man who ranks ahead of me, because he existed before me.'

[31]I did not know him, but for this reason I came baptizing in water so that he would be revealed to Israel." [32]And John testified, saying, "I saw the Spirit descending like a dove out of heaven, and it remained on him. [33]And I did not recognize him, but he who sent me to baptize in water, he said to me, 'On whomever you will see the Spirit descending, and remaining on him, this is he who baptizes in the Holy Spirit.' [34]And I have seen and have testified that this is the Chosen One of God."[j]

[35]Again, the next day, John was standing with two of his disciples, [36]and he looked at Jesus as he walked, and said, "Look, the Lamb of God." [37]And the two disciples heard him say this, and they followed Jesus. [38]And Jesus turned and saw them following, and said to them, "What are you looking for?"

They said to him, "Rabbi" (which translated means Teacher), "where are you staying?"

[39]He said to them, "Come, and you will[k] see."

They came and saw where he was staying, and they stayed with him that day. It was about four in the afternoon.[l] [40]One of the two who heard John, and followed him, was Andrew, Simon Peter's brother. [41]He first found his own brother, Simon, and said to him, "We have found the Messiah." (which is translated, Christ). [42]He brought him to Jesus. Jesus looked at him, and said,

---

a　1:18 Some Mss read "God," possibly a primitive transcriptional error in nomina sacra in the Alexandrian tradition

b　1:18 Lit., who is in the bosom of the Father

c　1:19 Gk. ioudaioi. See R. J. Bratcher, "The Jews' in the Gospel of John." The Bible Translator 26 (1975): 401-9

d　1:19 Some Mss lack "to him"

e　1:21 Malachi 4:5

f　1:21 Deuteronomy 18:15, 18

g　1:23 Isaiah 40:3. John condenses the 14+ words in Isaiah 40:3 LXX to 9

h　1:27 Some Mss add "who is preferred before me"

i　1:28 Some Mss read "Bethabara"

j　1:34 Some Mss read "Son." Other Mss have both readings together: "Chosen One, the Son of God." See Isaiah 42:1; Luke 9:35, 23:35

k　1:39 Some Mss lack "you will"

l　1:39 Lit. the tenth hour

"You are Simon the son of John[a]. You will be called Cephas" (which is translated, Peter). [43]On the next day, he was determined to go out into Galilee, and he found Philip. And Jesus said to him, "Follow me." [44]Now Philip was from Bethsaida, of the city of Andrew and Peter. [45]Philip found Nathanael, and said to him, "We have found him of whom Moses in the Law and the Prophets wrote: Jesus of Nazareth,[b] the son of Joseph."

[46]And Nathanael said to him, "Can any good thing come out of Nazareth?"

Philip said to him, "Come and see."

[47]Jesus saw Nathanael coming to him, and said about him, "Look, a true Israelite in whom there is no deceit."

[48]Nathanael said to him, "How do you know me?"

Jesus answered him, "Before Philip called you, when you were under the fig tree, I saw you."

[49]Nathanael answered him, "Rabbi, you are the Son of God. You are King of Israel."

[50]Jesus answered and said to him, "Because I told you, 'I saw you underneath the fig tree,' do you believe? You will see greater things than these." [51]And he said to him, "Truly, truly,[c] I tell you,[d] you will see heaven opened, and the angels of God ascending and descending on the Son of Man."

2 And the third day there was a wedding in Cana of Galilee, and the mother of Jesus was there. [2]Now Jesus also was invited, with his disciples, to the wedding. [3]And when the wine ran out, Jesus' mother said to him, "They have no wine."

[4]Jesus said to her, "Woman, what does that have to do with you and me? My hour has not yet come."

[5]His mother said to the servants, "Whatever he says to you, do it." [6]Now there were six stone water jars set there after the Jewish manner of purifying, containing two or three metretes[e] apiece. [7]Jesus said to them, "Fill the water jars with water." They filled them up to the brim. [8]He said to them, "Now draw some out, and take it to the ruler of the feast." So they took it. [9]When the ruler of the feast tasted the water now become wine, and did not know where it came from (but the servants who had drawn the water knew), the ruler of the feast called the bridegroom, [10]and said to him, "Everyone serves the good wine first, and when the guests have drunk freely, then that which is worse. You have kept the good wine until now." [11]This beginning of his signs Jesus did in Cana of Galilee, and revealed his glory; and his disciples believed in him.

[12]After this, he went down to Capernaum, he, and his mother, his brothers, and his disciples; and they stayed there a few days. [13]The Jewish Passover was near, and Jesus went up to Jerusalem. [14]And he found in the temple those who sold oxen, sheep, and doves, and the money changers sitting. [15]And he made a whip of cords, and threw all out of the temple, both the sheep and the oxen; and he poured out the changers' money, and overthrew their tables. [16]To those who sold the doves, he said, "Take these things out of here. Do not make my Father's house a marketplace." [17]His disciples remembered that it was written, "Zeal for your house will consume me."[f]

[18]The Jewish leaders therefore answered him, "What sign do you show us, seeing that you do these things?"

[19]Jesus answered them, "Destroy this temple, and in three days I will raise it up."

[20]The Jewish leaders therefore said, "Forty-six years was this temple in building, and will you raise it up in three days?" [21]But he spoke of the temple of his body. [22]When therefore he was raised from the dead, his disciples remembered that he said this[g], and they believed the Scripture, and the word which Jesus had said.

[23]Now when he was in Jerusalem at the Passover, during the feast, many believed

a   1:42 Some Mss read "Jonah"
b   1:45 Isaiah 11:1 Hebrew "netzer"
c   1:51 Lit. "Amen, amen"
d   1:51 Some Mss add "hereafter"
e   2:6 2 to 3 metretes is about 20 to 30 U. S. Gallons, 16 to 25 imperial gallons, or 75 to 115 liters.
f   2:17 Psalm 69:9
g   2:22 Some Mss add "to them"

in his name after seeing his signs which he did. [24]But Jesus did not trust himself to them, because he knew everyone, [25]and because he did not need anyone to testify concerning man; for he himself knew what was in man.

3 Now there was a man of the Pharisees named Nicodemus, a ruler of the Jewish people. [2]This man came to him at night, and said to him, "Rabbi, we know that you are a teacher come from God, for no one can do these signs that you do, unless God is with him."

[3]Jesus answered him, "Truly, truly, I tell you, unless one is born again he cannot see the kingdom of God."

[4]Nicodemus said to him, "How can anyone be born when he is old? Can he enter a second time into his mother's womb, and be born?"

[5]Jesus answered, "Truly, truly, I tell you, unless one is born of water and the Spirit he cannot enter into the kingdom of God. [6]That which is born of the flesh is flesh. That which is born of the Spirit is spirit. [7]Do not marvel that I said to you, 'You must be born again.' [8]The wind blows where it wants to, and you hear its sound, but do not know where it comes from and where it is going. So is everyone who is born of the Spirit."

[9]Nicodemus answered and said to him, "How can these things be?"

[10]Jesus answered him, "Are you the teacher of Israel, and do not understand these things? [11]Truly, truly, I tell you, we speak that which we know, and testify of that which we have seen, and you do not receive our witness. [12]If I told you earthly things and you do not believe, how will you believe if I tell you heavenly things? [13]And no one has ascended into heaven, but he who descended out of heaven, the Son of Man, who is in heaven.[a] [14]And as Moses lifted up the serpent in the wilderness, even so must the Son of Man be lifted up, [15]that whoever believes in him[b] may have everlasting life. [16]For God so loved the world that he gave his only Son, so that

whoever believes in him will not perish, but have everlasting life. [17]For God did not send his Son into the world to judge the world, but that the world should be saved through him. [18]He who believes in him is not judged. He who does not believe has been judged already, because he has not believed in the name of the only Son of God. [19]And this is the judgment, that the light has come into the world, and people loved the darkness rather than the light; for their works were evil. [20]For everyone who does evil hates the light, and does not come to the light, lest his works would be exposed. [21]But he who does the truth comes to the light, that his works may be revealed, that they have been done in God."

[22]After these things, Jesus came with his disciples into the land of Judea. He stayed there with them, and baptized. [23]Now John also was baptizing in Aenon near Salim, because there was much water there. They came, and were baptized. [24]For John was not yet thrown into prison. [25]Now a dispute arose between John's disciples with a Jew[c] about purification. [26]And they came to John, and said to him, "Rabbi, he who was with you beyond the Jordan, to whom you have testified, look, he is baptizing, and everyone is coming to him."

[27]John answered, "No one can receive anything, unless it has been given to him from heaven. [28]You yourselves bear me witness[d] that I said, 'I am not the Messiah,' but, 'I have been sent before him.' [29]He who has the bride is the bridegroom; but the friend of the bridegroom, who stands and hears him, rejoices greatly because of the bridegroom's voice. So this joy of mine is now complete. [30]He must increase, but I must decrease. [31]He who comes from above is above all. He who is from the earth belongs to the earth, and speaks of the earth.

---

a   3:13 Some Mss lack "who is in heaven," possibly a primitive excision in the Alexandrian tradition due to the difficulty of the term

b   3:15 Or, "that whoever believes, will in him." Some Mss add "should not perish, but"

c   3:25 Some Mss read "Jews"

d   3:28 Some Mss read "testify"

He who comes from heaven is above all. [32]What he has seen and heard, of that he testifies; and no one receives his witness. [33]He who has received his witness has set his seal to this, that God is true. [34]For he whom God has sent speaks the words of God; for he[a] does not give the Spirit by measure. [35]The Father loves the Son, and has given all things into his hand. [36]Whoever believes in the Son has everlasting life, but whoever refuses to believe in the Son won't see life, but the wrath of God remains on him."

4 Therefore when the Lord[b] knew that the Pharisees had heard that Jesus was making and baptizing more disciples than John [2](although Jesus himself did not baptize, but his disciples), [3]he left Judea, and departed again[c] into Galilee. [4]He needed to pass through Samaria. [5]So he came to a city of Samaria, called Sychar, near the parcel of ground that Jacob gave to his son, Joseph. [6]Jacob's well was there. Jesus therefore, being tired from his journey, sat down by the well. It was about about noon[d]. [7]A woman of Samaria came to draw water. Jesus said to her, "Give me a drink." [8]For his disciples had gone away into the city to buy food.

[9]The Samaritan woman therefore said to him, "How can you, being a Jew, ask for a drink from me, a Samaritan woman?" (For Jews have no dealings with Samaritans.)

[10]Jesus answered her, "If you knew the gift of God, and who it is who says to you, 'Give me a drink,' you would have asked him, and he would have given you living water."

[11]The woman said to him, "Sir, you have nothing to draw with, and the well is deep. From where do you get that living water? [12]Are you greater than our father, Jacob, who gave us the well, and drank of it himself, as did his children, and his livestock?"

[13]Jesus answered her, "Everyone who drinks of this water will thirst again, [14]but whoever drinks of the water that I will give him will never thirst again; but the water that I will give him will become in him a well of water springing up to everlasting life."

[15]The woman said to him, "Sir, give me this water, so that I do not get thirsty, neither come all the way here to draw."

[16]Jesus said to her, "Go, call your husband, and come here."

[17]The woman answered and said to him,[e] "I have no husband."

Jesus said to her, "You said well, 'I have no husband,' [18]for you have had five husbands; and he whom you now have is not your husband. This you have said truly."

[19]The woman said to him, "Sir, I perceive that you are a prophet. [20]Our fathers worshiped in this mountain, and you say that in Jerusalem is the place where people ought to worship."

[21]Jesus said to her, "Woman, believe me, the hour comes, when neither in this mountain, nor in Jerusalem, will you worship the Father. [22]You worship that which you do not know. We worship that which we know; for salvation is from the Jews. [23]But the hour comes, and now is, when the true worshippers will worship the Father in spirit and truth, for the Father seeks such to be his worshippers. [24]God is spirit, and those who worship him must worship in spirit and truth."

[25]The woman said to him, "I know that Messiah comes," (he who is called Christ). "When he has come, he will declare to us all things."

[26]Jesus said to her, "I am he, the one who speaks to you." [27]At this, his disciples came. They marveled that he was speaking with a woman; yet no one said, "What are you looking for?" or, "Why do you speak with her?" [28]So the woman left her water pot, and went away into the city, and said to the people, [29]"Come, see a man who told me everything that I did. Can this be the Messiah?"

---

a   3:34 Some Mss read "God"
b   4:1 Some Mss read "Jesus"
c   4:3 Some Mss lack "again"
d   4:6 Lit. the sixth hour
e   4:17 Some Mss lack "to him"

³⁰They went out of the city, and were coming to him. ³¹In the meanwhile, the disciples urged him, saying, "Rabbi, eat."

³²But he said to them, "I have food to eat that you do not know about."

³³The disciples therefore said one to another, "Has anyone brought him something to eat?"

³⁴Jesus said to them, "My food is to do the will of him who sent me, and to accomplish his work. ³⁵Do you not say, 'There are yet four months until the harvest?' Look, I tell you, lift up your eyes and see the fields, that they are white for harvest already. ³⁶He who reaps receives wages, and gathers fruit to everlasting life; that both he who sows and he who reaps may rejoice together. ³⁷For in this the saying is true, 'One sows, and another reaps.' ³⁸I sent you to reap that for which you have not labored. Others have labored, and you have entered into their labor."

³⁹From that city many of the Samaritans believed in him because of the word of the woman, who testified, "He told me everything that I did." ⁴⁰So when the Samaritans came to him, they begged him to stay with them. He stayed there two days. ⁴¹Many more believed because of his word. ⁴²They said to the woman, "Now we believe, not because of your speaking; for we have heard for ourselves, and know that this is indeed theᵃ Savior of the world."

⁴³After the two days he went out from there and went into Galilee. ⁴⁴For Jesus himself testified that a prophet has no honor in his own country. ⁴⁵So when he came into Galilee, the Galileans received him, having seen all the things that he did in Jerusalem at the feast, for they also went to the feast. ⁴⁶Jesus came therefore again to Cana of Galilee, where he made the water into wine. There was a certain nobleman whose son was sick at Capernaum. ⁴⁷When he heard that Jesus had come out of Judea into Galilee, he went to him, and begged him that he would come down and heal his son, for he was at the point of death. ⁴⁸Jesus therefore said to him, "Unless you see signs and wonders, you will in no way believe."

⁴⁹The nobleman said to him, "Sir, come down before my child dies." ⁵⁰Jesus said to him, "Go your way. Your son lives." The man believed the word that Jesus spoke to him, and he went his way. ⁵¹As he was now going down, his servants met him,ᵇ saying that his son was alive.ᶜ ⁵²So he inquired of them the hour when he began to get better. They said therefore to him, "Yesterday at one in the afternoon,ᵈ the fever left him." ⁵³So the father knew that it was at that hour in which Jesus said to him, "Your son lives." He believed, as did his whole house. ⁵⁴This is again the second sign that Jesus did, having come out of Judea into Galilee.

5 After these things, there was a Jewish festival,ᵉ and Jesus went up to Jerusalem. ²Now in Jerusalem by the sheep areaᶠ there is a pool, which is called in Hebrew Bethesda,ᵍ having five porches. ³In these lay aʰ multitude of those who were sick, blind, lame, or paralyzed.⁴ⁱ

⁵A certain man was there, who had been sick for thirty-eight years. ⁶When Jesus saw him lying there, and knew that he had been sick for a long time, he asked him, "Do you want to be made well?"

⁷The sick man answered him, "Sir, I have no one to put me into the pool when the water is stirred up, but while I'm coming, another steps down before me."

⁸Jesus said to him, "Arise, take up your mat, and walk."

---

a 4:42 Some Mss add "the Christ"
b 4:51 Some Mss add "and reported"
c 4:51 Some Mss read "saying, Your son lives"
d 4:52 Lit. the seventh hour
e 5:1 Possibly Purim
f 5:2 Gk. probatike, meaning "of sheep," a possible ellipsis which has been thought to suggest a place, market, gate or pool
g 5:2 Meaning, "House of Mercy." Some Mss read "Bethzatha"
h 5:3 Some Mss add "great"
i 5:3b-4 Some Mss add "waiting for the moving of the water; for an angel of the Lord went down at certain times into the pool, and stirred up the water. Whoever stepped in first after the stirring of the water was made whole of whatever disease he had"

⁹Immediately, the man was made well, and took up his mat and walked.

Now it was the Sabbath on that day. ¹⁰So the Jewish leaders said to him who was cured, "It is the Sabbath. It is not lawful for you to carry the mat."

¹¹He answered them, "He who made me well, the same said to me, 'Take up your mat, and walk.'"

¹²Then they asked him, "Who is the man who said to you to pick it up and walk?ª"

¹³But he who was healed did not know who it was, for Jesus had withdrawn, a crowd being in the place.

¹⁴Afterward Jesus found him in the temple, and said to him, "See, you are made well. Sin no more, so that nothing worse happens to you."

¹⁵The man went away, and told the Jewish leaders that it was Jesus who had made him well. ¹⁶For this cause the Jewish leaders persecuted Jesus,ᵇ because he did these things on the Sabbath. ¹⁷But heᶜ answered them, "My Father is still working, so I am working, too." ¹⁸For this cause therefore the Jewish leaders sought all the more to kill him, because he not only broke the Sabbath, but also called God his own Father, making himself equal with God. ¹⁹Jesus therefore answered them, "Truly, truly, I tell you, the Son can do nothing of himself, but what he sees the Father doing. For whatever things he does, these the Son also does likewise. ²⁰For the Father loves the Son, and shows him all things that he himself does. He will show him greater works than these, that you may marvel. ²¹For as the Father raises the dead and gives them life, even so the Son also gives life to whom he desires. ²²For the Father judges no one, but he has given all judgment to the Son, ²³that all may honor the Son, even as they honor the Father. Whoever does not honor the Son does not honor the Father who sent him.

²⁴"Truly, truly, I tell you, he who hears my word, and believes him who sent me, has everlasting life, and does not come into judgment, but has passed out of death into life. ²⁵Truly, truly, I tell you, the hour comes, and now is, when the dead will hear the Son of God's voice; and those who hear will live. ²⁶For as the Father has life in himself, even so he gave to the Son also to have life in himself. ²⁷He also gave him authority to execute judgment, because he is the Son of Man. ²⁸Do not marvel at this, for the hour comes, in which all that are in the tombs will hear his voice, ²⁹and will come out; those who have done good, to the resurrection of life; and those who have done evil, to the resurrection of judgment.ᵈ ³⁰I can of myself do nothing. As I hear, I judge, and my judgment is righteous; because I do not seek my own will, but the will of the Oneᵉ who sent me.

³¹"If I testify about myself, my witness is not valid. ³²It is another who testifies about me. I know that the testimony which he testifies about me is true. ³³You have sent to John, and he has testified to the truth. ³⁴But the testimony which I receive is not from people. However, I say these things that you may be saved. ³⁵He was the burning and shining lamp, and you were willing to rejoice for a while in his light. ³⁶But the testimony which I have is greater than that of John, for the works which the Father gave me to accomplish, the very works that I do, testify about me, that the Father has sent me. ³⁷The Father himself, who sent me, has testified about me. You have neither heard his voice at any time, nor seen his form. ³⁸You do not have his word living in you; because you do not believe him whom he sent.

³⁹You search the Scriptures, because you think that in them you have everlasting life; and these are they which testify about me. ⁴⁰But you are unwilling to come to me so that you may have life. ⁴¹I do not receive glory from people. ⁴²But I know you, that you do not have God's love in yourselves. ⁴³I have come in my Father's name, and you do not receive me. If another comes in his own name, you will receive him. ⁴⁴How can

---

a   5:12 Some Mss read "you, Take up your mat, and walk"

b   5:16 Some Mss add "and sought to kill him"

c   5:17 Some Mss read "Jesus"

d   5:29 Daniel 12:2

e   5:30 Some Mss read "my Father"

you believe, who receive glory from one another, and you do not seek the glory that comes from the only God?[a]

⁴⁵"Do not think that I will accuse you to the Father. There is one who accuses you, even Moses, on whom you have set your hope. ⁴⁶For if you believed Moses, you would believe me; for he wrote about me. ⁴⁷But if you do not believe his writings, how will you believe my words?"

6 After these things, Jesus went away to the other side of the sea of Galilee, which is also called the Sea of Tiberias. ²A large crowd followed him, because they saw the[b] signs which he did on those who were sick. ³Jesus went up into the mountain, and he sat there with his disciples. ⁴Now the Passover, the Jewish festival, was near. ⁵Jesus therefore lifting up his eyes, and seeing that a large crowd was coming to him, said to Philip, "Where are we to buy bread, that these may eat?" ⁶This he said to test him, for he himself knew what he would do.

⁷Philip answered him, "Two hundred denarii worth of bread is not sufficient for them, that everyone of them may receive a little."

⁸One of his disciples, Andrew, Simon Peter's brother, said to him, ⁹"There is a boy here who has five barley loaves and two fish, but what are these among so many?"

¹⁰Jesus said, "Have the people sit down." Now there was much grass in that place. So the men sat down, in number about five thousand. ¹¹Jesus took the loaves; and having given thanks, he distributed to the disciples, and the disciples to[c] those who were sitting down; likewise also of the fish as much as they desired. ¹²When they were filled, he said to his disciples, "Gather up the broken pieces which are left over, that nothing be lost." ¹³So they gathered them up, and filled twelve baskets with broken pieces from the five barley loaves, which were left over by those who had eaten. ¹⁴When therefore the people saw the sign which he did, they said, "This is truly the Prophet who comes into the world." ¹⁵Jesus therefore, perceiving that they were about to come and take him by force, to make him king, withdrew again[d] to the mountain by himself.

¹⁶When evening came, his disciples went down to the sea, ¹⁷and they entered into the boat, and were going over the sea to Capernaum. It was now dark, and Jesus had not come to them. ¹⁸The sea was tossed by a great wind blowing. ¹⁹When therefore they had rowed about three or four miles,[e] they saw Jesus walking on the sea.[f] and drawing near to the boat; and they were afraid. ²⁰But he said to them, "It is I[g]. Do not be afraid." ²¹They were willing therefore to receive him into the boat. Immediately the boat was at the land where they were going.

²²On the next day, the crowd that stood on the other side of the sea saw that there was no other boat there, except one,[h] and that Jesus had not entered with his disciples into the boat, but his disciples had gone away alone. ²³Other boats from Tiberias came near to the place where they ate the bread after the Lord had given thanks. ²⁴When the crowd therefore saw that Jesus was not there, nor his disciples, they themselves got into the boats, and came to Capernaum, seeking Jesus. ²⁵When they found him on the other side of the sea, they asked him, "Rabbi, when did you come here?"

²⁶Jesus answered them, "Truly, truly, I tell you, you seek me, not because you saw signs, but because you ate of the loaves, and were filled. ²⁷Do not work for the food which perishes, but for the food which remains to everlasting life, which the Son of Man will give to you. For God the Father has sealed him."

---

a   5:44 Some Mss lack "God"
b   6:2 Some Mss read "his"
c   6:11 Some Mss lack "the disciples, and the disciples to"
d   6:15 Some Mss lack "again"
e   6:19 Or about 5 to 6 kilometers. Lit. 25 or 30 stadia
f   6:19 Job 9:8, Psalm 107:29
g   6:20 Or, "I AM"
h   6:22 Some Mss add "in which his disciples had embarked"

²⁸They said therefore to him, "What must we do, that we may work the works of God?"

²⁹Jesus answered them, "This is the work of God, that you believe in him whom he has sent."

³⁰They said therefore to him, "What then do you do for a sign, that we may see, and believe you? What work do you do? ³¹Our fathers ate the manna in the wilderness. As it is written, 'He gave them bread out of heaven to eat.'"ᵃ

³²Jesus therefore said to them, "Truly, truly, I tell you, it was not Moses who gave you the bread out of heaven, but my Father gives you the true bread out of heaven. ³³For the bread of God is that which comes down out of heaven, and gives life to the world."

³⁴They said therefore to him, "Lord, always give us this bread."

³⁵Jesus said to them, "I am the bread of life. He who comes to me will not be hungry, and he who believes in me will never be thirsty. ³⁶But I told you that you have seen me, and yet you do not believe. ³⁷All those whom the Father gives me will come to me. Him who comes to me I will in no way throw out. ³⁸For I have come down from heaven, not to do my own will, but the will of him who sent me. ³⁹This is the will of himᵇ who sent me, that of all he has given to me I should lose nothing, but should raise him up at the last day. ⁴⁰This is the will of my Father,ᶜ that everyone who sees the Son, and believes in him, should have everlasting life; and I will raise him up at the last day."

⁴¹The Jewish people therefore murmured concerning him, because he said, "I am the bread which came down out of heaven." ⁴²They said, "Is not this Jesus, the son of Joseph, whose father and motherᵈ we know? How then does he say, 'I have come down out of heaven'?"

⁴³Therefore Jesus answered them, "Do not murmur among yourselves. ⁴⁴No one can come to me unless the Father who sent me draws him, and I will raise him up in the last day. ⁴⁵It is written in the Prophets,

'And they will all be taught by God.'ᵉ Therefore everyone who hears and learns from the Father comes to me. ⁴⁶Not that anyone has seen the Father, except he who is from God. He has seen the Father. ⁴⁷Truly, truly, I tell you, he who believesᶠ has everlasting life. ⁴⁸I am the bread of life. ⁴⁹Your fathers ate the manna in the wilderness, and they died. ⁵⁰This is the bread which comes down out of heaven, that anyone may eat of it and not die. ⁵¹I am the living bread which came down out of heaven. If anyone eats of this bread, he will live forever; and the bread which I will give for the life of the worldᵍ is my flesh."

⁵²The Jews therefore argued with one another, saying, "How can this man give us his flesh to eat?"

⁵³Jesus therefore said to them, "Truly I tell you, unless you eat the flesh of the Son of Man and drink his blood, you do not have life in yourselves. ⁵⁴He who eats my flesh and drinks my blood has everlasting life, and I will raise him up at the last day. ⁵⁵For my flesh is food indeed, and my blood is drink indeed. ⁵⁶He who eats my flesh and drinks my blood lives in me, and I in him. ⁵⁷As the living Father sent me, and I live because of the Father; so he who feeds on me, he will also live because of me. ⁵⁸This is the bread which came down out of heaven—not as the fathers ateʰ, and died. He who eats this bread will live forever." ⁵⁹He said these things in the synagogue, as he taught in Capernaum.

⁶⁰Therefore many of his disciples, when they heard this, said, "This is a hard saying. Who can listen to it?"

⁶¹But Jesus knowing in himself that his disciples murmured at this, said to them, "Does this cause you to stumble? ⁶²Then what if you would see the Son of Man as-

---

a 6:31 Exodus 16:4; Nehemiah 9:15; Psalm 78:24-25
b 6:39 Some Mss read "my Father"
c 6:40 Some Mss read "the one who sent me"
d 6:42 Some Mss lack "and mother"
e 6:45 Isaiah 54:13
f 6:47 Some Mss add "in me"
g 6:51 Some Mss add "which I will give"
h 6:58 Some Mss read "our fathers ate the manna, and died"

cending to where he was before? ⁶³It is the spirit who gives life. The flesh profits nothing. The words that I speak to you are spirit, and are life. ⁶⁴But there are some of you who do not believe." For Jesus knew from the beginning who they were who did not believe, and who it was who would betray him. ⁶⁵He said, "For this cause have I said to you that no one can come to me, unless it is given to him by the^a Father."

⁶⁶At this, many of his disciples went back, and walked no more with him. ⁶⁷Jesus said therefore to the twelve, "You do not also want to go away, do you?"

⁶⁸Simon Peter answered him, "Lord, to whom would we go? You have the words of everlasting life. ⁶⁹We have come to believe and know that you are the Holy One of God.^b"

⁷⁰Jesus answered them, "Did I not choose you, the twelve, and one of you is a devil?" ⁷¹Now he spoke of Judas, the son of Simon Iscariot, for it was he who would betray him, being one of the twelve.

7 After these things, Jesus was walking in Galilee, for he would not walk in Judea, because the Jewish leaders sought to kill him. ²Now the Jewish festival, the Feast of Tabernacles, was near. ³So his brothers said to him, "Depart from here, and go into Judea, that your disciples also may see your works that you are doing. ⁴For no one does anything in secret when he himself seeks to be known openly. If you do these things, show yourself to the world." ⁵For even his brothers did not believe in him.^c

⁶Jesus therefore said to them, "My time has not yet come, but your time is always ready. ⁷The world cannot hate you, but it hates me, because I testify about it, that its works are evil. ⁸You go up to the feast. I am not yet^d going up to this feast, because my time is not yet fulfilled."

⁹Having said these things to them, he stayed in Galilee. ¹⁰But when his brothers had gone up to the feast, then he also went up, not publicly, but as it were in secret. ¹¹The Jewish leaders therefore sought him at the feast, and said, "Where is he?"

¹²There was much murmuring among the crowds concerning him. Some said, "He is a good man." Others said, "Not so, but he leads the crowd astray." ¹³Yet no one spoke openly of him for fear of the Jewish leaders. ¹⁴But when it was now the midst of the feast, Jesus went up into the temple and taught. ¹⁵The Jewish leaders therefore marveled, saying, "How does this man know letters, having never been educated?"

¹⁶Jesus therefore answered them, "My teaching is not mine, but his who sent me. ¹⁷If anyone desires to do his will, he will know about the teaching, whether it is from God, or if I am speaking from myself. ¹⁸He who speaks from himself seeks his own glory, but he who seeks the glory of him who sent him is true, and no unrighteousness is in him. ¹⁹Did not Moses give you the Law, and yet none of you keeps the Law? Why do you seek to kill me?"

²⁰The crowd answered, "You have a demon. Who seeks to kill you?"

²¹Jesus answered them, "I did one work, and you all marvel because of it. ²²Moses has given you circumcision (not that it is of Moses, but of the fathers), and on the Sabbath you circumcise a boy. ²³If a boy receives circumcision on the Sabbath, that the Law of Moses may not be broken, are you angry with me, because I made a man completely healthy on the Sabbath? ²⁴Do not judge according to appearance, but judge righteous judgment."

²⁵Therefore some of them of Jerusalem said, "Is not this he whom they seek to kill? ²⁶Look, he speaks openly, and they say nothing to him. Can it be that the rulers indeed know that this is^e the Messiah? ²⁷However we know where this man comes from, but when the Messiah comes, no one will know where he comes from."

²⁸Jesus therefore called out in the temple, teaching and saying, "You both know

---

a   6:65 Some Mss read "my Father"
b   6:69 Some Mss read "Christ, the Son of the living God." Other Mss read "Christ, the Son of God"
c   7:5 Psalm 69:8
d   7:8 Some Mss read "not"
e   7:26 Some Mss add "truly"

me, and know where I am from. I have not come of myself, but he who sent me is true, whom you do not know. [29]I know him, because I am from him, and he sent me."

[30]They sought therefore to take him; but no one laid a hand on him, because his hour had not yet come. [31]But many in the crowd believed in him. They said, "When the Messiah comes, he won't do more signs than those which this man has done, will he?" [32]The Pharisees heard the crowd murmuring these things concerning him, and the chief priests and the Pharisees sent officers to arrest him.

[33]Then Jesus said, "I will be with you a little while longer, then I go to him who sent me. [34]You will seek me, and won't find me; and where I am, you cannot come."

[35]The Jewish leaders therefore said among themselves, "Where will this man go that we won't find him? Will he go to the Diaspora among the Greeks, and teach the Greeks? [36]What is this word that he said, 'You will seek me, and won't find me; and where I am, you cannot come'?"

[37]Now on the last and greatest day of the feast, Jesus stood and said in a loud voice, "If anyone is thirsty, let him come to me and drink. [38]He who believes in me, as the Scripture has said, from within him will flow rivers of living water." [39]But he said this about the Spirit, which those believing in him were to receive. For the[a] Spirit was not yet given, because Jesus was not yet glorified.

[40]Some[b] of the crowd therefore, when they heard these[c] words, said, "This is truly the Prophet."[d] [41]Others said, "This is the Messiah." But some said, "What, does the Messiah come out of Galilee?[e] [42]Hasn't the Scripture said that the Messiah comes of the seed of David,[f] and from Bethlehem,[g] the village where David was?" [43]So there arose a division in the crowd because of him. [44]Some of them would have arrested him, but no one laid hands on him. [45]The officers therefore came to the chief priests and Pharisees, and they said to them, "Why did you not bring him?"

[46]The officers answered, "No one ever spoke like this man."[h]

[47]The Pharisees therefore answered them, "You are not also led astray, are you? [48]Have any of the rulers believed in him, or of the Pharisees? [49]But this crowd that does not know the Law is accursed."

[50]Nicodemus (he who came to him before,[i] being one of them) said to them, [51]"Does our Law judge a man, unless it first hears from him personally and knows what he does?"

[52]They answered him, "Are you also from Galilee? Search, and see that no prophet comes from Galilee."[j] [53]Then everyone went to his own house,

8 but Jesus went to the Mount of Olives. [2]Now very early in the morning, he came again into the temple, and all the people came to him,[k] and he sat down and taught them. [3]Then the scribes and the Pharisees brought[l] a woman taken in adultery, and having set her in the midst, [4]they said to him, "Teacher, we found this woman in adultery, in the very act. [5]Now in the[m] Law, Moses commanded us[n] to stone such.[o] So what do you say?" [6]Now they said this to test him, that they might have something to accuse him of. But Jesus stooped down, and wrote on the ground with his finger.[p] [7]But when they continued asking him, he looked up and said to them, "He who is without sin among you, let him throw the first stone at her." [8]And again he

---

a   7:39 Some Mss add "Holy"
b   7:40 Some Mss read "Many"
c   7:40 Some Mss lack "these"
d   7:40 Deuteronomy 18:15; Acts 3:22
e   7:41 Isaiah 9:1-2; Matthew 4:13-16
f   7:42 2 Samuel 7:12
g   7:42 Micah 5:2
h   7:46 Some Mss lack "this man"
i   7:50 Some Mss add "by night"
j   7:52 However, cf. Isaiah 9:1 and Matthew 4:13-16. The prophets Jonah and Elijah came from the Galilee region
k   8:2 Some Mss lack "to him"
l   8:3 Some Mss add "to him"
m   8:5 Some Mss "our"
n   8:5 Some Mss lack "us"
o   8:5 Leviticus 20:10; Deuteronomy 22:22
p   8:6 Some Mss add "not taking notice"

stooped down, and with his finger wrote on the ground.

[9]But when they heard it,[a] they went out one by one, beginning from the oldest, even to the last, and he[b] was left alone, with the woman where she was, in the middle. [10]Then Jesus, standing up,[c] said to her, "Woman,[d] where are they[e]? Did no one condemn you?"

[11]And she said, "No one, Lord." And Jesus said, "Neither do I condemn you. Go your way. From now on, sin no more."[f]

[12]Again, therefore, Jesus spoke to them, saying, "I am the light of the world.[g] He who follows me will not walk in the darkness, but will have the light of life."

[13]The Pharisees therefore said to him, "You testify about yourself. Your testimony is not valid."

[14]Jesus answered them, "Even if I testify about myself, my testimony is true, for I know where I came from, and where I am going; but you do not know where I came from, or where I am going. [15]You judge according to the flesh. I judge no one. [16]Even if I do judge, my judgment is true, for I am not alone, but I am with the Father who sent me. [17]It's also written in your Law that the testimony of two people is valid.[h] [18]I am one who testifies about myself, and the Father who sent me testifies about me."

[19]They said therefore to him, "Where is your Father?"

Jesus answered, "You know neither me, nor my Father. If you knew me, you would know my Father also." [20]Jesus spoke these words in the treasury, as he taught in the temple. Yet no one arrested him, because his hour had not yet come. [21]Jesus said therefore again to them, "I am going away, and you will seek me, and you will die in your sins. Where I go, you cannot come."

[22]The Jewish leaders therefore said, "Will he kill himself, that he says, 'Where I am going, you cannot come?'"

[23]He said to them, "You are from beneath. I am from above. You are of this world. I am not of this world. [24]I said therefore to you that you will die in your sins; for unless you believe that I am[i] he, you will die in your sins."

[25]They said therefore to him, "Who are you?"

Jesus said to them, "Just what I have been saying to you from the beginning. [26]I have many things to speak and to judge concerning you. However he who sent me is true; and the things which I heard from him, these I say to the world."

[27]They did not understand that he spoke to them about the Father. [28]Jesus therefore said to them, "When you have lifted up the Son of Man, then you will know that I am he, and I do nothing of myself, but as the[j] Father taught me, I say these things. [29]He who sent me is with me. The Father hasn't left me alone, for I always do the things that are pleasing to him."

[30]As he spoke these things, many believed in him. [31]Jesus therefore said to those Judeans who had believed him, "If you remain in my word, then you are truly my disciples. [32]You will know the truth, and the truth will make you free."[k]

[33]They answered him, "We are Abraham's descendants, and have never been in bondage to anyone. How can you say, 'You will be made free?'"

[34]Jesus answered them, "Truly I tell you, everyone who commits sin is the slave of sin. [35]A slave does not live in the house forever. A son remains forever. [36]So if the Son sets you free, you will be free indeed.

---

a 8:9 Some Mss add "being convicted by their conscience"
b 8:9 Some Mss add "Jesus"
c 8:10 Some Mss add "and having seen no one but the woman"
d 8:10 Some Mss lack "Woman"
e 8:10 Some Mss read "your accusers" instead of "they"
f 7:53-8:11 Some Mss lack these verses, possibly because they seemed offensive to pious ears. The Johannine vocabulary suggests the authenticity of the words
g 8:12 Isaiah 60:1
h 8:17 Deuteronomy 17:6; 19:15
i 8:24 Or, "I AM"
j 8:28 Some Mss read "my"
k 8:32 Psalm 119:45

³⁷I know that you are Abraham's descendants, yet you seek to kill me, because my word finds no place in you. ³⁸I say the things which I have seen with my Father; and you also do the things which you have heard from[a] your father."

³⁹They answered him, "Our father is Abraham."

Jesus said to them, "If you were Abraham's children, you would do the works of Abraham. ⁴⁰But now you seek to kill me, a man who has told you the truth, which I heard from God. Abraham did not do this. ⁴¹You do the works of your father."

They said to him, "We were not born of sexual immorality. We have one Father, God."

⁴²Therefore Jesus said to them, "If God were your father, you would love me, for I came out and have come from God. For I have not come of myself, but he sent me. ⁴³Why do you not understand my speech? Because you cannot hear my word. ⁴⁴You are of your father, the devil, and you want to do the desires of your father. He was a murderer from the beginning, and does not stand in the truth, because there is no truth in him. When he speaks a lie, he speaks on his own; for he is a liar, and its father. ⁴⁵But because I tell the truth, you do not believe me. ⁴⁶Which of you convicts me of sin? If I tell the truth, why do you not believe me? ⁴⁷He who is of God hears the words of God. For this cause you do not hear, because you are not of God."

⁴⁸Then the Judeans answered him, "Do not we say well that you are a Samaritan, and have a demon?"

⁴⁹Jesus answered, "I do not have a demon, but I honor my Father, and you dishonor me. ⁵⁰But I do not seek my own glory. There is one who seeks and judges. ⁵¹Truly, truly, I tell you, if a person keeps my word, he will never see death."

⁵²Then the Judeans said to him, "Now we know that you have a demon. Abraham died, and the prophets; and you say, 'If anyone keeps my word, he will never taste of death.' ⁵³Are you greater than our father, Abraham, who died? The prophets died. Who do you make yourself out to be?"

⁵⁴Jesus answered, "If I glorify myself, my glory is nothing. It is my Father who glorifies me, of whom you say 'He is our God.' ⁵⁵You have not known him, but I know him. If I said, 'I do not know him,' I would be like you, a liar. But I know him, and keep his word. ⁵⁶Your father Abraham rejoiced to see my day. He saw it, and was glad."

⁵⁷The Judeans therefore said to him, "You are not yet fifty years old, and have you seen Abraham?"

⁵⁸Jesus said to them, "Truly, truly, I tell you, before Abraham came into existence, I AM.[b]"

⁵⁹Therefore they took up stones to throw at him, but Jesus was concealed, and went out of the temple.[c]

9 And as he passed by, he saw a man blind from birth. ²And his disciples asked him, "Rabbi, who sinned, this man or his parents, that he was born blind?"

³Jesus answered, "Neither did this man sin, nor his parents; but, that the works of God might be revealed in him. ⁴We[d] must work the works of him who sent me, while it is day. The night is coming, when no one can work. ⁵While I am in the world, I am the light of the world." ⁶When he had said this, he spat on the ground, made mud with the saliva, anointed the blind man's eyes with the mud, ⁷and said to him, "Go, wash in the pool of Siloam[e]" (which means "Sent"). So he went away, washed, and came back seeing. ⁸The neighbors therefore, and those who saw that he was a beggar[f] before, said, "Is not this he who sat and begged?" ⁹Some said, "It is he." Others said, "He looks like him."

He said, "I am he." ¹⁰They therefore were asking him, "How were your eyes opened?"

---

a   8:38 Some Mss read "seen with"
b   8:58 Gk. ego eimi. Cf. Exodus 3:14 LXX
c   8:59 Some Mss add "having gone through their midst, and so passed by." Other Mss add "and having gone through their midst he started going, and so passed by"
d   9:4 Some Mss read "I"
e   9:7 Lit. Gk. Aramaic: "Shilokha." Hebrew: "Shiloach"
f   9:8 Some Mss read "blind"

¹¹He answered, "A man called Jesus made mud, anointed my eyes, and said to me, 'Go to[a] Siloam, and wash.' So I went away and washed, and I received sight."

¹²Then they asked him, "Where is he?"

He said, "I do not know."

¹³They brought him who had been blind to the Pharisees. ¹⁴Now it was a Sabbath on the day[b] when Jesus made the mud and opened his eyes. ¹⁵Again therefore the Pharisees also asked him how he received his sight. He said to them, "He put mud on my eyes, I washed, and I see."

¹⁶Some therefore of the Pharisees said, "This man is not from God, because he does not keep the Sabbath." Others said, "How can a man who is a sinner do such signs?" There was division among them. ¹⁷Therefore they asked the blind man again, "What do you say about him, because he opened your eyes?"

He said, "He is a prophet."

¹⁸The Jewish leaders therefore did not believe concerning him, that he had been blind, and had received his sight, until they called the parents of him who had received his sight, ¹⁹and asked them, "Is this your son, who you say was born blind? How then does he now see?"

²⁰His parents answered them, "We know that this is our son, and that he was born blind; ²¹but how he now sees, we do not know; or who opened his eyes, we do not know. He is of age. Ask him. He will speak for himself." ²²His parents said these things because they feared the Jewish leaders; for the Jewish leaders had already agreed that if anyone would confess him as the Messiah, he would be put out of the synagogue. ²³Therefore his parents said, "He is of age. Ask him."

²⁴So they called the man who was blind a second time, and said to him, "Give glory to God. We know that this man is a sinner."

²⁵He therefore answered, "I do not know if he is a sinner. One thing I do know: that though I was blind, now I see."

²⁶They said to him[c], "What did he do to you? How did he open your eyes?"

²⁷He answered them, "I told you already, and you did not listen. Why do you want to hear it again? You do not also want to become his disciples, do you?"

²⁸They insulted him and said, "You are his disciple, but we are disciples of Moses. ²⁹We know that God has spoken to Moses. But as for this man, we do not know where he comes from."

³⁰The man answered them, "How amazing. You do not know where he comes from, yet he opened my eyes. ³¹We know that God does not listen to sinners, but if anyone is a worshipper of God, and does his will, he listens to him.[d] ³²Since the world began it has never been heard of that anyone opened the eyes of someone born blind. ³³If this man were not from God, he could do nothing."

³⁴They answered him, "You were altogether born in sins, and do you teach us?" They threw him out.

³⁵Jesus heard that they had thrown him out, and finding him, he said, "Do you believe in the Son of Man[e]?"

³⁶He answered, "Who is he, Lord, that I may believe in him?"

³⁷Jesus said to him, "You have both seen him, and it is he who speaks with you."

³⁸He said, "Lord, I believe." and he worshiped him.

³⁹Jesus said, "I came into this world for judgment, that those who do not see may see; and that those who see may become blind."

⁴⁰Those of the Pharisees who were with him heard these things, and said to him, "Are we also blind?"

⁴¹Jesus said to them, "If you were blind, you would have no sin; but since you say, 'We see,' your[f] sin remains.

10 "Truly, truly, I tell you, one who does not enter by the door into the

---

a 9:11 Some Mss add "the pool of"
b 9:14 Some Mss lack "on the day"
c 9:26 Some Mss add "again"
d 9:31 Psalm 66:18, Proverbs 15:29; 28:9
e 9:35 Some Mss read "God"
f 9:41 Some Mss read "Therefore your"

sheep fold, but climbs up some other way, the same is a thief and a robber. [2]But one who enters in by the door is the shepherd of the sheep. [3]The gatekeeper opens the gate for him, and the sheep listen to his voice. He calls his own sheep by name, and leads them out. [4]Whenever he brings out his own sheep, he goes before them, and the sheep follow him, for they know his voice. [5]They will by no means follow a stranger, but will flee from him; for they do not know the voice of strangers." [6]Jesus spoke this parable to them, but they did not understand what he was telling them.

[7]Jesus therefore said to them again, "Truly, truly, I tell you, I am the sheep's door. [8]All who came before me are thieves and robbers, but the sheep did not listen to them. [9]I am the door. If anyone enters in by me, he will be saved, and will go in and go out, and will find pasture. [10]The thief only comes to steal, kill, and destroy. I came that they may have life, and may have it abundantly. [11]I am the good shepherd.[a] The good shepherd lays down his life for the sheep. [12]He who is a hired hand and not a shepherd, who does not own the sheep, sees the wolf coming and leaves the sheep and runs away; and the wolf snatches them and scatters them. [13]And the hired hand flees[b] because he is a hired hand and the sheep means nothing to him. [14]I am the good shepherd. I know my own, and my own know me[c]; [15]even as the Father knows me, and I know the Father. I lay down my life for the sheep. [16]I have other sheep, which are not of this fold.[d] I must bring them also, and they will hear my voice. They will become one flock with one shepherd. [17]Therefore the[e] Father loves me, because I lay down my life,[f] that I may take it again. [18]No one takes it away from me, but I lay it down by myself. I have power to lay it down, and I have power to take it again. I received this commandment from my Father."

[19]A[g] division arose again among the Jewish people because of these words. [20]Many of them said, "He has a demon, and is insane. Why do you listen to him?" [21]Others said, "These are not the sayings of one possessed by a demon. It is not possible for a demon to open the eyes of the blind, is it?"[h]

[22]It was then the Feast of the Dedication[i] at Jerusalem. [23]It was winter, and Jesus was walking in the temple, in Solomon's porch. [24]The Jewish leaders therefore came around him and said to him, "How long will you keep us in suspense? If you are the Messiah, tell us plainly."

[25]Jesus answered them, "I told you, and you do not believe. The works that I do in my Father's name, these testify about me. [26]But you do not believe, because you are not of my sheep[j]. [27]My sheep hear my voice, and I know them, and they follow me. [28]I give everlasting life to them. They will never perish, and no one will snatch them out of my hand. [29]That which my Father has given me is more important than anything. No one is able to snatch them out of the[k] Father's hand. [30]I and the Father are one."

[31]Therefore the Jewish leaders took up stones again to stone him. [32]Jesus answered them, "I have shown you many good works from the[l] Father. For which of those works do you stone me?"

[33]The Jewish leaders answered him, "We do not stone you for a good work, but for blasphemy: because you, being a man, make yourself God."

[34]Jesus answered them, "Is it not written in your law, 'I said, you are gods?'[m] [35]If he called them gods, to whom the word of God came (and the Scripture cannot be broken), [36]do you say of him whom the

---

a   10:11 Isaiah 40:11; Ezekiel 34:11-12, 15, 22
b   10:13 Some Mss lack "And the hired hand flees"
c   10:14 Some Mss read "I'm known by my own"
d   10:16 Isaiah 56:8
e   10:17 Some Mss read "my"
f   10:17 Isaiah 53:7-8
g   10:19 Some Mss add "Therefore"
h   10:21 Exodus 4:11
i   10:22 The Feast of the Dedication is known in Hebrew as "Hanukkah," a celebration of the rededication of the Temple.
j   10:26 Some Mss add "as I told you"
k   10:29 Some Mss read "my"
l   10:32 Some Mss read "my"
m   10:34 Psalm 82:6: As messengers of the word of God (v.35), and as children of God (Psalm 82:6)

Father sanctified and sent into the world, 'You blaspheme,' because I said, 'I am the Son of God?' ³⁷If I do not do the works of my Father, do not believe me. ³⁸But if I do them, though you do not believe me, believe the works; that you may know and understandᵃ that the Father is in me, and I in the Father."

³⁹Nowᵇ they sought again to seize him, and he went out of their hand. ⁴⁰He went away again beyond the Jordan into the place where John was baptizing at first, and there he stayed. ⁴¹Many came to him. They said, "John indeed did no sign, but everything that John said about this man is true." ⁴²And many believed in him there.

11 Now a certain man was sick, Lazarus from Bethany, of the village of Mary and her sister, Martha. ²It was that Mary who had anointed the Lord with ointment, and wiped his feet with her hair, whose brother, Lazarus, was sick. ³The sisters therefore sent to him, saying, "Lord, look, the one you love is sick." ⁴But when Jesus heard it, he said, "This sickness is not to death, but for the glory of God, that God's Son may be glorified by it." ⁵Now Jesus loved Martha, and her sister, and Lazarus. ⁶When therefore he heard that he was sick, he stayed two days in the place where he was. ⁷Then after this he said to the disciples, "Let us go into Judea again."

⁸The disciples told him, "Rabbi, the Jewish leaders were just trying to stone you, and are you going there again?"

⁹Jesus answered, "Are there not twelve hours of daylight? If anyone walks in the day, he does not stumble, because he sees the light of this world. ¹⁰But if anyone walks in the night, he stumbles, because the light is not in him." ¹¹He said these things, and after that, he said to them, "Our friend, Lazarus, has fallen asleep, but I am going so that I may awake him out of sleep."

¹²Then the disciples said to himᶜ, "Lord, if he has fallen asleep, he will recover."

¹³Now Jesus had spoken of his death, but they thought that he spoke of taking rest in sleep. ¹⁴So Jesus said to them plainly then,

"Lazarus is dead. ¹⁵I am glad for your sakes that I was not there, so that you may believe. Nevertheless, let us go to him."

¹⁶Thomas therefore, who is called Didymus, said to his fellow disciples, "Let us go also, that we may die with him."

¹⁷So when Jesus came, he found that he had been in the tomb four days already. ¹⁸Now Bethany was near Jerusalem, about two milesᵈ away. ¹⁹Many of the Jewish people had come toᵉ Martha and Mary, to console them concerning their brother. ²⁰Then when Martha heard that Jesus was coming, she went and met him, but Mary stayed in the house. ²¹Therefore Martha said to Jesus, "Lord, if you would have been here, my brother would not have died. ²²Even now I know that whatever you ask of God, God will give you." ²³Jesus said to her, "Your brother will rise again."

²⁴Martha said to him, "I know that he will rise again in the resurrection at the last day."

²⁵Jesus said to her, "I am the resurrection and the life. He who believes in me will still live, even if he dies. ²⁶And whoever lives and believes in me will never die. Do you believe this?"

²⁷She said to him, "Yes, Lord. I have come to believe that you are the Messiah, the Son of God, he who comes into the world."

²⁸And when she had said this, she went away, and called Mary, her sister, secretly, saying, "The Teacher is here, and is calling you."

²⁹When she heard this, she arose quickly, and went to him. ³⁰Now Jesus had not yet come into the village, but was stillᶠ in the place where Martha met him. ³¹Then the Judeans who were with her in the house, and were consoling her, when they saw Mary, that she rose up quickly and went out, followed her, supposing that she was going to the tomb to weep there.ᵍ

---

a   10:38 Some Mss read "believe"
b   10:39 Some Mss lack "Now"
c   11:12 Some Mss read "His disciples said"
d   11:18 Or, 2.8 kilometers. Lit. 15 stadia
e   11:19 Some Mss add "the women around"
f   11:30 Some Mss lack "still"
g   11:31 Some Mss read "saying, "She is going to the tomb to weep there"

³²Therefore when Mary came to where Jesus was, and saw him, she fell down at his feet, saying to him, "Lord, if you would have been here, my brother would not have died."

³³When Jesus therefore saw her weeping, and the Judeans weeping who came with her, he was deeply moved in spirit and was troubled, ³⁴and said, "Where have you put him?"

They told him, "Lord, come and see."

³⁵Jesus wept.

³⁶The Judeans therefore said, "See how he loved him." ³⁷But some of them said, "Could not this man, who opened the eyes of him who was blind, have also kept this man from dying?"

³⁸So Jesus, deeply moved again, came to the tomb. Now it was a cave, and a stone lay against it. ³⁹Jesus said, "Take away the stone."

Martha, the sister of the dead man, said to him, "Lord, by this time there is a stench, for he has been dead four days."

⁴⁰Jesus said to her, "Did I not tell you that if you believed, you would see God's glory?"

⁴¹So they took away the stone.ᵃ And Jesus lifted up his eyes, and said, "Father, I thank you that you listened to me. ⁴²I know that you always listen to me, but because of the crowd that stands around I said this, that they may believe that you sent me."

⁴³When he had said this, he shouted with a loud voice, "Lazarus, come out."

⁴⁴The man who had died came out, bound hand and foot with wrappings, and his face was wrapped around with a cloth.

Jesus said to them, "Free him, and let him go."

⁴⁵Therefore many of the Judeans, who came to Mary and had seen the things which he did, believed in him. ⁴⁶But some of them went away to the Pharisees, and told them the things which Jesus had done. ⁴⁷The chief priests therefore and the Pharisees gathered a council, and said, "What are we doing? For this man does many signs. ⁴⁸If we leave him alone like

this, everyone will believe in him, and the Romans will come and take away both our place and our nation."

⁴⁹But a certain one of them, Caiaphas, being high priest that year, said to them, "You know nothing at all, ⁵⁰nor do you consider that it is advantageous for youᵇ that one man should die for the people, and that the whole nation not perish." ⁵¹Now he did not say this of himself, but being high priest that year, he prophesied that Jesus would die for the nation, ⁵²and not for the nation only, but that he might also gather together into one the children of God who are scattered abroad. ⁵³So from that day on they plotted to kill him. ⁵⁴Jesus therefore walked no more openly among the Judeans, but departed from there into the country near the wilderness, to a city called Ephraim; and stayed there with his disciples.

⁵⁵Now the Jewish Passover was near, and many went up from the country to Jerusalem before the Passover, to purify themselves. ⁵⁶Then they sought for Jesus and spoke one with another, as they stood in the temple, "What do you think—that he is not coming to the feast at all?" ⁵⁷Now the chief priests and the Pharisees had given orders that if anyone knew where he was, he should report it, that they might arrest him.

12 Then six days before the Passover, Jesus came to Bethany, where Lazarus was,ᶜ whom Jesusᵈ raised from the dead. ²So they prepared a dinner for him there; and Martha served, but Lazarus was one of those reclining at the table with him. ³Mary, therefore, took a poundᵉ of ointment of pure nard, very precious, and anointed the feet of Jesus, and wiped his feet with her hair. And the house was filled with the fragrance of the ointment. ⁴Then Judas Is-

---

a   11:41 Some Mss add "from the place where the dead was lying"
b   11:50 Some Mss read "us"
c   12:1 Some Mss add "who had been dead"
d   12:1 Some Mss lack "Jesus"
e   12:3 A Roman pound of 12 ounces, or about 340 grams

cariot,[a] one of his disciples, who would betray him, said, [5]"Why was this ointment not sold for three hundred denarii,[b] and given to the poor?" [6]Now he said this, not because he cared for the poor, but because he was a thief, and having the money box, used to steal what was put into it. [7]But Jesus said, "Leave her alone, that she may keep[c] this for the day of my burial. [8]For you always have the poor with you, but you do not always have me."

[9]A large crowd therefore of the Judeans learned that he was there, and they came, not for Jesus' sake only, but that they might see Lazarus also, whom he had raised from the dead. [10]But the chief priests plotted to kill Lazarus also, [11]because on account of him many of the Jewish people went away and believed in Jesus.

[12]On the next day the large crowd that had come to the feast heard that Jesus was coming to Jerusalem, [13]they took the branches of the palm trees, and went out to meet him, and were shouting, "Hosanna[d]. Blessed is he who comes in the name of the Lord,[e] the King of Israel."

[14]And Jesus, having found a young donkey, sat on it. As it is written, [15]"Do not be afraid,[f] daughter of Zion. Look, your King comes, sitting on a donkey's colt."[g] [16]His disciples did not understand these things at first, but when Jesus was glorified, then they remembered that these things were written about him, and that they had done these things to him. [17]The crowd therefore that was with him when he called Lazarus out of the tomb, and raised him from the dead, was testifying about it. [18]For this cause also the crowd went and met him, because they heard that he had done this sign. [19]The Pharisees therefore said among themselves, "See how you accomplish nothing. Look, the whole[h] world has gone after him."

[20]Now there were certain Greeks among those that went up to worship at the feast. [21]These, therefore, came to Philip, who was from Bethsaida of Galilee, and asked him, saying, "Sir, we want to see Jesus." [22]Philip came and told Andrew, and in turn, Andrew came with Philip, and they told Jesus. [23]And Jesus answered them, "The time has come for the Son of Man to be glorified. [24]Truly, truly, I tell you, unless a grain of wheat falls into the earth and dies, it remains by itself alone. But if it dies, it bears much fruit. [25]He who loves his life loses[i] it, and he who hates his life in this world will keep it to everlasting life. [26]If anyone serves me, let him follow me; and where I am, there will my servant also be. If anyone serves me, the Father will honor him.

[27]"Now my soul is troubled. And what should I say? 'Father, save me from this hour?' But for this cause I came to this hour. [28]Father, glorify your name."

Then there came a voice out of the sky, saying, "I have both glorified it, and will glorify it again."

[29]The crowd therefore, who stood by and heard it, said that it had thundered. Others said, "An angel has spoken to him." [30]Jesus answered, "This voice hasn't come for my sake, but for your sakes. [31]Now is the judgment of this world. Now the prince of this world will be cast out. [32]And I, if I am lifted up from the earth, will draw everyone to myself." [33]But he said this, signifying by what kind of death he should die. [34]The crowd answered him, "We have heard out of the law that the Messiah remains forever.[j] Then how can you say, 'The Son of Man must be lifted up?' Who is this Son of Man?"

[35]Jesus therefore said to them, "Yet a little while the light is with you. Walk while you have the light, that darkness does not overtake you. He who walks in the darkness does not know where he is going.

---

a   12:4 Some Mss add "Simon's son"
b   12:5 300 denarii was about a year's wages for an agricultural laborer.
c   12:7 Some Mss read "alone. She has kept"
d   12:13 "Hosanna" means "save us" or "help us, we pray"
e   12:13 Psalm 118:25-26
f   12:15 See Isaiah 54:4
g   12:15 Zechariah 9:9
h   12:19 Some Mss lack "whole"
i   12:25 Some Mss read "will lose it"
j   12:34 Isaiah 9:7; Daniel 2:44. See also Isaiah 53:8

³⁶While you have the light, believe in the light, that you may become children of light." Jesus said these things, and he departed and hid himself from them. ³⁷But though he had done so many signs before them, yet they did not believe in him, ³⁸that the word of Isaiah the prophet might be fulfilled, which he spoke,

"Lord, who has believed our report, and
to whom has the arm of the
Lord been revealed?"ª

³⁹For this cause they could not believe, for Isaiah said again,

⁴⁰He has blinded their eyes and
hardened their heart,
lest they should see with their eyes,
and understand with their heart,
and turn,ᵇ
and I would heal them.ᶜ

⁴¹Isaiah said these things becauseᵈ he saw his glory, and spoke of him.ᵉ ⁴²Nevertheless even of the rulers many believed in him, but because of the Pharisees they did not confess it, so that they would not be put out of the synagogue, ⁴³for they loved men's praise more than God's praise.

⁴⁴Then Jesus shouted out and said, "Whoever believes in me, believes not in me, but in him who sent me. ⁴⁵And he who sees me sees him who sent me. ⁴⁶I have come as a light into the world, that whoever believes in me may not remain in the darkness. ⁴⁷And if anyone hears my words and does not keep them,ᶠ I do not judge him. For I came not to judge the world, but to save the world. ⁴⁸He who rejects me, and does not accept my words, has one who judges him. The word that I spoke will judge him on the last day. ⁴⁹For I spoke not from myself, but the Father who sent me, he gave me a commandment, what I should say, and what I should speak. ⁵⁰I know that his commandment is everlasting life. The things therefore which I speak, even as the Father has said to me, so I speak."

13 Now before the feast of the Passover, Jesus, knowing that his time had come that he would depart from this world to the Father, having loved his own who were in the world, he loved them to the end. ²And duringᵍ the evening meal, the devil had already put into the heart of Judas Iscariot, Simon's son, to betray him. ³Because heʰ knew that the Father had given all things into his hands, and that he came forth from God, and was going to God, ⁴arose from the meal, and removed his outer garments. He took a towel, and wrapped a towel around his waist. ⁵Then he poured water into the basin, and began to wash the disciples' feet, and to wipe them with the towel that was wrapped around him. ⁶Then he came to Simon Peter. He said to him, "Lord, do you wash my feet?"

⁷Jesus answered him, "You do not know what I am doing now, but you will understand later."

⁸Peter said to him, "You will never wash my feet."

Jesus answered him, "If I do not wash you, you have no part with me."

⁹Simon Peter said to him, "Lord, not my feet only, but also my hands and my head."

¹⁰Jesus said to him, "Someone who has bathed only needs to have his feet washed, but is completely clean. You are clean, but not all of you." ¹¹For he knew him who would betray him, therefore he said, "You are not all clean." ¹²So when he had washed their feet, put his outer garment back on, and sat down again, he said to them, "Do you know what I have done to you? ¹³You call me, 'Teacher' and 'Lord.' You say so correctly, for so I am. ¹⁴If I then, the Lord and the Teacher, have washed your feet, you also ought to wash one another's feet. ¹⁵For I have given you an example, that you also should do as I have done to you. ¹⁶Truly, truly, I tell you, a servant is not greater than his master, neither one who is sent greater than he who sent him. ¹⁷If you know these

---

a 12:38 Isaiah 53:1
b 12:40 Or, "repent" or "change their ways"
c 12:40 An allusion to Isaiah 6:10 with some quotation
d 12:41 Some Mss read "when"
e 12:41 Isaiah 6:1
f 12:47 Some Mss read "believe"
g 13:2 Some Mss read "After"
h 13:3 Some Mss read "Jesus"

things, blessed are you if you do them. ¹⁸I do not speak concerning all of you. I know whom I have chosen. But that the Scripture may be fulfilled, 'He who ate my bread[a] has lifted up his heel against me.'[b] ¹⁹I am telling you this now before it happens, so that when it does happen you may believe that I am he. ²⁰Truly, truly, I tell you, he who receives whomever I send, receives me; and he who receives me, receives him who sent me."

²¹When Jesus had said this, he was troubled in spirit, and testified, "Truly, truly, I tell you that one of you will betray me."

²²The disciples looked at one another, perplexed about whom he spoke. ²³One of his disciples, whom Jesus loved, was reclining against Jesus' chest. ²⁴Simon Peter therefore motioned to him to inquire who it was he was talking about.

²⁵He, leaning back, as he was, on Jesus' chest, asked him, "Lord, who is it?"

²⁶Jesus therefore answered, "It is he to whom I will give this piece of bread when I have dipped it." So when he had dipped the piece of bread, he gave it to Judas, the son of Simon Iscariot. ²⁷After the piece of bread, then Satan entered into him.

Then Jesus said to him, "What you do, do quickly."

²⁸Now none of those reclining knew why he said this to him. ²⁹For some thought, because Judas had the money box, that Jesus said to him, "Buy what things we need for the feast," or that he should give something to the poor. ³⁰Therefore, having received the piece of bread, he went out immediately; and it was night.

³¹When he had gone out, Jesus said, "Now the Son of Man has been glorified, and God has been glorified in him. ³²If God has been glorified in him,[c] God will also glorify him in himself, and he will glorify him at once. ³³Little children, I will be with you a little while longer. You will seek me, and as I said to the Jewish leaders, 'Where I am going, you cannot come,' so now I tell you. ³⁴A new commandment I give to you, that you love one another. Just as I have loved you, you also must love one another.

³⁵By this everyone will know that you are my disciples, if you have love for one another."

³⁶Simon Peter said to him, "Lord, where are you going?"

Jesus answered, "Where I am going, you cannot follow now, but you will follow afterwards."

³⁷Peter said to him, "Lord, why can I not follow you now? I will lay down my life for you."

³⁸Jesus answered him, "Will you lay down your life for me? Truly, truly, I tell you, the rooster won't crow until you have denied me three times.

14 "Do not let your heart be troubled. Believe in God. Believe also in me. ²In my Father's house are many dwelling places. If it weren't so, I would have told you; for I go[d] to prepare a place for you. ³And if I go and prepare a place for you, I will come again, and will receive you to myself; that where I am, you may be there also. ⁴And you know the way[e] where I am going."

⁵Thomas said to him, "Lord, we do not know where you are going. How can we know the way?"

⁶Jesus said to him, "I am the way, the truth, and the life. No one comes to the Father except through me. ⁷If you have known me, you will know my Father also. From now on you do know him and have seen him."

⁸Philip said to him, "Lord, show us the Father, and that will be enough for us."

⁹Jesus said to him, "Have I been with you all this time, and still you do not know me, Philip? He who has seen me has seen the Father. How can you say, 'Show us the Father?' ¹⁰Do you not believe that I am in the Father, and the Father is in me? The words that I say to you I do not speak from myself; but the Father who lives in me

---

a   13:18 Some Mss read "bread with me"
b   13:18 Psalm 41:9
c   13:32 Some Mss lack "If God has…him"
d   14:2 Some Mss read "I am going"
e   14:4 Some Mss add "and you know"

does his[a] works. [11]Believe me that I am in the Father, and the Father is in me; or else believe[b] because of the works themselves. [12]Truly, truly, I tell you, he who believes in me, the works that I do, he will do also; and he will do greater works than these, because I am going to the[c] Father. [13]And whatever you ask in my name, this I will do, that the Father may be glorified in the Son. [14]If you ask me[d] anything in my name, I will do it. [15]If you love me, you will[e] keep my commandments. [16]I will pray to the Father, and he will give you another Helper,[f] that he may be with you forever,—[17]the Spirit of truth, whom the world cannot receive; because it neither sees him nor knows him; but you know him, for he lives with you, and will be in you. [18]I will not leave you orphans. I will come to you. [19]Yet a little while, and the world will see me no more; but you will see me. Because I live, you will live also. [20]In that day you will know that I am in my Father, and you in me, and I in you. [21]The one who has my commandments and keeps them is the one who loves me. And the one who loves me will be loved by my Father, and I will love him, and will reveal myself to him."

[22]Judas (not Iscariot) said to him, "Lord, what has happened that you are about to reveal yourself to us, and not to the world?"

[23]Jesus answered and said to him, "If anyone loves me, he will keep my word; and my Father will love him, and we will come to him and make our dwelling place with him. [24]He who does not love me does not keep my words. The word which you hear is not mine, but the Father's who sent me. [25]All this I have spoken to you while I am still with you. [26]But the Helper, the Holy Spirit, whom the Father will send in my name, he will teach you all things, and will remind you of all that I said to you. [27]Peace I leave with you. My peace I give to you. I do not give to you as the world gives. Do not let your heart be troubled, neither let it be afraid. [28]You heard how I told you, 'I am going away, and I will come to you.' If you loved me, you would rejoice that[g] I am going to the[h] Father; for the Father is greater than I. [29]Now I have told you before it happens so that, when it happens, you may believe. [30]I will not speak with you much longer, for the ruler of this world is coming, and he has no hold on me. [31]But that the world may know that I love the Father, and as the Father commanded me, so I do. Arise, let us go from here.

15 "I am the true vine, and my Father is the gardener. [2]Every branch in me that does not bear fruit, he takes away. Every branch that bears fruit, he prunes, that it may bear more fruit. [3]You are already clean because of the word which I have spoken to you. [4]Remain in me, and I in you. As the branch cannot bear fruit by itself, unless it remains in the vine, so neither can you, unless you remain in me. [5]I am the vine. You are the branches. He who remains in me, and I in him, the same bears much fruit, for apart from me you can do nothing. [6]If anyone does not remain in me, he is thrown out as a branch, and withers; and they gather them, throw them into the fire, and they are burned. [7]If you remain in me, and my words remain in you,[i] ask whatever you desire, and it will be done for you.

[8]"In this is my Father glorified, that you bear much fruit and so prove to be my disciples. [9]Even as the Father has loved me, I also have loved you. Remain in my love. [10]If you keep my commandments, you will remain in my love; even as I have kept my Father's commandments, and remain in his love. [11]I have spoken these things to you, that my joy may be[j] in you, and that your joy may be made full.

---

a   14:10 Some Mss read "the"
b   14:11 Some Mss add "me"
c   14:12 Some Mss: "my"
d   14:14 Some Mss lack "me"
e   14:15 Some Mss lack "you will"
f   14:16 Gk. Parakleton: Helper, Counselor, Intercessor, Advocate, and Comforter.
g   14:28 Some Mss add "I said"
h   14:28 Some Mss read "my"
i   15:7 Some Mss add "you will"
j   15:11 Some Mss read "may abide"

[12]"This is my commandment, that you love one another, even as I have loved you. [13]Greater love has no one than this, that someone lay down his life for his friends. [14]You are my friends, if you do whatever I command you. [15]No longer do I call you servants, for the servant does not know what his master is doing. But I have called you friends, for everything that I heard from my Father I have made known to you. [16]You did not choose me, but I chose you, and appointed you, that you should go and bear fruit, and that your fruit should remain; that whatever you will ask of the Father in my name, he may give it to you.

[17]"I command these things to you, that you may love one another. [18]If the world hates you, you know that it has hated me before it hated you. [19]If you were of the world, the world would love its own. But because you are not of the world, since I chose you out of the world, therefore the world hates you. [20]Remember the word that I said to you: 'A servant is not greater than his master.'[a] If they persecuted me, they will also persecute you. If they kept my word, they will keep yours also. [21]But all these things will they do to you because of my name, because they do not know him who sent me. [22]If I had not come and spoken to them, they would not have had sin; but now they have no excuse for their sin. [23]He who hates me hates my Father also. [24]If I had not done among them the works which no one else did, they would not have had sin. But now have they seen and also hated both me and my Father. [25]But this happened so that the word may be fulfilled which is written in their law, 'They hated me without a cause.'[b]

[26]"When the Helper has come, whom I will send to you from the Father, the Spirit of truth, who proceeds from the Father, he will testify about me. [27]And you will also testify, because you have been with me from the beginning.

16 "I have said all these things to you so that you may be kept from stumbling. [2]They will put you out of the synagogues, but an hour is coming when whoever kills you will think that he is offering a service to God. [3]They will do these things because they have not known the Father or me. [4]But I have told you these things, so that when their[c] hour comes, you may remember that I told you about them. I did not tell you these things from the beginning, because I was with you. [5]But now I am going to him who sent me, and none of you asks me, 'Where are you going?' [6]But because I have told you these things, sorrow has filled your heart. [7]Nevertheless I tell you the truth: It is to your advantage that I go away, for if I do not go away, the Helper won't come to you. But if I go, I will send him to you. [8]When he has come, he will convict the world about sin, and about righteousness, and about judgment; [9]about sin, because they do not believe in me; [10]about righteousness, because I am going to the[d] Father, and you won't see me any more; [11]about judgment, because the prince of this world has been judged.

[12]"I have yet many things to tell you, but you cannot bear them now. [13]However when he, the Spirit of truth, has come, he will guide you into all truth, for he will not speak on his own; but whatever he hears he will speak, and he will declare to you things that are coming. [14]He will glorify me, for he will take from what is mine, and will declare it to you. [15]All things that the Father has are mine; that is why I said that he takes of mine, and will declare it to you. [16]A little while, and you will no longer see me. Again a little while, and you will see me.[e]"

[17]Some of his disciples therefore said to one another, "What is this that he says to us, 'A little while, and you won't see me, and again a little while, and you will see me;' and, 'Because I go to the Father?'" [18]They said therefore, "What is this that he says, 'A little while?' We do not know what he is saying."

---

a   15:20 John 13:16
b   15:25 Psalms 35:19; 69:4
c   16:4 Some Mss read "the"
d   16:10 Some Mss read "my"
e   16:16 Some Mss add "because I go to the Father"

¹⁹Jesus knew that they wanted to ask him, so he said to them, "Do you inquire among yourselves concerning this, that I said, 'A little while, and you won't see me, and again a little while, and you will see me?' ²⁰Truly, truly, I tell you, that you will weep and lament, but the world will rejoice. You will be sorrowful, but your sorrow will be turned into joy. ²¹A woman, when she gives birth, has pain, because her time has come. But when she has delivered the child, she does not remember the anguish any more, for the joy that a human being is born into the world. ²²Therefore you have sorrow now, but I will see you again, and your heart will rejoice, and no one will take your joy away from you.

²³"And in that day you will ask nothing of me. Truly, truly I tell you, whatever you may ask of the Father in my name, he will give it to you. ²⁴Until now, you have asked nothing in my name. Ask, and you will receive, that your joy may be made full. ²⁵I have spoken these things to you in figures of speech. The[a] hour is coming when I will no more speak to you in figures of speech, but will tell you plainly about the Father. ²⁶In that day you will ask in my name, and I am not saying to you that I will ask the Father on your behalf, ²⁷for the Father himself loves you, because you have loved me, and have believed that I came forth from God. ²⁸I came forth from the Father and have come into the world. Again, I leave the world, and go to the Father."

²⁹His disciples said to him, "Look, now you are speaking plainly and not in any figure of speech. ³⁰Now we know that you know all things and do not need anyone to question you. By this we believe that you came forth from God."

³¹Jesus answered them, "Do you now believe? ³²Look, the time is coming, and has[b] come, that you will be scattered, everyone to his own place, and you will leave me alone. But I am not alone, because the Father is with me. ³³I have told you these things, that in me you may have peace. In the world you have oppression; but cheer up. I have overcome the world."

17 Jesus said these things, and lifting up his eyes to heaven, he said, "Father, the time has come. Glorify your Son, that your Son may also glorify you; ²even as you gave him authority over all flesh, he will give everlasting life to all whom you have given him. ³This is everlasting life, that they may know you, the only true God, and him whom you sent, Jesus Christ. ⁴I glorified you on the earth. I have accomplished the work which you have given me to do. ⁵Now, Father, glorify me with your own self with the glory which I had with you before the world existed. ⁶I revealed your name to the people whom you have given me out of the world. They were yours, and you have given them to me. They have kept your word. ⁷Now they have known that all things whatever you have given me are from you, ⁸for the words which you have given me I have given to them, and they received them, and knew for sure that I came forth from you, and they have believed that you sent me. ⁹I pray for them. I do not pray for the world, but for those whom you have given me, for they are yours. ¹⁰All things that are mine are yours, and yours are mine, and I am glorified in them. ¹¹I am no more in the world, but these are in the world, and I am coming to you. Holy Father, keep them through your name which you have given me, that they may be one, even as we are. ¹²While I was with them[c], I kept them in your name[d] which you have given me, and I guarded them, and not one of them perished, except the son of destruction, that the Scripture might be fulfilled. ¹³But now I come to you, and I say these things in the world, that they may have my joy made full in themselves. ¹⁴I have given them your word. The world hated them, because they are not of the world, even as I am not of the world. ¹⁵I pray not that you would take them from the world, but that you would keep them from the evil one. ¹⁶They are not of the world even as I am not of the world. ¹⁷Sanctify

---

a   16:25 Some Mss read "But the"
b   16:32 Some Mss add "now"
c   17:12 Some Mss add "in the world"
d   17:12 Some Mss add "Those whom"

them in the[a] truth. Your word is truth.[b] [18]As you sent me into the world, even so I have sent them into the world. [19]For their sakes I sanctify myself, that they themselves also may be sanctified in truth. [20]Not for these only do I pray, but for those also who believe in me through their word, [21]that they may all be one; even as you, Father, are in me, and I in you, that they also may be[c] in us; that the world may believe that you sent me. [22]The glory which you have given me, I have given to them; that they may be one, even as we are one; [23]I in them, and you in me, that they may be perfected into one; that the world may know that you sent me, and loved them, even as you loved me. [24]Father, I desire that they also whom you have given me be with me where I am, that they may see my glory, which you have given me, for you loved me before the foundation of the world. [25]Righteous Father, the world hasn't known you, but I knew you; and these knew that you sent me. [26]I made known to them your name, and will make it known; that the love with which you loved me may be in them, and I in them."

18 When Jesus had spoken these words, he went out with his disciples over the brook Kidron, where there was a garden, into which he and his disciples entered. [2]Now Judas, who betrayed him, also knew the place, for Jesus often met there with his disciples. [3]Judas then, having taken a detachment of soldiers and officers from the chief priests and the Pharisees, came there with lanterns, torches, and weapons. [4]Jesus therefore, knowing all the things that were happening to him, went forth, and said to them, "Who are you looking for?"

[5]They answered him, "Jesus the Nazorean."

Jesus said to them, "I AM."

Judas also, who betrayed him, was standing with them. [6]When therefore he said to them, "I AM," they went backward, and fell to the ground.

[7]Again therefore he asked them, "Who are you looking for?"

They said, "Jesus the Nazorean."

[8]Jesus answered, "I told you that I AM. If therefore you seek me, let these go their way," [9]that the word might be fulfilled which he spoke, "Of those whom you have given me, I have lost none."[d]

[10]Simon Peter therefore, having a sword, drew it, and struck the high priest's servant, and cut off his right ear. The servant's name was Malchus. [11]Jesus therefore said to Peter, "Put the sword into its sheath. Am I not to drink the cup which the[e] Father has given me?"

[12]So the detachment, the commanding officer, and the officers of the Jewish leaders, seized Jesus and bound him, [13]and led him to Annas first, for he was father-in-law to Caiaphas, who was high priest that year. [14]Now it was Caiaphas who advised the Jewish leaders that it was expedient that one man should perish for the people. [15]Simon Peter followed Jesus, as did another disciple. Now that disciple was known to the high priest, and entered in with Jesus into the court of the high priest; [16]but Peter was standing at the door outside. So the other disciple, who was known to the high priest, went out and spoke to her who kept the door, and brought in Peter. [17]Then the maid who kept the door said to Peter, "Are you also one of this man's disciples?"

He said, "I am not."

[18]Now the servants and the officers were standing there, having made a fire of coals, for it was cold. They were warming themselves. Peter was with them, standing and warming himself. [19]The high priest therefore asked Jesus about his disciples, and about his teaching. [20]Jesus answered him, "I spoke openly to the world. I always taught in synagogues, and in the temple, where all the Jewish people come together[f]. I said nothing in secret. [21]Why do you

---

a   17:17 Some Mss read "your"
b   17:17 Psalm 119:142
c   17:21 Some Mss add "one"
d   18:9 John 6:39
e   18:11 Some Mss read "my"
f   18:20 Some Mss read "where the Jews always meet"

ask me? Ask those who have heard what I spoke to them; surely they know what I said."

²²When he had said this, one of the officers standing by slapped Jesus with his hand, saying, "Do you answer the high priest like that?"

²³Jesus answered him, "If I have spoken evil, testify of the evil; but if well, why do you beat me?"

²⁴Annas sent him bound to Caiaphas, the high priest. ²⁵Now Simon Peter was standing and warming himself. They said therefore to him, "You are not also one of his disciples, are you?"

He denied it, and said, "I am not."

²⁶One of the servants of the high priest, being a relative of him whose ear Peter had cut off, said, "Did I not see you in the garden with him?"

²⁷Peter therefore denied it again, and immediately the rooster crowed.

²⁸They led Jesus therefore from Caiaphas into the Praetorium. It was early, and they themselves did not enter into the Praetorium, that they might not be defiled, but might eat the Passover. ²⁹Pilate therefore went out to them, and said, "What accusation do you bring against this man?"

³⁰They answered him, "If this man weren't an evildoer, we would not have delivered him up to you."

³¹Pilate therefore said to them, "Take him yourselves, and judge him according to your law."

Therefore the Jewish leaders said to him, "It is not lawful for us to put anyone to death," ³²that the word of Jesus might be fulfilled, which he spoke, signifying by what kind of death he should die.

³³Pilate therefore entered again into the Praetorium, called Jesus, and said to him, "Are you the King of the Jews?"

³⁴Jesus answered him, "Do you say this by yourself, or did others tell you about me?"

³⁵Pilate answered, "I'm not a Jew, am I? Your own nation and the chief priests delivered you to me. What have you done?"

³⁶Jesus answered, "My kingdom is not of this world. If my kingdom were of this world, then my servants would fight, that I would not be delivered to the Jewish leaders. But now my kingdom is not from here."

³⁷Pilate therefore said to him, "Are you a king then?"

Jesus answered, "You say that I am a king. For this reason I have been born, and for this reason I have come into the world, that I should testify to the truth. Everyone who is of the truth listens to my voice."

³⁸Pilate said to him, "What is truth?"

When he had said this, he went out again to the Jewish leaders, and said to them, "I find no basis for a charge against him. ³⁹But you have a custom, that I should release someone to you at the Passover. Therefore do you want me to release to you the King of the Jews?"

⁴⁰Then they[a] shouted again, saying, "Not this man, but Barabbas." Now Barabbas was a robber.

19 So Pilate then took Jesus, and flogged him. ²The soldiers twisted thorns into a crown, and put it on his head, and dressed him in a purple garment. ³And they kept coming up to him and[b] saying, "Hail, King of the Jews." and they struck him with their hands.

⁴Then Pilate went out again, and said to them, "Look, I am bringing him out to you, that you may know that I find no basis for a charge against him."

⁵Then Jesus came out, wearing the crown of thorns and the purple garment. Pilate said to them, "Look, here is the man."

⁶When therefore the chief priests and the officers saw him, they shouted, saying, "Crucify. Crucify."

Pilate said to them, "Take him yourselves, and crucify him, for I find no basis for a charge against him."

⁷The Jewish leaders answered him, "We have a law, and by that[c] law he ought to die, because he made himself the Son of God."

---

a 18:40 Some Mss add "all"
b 19:3 Some Mss lack "coming up to him and"
c 19:7 Some Mss read "our"

[8]When therefore Pilate heard this saying, he was more afraid. [9]He entered into the Praetorium again, and said to Jesus, "Where are you from?" But Jesus gave him no answer. [10]Pilate therefore said to him, "Are you not speaking to me? Do you not know that I have power to release you, and have power to crucify you?"

[11]Jesus answered, "You would have no power at all against me, unless it were given to you from above. Therefore he who delivered me to you has greater sin."

[12]At this, Pilate was seeking to release him, but the Jewish leaders shouted, saying, "If you release this man, you are not Caesar's friend. Everyone who makes himself a king speaks against Caesar."

[13]When Pilate therefore heard these words, he brought Jesus out, and sat down on the judgment seat at a place called "The Pavement," but in Hebrew, "Gabbatha."[a] [14]Now it was the Preparation Day of the Passover, at about noon.[b] He said to the Jewish leaders, "Look, here is your King."

[15]They shouted, "Away with him. Away with him. Crucify him."

Pilate said to them, "Should I crucify your King?"

The chief priests answered, "We have no king but Caesar."

[16]So then he delivered him to them to be crucified. So they took Jesus.[c] [17]And he went out, carrying the cross himself, to the place called "The Place of a Skull,[d]" which is called in Hebrew, "Golgotha," [18]where they crucified him, and with him two others, on either side one, and Jesus in the middle. [19]Pilate wrote a title also, and put it on the cross. There was written, "JESUS THE NAZOREAN, THE KING OF THE JEWS." [20]Therefore many Jews read this title, for the place where Jesus was crucified was near the city; and it was written in Hebrew, in Latin, and in Greek. [21]The chief priests of the Jewish people therefore said to Pilate, "Do not write, 'The King of the Jews,' but, 'he said, I am King of the Jews.'"

[22]Pilate answered, "What I have written, I have written."

[23]Then the soldiers, when they had crucified Jesus, took his clothes and made four parts, to every soldier a part; and also the tunic. Now the tunic was without seam, woven from the top throughout. [24]Then they said to one another, "Let us not tear it, but cast lots for it to decide whose it will be," that the Scripture might be fulfilled, which says,

"They divided my clothes among themselves, and
　　for my clothing they cast a lot."[e]

Therefore the soldiers did these things. [25]But there were standing by the cross of Jesus his mother, and his mother's sister, Mary the wife of Cleopas, and Mary Magdalene. [26]Therefore when Jesus saw his mother, and the disciple whom he loved standing there, he said to his mother, "Woman, look, your son." [27]Then he said to the disciple, "Look, your mother." From that hour, the disciple took her to his own home.

[28]After this, Jesus, knowing[f] that all things were now finished, that the Scripture might be fulfilled, said, "I am thirsty."[g] [29]Now a vessel full of vinegar was set there; so they put a sponge full of the vinegar on hyssop, and held it at his mouth. [30]When Jesus therefore had received the vinegar, he said, "It is finished." He bowed his head, and gave up his spirit.

[31]Therefore the Jewish leaders, because it was the Preparation Day, so that the bodies would not remain on the cross on the Sabbath (for that Sabbath was a special one), asked of Pilate that their legs might be broken, and that they might be taken away. [32]Therefore the soldiers came, and broke the legs of the first, and of the other who was crucified with him; [33]but when they came to Jesus, and saw that he was

---

a　19:13 In late Second Temple era, the Hebrew language had assimilated many Aramaic words, including Gabbatha

b　19:14 Lit. the sixth hour

c　19:16 Some Mss add "and led (him) away"

d　19:17 Latin: Calvary

e　19:24 Psalm 22:18

f　19:28 Some Mss read "seeing"

g　19:28 Psalm 22:15; Psalm 69:21

already dead, they did not break his legs. [34]However one of the soldiers pierced his side with a spear, and immediately blood and water came out. [35]He who has seen has testified, and his testimony is true. He knows that he tells the truth, that you may believe. [36]For these things happened, that the Scripture might be fulfilled, "A bone of him will not be broken."[a] [37]Again another Scripture says, "They will look on him whom they pierced."[b]

[38]After these things, Joseph of Arimathaea, being a disciple of Jesus, but secretly for fear of the Jewish leaders, asked of Pilate that he might take away the body of Jesus. Pilate gave him permission. He came therefore and took away his body[c]. [39]Nicodemus, who at first came to Jesus by night, also came bringing a mixture of myrrh and aloes, about seventy-five pounds.[d] [40]So they took the body of Jesus, and bound it in linen cloths with the spices, according to Jewish burial practice. [41]Now in the place where he was crucified there was a garden. In the garden was a new tomb in which no one had ever yet been placed. [42]Then because of the Jewish Preparation Day (for the tomb was nearby) they put Jesus there.

20 Now on the first day of the week, Mary Magdalene went early, while it was still dark, to the tomb, and saw the stone taken away from the tomb. [2]Therefore she ran and came to Simon Peter, and to the other disciple whom Jesus loved, and said to them, "They have taken away the Lord out of the tomb, and we do not know where they have put him."

[3]Therefore Peter and the other disciple went out, and they went toward the tomb. [4]They both ran together. The other disciple outran Peter, and came to the tomb first. [5]Stooping and looking in, he saw the linen cloths lying, yet he did not enter in. [6]Then Simon Peter came, following him, and entered into the tomb. He saw the linen cloths lying, [7]and the cloth that had been on his head, not lying with the linen cloths, but rolled up in a place by itself. [8]So then the other disciple who came first to the tomb

also entered in, and he saw and believed. [9]For as yet they did not know the Scripture, that he must rise from the dead.[e] [10]So the disciples went away again to their own homes.

[11]But Mary was standing outside at the tomb weeping. So, as she wept, she stooped and looked into the tomb, [12]and she saw two angels in white sitting, one at the head, and one at the feet, where the body of Jesus had lain. [13]They told her, "Woman, why are you weeping?"

She said to them, "Because they have taken away my Lord, and I do not know where they have put him." [14]When she had said this, she turned around and saw Jesus standing, and did not know that it was Jesus.

[15]Jesus said to her, "Woman, why are you weeping? Who are you looking for?"

She, supposing him to be the gardener, said to him, "Sir, if you have carried him away, tell me where you have put him, and I will take him away."

[16]Jesus said to her, "Mary." She turned and said to him in Hebrew,[f] "Rabboni." which is to say, "Teacher."

[17]Jesus said to her, "Do not touch me, for I have not yet ascended to the[g] Father; but go to my brothers, and tell them, 'I am ascending to my Father and your Father, to my God and your God.'"

[18]Mary Magdalene came and told the disciples, "I have seen the Lord,"[h] and that he had said these things to her. [19]When therefore it was evening, on that day, the first day of the week, and when the doors were locked where the disciples were,[i] for fear of the Jewish leaders, Jesus came and stood in the midst, and said to them, "Peace be to you."

---

a   19:36 Exodus 12:46; Numbers 9:12; Psalm 34:20
b   19:37 Zechariah 12:10
c   19:38 Some Mss read "the body of Jesus"
d   19:39 Or, 32.5 kg. Lit. 100 litrai.
e   20:9 Psalm 16:10; Isaiah 53:11 (see DSS and LXX)
f   20:16 Some Mss lack "in Hebrew"
g   20:17 Some Mss read "my"
h   20:18 Some Mss read "that she had seen the Lord"
i   20:19 Some Mss add "assembled"

²⁰When he had said this, he showed them his hands and his side. The disciples therefore were glad when they saw the Lord. ²¹Jesus therefore said to them again, "Peace be to you. As the Father has sent me, even so I send you." ²²When he had said this, he breathed on them, and said to them, "Receive the Holy Spirit. ²³Whoever's sins you forgive, they are forgiven them. Whoever's sins you retain, they have been retained."

²⁴But Thomas, one of the twelve, called Didymus, was not with them when Jesus came. ²⁵The other disciples therefore said to him, "We have seen the Lord."

But he said to them, "Unless I see in his hands the mark of the nails, and put my finger into the mark of the nails, and put my hand into his side, I will not believe."

²⁶After eight days again his disciples were inside, and Thomas was with them. Jesus came, the doors being locked, and stood in the midst, and said, "Peace be to you." ²⁷Then he said to Thomas, "Put your finger here, and observe my hands. Reach out your hand, and put it into my side; and do not be unbelieving, but believing."

²⁸Thomas answered and said to him, "My Lord and my God."

²⁹Jesus said to him, "Because you have seen me,ᵃ you have believed. Blessed are those who have not seen, and have believed."

³⁰Therefore Jesus did many other signs in the presence of his disciples, which are not written in this book; ³¹but these are written, that you may believe that Jesus is the Messiah, the Son of God, and that believing you may have life in his name.

21 After these things, Jesus revealed himself again to the disciples at the sea of Tiberias. He revealed himself this way. ²Simon Peter, Thomas called Didymus, Nathanael of Cana in Galilee, and the sons of Zebedee, and two others of his disciples were together. ³Simon Peter said to them, "I'm going fishing."

They told him, "We are also coming with you." Theyᵇ went out, and entered into the boat. That night, they caught nothing. ⁴But when day had already come, Jesus stood on the beach, yet the disciples did not know that it was Jesus. ⁵Jesus therefore said to them, "Children, have you anything to eat?" They answered him, "No."

⁶And he said to them, "Cast the net on the right side of the boat, and you will find some."

They cast it therefore, and now they weren't able to draw it in for the multitude of fish. ⁷That disciple therefore whom Jesus loved said to Peter, "It's the Lord."

So when Simon Peter heard that it was the Lord, he wrapped his coat around him (for he was naked), and threw himself into the sea. ⁸But the other disciples came in the little boat (for they were not far from the land, but about one hundred yardsᶜ away), dragging the net full of fish. ⁹So when they got out on the land, they saw a fire of coals there, and fish placed on it, and bread. ¹⁰Jesus said to them, "Bring some of the fish which you have just caught."

¹¹Simon Peter went up, and drew the net to land, full of great fish, one hundred fifty-three; and even though there were so many, the net was not torn.

¹²Jesus said to them, "Come and eat breakfast."

None of the disciples dared inquire of him, "Who are you?" knowing that it was the Lord.

¹³Then Jesus came and took the bread, gave it to them, and the fish likewise. ¹⁴This is now the third time that Jesus was revealed to his disciples, after he had risen from the dead. ¹⁵So when they had eaten their breakfast, Jesus said to Simon Peter, "Simon, son of John,ᵈ do you love me more than these?" He said to him, "Yes, Lord; you know that I love you." He said to him, "Feed my lambs."

¹⁶He said to him again a second time, "Simon, son of John, do you love me?" He said

---

a   20:29 Some Mss add "Thomas"

b   21:3 Some Mss add "immediately"

c   21:8 Or, 90 meters. Lit. 200 cubits

d   21:15 Some Mss read "Jonah," also in vv. 16 and 17

to him, "Yes, Lord; you know that I love you." He said to him, "Tend my sheep."

[17]He said to him the third time, "Simon, son of John, do you love me?"

Peter was grieved because he asked him the third time, "Do you love me?" He said to him, "Lord, you know everything. You know that I love you."

Jesus said to him, "Feed my sheep. [18]Truly I tell you, when you were young, you dressed yourself, and walked where you wanted to. But when you are old, you will stretch out your hands, and another will dress you, and carry you where you do not want to go."

[19]Now he said this, signifying by what kind of death he would glorify God. When he had said this, he said to him, "Follow me."

[20]Then Peter, turning around, saw a disciple following. This was the disciple whom Jesus sincerely loved, the one who had also leaned on Jesus' chest at the evening meal and asked, "Lord, who is going to betray You?" [21]Peter seeing him, said to Jesus, "Lord, what about this man?"

[22]Jesus said to him, "If I desire that he stay until I come, what is that to you? You follow me." [23]This saying therefore went out among the brothers, that this disciple would not die. Yet Jesus did not say to him that he would not die, but, "If I desire that he stay until I come, what is that to you?" [24]This is the disciple who testifies about these things, and wrote these things. We know that his witness is true. [25]There are also many other things which Jesus did, which if they would all be written, I suppose that even the world itself would not have room for the books that would be written.

Acts

1 The first account[a] I wrote, Theophilus, concerned all that Jesus began both to do and to teach, [2]until the day in which he was received up, after he had given commandment through the Holy Spirit to the apostles whom he had chosen. [3]To these he also showed himself alive after he suffered, by many proofs, appearing to them over a period of forty days, and speaking about God's kingdom. [4]Being assembled together with them, he commanded them, "Do not depart from Jerusalem, but wait for the promise of the Father, which you heard from me. [5]For John indeed baptized in water, but you will be baptized in the Holy Spirit not many days from now."

[6]Therefore, when they had come together, they asked him, "Lord, are you now restoring the kingdom to Israel?"

[7]He said to them, "It is not for you to know times or seasons which the Father has set within his own authority. [8]But you will receive power when the Holy Spirit has come upon you. You will be my witnesses[b] in Jerusalem, in all Judea and Samaria, and to the farthest part of the earth."

[9]When he had said these things, as they were looking, he was taken up, and a cloud took him out of their sight. [10]While they were looking steadfastly into the sky as he went, look, two men stood by them in white clothing, [11]who also said, "You men of Galilee, why do you stand looking into the sky? This Jesus, who was received up from you into the sky will come back in the same way as you saw him going into the sky."

[12]Then they returned to Jerusalem from the mountain called Olivet, which is near Jerusalem, a Sabbath day's journey away. [13]When they had come in, they went up into the upper room, where they were staying; that is Peter, John, James, Andrew, Philip, Thomas, Bartholomew, Matthew, James the son of Alphaeus, Simon the Zealot, and Judas the son of James. [14]All

---

a   1:1 Or, "word," "treatise," "book." Gk. Logos
b   1:8 Some Mss read "witnesses to me"

these with one accord continued steadfastly in prayer,[a] along with the women, and Mary the mother of Jesus, and with his brothers.

[15]In these days, Peter stood up in the midst of the brothers[b] (and the number of names was about one hundred twenty), and said, [16]"Brothers, it was necessary that this Scripture should be fulfilled, which the Holy Spirit spoke before by the mouth of David concerning Judas, who was guide to those who took Jesus. [17]For he was numbered with us, and received his portion in this ministry. [18]Now this man obtained a field with the reward for his wickedness, and falling headlong, his body burst open, and all his intestines gushed out. [19]It became known to everyone who lived in Jerusalem that in their language that field was called 'Hakel-Dema,' that is, 'The field of blood.' [20]For it is written in the scroll of Psalms,

'Let his habitation be made desolate,
    And let no one dwell in it;'[c]
        and,
'Let another take his office.'[d]

[21]"Of the men therefore who have accompanied us all the time that the Lord Jesus went in and out among us, [22]beginning from the baptism of John, to the day that he was received up from us, of these one must become a witness with us of his resurrection."

[23]They put forward two, Joseph called Barsabbas, who was surnamed Justus, and Matthias. [24]They prayed, and said, "You, Lord, who know the hearts of all people, show which one of these two you have chosen [25]to take part in this ministry and office of apostle from which Judas fell away, that he might go to his own place." [26]They drew lots for them, and the lot fell on Matthias, and he was numbered with the eleven apostles.

2 Now when the day of Pentecost[e] had come, they were all together[f] in one place. [2]Suddenly there came from the sky a sound like the rushing of a mighty wind, and it filled all the house where they were sitting. [3]Tongues like fire appeared and were distributed to them, and one sat on each of them. [4]They were all filled with the Holy Spirit, and began to speak with other tongues, as the Spirit gave them the ability to speak. [5]Now there were dwelling in Jerusalem Jews, devout men, from every nation under the sky. [6]When this sound was heard, the crowd came together, and were bewildered, because everyone heard them speaking in his own language. [7]They were all amazed and marveled, saying,[g] "Look, are not all these who speak Galileans? [8]How do we hear, everyone in our own native language? [9]Parthians, Medes, Elamites, and people from Mesopotamia, Judea, Cappadocia, Pontus, Asia, [10]Phrygia, Pamphylia, Egypt, the parts of Libya around Cyrene, visitors from Rome, both Jews and proselytes, [11]Cretans and Arabians: we hear them speaking in our tongues the mighty works of God." [12]They were all amazed, and were perplexed, saying one to another, "What does this mean?" [13]Others, mocking, said, "They are filled with new wine."

[14]But Peter, standing up with the eleven, lifted up his voice, and spoke out to them, "You men of Judea, and all you who dwell at Jerusalem, let this be known to you, and listen to my words. [15]For these are not drunk, as you suppose, seeing it is only nine in the morning of the day[h].[16]But this is what has been spoken through the prophet Joel:

[17]"And it will be in the last days, says
        God,
    that I will pour out my Spirit on all
        flesh;
and your sons and your daughters will
        prophesy,
    and your young men will see visions,
    and your old men will dream
        dreams.

a   1:14 Some Mss add "and petition"
b   1:15 Some Mss read "disciples"
c   1:20 Psalm 69:25
d   1:20 Psalm 109:8
e   2:1 For Heb. Shavuot
f   2:1 Some Mss read "with one accord"
g   2:7 Some Mss add "to one another"
h   2:15 Lit. the third hour

[18]And even on my servants and on my handmaidens in those days
I will pour out my Spirit, and they will prophesy.
[19]And I will show wonders in the sky above,
and signs on the earth beneath;
blood, and fire, and billows[a] of smoke.
[20]The sun will be turned into darkness, and the moon into blood,
before the great and glorious day of the Lord comes.
[21]And it will be that whoever will call on the name of the Lord will be saved.'[b]

[22]"Men of Israel, hear these words. Jesus the Nazorean, a man approved by God to you by mighty works and wonders and signs which God did by him in the midst of you, even as you yourselves know, [23]him, being delivered up by the determined counsel and foreknowledge of God,[c] by the hand of lawless men, crucified and killed; [24]whom God raised up, having freed him from the pains of death, because it was not possible that he should be held by it. [25]For David says concerning him,

'I saw the Lord always before me,
for he is at my right hand, that I should not be shaken.
[26]Therefore my heart was glad, and my tongue rejoiced,
and moreover my flesh also will dwell in hope;
[27]because you will not abandon my soul in Sheol,[d]
neither will you allow your Holy One to see decay.
[28]You made known to me the paths of life.
You will make me full of joy in your presence.'[e]

[29]"Brothers, I may tell you freely of the patriarch David, that he both died and was buried, and his tomb is with us to this day. [30]Therefore, being a prophet, and knowing that God had sworn with an oath to him that one from the fruit of his body[f] would sit on his throne,[g] [31]he foreseeing this spoke about the resurrection of the Messiah, that neither was he[h] abandoned in Sheol, nor did his flesh see decay.[i] [32]This Jesus God raised up, to which we all are witnesses. [33]Being therefore exalted by the right hand of God, and having received from the Father the promise of the Holy Spirit, he has poured out this, which you[j] see and hear. [34]For David did not ascend into the heavens, but he says himself,

'The Lord said to my Lord, "Sit by my right hand,
[35]until I make your enemies a footstool for your feet." '[k]

[36]"Let all the house of Israel therefore know certainly that God has made him both Lord and Messiah, this Jesus whom you crucified."

[37]Now when they heard this, they were cut to the heart, and said to Peter and the rest[l] of the apostles, "Brothers, what should we do?"

[38]Peter said to them, "Repent, and be baptized, every one of you, in the name of Jesus Christ for the forgiveness of your[m] sins, and you will receive the gift of the Holy Spirit. [39]For to you is the promise, and to your children, and to all who are far off, even as many as the Lord our God will call to himself." [40]With many other words he testified, and exhorted them, saying, "Save yourselves from this crooked generation."

[41]Then those who[n] received his word were baptized. There were added that day about three thousand souls. [42]They continued steadfastly in the apostles' teaching and fellowship, in the breaking of bread,

a   2:19 Lit., steam, mist, vapor
b   2:21 Joel 2:28-32
c   2:23 Some Mss add "you have taken"
d   2:27 Gk. Hades
e   2:28 Psalm 16:8-11
f   2:30 Some Mss add "according to the flesh, he would raise up the Messiah"
g   2:30 See 2 Samuel 7:12-13; Psalm 132:11
h   2:31 Some Mss read "his soul"
i   2:31 Psalm 16:10
j   2:33 Some Mss add "now"
k   2:35 Psalm 110:1
l   2:37 Some Mss lack "the rest"
m   2:38 Some Mss lack "your"
n   2:41 Some Mss add "gladly"

and prayer. ⁴³Fear came on every soul, and many wonders and signs were done through theᵃ apostles.ᵇ ⁴⁴All who believed were together, and had all things in common. ⁴⁵They sold their possessions and goods, and distributed them to all, according as anyone had need. ⁴⁶Day by day, continuing steadfastly with one accord in the temple, and breaking bread at home, they took their food with gladness and singleness of heart, ⁴⁷praising God, and having favor with all the people. The Lord added to their numberᶜ day by day those who were being saved.

3 Now Peter and John were going up into the temple at the hour of prayer, at three in the afternoon.ᵈ ²A certain man who was lame from his mother's womb was being carried, whom they put daily at the door of the temple which is called Beautiful,ᵉ to ask gifts for the needy of those who entered into the temple. ³Seeing Peter and John about to go into the temple, he asked to receive gifts for the needy. ⁴Peter, fastening his eyes on him, with John, said, "Look at us." ⁵He listened to them, expecting to receive something from them. ⁶But Peter said, "Silver and gold have I none, but what I have, that I give you. In the name of Jesus Christ the Nazorean, get up and walk." ⁷He took him by the right hand, and raised him up. Immediately his feet and his ankle bones received strength. ⁸Leaping up, he stood, and began to walk. He entered with them into the temple, walking, leaping, and praising God. ⁹All the people saw him walking and praising God. ¹⁰They recognized him, that it was he who used to sit begging for gifts for the needy at the Beautiful Gate of the temple. They were filled with wonder and amazement at what had happened to him. ¹¹And as heᶠ held on to Peter and John, all the people ran together to them in the porch that is called Solomon's, greatly wondering.

¹²When Peter saw it, he responded to the people, "You men of Israel, why do you marvel at this? Why do you fasten your eyes on us, as though by our own power or godliness we had made him walk? ¹³The God of Abraham, Isaac, and Jacob, the God of our fathers, has glorified his Servant Jesus, whom you delivered up, and denied in the presence of Pilate, when he had determined to release him. ¹⁴But you denied the Holy and Righteous One, and asked for a man who was a murderer to be granted to you, ¹⁵and killed the Prince of life, whom God raised from the dead, to which we are witnesses. ¹⁶By faith in his name, his name has made this man strong, whom you see and know. Yes, the faith which is through him has given him this perfect soundness in the presence of you all.

¹⁷"Now, brothers, I know that you did this in ignorance, as did also your rulers. ¹⁸But the things which God announced by the mouth of all his prophets, that the Messiah should suffer, he thus fulfilled.

¹⁹"Repent therefore, and turn again, that your sins may be blotted out, so that there may come times of refreshing from the presence of the Lord, ²⁰and that he may send Jesus, the Messiah who was ordained for you before, ²¹whom heaven must receive until the times of restoration of all things, which God spoke long ago by the mouth ofᵍ his holy prophets. ²²For Moses indeed said to the fathers, 'The Lord yourʰ God will raise up a prophet for you from among your brothers, like me. You must listen to him in all things whatever he says to you. ²³It will be, that every soul that will not listen to that prophet will be utterly destroyed from among the people.'ⁱ ²⁴Yes, and all the prophets from Samuel and those who followed after, as many as have spoken, they also told of these days.

---

a   2:43 Some Mss add "the hands of"
b   2:43 Some Mss add "in Jerusalem." Other Mss read "in Jerusalem; and great fear was on all. And"
c   2:47 Some Mss read "the church"
d   3:1 Lit. the ninth hour
e   3:2 Gk. horaios, meaning "beautiful"
f   3:11 Some Mss read "the lame man who was healed"
g   3:21 Some Mss add "all"
h   3:22 Some Mss read "our"
i   3:23 For the consequences for ignoring the required sacrifice of God, see Leviticus 23:29; Deuteronomy 18:15, 18-19

²⁵You are the children of the prophets, and of the covenant which God made with our fathers, saying to Abraham, 'And in your offspring all the families of the earth will be blessed.'ᵃ ²⁶God, having raised up his Servant,ᵇ sent him to you first, to bless you, in turning away everyone of you from your wickedness."

4 As they spoke to the people, the priests and the captain of the temple and the Sadducees came to them, ²being upset because they taught the people and proclaimed in Jesus the resurrection from the dead. ³They laid hands on them, and put them in custody until the next day, for it was now evening. ⁴But many of those who heard the word believed, and the number of the men came to be about five thousand.

⁵It happened in the morning, that their rulers, elders, and scribes were gathered together in Jerusalem. ⁶Annas the high priest was there, with Caiaphas, John, Alexander, and as many as were relatives of the high priest. ⁷When they had stood them in the middle of them, they inquired, "By what power, or in what name, have you done this?"

⁸Then Peter, filled with the Holy Spirit, said to them, "Rulers of the people, and elders,ᶜ ⁹if we are examined today concerning a good deed done to a crippled man, by what means this man has been healed, ¹⁰be it known to you all, and to all the people of Israel, that in the name of Jesus Christ the Nazorean, whom you crucified, whom God raised from the dead, in him does this man stand here before you whole. ¹¹This one is the stone which was regarded as worthless by you, the builders, which has become the head of the corner.ᵈ ¹²And there is salvation in no one else, for there is no other name under heaven that is given among people by which we must be saved."

¹³Now when they saw the boldness of Peter and John, and had perceived that they were unlearned and ignorant men, they were amazed. They recognized that they had been with Jesus. ¹⁴Seeing the man who was healed standing with them, they could say nothing against it. ¹⁵But when they had commanded them to go aside out of the council, they conferred among themselves, ¹⁶saying, "What should we do with these men? Because indeed a notable miracle has been done through them, as can be plainly seen by all who dwell in Jerusalem, and we cannot deny it. ¹⁷But so this does not spread any further among the people, let us severelyᵉ threaten them, that from now on they do not speak to anyone in this name." ¹⁸They called them, and commanded them not to speak at all nor teach in the name of Jesus.

¹⁹But Peter and John answered them, "Whether it is right in the sight of God to listen to you rather than to God, judge for yourselves, ²⁰for we cannot help telling the things which we saw and heard."

²¹When they had further threatened them, they let them go, finding no way to punish them, because of the people; for everyone glorified God for that which was done. ²²For the man on whom this miracle of healing was performed was more than forty years old.

²³Being let go, they came to their own company, and reported all that the chief priests and the elders had said to them. ²⁴When they heard it, they lifted up their voice to God with one accord, and said, "Lord, you are the God whoᶠ made the heaven and the earth and the sea, and all that is in them.ᵍ ²⁵You said through the Holy Spirit,ʰ through the mouth of our father David your servant:

'Why do the nations rage,
    and the peoples plot in vain?
²⁶The kings of the earth take a stand,
    and the rulers take council together,
    against the Lord, and against his
        Messiah.'ⁱ

---

a   3:25 Genesis 22:18; 26:4; 28:14
b   3:26 Some Mss add "Jesus"
c   4:8 Some Mss add "of Israel"
d   4:11 An allusion to Psalm 118:22
e   4:17 Some Mss lack "severely"
f   4:24 Some Mss lack "[are] the God, [who]"
g   4:24 Exodus 20:11
h   4:25 Some Mss lack "Holy Spirit"
i   4:26 Psalm 2:1-2

²⁷"For truly, in this city[a] against your holy servant, Jesus, whom you anointed, both Herod and Pontius Pilate, with the non-Jews and the people of Israel, were gathered together ²⁸to do whatever your hand and your council foreordained to happen. ²⁹Now, Lord, look at their threats, and grant to your servants to speak your word with all boldness, ³⁰while you stretch out your hand to heal; and that signs and wonders may be done through the name of your holy Servant Jesus."

³¹When they had prayed, the place was shaken where they were gathered together. They were all filled with the Holy Spirit, and they spoke the word of God with boldness. ³²And the full number of those who believed were of one heart and soul. Not one of them claimed that anything of the things which he possessed[b] was his own, but they had all things in common. ³³With great power, the apostles gave their testimony of the resurrection of the Lord Jesus. Great grace was on them all. ³⁴For neither was there among them any who lacked, for as many as were owners of lands or houses sold them, and brought the proceeds of the things that were sold, ³⁵and put them at the apostles' feet, and distribution was made to each, according as anyone had need. ³⁶Joseph,[c] who by the apostles was surnamed Barnabas (which is translated, Son of Encouragement), a Levite, a native of Cyprus by birth, ³⁷having a field, sold it, and brought the money and put it at the apostles' feet.

5 But a certain man named Ananias, with Sapphirah, his wife, sold a possession, ²and kept back part of the price, his wife also being aware of it, and brought a certain part, and put it at the apostles' feet. ³But Peter said, "Ananias, why has Satan filled your heart[d] to lie to the Holy Spirit, and to keep back part of the price of the land? ⁴While you kept it, did not it remain your own? After it was sold, was not it in your power? How is it that you have conceived this thing in your heart? You have not lied to people, but to God."

⁵Ananias, hearing these words, fell down and died. Great fear came on all who heard it.[e] ⁶The young men arose and wrapped him up, and they carried him out and buried him. ⁷About three hours later, his wife, not knowing what had happened, came in. ⁸Peter answered her, "Tell me whether you sold the land for so much."

She said, "Yes, for so much."

⁹But Peter asked her, "How is it that you have agreed together to tempt the Spirit of the Lord? Look, the feet of those who have buried your husband are at the door, and they will carry you out."

¹⁰She fell down immediately at his feet, and died. The young men came in and found her dead, and they carried her out and buried her by her husband. ¹¹Great fear came on the whole church, and on all who heard these things. ¹²By the hands of the apostles many signs and wonders were done among the people. They were all with one accord in Solomon's porch. ¹³None of the rest dared to join them, however the people honored them. ¹⁴More believers were added to the Lord, crowds of both men and women. ¹⁵They even carried out the sick into the streets, and put them on cots and mats, so that as Peter came by at the least his shadow would fall on some of them. ¹⁶Crowds also came together from the cities around Jerusalem, bringing sick people, and those who were tormented by unclean spirits: and they were all healed.

¹⁷But the high priest rose up, and all those who were with him (which is the sect of the Sadducees), and they were filled with jealousy, ¹⁸and laid hands on the apostles, and put them in public custody. ¹⁹But an angel of the Lord opened the prison doors by night, and brought them out, and said, ²⁰"Go stand and speak in the temple to the people all the words of this life." ²¹When they heard this, they entered into the temple about daybreak, and taught. But

---

a   4:27 Some Mss lack "in this city"
b   4:32 Some Mss read "of their belongings"
c   4:36 Some Mss read "Josi"
d   5:3 Some Mss add "for you"
e   5:5 Some Mss add "these things"

the high priest came, and those who were with him, and called the council together, and all the senate of the children of Israel, and sent to the prison to have them brought. ²²But the officers who came did not find them in the prison. They returned and reported, ²³"We found the prison shut and locked, and the guards standing before the doors, but when we opened them, we found no one inside."

²⁴Now when the[a] captain of the temple, and the chief priests heard these words, they were very perplexed about them and what might become of this. ²⁵One came and told them, "Look, the men whom you put in prison are in the temple, standing and teaching the people." ²⁶Then the captain went with the officers, and brought them without violence, for they were afraid that the people might stone them.

²⁷When they had brought them, they set them before the council. The high priest questioned them, ²⁸saying, "Did not we strictly command you not to teach in this name? And look, you have filled Jerusalem with your teaching, and intend to bring this man's blood on us."

²⁹But Peter and the apostles answered, "We must obey God rather than people. ³⁰The God of our fathers raised up Jesus, whom you killed, hanging him on a tree. ³¹God exalted him with his right hand to be a Prince and a Savior, to give repentance to Israel, and remission of sins. ³²We are[b] witnesses of these things; and so also is the Holy Spirit, whom God has given to those who obey him."

³³But they, when they heard this, were cut to the heart, and wanted[c] to kill them. ³⁴But one stood up in the council, a Pharisee named Gamaliel, a teacher of the Law, honored by all the people, and commanded to put the men[d] out for a little while. ³⁵He said to them, "You men of Israel, be careful concerning these men, what you are about to do. ³⁶For before these days Todah rose up, making himself out to be somebody; to whom a number of men, about four hundred, joined themselves: who was slain; and all, as many as obeyed him, were dispersed,

and came to nothing. ³⁷After this man, Judas of Galilee rose up in the days of the enrollment, and drew away some people after him. He also perished, and all, as many as obeyed him, were scattered abroad. ³⁸Now I tell you, withdraw from these men, and leave them alone. For if this counsel or this work is of man, it will be overthrown. ³⁹But if it is of God, you will not be able to overthrow them[e], and you would be found even to be fighting against God."

⁴⁰They agreed with him. Summoning the apostles, they beat them and commanded them not to speak in the name of Jesus, and let them go. ⁴¹They therefore departed from the presence of the council, rejoicing that they were counted worthy to suffer dishonor for the Name[f].

⁴²Every day, in the temple and at home, they never stopped teaching and proclaiming that Jesus is the Messiah.

6 Now in those days, when the number of the disciples was multiplying, a complaint arose from the Hellenists against the Hebrews, because their widows were neglected in the daily service. ²So the twelve summoned the full number of the disciples and said, "It is not appropriate for us to forsake the word of God and serve tables. ³Therefore select from among you, brothers, seven men of good report, full of the[g] Spirit and of wisdom, whom we may appoint over this business. ⁴But we will continue steadfastly in prayer and in the ministry of the word."

⁵And these words pleased the whole gathering. They chose Stephen, a man full of faith and of the Holy Spirit, Philip, Prochorus, Nicanor, Timon, Parmenas, and Nicolaus, a proselyte of Antioch; ⁶whom they set before the apostles. When they had prayed, they laid their hands on them. ⁷The

---

a   5:24 Some Mss add "high priest the"
b   5:32 Some Mss add "his"
c   5:33 Some Mss read "plotted"
d   5:34 Some Mss read "apostles"
e   5:39 Some Mss read "you are not able to overthrow it"
f   5:41 Some Mss add "of Jesus"
g   6:3 Some Mss add "Holy"

word of God increased and the number of the disciples multiplied greatly in Jerusalem; and a large group of the priests were obedient to the faith.

[8]Stephen, full of grace[a] and power, performed great wonders and signs among the people. [9]But some of those who were of the synagogue called "The Libertines," and of the Cyrenians, of the Alexandrians, and of those of Cilicia and Asia arose, disputing with Stephen. [10]They weren't able to withstand the wisdom and the Spirit by which he spoke. [11]Then they secretly induced men to say, "We have heard him speak blasphemous words against Moses and God." [12]They stirred up the people, the elders, and the scribes, and came against him and seized him, and brought him in to the council, [13]and set up false witnesses who said, "This man never stops speaking blasphemous words against this holy place and the Law. [14]For we have heard him say that this Jesus the Nazorean will destroy this place, and will change the customs which Moses delivered to us." [15]All who sat in the council, fastening their eyes on him, saw his face like it was the face of an angel.

7 The high priest said, "Are these things so?"

[2]He said, "Brothers and fathers, listen. The God of glory appeared to our father Abraham, when he was in Mesopotamia, before he lived in Haran, [3]and said to him, 'Get out of your land, and from your relatives, and come into a land which I will show you.'[b] [4]Then he came out of the land of the Kasdim[c], and lived in Haran. From there, after his father died, he moved him into this land, where you are now living. [5]He gave him no inheritance in it, no, not so much as to set his foot on. He promised that he would give it to him for a possession, and to his descendants after him, when he still had no child. [6]God spoke in this way, that his descendants would live as foreigners in a strange land, and that they would be enslaved and oppressed for four hundred years. [7]But I will judge the nation to which they will be in bondage,' said God,

'and after that will they come out,[d] and serve me in this place.'[e] [8]He gave him the covenant of circumcision. So Abraham became the father of Isaac, and circumcised him the eighth day. Isaac became the father of Jacob, and Jacob became the father of the twelve patriarchs.

[9]"The patriarchs, moved with jealousy against Joseph, sold him into Egypt; and God was with him, [10]and delivered him out of all his afflictions, and gave him favor and wisdom before Pharaoh, king of Egypt. He made him governor over Egypt and all his house. [11]Now a famine came over all the land of[f] Egypt and Canaan, and great affliction, and our fathers found no food. [12]But when Jacob heard that there was grain in Egypt, he sent out our fathers the first time. [13]On the second time Joseph was made known to his brothers, and Joseph's race was revealed to Pharaoh. [14]Then Joseph sent, and summoned Jacob, his father, and all his relatives, seventy-five souls.[g] [15]Jacob went down into Egypt, and he died, himself and our fathers, [16]and they were brought back to Shechem, and placed in the tomb that Abraham bought for a price in silver from the children of Hamor in[h] Shechem.[i]

[17]"But as the time of the promise came close which God had made[j] to Abraham, the people grew and multiplied in Egypt, [18]until 'there arose a different king over Egypt,[k] who did not know Joseph.'[l] [19]The same took advantage of our race, and mistreated our fathers, and forced them to throw out their babies, so that they would

a 6:8 Some Mss read "faith"
b 7:3 Genesis 12:1
c 7:4 Or, Chaldeans
d 7:7 Genesis 15:13-14
e 7:7 Exodus 3:12
f 7:11 Some Mss lack "the land of"
g 7:14 Exodus 1:5
h 7:16 Some Mss read "the father of"
i 7:16 In Genesis 12:6-7 Abraham built an altar in Shechem, which would have required the purchase of land, apparently from the sons of Hamor. A descendant of the latter also named Hamor sold land in Shechem to Jacob in Genesis 33:19
j 7:17 Some Mss read "sworn"
k 7:18 Some Mss lack "over Egypt"
l 7:18 Exodus 1:8

not stay alive. ²⁰At that time Moses was born, and was exceedingly handsome. He was nourished three months in his father's house. ²¹When he was thrown out, Pharaoh's daughter took him up, and reared him as her own son. ²²Moses was instructed in all the wisdom of the Egyptians. He was mighty in his[a] words and works. ²³But when he was forty years old, it came into his heart to visit his brothers, the children of Israel. ²⁴Seeing one of them suffer wrong, he defended him, and avenged him who was oppressed, striking the Egyptian. ²⁵He supposed that his brothers understood that God, by his hand, was giving them deliverance; but they did not understand.

²⁶"The day following, he appeared to them as they fought, and urged them to be at peace again, saying, 'Men, you are brothers. Why do you wrong one another?' ²⁷But he who did his neighbor wrong pushed him away, saying, 'Who made you a ruler and a judge over us? ²⁸Do you want to kill me, as you killed the Egyptian yesterday?'[b] ²⁹Moses fled at this saying, and became a stranger in the land of Midian, where he became the father of two sons.

³⁰"When forty years were fulfilled, an angel[c] appeared to him in the wilderness of Mount Sinai, in a flame of fire in a bush. ³¹When Moses saw it, he wondered at the sight. As he came close to see, a voice of the Lord came,[d] ³²'I am the God of your fathers, the God of Abraham, and[e] of Isaac, and of Jacob.'[f] Moses trembled, and dared not look. ³³The Lord said to him, 'Take your sandals off of your feet, for the place where you stand is holy ground. ³⁴I have surely seen the affliction of my people that is in Egypt, and have heard their groaning. I have come down to deliver them. Now come, I will send you into Egypt.'[g]

³⁵"This Moses, whom they refused, saying, 'Who made you a ruler and a judge?'— God has sent him as both a ruler and a deliverer by the hand of the angel who appeared to him in the bush. ³⁶This man led them out, having worked wonders and signs in Egypt, in the Red Sea,[h] and in the

wilderness for forty years. ³⁷This is that Moses, who said to the children of Israel, 'God[i] will raise up a prophet for you from among your brothers, like me[j].'[k] ³⁸This is he who was in the assembly in the wilderness with the angel that spoke to him on Mount Sinai, and with our fathers, who received words of life[l] to give to us, ³⁹to whom our fathers would not be obedient, but rejected him, and turned back in their hearts to Egypt, ⁴⁰saying to Aaron, 'Make us gods that will go before us, for as for this Moses, who led us out of the land of Egypt, we do not know what has become of him.'[m] ⁴¹They made a calf in those days, and brought a sacrifice to the idol, and rejoiced in the works of their hands. ⁴²But God turned, and gave them over to worship the host of heaven, as it is written in the book of the prophets,

'Did you offer to me sacrifices and
offerings
forty years in the wilderness, O
house of Israel?
⁴³You took up the tabernacle of Moloch,
and the star of your[n] god Rephan,
the images which you made to worship
them.
I will carry you away[o] beyond
Babylon.'[p]

⁴⁴"Our fathers had the tabernacle of the testimony in the wilderness, even as he who spoke to Moses commanded him to make it according to the pattern that he had seen; ⁴⁵which also our fathers, in

---

a   7:22 Some Mss read "in"
b   7:28 Exodus 2:14
c   7:30 Some Mss add "of the Lord"
d   7:31 Some Mss add "to him"
e   7:32 Some Mss add (and before Jacob) "the God"
f   7:32 Exodus 3:6
g   7:34 Exodus 3:5,7-8,10
h   7:36 Gk. "Red Sea" for Hebrew Yam Suf, meaning "Sea of Reeds" or "Sea at the End"
i   7:37 Some Mss read "The Lord our God"
j   7:37 Some Mss add "him shall you hear"
k   7:37 Deuteronomy 18:15
l   7:38 Some Mss read "a living word"
m   7:40 Exodus 32:1
n   7:43 Some Mss lack "your"
o   7:43 Amos 5:25-27
p   7:43 They were taken beyond Damascus (Amos 5:27) and beyond Babylon, to as far as the cities of the Medes (2 Kings 17:6)

their turn, brought in with Joshua when they entered into the possession of the nations, whom God drove out before the face of our fathers, to the days of David, [46]who found favor in the sight of God, and asked to find a habitation for the God[a] of Jacob. [47]But Solomon built him a house. [48]However, the Most High does not dwell in temples made with hands, as the prophet says,

[49]'Heaven is my throne,

and the earth a footstool for my feet.
What kind of house will you build me?'
says the Lord;
'or what is the place of my rest?
[50]Did not my hand make all these
things?'[b]

[51]"You stiff-necked and uncircumcised in heart and ears, you always resist the Holy Spirit. As your fathers did, so you do. [52]Which of the prophets did not your fathers persecute? They killed those who foretold the coming of the Righteous One, of whom you have now become betrayers and murderers. [53]You received the Law as it was ordained by angels, and did not keep it."

[54]Now when they heard these things, they were cut to the heart, and they gnashed at him with their teeth. [55]But he, being full of the Holy Spirit, looked up steadfastly into heaven, and saw the glory of God, and Jesus standing on the right hand of God. [56]And he said, "Look, I see the heavens opened, and the Son of Man standing at the right hand of God."[c]

[57]But they shouted out with a loud voice, and stopped their ears, and rushed at him with one accord. [58]They threw him out of the city, and stoned him. The witnesses placed their garments at the feet of a young man named Saul. [59]They stoned Stephen as he called out, saying, "Lord Jesus, receive my spirit." [60]He kneeled down, and shouted out, "Lord, do not hold this sin against them." When he had said this, he fell asleep.

8 Saul was consenting to his death. A great persecution arose against the church which was in Jerusalem in that day.

They were all scattered abroad throughout the regions of Judea and Samaria, except for the apostles. [2]Devout men buried Stephen, and lamented greatly over him. [3]But Saul ravaged the church, entering into every house, and dragged both men and women off to prison. [4]Therefore those who were scattered abroad went around proclaiming the word. [5]And Philip[d] went down to the[e] city of Samaria, and proclaimed to them the Messiah. [6]The crowds listened with one accord to the things that were spoken by Philip, when they heard and saw the signs which he did. [7]For unclean spirits came out of many of those who had them. They came out, crying with a loud voice. Many who had been paralyzed and lame were healed. [8]There was great joy in that city.

[9]But there was a certain man, Simon by name, who used to practice sorcery in the city, and amazed the people of Samaria, making himself out to be some great one, [10]to whom they all listened, from the least to the greatest, saying, "This man is that power of God which is called Great.'" [11]They listened to him, because for a long time he had amazed them with his sorceries. [12]But when they believed Philip as he preached good news concerning the kingdom of God and the name of Jesus Christ, they were baptized, both men and women. [13]Simon himself also believed. Being baptized, he continued with Philip. Seeing signs and great[g] miracles occurring, he was amazed.

[14]Now when the apostles who were at Jerusalem heard that Samaria had received the word of God, they sent Peter and John to them, [15]who, when they had come down, prayed for them, that they might receive the Holy Spirit; [16]for he had not yet fallen upon any of them. They had

---

a   7:46 Some Mss read "house"
b   7:50 Isaiah 66:1-2
c   7:56 Daniel 7:13
d   8:5 This is apparently the Philip mentioned in Acts 6:5, also known in Acts 21:8 as an evangelist
e   8:5 Some Mss read "a city"
f   8:10 Some Mss read "great power of God"
g   8:13 Some Mss lack "great"

only been baptized in the name of the Lord Jesus[a]. [17]Then they laid their hands on them, and they received the Holy Spirit. [18]Now when Simon saw that the[b] Spirit was given through the laying on of the apostles' hands, he offered them money, [19]saying, "Give me also this power, that whomever I lay my hands on may receive the Holy Spirit." [20]But Peter said to him, "May your silver perish with you, because you thought you could obtain the gift of God with money. [21]You have neither part nor lot in this matter, for your heart is not right before God. [22]Repent therefore of this, your wickedness, and ask the Lord[c] if perhaps the thought of your heart may be forgiven you. [23]For I see that you are in the gall of bitterness and in the bondage of iniquity."

[24]Simon answered, "Pray for me to the Lord, that none of the things which you have spoken happen to me."

[25]They therefore, when they had testified and spoken the word of the Lord, returned to Jerusalem, and preached the Good News to many villages of the Samaritans. [26]But an angel of the Lord spoke to Philip, saying, "Arise, and go toward the south to the way that goes down from Jerusalem to Gaza. This is a desert."

[27]And he arose and went; and look, there was a man from Ethiopia, a eunuch of great authority under Candace, queen of the Ethiopians, who was over all her treasure, who had come to Jerusalem to worship. [28]He was returning and sitting in his chariot, and was reading the prophet Isaiah.

[29]The Spirit said to Philip, "Go near, and join yourself to this chariot."

[30]Philip ran to him, and heard him reading Isaiah the prophet, and said, "Do you understand what you are reading?"

[31]He said, "How can I, unless someone explains it to me?" He begged Philip to come up and sit with him. [32]Now the passage of the Scripture which he was reading was this,

"He was led as a sheep to the slaughter.
As a lamb before his shearer is silent,

so he does not open his mouth.
[33]In his[d] humiliation his justice was
    taken away.[e]
Who will declare his generation?
For his life is taken from the earth."[f]
[34]The eunuch answered Philip, "Who is the prophet talking about? About himself, or about someone else?"

[35]Philip opened his mouth, and beginning from this Scripture, preached to him Jesus. [36]And as they went on the way, they came to some water, and the eunuch said, "Look, here is water. What is keeping me from being baptized?" [37g] [38]He commanded the chariot to stand still, and they both went down into the water, both Philip and the eunuch, and he baptized him.

[39]When they came up out of the water, the Spirit of the Lord caught Philip away, and the eunuch did not see him any more, for he went on his way rejoicing. [40]But Philip was found at Azotus. Passing through, he preached the Good News to all the cities, until he came to Caesarea.

9 But Saul, still breathing threats and slaughter against the disciples of the Lord, went to the high priest, [2]and asked for letters from him to the synagogues of Damascus, that if he found any who were of the Way, whether men or women, he might bring them bound to Jerusalem. [3]As he traveled, it happened that he got close to Damascus, and suddenly a light from the sky shone around him. [4]He fell on the earth, and heard a voice saying to him, "Saul, Saul, why do you persecute me?[h]"

[5]He said, "Who are you, Lord?"

---

a   8:16 Some Mss read "Christ Jesus"

b   8:18 Some Mss add "Holy"

c   8:22 Some Mss read "God"

d   8:33 Some Mss lack "his"

e   8:33 Some Mss add "and"

f   8:33 Isaiah 53:7, 8

g   8:37 Some Mss add "Philip said, 'If you believe with all your heart, you may.' He answered, 'I believe that Jesus Christ is the Son of God." The earliest manuscript having this verse is the sixth century

h   9:4 Some Mss add "It is hard for you to kick against the goads." See Acts 26:14

The Lord said, "I am Jesus, whom you are persecuting. [6]But rise up, and enter into the city, and you will be told what you must do."

[7]The men who traveled with him stood speechless, hearing the sound, but seeing no one. [8]Saul arose from the ground, and when his eyes were opened, he saw no one. They led him by the hand, and brought him into Damascus. [9]He was without sight for three days, and neither ate nor drank.

[10]Now there was a certain disciple at Damascus named Ananias. The Lord said to him in a vision, "Ananias." And he said, "Look, it's me, Lord."

[11]The Lord said to him, "Arise, and go to the street which is called Straight, and inquire in the house of Judas for one named Saul, a man of Tarsus. For look, he is praying, [12]and in a vision he has seen a man named Ananias coming in, and laying his hands on him, that he might receive his sight."

[13]But Ananias answered, "Lord, I have heard from many about this man, how much evil he did to your saints at Jerusalem. [14]Here he has authority from the chief priests to bind all who call on your name."

[15]But the Lord said to him, "Go your way, for he is my chosen vessel to bear my name before the nations and kings, and the sons of Israel. [16]For I will show him how many things he must suffer for my name's sake."

[17]Ananias departed, and entered into the house. Laying his hands on him, he said, "Brother Saul, the Lord, who appeared to you on the road by which you came, has sent me, that you may receive your sight, and be filled with the Holy Spirit." [18]Immediately something like scales fell from his eyes, and he received his sight. He arose and was baptized. [19]He took food and was strengthened. He[a] stayed several days with the disciples who were at Damascus. [20]Immediately in the synagogues he proclaimed Jesus,[b] that he is the Son of God. [21]All who heard him were amazed, and said, "Is not this he who in Jerusalem made havoc of those who called on this name? And he had come here intending to bring them bound before the chief priests."

[22]But Saul increased more in strength, and confounded the Jews who lived at Damascus, proving that this is the Messiah. [23]When many days were fulfilled, the Jews conspired together to kill him, [24]but their plot became known to Saul. They watched the gates both day and night that they might kill him, [25]but his disciples took him by night, and let him down through the wall, lowering him in a basket. [26]When Saul had come to Jerusalem, he tried to join himself to the disciples; but they were all afraid of him, not believing that he was a disciple. [27]But Barnabas took him, and brought him to the apostles, and declared to them how he had seen the Lord in the way, and that he had spoken to him, and how at Damascus he had preached boldly in the name of Jesus. [28]He was with them coming in and going out[c] in Jerusalem, speaking boldly in the name of the Lord.[d] [29]He spoke and disputed against the Hellenists, but they were seeking to kill him. [30]When the brothers knew it, they brought him down to Caesarea, and sent him off to Tarsus. [31]So the church[e] throughout all Judea and Galilee and Samaria had peace, and were built up. They were multiplied, walking in the fear of the Lord and in the comfort of the Holy Spirit.

[32]It happened, as Peter went throughout all those parts, he came down also to the saints who lived at Lydda. [33]There he found a certain man named Aeneas, who had been bedridden for eight years, because he was paralyzed. [34]Peter said to him, "Aeneas, Jesus Christ heals you. Get up and make your bed." Immediately he arose. [35]All who lived at Lydda and in Sharon saw him, and they turned to the Lord.

[36]Now there was at Joppa a certain disciple named Tabitha (which when

---

a   9:19 Some Mss read "Saul"
b   9:20 Some Mss read "Christ"
c   9:28 Some Mss lack "and going out"
d   9:29 Some Mss add "Jesus"
e   9:31 Some Mss read "churches"

translated, means Dorcas).[a] This woman was full of good works and acts of mercy which she did. [37]It happened in those days that she fell sick, and died. When they had washed her, they placed her in an upper chamber. [38]As Lydda was near Joppa, the disciples, hearing that Peter was there, sent two men[b] to him, imploring him not to delay in coming to us.[c] [39]Peter got up and went with them. When he had come, they brought him into the upper chamber. All the widows stood by him weeping, and showing the coats and garments which Dorcas had made while she was with them. [40]Peter put them all out, and kneeled down and prayed. Turning to the body, he said, "Tabitha, get up." She opened her eyes, and when she saw Peter, she sat up. [41]He gave her his hand, and raised her up. Calling the saints and widows, he presented her alive. [42]And it became known throughout all Joppa, and many believed in the Lord. [43]It happened, that he stayed many days in Joppa with one Simon, a tanner.

10 Now there was a certain man in Caesarea, Cornelius by name, a centurion of what was called the Italian Regiment, [2]a devout man, and one who feared God with all his house, who gave gifts for the needy generously to the people, and always prayed to God. [3]At about three in the afternoon[d] he clearly saw in a vision an angel of God coming to him, and saying to him, "Cornelius."

[4]He, fastening his eyes on him, and being frightened, said, "What is it, Lord?"

He said to him, "Your prayers and your gifts to the needy have gone up for a memorial before God. [5]Now send men to Joppa, and get Simon, who is surnamed Peter. [6]He lodges with one Simon, a tanner, whose house is by the seaside.[e]"

[7]When the angel who spoke to him[f] had departed, he called two of his household servants and a devout soldier of those who waited on him continually. [8]Having explained everything to them, he sent them to Joppa. [9]Now on the next day as they were on their journey, and got close to the city, Peter went up on the housetop to pray at about noon. [10]He became hungry and desired to eat, but while they were preparing, he fell into a trance. [11]He saw heaven opened and a certain container descending to him, like a great sheet let down[g] by four corners on the earth, [12]in which were all kinds of four-footed animals of the earth,[h] crawling creatures and birds of the sky. [13]A voice came to him, "Rise, Peter, kill and eat."

[14]But Peter said, "Not so, Lord; for I have never eaten anything that is common or unclean."

[15]A voice came to him again the second time, "What God has cleansed, you must not call unclean." [16]This was done three times, and immediately the vessel was received up into heaven. [17]Now while Peter was very perplexed in himself what the vision which he had seen might mean, look, the men who were sent by Cornelius, having made inquiry for Simon's house, stood before the gate, [18]and called and asked whether Simon, who was surnamed Peter, was lodging there. [19]While Peter was pondering the vision, the Spirit said to him, "Look, three[i] men seek you. [20]But arise, get down, and go with them, doubting nothing; for I have sent them."

[21]Peter went down to the men,[j] and said, "Look, I am the one whom you seek. Why have you come?"

[22]They said, "Cornelius, a centurion, a righteous man and one who fears God, and well spoken of by all the Jewish nation, was directed by a holy angel to invite you

---

a   9:36 "Dorcas" is Greek for "Gazelle"
b   9:38 Some Mss read "messengers"
c   9:38 Some Mss read "them"
d   10:3 Lit. the ninth hour
e   10:6 Some Mss add "This one will tell you what it is necessary for you to do"
f   10:7 Some Mss read "Cornelius"
g   10:11 Some Mss read "tied"
h   10:12 Some Mss add "wild beasts"
i   10:19 Some Mss lack "three"
j   10:21 Some Mss add "which were sent to him from Cornelius"

to his house, and to listen to what you say." [23]So he called them in and lodged them. On the next day he[a] arose and went out with them, and some of the brothers from Joppa accompanied him. [24]On the next day he[b] entered into Caesarea. Cornelius was waiting for them, having called together his relatives and his near friends. [25]When it happened that Peter entered, Cornelius met him, fell down at his feet, and worshiped him. [26]But Peter raised him up, saying, "Stand up. I myself am also a man." [27]And as he talked with him, he went in and found many gathered together. [28]He said to them, "You yourselves know how it is an unlawful thing for a man who is a Jew to join himself or come to one of another nation, but God has shown me that I should not call any man unholy or unclean. [29]Therefore also I came without complaint when I was sent for. I ask therefore, why did you send for me?"

[30]Cornelius said, "Four days ago[c] until this hour, at three in the afternoon[d], I was praying in my house, and look, a man stood before me in bright clothing, [31]and said, 'Cornelius, your prayer is heard, and your gifts to the needy are remembered in the sight of God. [32]Send therefore to Joppa and summon Simon, who is surnamed Peter. He lodges in the house of Simon, a tanner,[e] by the seaside.'[f] [33]Therefore I sent to you at once, and it was good of you to come. Now therefore we are all here present in the sight of God to hear all things that have been commanded you by the Lord.[g]"

[34]And Peter opened his mouth and said, "Truly I perceive that God does not show favoritism; [35]but in every nation he who fears him and works righteousness is acceptable to him. [36]The word which[h] he sent to the sons of Israel, preaching good news of peace through Jesus Christ—he is Lord of all—[37]that spoken word you yourselves know, which was proclaimed throughout all Judea, beginning from Galilee, after the baptism which John preached; [38]even Jesus of Nazareth, how God anointed him with the Holy Spirit and with power, who went about doing good and healing all who were oppressed by the devil, for God was with him. [39]We are witnesses of everything he did both in the land of the Jews and in Jerusalem, whom they also[i] killed by hanging on a tree. [40]God raised him up the third day, and gave him to be revealed, [41]not to all the people, but to witnesses who were chosen before by God, to us, who ate and drank with him after he rose from the dead. [42]He commanded us to proclaim to the people and to testify that this is he who is appointed by God as the Judge of the living and the dead. [43]All the prophets testify about him, that through his name everyone who believes in him receives forgiveness of sins."

[44]While Peter was still speaking these words, the Holy Spirit fell on all those who heard the word. [45]They of the circumcision who believed were amazed, as many as came with Peter, because the gift of the Holy Spirit was also poured out on the non-Jewish people. [46]For they heard them speaking in other tongues and magnifying God.

Then Peter answered, [47]"Can anyone withhold the water, that these who have received the Holy Spirit as well as we should not be baptized?" [48]He commanded them to be baptized in the name of Jesus Christ.[j] Then they asked him to stay some days.

11 Now the apostles and the brothers who were in Judea heard that the non-Jewish people had also received the word of God. [2]When Peter had come up to Jerusalem, those who were of the circumcision contended with him, [3]saying, "You went in to uncircumcised men, and ate with them."

---

a   10:23 Some Mss read "Peter"
b   10:24 Some Mss read "they"
c   10:30 Some Mss add "I was fasting"
d   10:30 Lit. the ninth hour
e   10:32 Or, Simon Berseus
f   10:32 Some Mss add "When he comes, he will speak to you"
g   10:33 Some Mss read "God"
h   10:36 Some Mss lack "which"
i   10:39 Some Mss lack "also"
j   10:48 Some Mss read "the Lord"

[4]But Peter began, and explained to them in order, saying, [5]"I was in the city of Joppa praying, and in a trance I saw a vision: a certain container descending, like it was a great sheet let down from heaven by four corners. It came as far as me. [6]When I had looked intently at it, I considered, and saw the four-footed animals of the earth, wild animals, crawling creatures, and birds of the sky. [7]I also heard a voice saying to me, 'Rise, Peter, kill and eat.' [8]But I said, 'Not so, Lord, for nothing unholy or unclean has ever entered into my mouth.' [9]But a voice answered[a] the second time out of heaven, 'What God has cleansed, do not call unclean.' [10]This was done three times, and all were drawn up again into heaven. [11]And look, immediately three men stood before the house where we were, having been sent from Caesarea to me. [12]The Spirit told me to go with them, without discriminating.[b] These six brothers also accompanied me, and we entered into the man's house. [13]He told us how he had seen the angel standing in his house, and saying to him, 'Send to Joppa, and get Simon, whose surname is Peter, [14]who will speak to you words by which you will be saved, you and all your house.' [15]As I began to speak, the Holy Spirit fell on them, even as on us at the beginning. [16]I remembered the word of the Lord, how he said, 'John indeed baptized in water, but you will be baptized in the Holy Spirit.'[c] [17]If then God gave to them the same gift as us, when we believed in the Lord Jesus Christ, who was I, that I could withstand God?"

[18]When they heard these things, they held their peace, and glorified God, saying, "Then God has also granted to the non-Jews repentance to life."

[19]They therefore who were scattered abroad by the oppression that arose about Stephen traveled as far as Phoenicia, Cyprus, and Antioch, speaking the word to no one except to Jews only. [20]But there were some of them, men of Cyprus and Cyrene, who, when they had come to Antioch, spoke to the Greeks,[d] proclaiming the good news of the Lord Jesus. [21]The hand of the Lord was with them, and a great number believed and turned to the Lord. [22]The report concerning them came to the ears of the church which was in Jerusalem. They sent out Barnabas to go as far as Antioch, [23]who, when he had come, and had seen the grace of God, was glad. He exhorted them all, that with purpose of heart they should remain true to the Lord. [24]For he was a good man, and full of the Holy Spirit and of faith, and many people were added to the Lord.

[25]Barnabas went out to Tarsus to look for Saul. [26]When he had found him, he brought him to Antioch. It happened, that for a whole year they were gathered together with the church, and taught many people. The disciples were first called Christians in Antioch.

[27]Now in these days, prophets came down from Jerusalem to Antioch. [28]One of them named Agabus stood up, and indicated by the Spirit that there should be a great famine all over the world, which also happened in the days of Claudius.[e] [29]As any of the disciples had plenty, each determined to send relief to the brothers who lived in Judea; [30]which they also did, sending it to the elders by the hands of Barnabas and Saul.

12 Now about that time, Herod the king stretched out his hands to oppress some of the church. [2]He killed James, the brother of John, with the sword. [3]When he saw that it pleased the Jewish people, he proceeded to seize Peter also. This was during the days of unleavened bread. [4]When he had arrested him, he put him in prison, and delivered him to four squads of four soldiers each to guard him, intending to bring him out to the people after the Passover. [5]Peter therefore was kept in the prison, but constant prayer was made by the church to God for him. [6]The same night

a   11:9 Some Mss add "me"
b   11:12 Some Mss read "doubting nothing"
c   11:16 Acts 1:5
d   11:20 Or, "Hellenists," someone who spoke Greek
e   11:28 Some Mss add "Caesar"

when Herod was about to bring him out, Peter was sleeping between two soldiers, bound with two chains. Guards in front of the door kept the prison. [7]And look, an angel of the Lord stood by him, and a light shone in the cell. He struck Peter on the side, and woke him up, saying, "Stand up quickly." His chains fell off from his hands. [8]The angel said to him, "Get dressed and put on your sandals." He did so. He said to him, "Put on your cloak, and follow me." [9]And he went out and followed him. He did not know that what was being done by the angel was real, but thought he saw a vision. [10]When they were past the first and the second guard, they came to the iron gate that leads into the city, which opened to them by itself. They went out, and went down one street, and immediately the angel departed from him.

[11]When Peter had come to himself, he said, "Now I truly know that the Lord has sent out his angel and delivered me out of the hand of Herod, and from everything the Jewish people were expecting." [12]Thinking about that, he came to the house of Mary, the mother of John whose surname was Mark, where many were gathered together and were praying. [13]And when Peter knocked at the door of the gate, a servant girl named Rhoda came to answer. [14]When she recognized Peter's voice, she did not open the gate for joy, but ran in, and reported that Peter was standing in front of the gate.

[15]They said to her, "You are crazy." But she insisted that it was so. They said, "It is his angel." [16]But Peter continued knocking. When they had opened, they saw him, and were amazed. [17]But he, beckoning to them with his hand to be silent, declared to them how the Lord had brought him out of the prison. He said, "Tell these things to James, and to the brothers." Then he departed, and went to another place.

[18]Now as soon as it was day, there was no small stir among the soldiers about what had become of Peter. [19]When Herod had sought for him, and did not find him, he examined the guards, and commanded that they should be put to death. He went down from Judea to Caesarea, and stayed there. [20]Now Herod was very angry with the people of Tyre and Sidon. They came with one accord to him, and, having made Blastus, the king's personal aide, their friend, they asked for peace, because their country depended on the king's country for food. [21]On an appointed day, Herod dressed himself in royal clothing, and[a] sat on the throne, and gave a speech to them. [22]But the crowd shouted, "The voice of a god, and not of a man." [23]Immediately an angel of the Lord struck him, because he did not give God the glory, and he was eaten by worms and died.

[24]But the word of God grew and multiplied. [25]Barnabas and Saul returned to[b] Jerusalem, when they had fulfilled their service, also taking with them John whose surname was Mark.

13 Now in the church that was at Antioch there were some prophets and teachers: Barnabas, Simeon who was called Niger, Lucius of Cyrene, Manaen the foster brother of Herod the tetrarch, and Saul. [2]As they served the Lord and fasted, the Holy Spirit said, "Separate Barnabas and Saul for me, for the work to which I have called them."

[3]Then, when they had fasted and prayed and laid their hands on them, they sent them away. [4]So, being sent out by the Holy Spirit, they went down to Seleucia. From there they sailed to Cyprus. [5]When they were at Salamis, they proclaimed the word of God in the Jewish synagogues. They had also John as their attendant. [6]When they had gone through the whole[c] island as far as Paphos, they found a certain man, a sorcerer, a false prophet, a Jew, whose name was Bar-Jesus, [7]who was with the proconsul, Sergius Paulus, a man of understanding. This man summoned Barnabas

---

a   12:21 Some Mss lack "and"
b   12:25 Some Mss read "from"
c   13:6 Some Mss lack "whole"

and Saul, and sought to hear the word of God. [8]But Elymas the sorcerer (for so is his name by interpretation) withstood them, seeking to turn aside the proconsul from the faith. [9]But Saul, who is also called Paul, filled with the Holy Spirit, fastened his eyes on him, [10]and said, "Full of all deceit and all fraud, you son of the devil, you enemy of all righteousness, will you not cease to pervert the right ways of the Lord? [11]Now, look, the hand of the Lord is on you, and you will be blind, unable to see the sun for a time."

Immediately a mist and darkness fell on him. He went around seeking someone to lead him by the hand. [12]Then the proconsul, when he saw what was done, believed, being astonished at the teaching of the Lord.

[13]Now Paul and his company set sail from Paphos, and came to Perga in Pamphylia, and John departed from them and returned to Jerusalem. [14]But they, passing on from Perga, came to Antioch of Pisidia. They went into the synagogue on the Sabbath day, and sat down. [15]After the reading of the Law and the Prophets, the rulers of the synagogue sent to them, saying, "Brothers, if you have any word of exhortation for the people, speak."

[16]Paul stood up, and beckoning with his hand said, "Men of Israel, and you who fear God, listen. [17]The God of this people Israel[a] chose our fathers, and exalted the people when they stayed as foreigners in the land of Egypt, and with an uplifted arm, he led them out of it. [18]For a period of about forty years he put up with them in the wilderness. [19]When he had destroyed seven nations in the land of Canaan, he gave them their land as an inheritance. [20]And after these things, about four hundred and fifty years,[b] he gave them judges, until Samuel the prophet. [21]Afterward they asked for a king, and God gave to them Saul the son of Kish, a man of the tribe of Benjamin, for forty years. [22]When he had removed him, he raised up David to be their king, to whom he also testified, 'I have found David the son of Jesse, a man after my heart, who will do all my will.' [23]From this man's off-

spring, according to his promise,[c] God has brought to Israel a Savior, Jesus,[d] [24]before his coming, when John had first preached the baptism of repentance to all the people of Israel.[e] [25]As John was fulfilling his course, he said, 'What do you suppose that I am? I am not he. But look, one comes after me the sandals of whose feet I am not worthy to untie.' [26]Brothers, children of the stock of Abraham, and those among you who fear God, the word of this salvation is sent out to us.[f] [27]For those who dwell in Jerusalem, and their rulers, because they did not know him, nor the voices of the prophets which are read every Sabbath, fulfilled them by condemning him. [28]Though they found no cause for death, they still asked Pilate to have him killed. [29]When they had fulfilled all things that were written about him, they took him down from the tree, and placed him in a tomb. [30]But God raised him from the dead, [31]and he was seen for many days by those who came up with him from Galilee to Jerusalem, who are his witnesses to the people. [32]We bring you good news of the promise made to the fathers, [33]that God has fulfilled the same to us, their children, in that he raised up Jesus. As it is also written in the second psalm, 'You are my Son. Today I have become your father.'[g]

[34]"Concerning that he raised him up from the dead, now no more to return to corruption, he has spoken thus: 'I will give to you the faithful sacred things of David.' [35]Therefore he says also in another psalm, 'You will not allow your Holy One to see decay.'[h] [36]For David, after he had in his own generation served the counsel of God, fell asleep, and was placed with his

---

a   13:17 Some Mss lack "Israel"
b   13:20 E.g., 400 (years of slavery in Egypt) + 40 (years of wilderness sojourn) + 7 years (approx. years of conquest of Canaan) = 447 years, which is "about 450 years"
c   13:23 Psalm 132:11
d   13:23 Some Mss read "salvation"
e   13:24 Some Mss read "to Israel"
f   13:26 Some Mss read "you"
g   13:33 Psalm 2:7
h   13:35 Psalm 16:10

fathers, and saw decay. [37]But he whom God raised up saw no decay. [38]Be it known to you therefore, brothers, that through this man is proclaimed to you remission of sins, [39]and by him everyone who believes is justified from all things, from which you could not be justified by the Law of Moses. [40]Beware therefore, lest that come on you which is spoken in the Prophets:

[41]'Look, you scoffers, and be amazed,
and perish; for I am working
a work in your days, a work[a]
which you will not believe, if
one tells it to you.'"[b]

[42]So when they went out they[c] begged that these words might be preached to them the next Sabbath. [43]Now when the synagogue broke up, many of the Jews and of the devout proselytes followed Paul and Barnabas; who, speaking to them, urged them to continue in the grace of God. [44]The next Sabbath almost the whole city was gathered together to hear the word of the Lord.[d] [45]But when the Jews saw the crowds, they were filled with jealousy, and contradicted the things which were spoken by Paul, and reviled him.

[46]Paul and Barnabas spoke out boldly, and said, "It was necessary that God's word should be spoken to you first. Since indeed you thrust it from you, and judge yourselves unworthy of everlasting life, look, we turn to the non-Jewish people. [47]For so has the Lord commanded us, saying, 'I have set you as a light to the nations, that you may bring salvation to the farthest part of the earth.'"[e]

[48]As the non-Jewish people heard this, they were glad, and glorified the word of God. As many as were appointed to everlasting life believed. [49]The Lord's word was spread abroad throughout all the region. [50]But the Jews stirred up the devout and prominent women and the chief men of the city, and stirred up a persecution against Paul and Barnabas, and threw them out of their borders. [51]But they shook off the dust of their feet against them, and came to Iconium. [52]The disciples were filled with joy with the Holy Spirit.

14 It happened in Iconium that they entered together into the Jewish synagogue, and so spoke that a great number of both of Jews and of Greeks believed. [2]But the disbelieving[f] Jews stirred up and embittered the souls of the non-Jewish people against the brothers. [3]Therefore they stayed there a long time, speaking boldly in the Lord, who testified to the word of his grace, granting signs and wonders to be done by their hands. [4]But the population of the city was divided. Some sided with the Jews, and some with the apostles. [5]When some of both the non-Jewish people and the Jews, with their rulers, made a violent attempt to mistreat and stone them, [6]they became aware of it, and fled to the cities of Lycaonia, Lystra, Derbe, and the surrounding region. [7]There they preached the Good News.

[8]At Lystra a certain man sat, without strength in his feet, a cripple from his mother's womb, who never had walked. [9]He was listening to Paul speaking, who, fastening eyes on him, and seeing that he had faith to be made whole, [10]said with a loud voice, "Stand upright on your feet." He leaped up and walked. [11]When the crowd saw what Paul had done, they lifted up their voice, saying in the language of Lycaonia, "The gods have come down to us in human form." [12]They called Barnabas "Jupiter," and Paul "Mercury," because he was the chief speaker. [13]The priest of Jupiter, whose temple was in front of their city, brought oxen and garlands to the gates, and would have made a sacrifice along with the crowds. [14]But when the apostles, Barnabas and Paul, heard of it, they tore their clothes, and sprang into the crowd, crying out, [15]"Men, why are you doing these things? We also are men of like passions with you, and bring you good news, that you should turn from these

---

a   13:41 Some Mss lack "a work"
b   13:41 Habakkuk 1:5
c   13:42 Some Mss read "the Jews went out of the synagogue, the non-Jews"
d   13:44 Some Mss read "God"
e   13:47 Isaiah 49:6
f   14:2 Or, "disobedient"

vain things to the living God, who made the sky and the earth and the sea, and all that is in them; [16]who in the generations gone by allowed all the nations to walk in their own ways. [17]Yet he did not leave himself without witness, in that he did good and gave you rains from the sky and fruitful seasons, filling your[a] hearts with food and gladness."

[18]Even saying these things, they hardly stopped the crowds from making a sacrifice to them. [19]But some Jews from Antioch and Iconium came there, and having persuaded the crowds, they stoned Paul, and dragged him out of the city, supposing that he was dead.

[20]But as the disciples stood around him, he rose up, and entered into the city. On the next day he went out with Barnabas to Derbe. [21]When they had preached the Good News to that city, and had made many disciples, they returned to Lystra, Iconium, and Antioch, [22]confirming the souls of the disciples, exhorting them to continue in the faith, and that through many afflictions we must enter into the kingdom of God. [23]When they had appointed elders for them in every church, and had prayed with fasting, they commended them to the Lord, on whom they had believed.

[24]They passed through Pisidia, and came to Pamphylia. [25]When they had spoken the word in Perga, they went down to Attalia. [26]From there they sailed to Antioch, from where they had been committed to the grace of God for the work which they had fulfilled. [27]When they had arrived, and had gathered the church together, they reported all the things that God had done with them, and that he had opened a door of faith to the nations. [28]They stayed there with the disciples for a long time.

15 Some men came down from Judea and taught the brothers, "Unless you are circumcised after the custom of Moses, you cannot be saved." [2]Therefore when Paul and Barnabas had no small discord and discussion with them, they appointed Paul and Barnabas, and some others of them, to go up to Jerusalem to the apostles and elders about this question. [3]They, being sent on their way by the church, passed through both Phoenicia and Samaria, declaring the conversion of the non-Jewish people. They caused great joy to all the brothers. [4]When they had come to Jerusalem, they were received by the church and the apostles and the elders, and they reported all things that God had done with them.

[5]But some of the sect of the Pharisees who believed rose up, saying, "It is necessary to circumcise them, and to command them to keep the Law of Moses."

[6]The apostles and the elders were gathered together to see about this matter. [7]When there had been much discussion, Peter rose up and said to them, "Brothers, you know that a good while ago God made a choice among you,[b] that by my mouth the nations should hear the word of the Good News, and believe. [8]God, who knows the heart, testified about them, giving them the Holy Spirit, just like he did to us. [9]He made no distinction between us and them, cleansing their hearts by faith. [10]Now therefore why do you tempt God, that you should put a yoke on the neck of the disciples which neither our fathers nor we were able to bear? [11]But we believe that we are saved through the grace of the Lord Jesus, just as they are."

[12]And all the people kept quiet, and they listened to Barnabas and Paul reporting what signs and wonders God had done among the nations through them. [13]After they were silent, James answered, "Brothers, listen to me. [14]Simeon has reported how God first visited the nations, to take out of them a people for his name. [15]This agrees with the words of the prophets. As it is written,

[16]"After these things I will return,
     and I will rebuild the tent of David,
          which has fallen.
     I will rebuild its ruins.
     I will set it up,

---

[17]that the rest of humanity may seek after the Lord,
and all the nations who are called by my name,
says the Lord, who makes[a] these things [18]known from long ago.[b]

[19]"Therefore my judgment is that we do not trouble those from among the non-Jewish people who turn to God, [20]but that we write to them that they abstain from the pollution of idols, from sexual immorality, from what is strangled, and from blood. [21]For Moses from generations of old has in every city those who proclaim him, being read in the synagogues every Sabbath."

[22]Then it seemed good to the apostles and the elders, with the whole church, to choose men out of their company, and send them to Antioch with Paul and Barnabas: Judas called Barsabbas, and Silas, chief men among the brothers. [23]They wrote these things by their hand:

"The apostles, the elders, and the brothers, to the brothers who are of the non-Jewish brothers in Antioch, Syria, and Cilicia: greetings. [24]Because we have heard that some who went out[c] from us have troubled you with words, unsettling your souls,[d] to whom we gave no commandment; [25]it seemed good to us, having come to one accord, to choose out men and send them to you with our beloved Barnabas and Paul, [26]who have risked their lives for the name of our Lord Jesus Christ. [27]We have sent therefore Judas and Silas, who themselves will also tell you the same things by word of mouth. [28]For it seemed good to the Holy Spirit, and to us, to lay no greater burden on you than these necessary things: [29]that you abstain from things sacrificed to idols, from blood, from things strangled, and from sexual immorality, from which if you keep yourselves, it will be well with you. Farewell."

[30]So, when they were sent off, they came to Antioch, and having gathered the congregation together, they delivered the letter. [31]When they had read it, they rejoiced over the encouragement. [32]Judas and Silas, also being prophets themselves, encouraged the brothers with many words, and strengthened them. [33]After they had spent some time there, they were sent back with greetings from the brothers to those that had sent them forth.[e] [34][f] [35]But Paul and Barnabas stayed in Antioch, teaching and proclaiming the word of the Lord, with many others also.

[36]After some days Paul said to Barnabas, "Let us return now and visit our brothers in every city in which we proclaimed the word of the Lord, to see how they are doing." [37]Barnabas planned to take John, who was called Mark, with them also. [38]But Paul did not think that it was a good idea to take with them someone who had withdrawn from them in Pamphylia, and did not go with them to do the work. [39]Then the contention grew so sharp that they separated from each other. Barnabas took Mark with him, and sailed away to Cyprus, [40]but Paul chose Silas, and went out, being commended by the brothers to the grace of the Lord.[g] [41]He went through Syria and Cilicia, strengthening the churches.

16 He came to Derbe and Lystra. And look, a certain disciple was there, named Timothy, the son of a Jewess who believed; but his father was a Greek. [2]The brothers who were at Lystra and Iconium gave a good testimony about him. [3]Paul wanted to have him go out with him, and he took and circumcised him because of the Jews who were in those parts; for they all knew that his father was a Greek. [4]As they went on their way through the cities, they delivered the decrees to them to keep which had been ordained by the apostles and elders who were at Jerusalem. [5]So the churches were strengthened in the faith, and increased in number daily.

---

a   15:17 Some Mss add "all"
b   15:17 Amos 9:11-12. Some Mss add "to God is all his works"
c   15:24 Some Mss lack "went out"
d   15:24 Some Mss add "saying, You must be circumcised and keep the law"
e   15:33 Some Mss read "the apostles"
f   15:34 Some Mss add "But it seemed good to Silas that they should remain"
g   15:40 Some Mss read "God"

[6]When they had gone through the region of Phrygia and Galatia, they were forbidden by the Holy Spirit to speak the word in Asia. [7]When they had come opposite Mysia, they tried to go into Bithynia, but the Spirit of Jesus[a] did not allow them. [8]Passing by Mysia, they came down to Troas. [9]A vision appeared to Paul in the night. There was a man of Macedonia standing, begging him, and saying, "Come over into Macedonia and help us." [10]When he had seen the vision, immediately we sought to go out to Macedonia, concluding that the Lord had called us to proclaim the Good News to them. [11]So, setting sail from Troas, we made a straight course to Samothrace, and the day following to Neapolis; [12]and from there to Philippi, which is a principle city of that district[b] of Macedonia, a colony. We were staying some days in this[c] city.

[13]On the Sabbath day we went forth outside of the gate[d] by a riverside, where we supposed there was a place of prayer,[e] and we sat down, and spoke to the women who had come together. [14]A certain woman named Lydia, a seller of purple, of the city of Thyatira, one who worshiped God, heard us; whose heart the Lord opened to listen to the things which were spoken by Paul. [15]When she and her household were baptized, she begged us, saying, "If you have judged me to be faithful to the Lord, come into my house, and stay." So she persuaded us.

[16]It happened, as we were going to prayer, that a certain girl having a spirit of Python[f] met us, who brought her masters much gain by fortune telling. [17]She followed Paul and us, shouting, "These men are servants of the Most High God, who proclaim to you[g] the way of salvation." [18]She was doing this for many days.

But Paul, becoming greatly annoyed, turned and said to the spirit, "I command you in the name of Jesus Christ to come out of her." And it came out at once. [19]But when her masters saw that the hope of their gain was gone, they seized Paul and Silas, and dragged them into the marketplace before the rulers. [20]When they had brought them to the magistrates, they said, "These men, being Jews, are agitating our city, [21]and set forth customs which it is not lawful for us to accept or to observe, being Romans."

[22]The crowd rose up together against them, and the magistrates tore their clothes off of them, and commanded them to be beaten with rods. [23]When they had laid many stripes on them, they threw them into prison, charging the jailer to keep them safely, [24]who, having received such a command, threw them into the inner prison, and secured their feet in the stocks.

[25]But about midnight Paul and Silas were praying and singing hymns to God, and the prisoners were listening to them. [26]Suddenly there was a great earthquake, so that the foundations of the prison were shaken; and immediately all the doors were opened, and everyone's bonds were loosened. [27]The jailer, being roused out of sleep and seeing the prison doors open, drew his sword and was about to kill himself, supposing that the prisoners had escaped. [28]But Paul shouted loudly, saying, "Do not harm yourself, for we are all here."

[29]He called for lights and sprang in, and, fell down trembling before Paul and Silas, [30]and brought them out and said, "Sirs, what must I do to be saved?"

[31]They said, "Believe in the Lord Jesus Christ, and you will be saved, you and your household." [32]They spoke the word of the Lord to him, and to all who were in his house.

[33]He took them the same hour of the night, and washed their stripes, and was immediately baptized, he and all his household. [34]He brought them up into his house, and set food before them, and rejoiced greatly, with all his household, having believed in God.

---

a   16:7 Some Mss lack "Jesus"
b   16:12 Lit., "first of that district"
d   16:12 Some Mss read "that very city"
d   16:13 Some Mss read "city"
e   16:13 Some Mss read "prayer was customarily to be"
f   16:16 Or, "divination"
g   16:17 Some Mss read "us"

[35]But when it was day, the magistrates sent the sergeants, saying, "Let those men go."

[36]The jailer reported these[a] words to Paul, saying, "The magistrates have sent to let you go; now therefore come out, and go in peace."

[37]But Paul said to them, "They have beaten us publicly, without a trial, men who are Romans, and have cast us into prison. Do they now release us secretly? No indeed. Let them come themselves and bring us out."

[38]The sergeants reported these words to the magistrates, and they were afraid when they heard that they were Romans, [39]and they came and begged them. When they had brought them out, they asked them to depart from the city. [40]They went out of the prison, and entered into Lydia's house. When they had seen the brothers, they encouraged them, and departed.

17 Now when they had passed through Amphipolis and Apollonia, they came to Thessalonica, where there was a Jewish synagogue. [2]Paul, as was his custom, went in to them, and for three Sabbath days reasoned with them from the Scriptures, [3]explaining and demonstrating that the Messiah had to suffer and rise again from the dead, and saying, "This Jesus, whom I proclaim to you, is the Messiah."

[4]Some of them were persuaded, and joined Paul and Silas, as did a large number of the devout Greeks, and not a few of the prominent women. [5]But the Jews, being moved with jealousy,[b] took along some wicked men from the marketplace, and gathering a crowd, set the city in an uproar. Assaulting the house of Jason, they sought to bring them out to the people. [6]When they did not find them, they dragged Jason and certain brothers before the rulers[c] of the city, crying, "These who have turned the world upside down have come here also, [7]whom Jason has received. These all act contrary to the decrees of Caesar, saying that there is another king, Jesus." [8]The crowd and the rulers of the city were troubled when they heard these things. [9]When they had taken security from Jason and the rest, they let them go. [10]The brothers immediately sent Paul and Silas away by night to Beroea. When they arrived, they went into the Jewish synagogue.

[11]Now these were more noble than those in Thessalonica, in that they received the word with all readiness of the mind, examining the Scriptures daily to see whether these things were so. [12]Many of them therefore believed; also of the prominent Greek women, and not a few men. [13]But when the Jews of Thessalonica had knowledge that the word of God was proclaimed by Paul at Beroea also, they came there likewise, agitating the crowds. [14]Then the brothers immediately sent out Paul to go as far as[d] to the sea, and Silas and Timothy still stayed there. [15]But those who escorted Paul brought him as far as Athens. Receiving a commandment to Silas and Timothy that they should come to him very quickly, they departed.

[16]Now while Paul waited for them at Athens, his spirit was provoked within him as he saw the city full of idols. [17]So he reasoned in the synagogue with the Jews and the devout persons, and in the marketplace every day with those who met him. [18]Some of the Epicurean and Stoic philosophers also were conversing with him. Some said, "What does this babbler want to say?"

Others said, "He seems to be advocating foreign deities," because he preached Jesus and the resurrection.

[19]They took hold of him, and brought him to the Areopagus, saying, "May we know what this new teaching is, which is spoken by you? [20]For you bring certain strange things to our ears. We want to know therefore what these things mean." [21]Now all the Athenians and the strangers living there spent their time in nothing

---

a   16:36 Some Mss lack "these"
b   17:5 Some Mss read "who were unpersuaded"
c   17:6 Gk. "Politarchs"
d   17:14 Some Mss read "as though by"

else, but either to tell or to hear some new thing. ²²Paul stood in the middle of the Areopagus, and said, "You men of Athens, I perceive that you are very religious in all things. ²³For as I passed along, and observed the objects of your worship, I found also an altar with this inscription: 'TO AN UNKNOWN GOD.' What therefore you worship in ignorance, this I announce to you. ²⁴The God who made the world and all things in it, he, being Lord of heaven and earth, does not dwell in temples made with hands, ²⁵neither is he served by human[a] hands, as though he needed anything, seeing he himself gives to all life and breath, and all things. ²⁶He made from one blood[b] every nation of the human race to dwell on all the surface of the earth, having determined appointed seasons, and the boundaries of their dwellings, ²⁷that they should seek God,[c] if perhaps they might reach out for him and find him, though he is not far from each one of us. ²⁸'For in him we live, and move, and have our being.'[d] As some of your own poets have said, 'For we are also his offspring.'[e] ²⁹Being then the offspring of God, we ought not to think that the Divine Nature is like gold, or silver, or stone, engraved by human art and design. ³⁰The times of ignorance therefore God overlooked. But now he commands that all people everywhere should repent, ³¹because he has appointed a day in which he will judge the world in righteousness by the man whom he has ordained; of which he has given assurance to everyone by raising him from the dead."

³²Now when they heard of the resurrection of the dead, some mocked; but others said, "We want to hear you again concerning this."

³³Thus Paul went out from among them. ³⁴But some people joined with him, and believed, among whom also was Dionysius the Areopagite, and a woman named Damaris, and others with them.

18 After these things Paul departed from Athens, and came to Corinth. ²He found a certain Jew named Aquila, a man of Pontus by race, who had recently come from Italy, with his wife Priscilla, because Claudius had commanded all the Jews to depart from Rome. He came to them, ³and because he practiced the same trade, he lived with them and worked, for by trade they were tent makers. ⁴He reasoned in the synagogue every Sabbath, and persuaded Jews and Greeks. ⁵But when Silas and Timothy came down from Macedonia, Paul was compelled by the word,[f] testifying to the Jews that Jesus was the Messiah. ⁶When they opposed him and blasphemed, he shook out his clothing and said to them, "Your blood be on your own heads. I am clean. From now on, I will go to the non-Jewish people."

⁷He departed there, and went into the house of a certain man named Titius[g] Justus, one who worshiped God, whose house was next door to the synagogue. ⁸Crispus, the ruler of the synagogue, believed in the Lord with all his house. Many of the Corinthians, when they heard, believed and were baptized. ⁹The Lord said to Paul in the night by a vision, "Do not be afraid, but speak and do not be silent; ¹⁰for I am with you, and no one will attack you to harm you, for I have many people in this city."

¹¹He lived there a year and six months, teaching the word of God among them. ¹²But when Gallio was proconsul of Achaia, the Jews with one accord rose up against Paul and brought him before the judgment seat, ¹³saying, "This one persuades people to worship God contrary to the law."

¹⁴But when Paul was about to open his mouth, Gallio said to the Jews, "If indeed it were a matter of wrong or of wicked crime, you Jews, it would be reasonable that I should bear with you; ¹⁵but if they are questions about words and names and

---

a   17:25 Some Mss read "men's"
b   17:26 Some Mss lack "blood"
c   17:27 Some Mss read "the Lord"
d   17:28 Epimenides, Cretica
e   17:28 Aratus, Phaenomena 5
f   18:5 Some Mss read "Spirit"
g   18:7 Some Mss lack "Titius"

your own law, look to it yourselves. For I do not want to be a judge of these matters." [16]He drove them from the judgment seat.

[17]Then all the Greeks[a] took hold of Sosthenes, the ruler of the synagogue, and beat him before the judgment seat. But none of these things were of concern to Gallio.

[18]Paul, having stayed after this many more days, took his leave of the brothers, and sailed from there for Syria, together with Priscilla and Aquila. He shaved his head in Cenchreae, for he had a vow. [19]They[b] came to Ephesus, and he left them there; but he himself entered into the synagogue, and reasoned with the Jews. [20]When they asked him to stay[c] a longer time, he declined; [21]but taking his leave of them, and saying,[d] "I will return again to you if God wills," he set sail from Ephesus.

[22]When he had landed at Caesarea, he went up and greeted the church, and went down to Antioch. [23]Having spent some time there, he departed, and went through the region of Galatia, and Phrygia, in order, establishing all the disciples. [24]Now a certain Jew named Apollos, an Alexandrian by race, an eloquent man, came to Ephesus. He was mighty in the Scriptures. [25]This man had been instructed in the way of the Lord; and being fervent in spirit, he spoke and taught accurately the things concerning Jesus,[e] although he knew only the baptism of John. [26]He began to speak boldly in the synagogue. But when Priscilla and Aquila heard him, they took him aside, and explained to him the way of God more accurately.

[27]When he had determined to pass over into Achaia, the brothers encouraged him, and wrote to the disciples to receive him. When he had come, he greatly helped those who had believed through grace; [28]for he powerfully refuted the Jews, publicly showing by the Scriptures that Jesus was the Messiah.

19 It happened that, while Apollos was at Corinth, Paul, having passed through the upper country, came to Ephesus, and found certain disciples. [2]He said to them, "Did you receive the Holy Spirit when you believed?"

They said to him, "No, we have not even heard that there is a Holy Spirit."

[3]He said, "Into what then were you baptized?"

They said, "Into John's baptism."

[4]Paul said, "John indeed baptized with the baptism of repentance, saying to the people that they should believe in the one who would come after him, that is, in Jesus."

[5]When they heard this, they were baptized in the name of the Lord Jesus. [6]When Paul had laid his hands on them, the Holy Spirit came on them, and they spoke with other tongues and prophesied. [7]They were about twelve men in all. [8]He entered into the synagogue, and spoke boldly for a period of three months, reasoning and persuading about the things concerning the kingdom of God.

[9]But when some were hardened and disobedient, speaking evil of the Way before the crowd, he departed from them, and separated the disciples, reasoning daily in the school of Tyrannus. [10]This continued for two years, so that all those who lived in Asia heard the word of the Lord Jesus, both Jews and Greeks.

[11]God worked special miracles by the hands of Paul, [12]so that even handkerchiefs[f] or aprons were carried away from his body to the sick, and the evil spirits went out. [13]But some of the itinerant Jews, exorcists, took on themselves to invoke over those who had the evil spirits the name of the Lord Jesus, saying, "I[g] adjure you by Jesus whom Paul preaches." [14]There were seven sons of one Sceva, a Jewish chief priest, who did this.

---

a   18:17 Some Mss lack "the Greeks"
b   18:19 Some Mss read "He"
c   18:20 Some Mss add "with them"
d   18:21 Some Mss add "I must by all means keep this coming feast in Jerusalem, but"
e   18:25 Some Mss read "the Lord"
f   19:12 Or, "face cloths"
g   19:13 Some Mss read "We"

¹⁵The evil spirit answered, "Jesus I know, and Paul I know, but who are you?" ¹⁶The man in whom the evil spirit was leaped on them, and overpowered them all, and prevailed against them, so that they fled out of that house naked and wounded. ¹⁷This became known to all, both Jews and Greeks, who lived at Ephesus. Fear fell on them all, and the name of the Lord Jesus was magnified. ¹⁸Many also of those who had believed came, confessing, and declaring their deeds. ¹⁹Many of those who practiced magical arts brought their books together and burned them in the sight of all. They counted the price of them, and found it to be fifty thousand pieces of silver. ²⁰So the word of the Lord was growing and becoming mighty.

²¹Now after these things had ended, Paul determined in the spirit, when he had passed through Macedonia and Achaia, to go to Jerusalem, saying, "After I have been there, I must also see Rome."

²²Having sent into Macedonia two of those who served him, Timothy and Erastus, he himself stayed in Asia for a while. ²³About that time there arose no small stir concerning the Way. ²⁴For a certain man named Demetrius, a silversmith, who made silver shrines of Artemis, brought no little business to the craftsmen, ²⁵whom he gathered together, with the workmen of like occupation, and said, "Sirs, you know that by this business we have our wealth. ²⁶You see and hear, that not at Ephesus alone, but almost throughout all Asia, this Paul has persuaded and turned away many people, saying that they are no gods, that are made with hands. ²⁷Not only is there danger that this our trade come into disrepute; but also that the temple of the great goddess Artemis will be counted as nothing, and that she should even be deposed from her magnificence, whom all Asia and the world worships."

²⁸When they heard this they were filled with anger, and began to shout, saying, "Great is Artemis of the Ephesians." ²⁹The[a] city was filled with confusion, and they rushed with one accord into the theater,

having seized Gaius and Aristarchus, Macedonians, Paul's companions in travel. ³⁰When Paul wanted to enter in to the people, the disciples did not allow him. ³¹Certain also of the Asiarchs, being his friends, sent to him and begged him not to venture into the theater. ³²Some therefore shouted one thing, and some another, for the assembly was in confusion. Most of them did not know why they had come together. ³³They brought Alexander out of the crowd, the Jews putting him forward. Alexander beckoned with his hand, and would have made a defense to the people. ³⁴But when they perceived that he was a Jew, all with one voice for a time of about two hours shouted, "Great is Artemis of the Ephesians."

³⁵When the town clerk had quieted the crowd, he said, "You men of Ephesus, is there anyone who does not know that the city of the Ephesians is temple keeper of the great[b] Artemis, and of the image which fell down from Zeus? ³⁶Seeing then that these things cannot be denied, you ought to be quiet, and to do nothing rash. ³⁷For you have brought these men here, who are neither robbers of temples nor blasphemers of our[c] goddess. ³⁸If therefore Demetrius and the craftsmen who are with him have a matter against anyone, the courts are open, and there are proconsuls. Let them press charges against one another. ³⁹But if you seek anything further, it will be settled in the regular assembly. ⁴⁰For indeed we are in danger of being accused concerning this day's riot, there being no cause. Concerning it, we would not be able to give an account of this commotion." ⁴¹When he had thus spoken, he dismissed the assembly.

20 After the uproar had ceased, Paul sent for the disciples and, after encouraging them, took leave of them,[d] and

---

a 19:29 Some Mss add "whole"
b 19:35 Some Mss add "goddess"
c 19:37 Some Mss read "your"
d 20:1 Some Mss lack "after encouraging them"

departed to go into Macedonia. [2]When he had gone through those parts, and had encouraged them with many words, he came into Greece. [3]When he had spent three months there, and a plot was made against him by Jews as he was about to set sail for Syria, he determined to return through Macedonia. [4]He was accompanied[a] by Sopater son of Pyrrhus[b] of Beroea; Aristarchus and Secundus of the Thessalonians; Gaius of Derbe; Timothy; and Tychicus and Trophimus of Asia. [5]But these had gone ahead, and were waiting for us at Troas. [6]We sailed away from Philippi after the days of Unleavened Bread, and came to them at Troas in five days, where we stayed seven days.

[7]On the first day of the week, when we[c] were gathered together to break bread, Paul talked with them, intending to depart on the next day, and continued his speech until midnight. [8]There were many lights in the upper chamber where we were gathered together. [9]A certain young man named Eutychus sat in the window, weighed down with deep sleep. As Paul spoke still longer, being weighed down by his sleep, he fell down from the third story, and was taken up dead. [10]Paul went down, and fell upon him, and embracing him said, "Do not be troubled, for his life is in him."

[11]When he had gone up, and had broken bread, and eaten, and had talked with them a long while, even until break of day, he departed. [12]They brought the boy in alive, and were greatly comforted.

[13]But we who went ahead to the ship set sail for Assos, intending to take Paul aboard there, for he had so arranged, intending himself to go by land. [14]When he met us at Assos, we took him aboard, and came to Mitylene. [15]Sailing from there, we came the following day opposite Chios. The next day we landed at Samos,[d] and the day after we came to Miletus. [16]For Paul had determined to sail past Ephesus, that he might not have to spend time in Asia; for he was hastening, if it were possible for him, to be in Jerusalem on the day of Pentecost.

[17]From Miletus he sent to Ephesus, and called to himself the elders of the church. [18]When they had come to him, he said to them, "You yourselves know, from the first day that I set foot in Asia, how I was with you all the time, [19]serving the Lord with all humility, with many tears, and with trials which happened to me by the plots of the Jews; [20]how I did not hold back from declaring to you anything that was profitable, and teaching you publicly and from house to house, [21]testifying both to Jews and to Greeks repentance toward God, and faith toward our Lord Jesus. [22]And now, look, I am going bound by the Spirit to Jerusalem, not knowing what will happen to me there; [23]except that the Holy Spirit testifies in every city, saying that bonds and afflictions wait for me. [24]But I make my life[e] an account of nothing[f] precious to myself, so that I may finish my race,[g] and the ministry which I received from the Lord Jesus, to fully testify to the Good News of the grace of God.

[25]"And now, look, I know that you all, among whom I went about proclaiming the kingdom,[h] will see my face no more. [26]Therefore I testify to you today that I am innocent of everyone's blood, [27]for I did not hold back from declaring to you the whole counsel of God. [28]Take heed, therefore, to yourselves, and to all the flock, in which the Holy Spirit has made you overseers, to shepherd the church of[i] God[j] which he purchased with his own blood. [29]For I know that after my departure, vicious wolves will enter in among you, not sparing the flock. [30]Men will arise from among your own selves, speaking perverse things, to draw away the disciples after them. [31]Therefore watch, remembering that for

---

a   20:4 Some Mss add "as far as Asia"
b   20:4 Some Mss lack "son of Pyrrhus"
c   20:7 Some Mss read "when the disciples"
d   20:15 Some Mss add "and stayed at Trogyllium"
e   20:24 Some Mss read "my self"
f   20:24 Some Mss add "neither do I hold my life"
g   20:24 Some Mss add "with joy"
h   20:25 Some Mss add "of God"
i   20:28 Some Mss add "the Lord and"
j   20:28 Some Mss read "Lord"

a period of three years I did not cease to admonish everyone night and day with tears. [32]Now[a] I entrust you to God, and to the word of his grace, which is able to build up, and to give you the inheritance among all those who are sanctified. [33]I coveted no one's silver, or gold, or clothing. [34]You yourselves know that these hands served my necessities, and those who were with me. [35]In all things I gave you an example, that so laboring you ought to help the weak, and to remember the words of the Lord Jesus, that he himself said, 'It is more blessed to give than to receive.'"

[36]When he had spoken these things, he knelt down and prayed with them all. [37]They all wept a lot, and fell on Paul's neck and kissed him, [38]sorrowing most of all because of the word which he had spoken, that they should see his face no more. And they accompanied him to the ship.

21 When it happened that we had parted from them and had set sail, we came with a straight course to Cos, and the next day to Rhodes, and from there to Patara.[b] [2]Having found a ship crossing over to Phoenicia, we went aboard, and set sail. [3]When we had come in sight of Cyprus, leaving it on the left hand, we sailed to Syria, and landed at Tyre, for there the ship was to unload her cargo. [4]Having found the[c] disciples, we stayed there seven days. These said to Paul through the Spirit, that he should not go up to Jerusalem. [5]When it happened that we had accomplished the days, we departed and went on our journey. They all, with wives and children, brought us on our way until we were out of the city. Kneeling down on the beach, we prayed. [6]After saying goodbye to each other, we went on board the ship, and they returned home again.

[7]When we had finished the voyage from Tyre, we arrived at Ptolemais. We greeted the brothers, and stayed with them one day. [8]On the next day,[d] we departed and came to Caesarea.

We entered into the house of Philip the evangelist, who was one of the seven, and stayed with him. [9]Now this man had four virgin daughters who prophesied. [10]As we stayed there some days, a certain prophet named Agabus came down from Judea. [11]Coming to us, and taking Paul's belt, he bound his own feet and hands, and said, "Thus says the Holy Spirit: 'So will the Jews in Jerusalem bind the man who owns this belt, and will deliver him into the hands of the non-Jewish people.'"

[12]When we heard these things, both we and they of that place begged him not to go up to Jerusalem. [13]Then Paul answered, "What are you doing, weeping and breaking my heart? For I am ready not only to be bound, but also to die at Jerusalem for the name of the Lord Jesus."

[14]When he would not be persuaded, we ceased, saying, "The Lord's will be done."

[15]After these days we took up our baggage and went up to Jerusalem. [16]Some of the disciples from Caesarea also went with us, bringing one Mnason of Cyprus, an early disciple, with whom we would stay.

[17]When we had come to Jerusalem, the brothers received us gladly. [18]The day following, Paul went in with us to James; and all the elders were present. [19]When he had greeted them, he reported one by one the things which God had worked among the non-Jewish people through his ministry. [20]They, when they heard it, glorified God.[e] They said to him, "You see, brother, how many thousands there are among the Jews of those who have believed, and they are all zealous for the Law. [21]They have been informed about you, that you teach all the Jews who are among the non-Jews to forsake Moses, telling them not to circumcise their children neither to walk after the customs. [22]What then? The multitude must certainly meet. [f]They will hear that you have come. [23]Therefore do what we tell

---

a   20:32 Some Mss add "brothers"
b   21:21 Some Mss add "and Myra"
c   21:4 Some Mss lack "the"
d   21:8 Some Mss add "who were Paul's companions"
e   21:20 Some Mss read "the Lord"
f   21:22 Or, "A multitude is sure to gather." Some Mss lack "The multitude must certainly meet"

you. We have four men who have taken a vow. [24]Take them, and purify yourself with them, and pay their expenses for them, that they may shave their heads. Then all will know that there is no truth in the things that they have been informed about you, but that you yourself also walk keeping the Law. [25]But concerning the non-Jewish who believe, we have written our decision that they should[a] keep themselves from food offered to idols, from blood, from strangled things, and from sexual immorality."

[26]Then Paul took the men, and the next day, purified himself and went with them into the temple, declaring the fulfillment of the days of purification, until the offering was offered for every one of them. [27]When the seven days were almost completed, the Jews from Asia, when they saw him in the temple, stirred up all the crowd and laid hands on him, [28]crying out, "Men of Israel, help. This is the man who teaches all men everywhere against the people, and the Law, and this place. Moreover, he also brought Greeks into the temple, and has defiled this holy place." [29]For they had previously[b] seen Trophimus, the Ephesian, with him in the city, and they supposed that Paul had brought him into the temple.

[30]All the city was moved, and the people ran together. They seized Paul and dragged him out of the temple. Immediately the doors were shut. [31]As they were trying to kill him, news came up to the commanding officer of the regiment that all Jerusalem was in an uproar. [32]Immediately he took soldiers and centurions, and ran down to them. They, when they saw the chief captain and the soldiers, stopped beating Paul. [33]Then the commanding officer came near, arrested him, commanded him to be bound with two chains, and inquired who he was and what he had done. [34]Some shouted one thing, and some another, among the crowd. When he could not find out the truth because of the noise, he commanded him to be brought into the barracks.

[35]When he came to the stairs, it happened that he was carried by the soldiers because of the violence of the crowd; [36]for the crowd of the people followed after, crying out, "Away with him." [37]As Paul was about to be brought into the barracks, he asked the commanding officer, "May I speak something[c] to you?"

He said, "Do you know Greek? [38]Are you not then the Egyptian, who before these days stirred up to sedition and led out into the wilderness the four thousand men of the Assassins?"

[39]But Paul said, "I am a Jew, from Tarsus in Cilicia, a citizen of no insignificant city. I beg you, allow me to speak to the people."

[40]When he had given him permission, Paul, standing on the stairs, beckoned with his hand to the people. When there was a great silence, he spoke to them in the Hebrew language, saying,

22 "Brothers and fathers, listen to the defense which I now make to you."

[2]When they heard that he spoke to them in the Hebrew language, they were even more quiet. He said, [3]"I am indeed a Jew, born in Tarsus of Cilicia, but brought up in this city at the feet of Gamaliel, instructed according to the strict manner of the Law of our fathers, being zealous for God, even as you all are this day. [4]I persecuted this Way to the death, binding and delivering into prisons both men and women. [5]As also the high priest and all the council of the elders testify, from whom also I received letters to the brothers, and traveled to Damascus to bring them also who were there to Jerusalem in bonds to be punished. [6]It happened that, as I made my journey, and came close to Damascus, about noon, suddenly there shone from the sky a great light around me. [7]I fell to the ground, and heard a voice saying to me, 'Saul, Saul, why are you persecuting me?' [8]I answered, 'Who are you, Lord?' He said

---

a   21:25 Some Mss add "observe no such thing, except to"

b   21:29 Some Mss lack "previously"

c   21:37 Some Mss lack "something"

to me, 'I am Jesus the Nazorean, whom you persecute.'

⁹"Those who were with me indeed saw the light, and were afraid,ᵃ but they did not understand the voice of him who spoke to me. ¹⁰I said, 'What should I do, Lord?' The Lord said to me, 'Arise, and go into Damascus. There you will be told about all things which are appointed for you to do.' ¹¹When I could not see for the glory of that light, being led by the hand of those who were with me, I came into Damascus. ¹²One Ananias, a devout man according to the Law, well reported of by all the Jews who lived in Damascus, ¹³came to me, and standing by me said to me, 'Brother Saul, receive your sight.' In that very hour I looked up at him. ¹⁴He said, 'The God of our fathers has appointed you to know his will, and to see the Righteous One, and to hear a voice from his mouth. ¹⁵For you will be a witness for him to all people of what you have seen and heard. ¹⁶Now why do you wait? Arise, be baptized, and wash away your sins, calling on his name.'ᵇ'

¹⁷"It happened that, when I had returned to Jerusalem, and while I prayed in the temple, I fell into a trance, ¹⁸and saw him saying to me, 'Hurry and get out of Jerusalem quickly, because they will not receive testimony concerning me from you.' ¹⁹I said, 'Lord, they themselves know that I imprisoned and beat in every synagogue those who believed in you. ²⁰When the blood of Stephen, your witness, was shed, I also was standing by,ᶜ and guarding the cloaks of those who killed him.'

²¹"He said to me, 'Depart, for I will send you out far from here to the non-Jewish people.'"

²²They listened to him until he said that; then they lifted up their voice, and said, "Rid the earth of this fellow, for he is not fit to live."

²³As they yelled, and threw off their cloaks, and threw dust into the air, ²⁴the commanding officer commanded him to be brought into the barracks, ordering him to be examined by scourging, that he might know for what crime they yelled at him like that. ²⁵When theyᵈ had tied him

up with thongs, Paul asked the centurion who stood by, "Is it lawful for you to scourge a man who is a Roman, and not found guilty?"

²⁶When the centurion heard it, he went to the commanding officer and told him, "What are you about to do?ᵉ For this man is a Roman."

²⁷The commanding officer came and asked him, "Tell me, are you a Roman?"

He said, "Yes."

²⁸The commanding officer answered, "I bought my citizenship for a great price."

Paul said, "But I was born a Roman."

²⁹Immediately those who were about to examine him departed from him, and the commanding officer also was afraid when he realized that he was a Roman, because he had bound him. ³⁰But on the next day, desiring to know the truth about why he was accused by the Jews, he freed himᶠ, and commanded the chief priests and all the council to come together, and brought Paul down and set him before them.

23 Paul, looking steadfastly at the council, said, "Brothers, I have lived before God in all good conscience until this day."

²The high priest, Ananias, commanded those who stood by him to strike him on the mouth.

³Then Paul said to him, "God will strike you, you whitewashed wall. Do you sit to judge me according to the Law, and command me to be struck contrary to the law?"

⁴Those who stood by said, "Do you malign God's high priest?"

⁵Paul said, "I did not know, brothers, that he was high priest. For it is written, 'You must not speak evil of a ruler of your people.'ᵍ ⁶But when Paul perceived that the one part were Sadducees and the other

---

a   22:9 Some Mss lack "and were afraid"
b   22:16 Some Mss read "the name of the Lord"
c   22:20 Some Mss add "and consenting to his death"
d   22:25 Some Mss read "he"
e   22:26 Some Mss read "Watch what you are about to be doing"
f   22:30 Some Mss add "from the bonds"
g   23:5 Exodus 22:28

Pharisees, he shouted in the council, "Men and brothers, I am a Pharisee, a son of Pharisees. Concerning the hope and resurrection of the dead I am being judged."

[7]When he had said this, an argument arose between the Pharisees and Sadducees, and the assembly was divided. [8]For the Sadducees say that there is no resurrection, nor angel, nor spirit; but the Pharisees confess all of these. [9]A great clamor arose, and some of[a] the scribes of the Pharisees part stood up, and contended, saying, "We find no evil in this man. What if a spirit spoke to him, or an angel?[b]"

[10]When a great argument arose, the commanding officer, fearing that Paul would be torn in pieces by them, commanded the soldiers to go down and take him by force from among them, and bring him into the barracks.

[11]The following night, the Lord stood by him, and said, "Cheer up[c], for as you have testified about me at Jerusalem, so you must testify also at Rome."

[12]When it was day,[d] the Jews formed a conspiracy, and bound themselves under a curse, saying that they would neither eat nor drink until they had killed Paul. [13]There were more than forty people who had made this conspiracy. [14]They came to the chief priests and the elders, and said, "We have bound ourselves under a great curse, to taste nothing until we have killed Paul. [15]Now therefore, you with the council inform the commanding officer that he should bring him down to you,[e] as though you were going to judge his case more exactly. We are ready to kill him before he comes near."

[16]But Paul's sister's son heard of their lying in wait, and he came and entered into the barracks and told Paul. [17]Paul summoned one of the centurions, and said, "Bring this young man to the commanding officer, for he has something to tell him."

[18]So he took him, and brought him to the commanding officer, and said, "Paul, the prisoner, summoned me and asked me to bring this young man to you, who has something to tell you."

[19]The commanding officer took him by the hand, and going aside, asked him privately, "What is it that you have to tell me?"

[20]And he said, "The Jews have agreed to ask you to bring Paul down to the council tomorrow, as though they intended to inquire somewhat more thoroughly concerning him. [21]Therefore do not yield to them, for more than forty men lie in wait for him, who have bound themselves under a curse neither to eat nor to drink until they have killed him. Now they are ready, looking for the promise from you."

[22]So the commanding officer let the young man go, charging him, "Tell no one that you have revealed these things to me." [23]He called to himself two of the centurions, and said, "Prepare two hundred soldiers to go as far as Caesarea, with seventy horsemen, and two hundred spearmen, at at nine tonight[f]." [24]He asked them to provide animals, that they might set Paul on one, and bring him safely to Felix the governor. [25]He wrote a letter like this:

[26]"Claudius Lysias to the most excellent governor Felix: Greetings.

[27]"This man was seized by the Jews, and was about to be killed by them, when I came with the soldiers and rescued him, having learned that he was a Roman. [28]Desiring to know the cause why they accused him, I brought him down to their council. [29]I found him to be accused about questions of their law, but not to be charged with anything worthy of death or of imprisonment. [30]When I was told that there would be a plot[g] against the man, I sent him to you immediately, charging his accusers also to bring their accusations against him before you.[h]"

---

a   23:9 Some Mss lack "some of"
b   23:9 Some Mss "Let's not fight against God"
c   23:11 Some Mss add "Paul"
d   23:12 Some Mss add "some of"
e   23:15 Some Mss add "tomorrow"
f   23:23 Lit. the third hour
g   23:30 Some Mss add "by the Jews"
h   23:30 Some Mss add "Farewell"

[31]So the soldiers, carrying out their orders, took Paul and brought him by night to Antipatris. [32]But on the next day they left the horsemen to go with him, and returned to the barracks. [33]When they came to Caesarea and delivered the letter to the governor, they also presented Paul to him. [34]When the governor had read it, he asked what province he was from. When he understood that he was from Cilicia, he said, [35]"I will hear you fully when your accusers also arrive." He commanded that he be kept in Herod's palace.

24 After five days, the high priest, Ananias, came down with certain[a] elders and an orator, one Tertullus. They informed the governor against Paul. [2]When he was called, Tertullus began to accuse him, saying, "Seeing that by you we enjoy much peace, and that by your foresight reforms[b] are coming to this nation, [3]we accept it in all ways and in all places, most excellent Felix, with all thankfulness. [4]But, that I do not delay you, I entreat you to bear with us and hear a few words. [5]For we have found this man to be a plague, an instigator of insurrections among all the Jews throughout the world, and a ringleader of the sect of the Nazarenes. [6]He even tried to profane the temple, and we arrested him.[7c] [8]By examining him yourself you may ascertain all these things of which we accuse him."

[9]The Jews also joined in the attack, affirming that these things were so. [10]When the governor had beckoned to him to speak, Paul answered, "Because I know that you have been a judge of this nation for many years, I cheerfully make my defense, [11]seeing that you can recognize that it is not more than twelve days since I went up to worship at Jerusalem. [12]In the temple they did not find me disputing with anyone or stirring up a crowd, either in the synagogues, or in the city. [13]Nor can they prove to you[d] the things of which they now accuse me. [14]But this I confess to you, that after the Way, which they call a sect, so I serve the God of our fathers, believing all things which are according to the Law, and which are written in the Prophets; [15]having hope toward God, which these also themselves look for, that there will be a resurrection[e], both of the just and unjust. [16]This being so, I also do my best to always have a clear conscience toward God and people. [17]Now after some years, I came to bring gifts for the needy to my nation, and offerings; [18]amid which certain Jews from Asia found me purified in the temple, not with a mob, nor with turmoil. [19]They ought to have been here before you, and to make accusation, if they had anything against me. [20]Or else let these men themselves say what injustice they found in me when I stood before the council, [21]unless it is for this one thing that I shouted out standing among them, 'Concerning the resurrection of the dead I am being judged before you today.'"

[22]But Felix,[f] having more exact knowledge concerning the Way, deferred them, saying, "When Lysias, the commanding officer, comes down, I will decide your case." [23]He ordered the centurion that he[g] should be kept in custody, and should have some privileges, and not to forbid any of his friends to serve him or to visit him. [24]But after some days, Felix came with Drusilla, his wife, who was a Jewess, and sent for Paul, and heard him concerning the faith in Christ Jesus. [25]As he reasoned about righteousness, self-control, and the judgment to come, Felix was terrified, and answered, "Go your way for this time, and when it is convenient for me, I will summon you." [26]Meanwhile, he also hoped that money would be given to him by Paul.[h] Therefore also he sent for him more often,

---

a   24:1 Some Mss read "the"
b   24:2 Some Mss read "prosperity"
c   24:6-8 Some Mss add "And we would have judged him according to our law, 7 but the chief captain Lysias came, and with great violence took him away out of our hands, 8commanding his accusers to come to you"
d   24:13 Some Mss lack "to you"
e   24:15 Some Mss add "of the dead"
f   24:22 Some Mss add "heard these things"
g   24:23 Some Mss read "Paul"
h   24:26 Some Mss add "that he might release him"

and talked with him. ²⁷But when two years were fulfilled, Felix was succeeded by Porcius Festus, and desiring to gain favor with the Jews, Felix left Paul in bonds.

25 Festus therefore, having come into the province, after three days went up to Jerusalem from Caesarea. ²Then the high priest and the principal men of the Jews informed him against Paul, and they urged him, ³asking a favor against him, that he would summon him to Jerusalem; plotting to kill him on the way. ⁴However Festus answered that Paul should be kept in custody at Caesarea, and that he himself was about to depart shortly. ⁵"Let them therefore," said he, "that are in power among you go down with me, and if there is anything wrongᵃ in the man, let them accuse him."

⁶When he had stayed among them more than eight orᵇ ten days, he went down to Caesarea, and on the next day he sat on the judgment seat, and commanded Paul to be brought. ⁷When he had come, the Jews who had come down from Jerusalem stood around him, bringing against him many and grievous charges which they could not prove, ⁸while he said in his defense, "Neither against the law of the Jews, nor against the temple, nor against Caesar, have I sinned at all."

⁹But Festus, desiring to gain favor with the Jews, answered Paul and said, "Are you willing to go up to Jerusalem, and be judged by me there concerning these things?"

¹⁰But Paul said, "I am standing before Caesar's judgment seat, where I ought to be tried. I have done no wrong to the Jews, as you also know very well. ¹¹For if I have done wrong, and have committed anything worthy of death, I do not refuse to die; but if none of those things is true that they accuse me of, no one can give me up to them. I appeal to Caesar."

¹²Then Festus, when he had conferred with the council, answered, "You have appealed to Caesar. To Caesar you will go."

¹³Now when some days had passed, Agrippa the King and Bernice arrived at Caesarea, and greeted Festus. ¹⁴As theyᶜ stayed there many days, Festus laid Paul's case before the king, saying, "There is a certain man left a prisoner by Felix; ¹⁵about whom, when I was at Jerusalem, the chief priests and the Jewish elders informed me, asking for a sentence against him. ¹⁶To whom I answered that it is not the custom of the Romans to give up anyone to destruction ᵈbefore the accused has met the accusers face to face, and has had opportunity to make his defense against the charge. ¹⁷When therefore they had come together here, I did not delay, but on the next day sat on the judgment seat, and commanded the man to be brought. ¹⁸Concerning whom, when the accusers stood up, they brought no charge of such things as I supposed; ¹⁹but had certain questions against him about their own religion, and about one Jesus, who was dead, whom Paul affirmed to be alive. ²⁰Being perplexed how to inquire concerning these things, I asked whether he was willing to go to Jerusalem and there be judged concerning these matters. ²¹But when Paul had appealed to be kept for the decision of the emperor, I commanded him to be kept until I could send him to Caesar."

²²Agrippa said to Festus, "I also would like to hear the man myself."

"Tomorrow," he said, "you will hear him."

²³So on the next day, when Agrippa and Bernice had come with great pomp, and they had entered into the place of hearing with the commanding officers and principal men of the city, at the command of Festus, Paul was brought in. ²⁴And Festus said, "King Agrippa, and all people who are here present with us, you see this man, about whom the whole assembly of the Jews petitioned me, both at Jerusalem and here, crying that he ought not to live any longer. ²⁵But when I found that he had committed

---

a   25:5 Some Mss lack "wrong"
b   25:6 Some Mss lack "eight or"
c   25:14 Some Mss read "he"
d   25:16 Some Mss lack "to destruction"

nothing worthy of death, and as he himself appealed to the emperor I determined to send him. [26]Of whom I have no certain thing to write to my lord. Therefore I have brought him forth before you, and especially before you, King Agrippa, that, after examination, I may have something to write. [27]For it seems to me unreasonable, in sending a prisoner, not to also specify the charges against him."

26 Agrippa said to Paul, "You may speak for yourself."

Then Paul stretched out his hand, and made his defense. [2]"I think myself happy, King Agrippa, that I am to make my defense before you this day concerning all the things that I am accused by the Jews, [3]especially because you are expert in all customs and questions which are among Jews. Therefore I beg you to hear me patiently.

[4]"Indeed, all Jews know my way of life from my youth up, which was from the beginning among my own nation and at Jerusalem; [5]having known me from the first, if they are willing to testify, that after the strictest sect of our religion I lived a Pharisee. [6]Now I stand here to be judged for the hope of the promise made by God to our fathers, [7]which our twelve tribes, earnestly serving night and day, hope to attain. Concerning this hope I am accused by the Jews, O King[a]. [8]Why is it judged incredible with you, if God does raise the dead?

[9]"In fact, I thought to myself that I ought to do many things against the name of Jesus the Nazorean. [10]This I also did in Jerusalem. I both shut up many of the saints in prisons, having received authority from the chief priests, and when they were put to death I gave my vote against them. [11]Punishing them often in all the synagogues, I tried to make them blaspheme. Being exceedingly enraged against them, I persecuted them even to foreign cities.

[12]"Whereupon as I traveled to Damascus with the authority and commission from the chief priests, [13]at noon, O King, I saw on the way a light from the sky, brighter than the sun, shining around me and those who traveled with me. [14]When we had all fallen to the earth, I heard a voice saying to me in the Hebrew language, 'Saul, Saul, why are you persecuting me? It is hard for you to kick against the goads.'

[15]"I said, 'Who are you, Lord?'

"He said, 'I am Jesus, whom you are persecuting. [16]But arise, and stand on your feet, for I have appeared to you for this purpose: to appoint you a servant and a witness both of the things which you have seen me,[b] and of the things which I will reveal to you; [17]delivering you from the people, and from the non-Jewish people, to whom I send you, [18]to open their eyes, that they may turn[c] from darkness to light and from the power of Satan to God, that they may receive remission of sins and an inheritance among those who are sanctified by faith in me.'

[19]"Therefore, King Agrippa, I was not disobedient to the heavenly vision, [20]but declared first to them of Damascus, at Jerusalem, and throughout all the country of Judea, and also to the non-Jews, that they should repent and turn to God, doing works worthy of repentance. [21]For this reason Jews seized me in the temple, and tried to kill me. [22]Having therefore obtained the help that is from God, I stand to this day testifying both to small and great, saying nothing but what the Prophets and Moses said would happen, [23]how the Messiah would suffer, and how, by the resurrection of the dead, he would be first to proclaim light both to these people and to the non-Jewish people."

[24]As he thus made his defense, Festus said with a loud voice, "Paul, you are crazy. Your great learning is driving you insane."

[25]But he said, "I am not crazy, most excellent Festus, but boldly declare words of truth and reasonableness. [26]For the king knows of these things, to whom also I speak freely. For I am persuaded that none

---

a 26:7 Some Mss add "Agrippa"
b 26:16 Some Mss lack "me"
c 26:18 Some Mss add "back"

of these things is hidden from him, for this has not been done in a corner. [27]King Agrippa, do you believe the prophets? I know that you believe."

[28]Agrippa said to Paul, "With a little persuasion are you trying to make me a Christian?"

[29]Paul said, "I pray to God, that whether with little or with much, not only you, but also all that hear me this day, might become such as I am, except for these bonds."

[30]The[a] king rose up with the governor, and Bernice, and those who sat with them. [31]When they had withdrawn, they spoke one to another, saying, "This man does nothing worthy of death or of bonds." [32]Agrippa said to Festus, "This man might have been set free if he had not appealed to Caesar."

27 When it was determined that we should sail for Italy, they delivered Paul and certain other prisoners to a centurion named Julius, of the Augustan band. [2]Embarking in a ship from Adramyttium, which was about to sail to places on the coast of Asia, we put to sea; Aristarchus, a Macedonian of Thessalonica, being with us. [3]The next day, we landed at Sidon. Julius treated Paul kindly, and gave him permission to go to his friends and refresh himself. [4]Putting to sea from there, we sailed under the lee of Cyprus, because the winds were contrary. [5]When we had sailed across the sea which is off Cilicia and Pamphylia, we came to Myra, a city of Lycia. [6]There the centurion found a ship of Alexandria sailing for Italy, and he put us on board. [7]When we had sailed slowly many days, and had come with difficulty opposite Cnidus, the wind not allowing us further, we sailed under the lee of Crete, opposite Salmone. [8]With difficulty sailing along it we came to a certain place called Fair Havens, near the city of Lasea.

[9]When much time had passed and the voyage was now dangerous, because the Fast had now already gone by, Paul admonished them, [10]and said to them, "Sirs, I perceive that the voyage will be with injury and much loss, not only of the cargo and the ship, but also of our lives." [11]But the centurion gave more heed to the master and to the owner of the ship than to those things which were spoken by Paul. [12]Because the haven was not suitable to winter in, the majority advised going to sea from there, if by any means they could reach Phoenix, and winter there, which is a port of Crete, looking northeast and southeast.

[13]When the south wind blew softly, supposing that they had obtained their purpose, they weighed anchor and sailed along Crete, close to shore. [14]But before long, a stormy wind beat down from shore, which is called Euraquilo.[b] [15]When the ship was caught, and could not face the wind, we gave way to it, and were driven along. [16]Running under the lee of a small island called Cauda[c], we were able, with difficulty, to secure the boat. [17]After they had hoisted it up, they used cables to help reinforce the ship. Fearing that they would run aground on the Syrtis, they lowered the sea anchor, and so were driven along. [18]As we labored exceedingly with the storm, the next day they began to throw things overboard. [19]On the third day, they[d] threw out the ship's tackle with their own hands. [20]When neither sun nor stars shone on us for many days, and no small storm pressed on us, all hope that we would be saved was now taken away.

[21]When they had been long without food, Paul stood up in the middle of them, and said, "Sirs, you should have listened to me, and not have set sail from Crete, and have gotten this injury and loss. [22]Now I exhort you to cheer up, for there will be no loss of life among you, but only of the ship. [23]For there stood by me this night an angel, belonging to the God whose I am and whom I serve, [24]saying, 'Do not be afraid, Paul. You must stand before Caesar. And

---

a   26:30 Some Mss add "And he having spoken these things"

b   27:14 Or, "a northeaster." Some Mss read "Euroclydon," a southeast wind

c   27:16 Some Mss read "Clauda"

d   27:16 Some Mss read "Clauda"

look, God has granted you all those who sail with you.' ²⁵Therefore, sirs, cheer up. For I believe God, that it will be just as it has been spoken to me. ²⁶But we must run aground on a certain island."

²⁷But when the fourteenth night had come, as we were driven back and forth in the Adriatic Sea, about midnight the sailors surmised that they were drawing near to some land. ²⁸They took soundings, and found twenty fathoms.ᵃ After a little while, they took soundings again, and found fifteen fathoms.ᵇ ²⁹Fearing that we would run aground on rocky ground, they let go four anchors from the stern, and wished for daylight. ³⁰As the sailors were trying to flee out of the ship, and had lowered the boat into the sea, pretending that they would lay out anchors from the bow, ³¹Paul said to the centurion and to the soldiers, "Unless these stay in the ship, you cannot be saved." ³²Then the soldiers cut away the ropes of the boat, and let it fall off.

³³While the day was coming on, Paul begged them all to take some food, saying, "This day is the fourteenth day that you wait and continue fasting, having taken nothing. ³⁴Therefore I urge you to take some food, for this is for your preservation; for not a hair will perishᶜ from any of your heads." ³⁵When he had said this, and had taken bread, he gave thanks to God in the presence of all, and he broke it, and began to eat. ³⁶Then they all cheered up, and they also took food. ³⁷In all, we were two hundred seventy-six souls on the ship. ³⁸When they had eaten enough, they lightened the ship, throwing out the wheat into the sea. ³⁹When it was day, they did not recognize the land, but they noticed a certain bay with a beach, and they decided to try to drive the ship onto it. ⁴⁰Casting off the anchors, they left them in the sea, at the same time untying the rudder ropes. Hoisting up the foresail to the wind, they made for the beach. ⁴¹But coming to a place where two seas met, they ran the vessel aground. The bow struck and remained immovable, but the stern began to break up by the violence of the waves.

⁴²The soldiers' counsel was to kill the prisoners, so that none of them would swim out and escape. ⁴³But the centurion, desiring to save Paul, stopped them from their purpose, and commanded that those who could swim should throw themselves overboard first to go toward the land; ⁴⁴and the rest should follow, some on planks, and some on other things from the ship. So it happened that they all escaped safely to the land.

28 When we had escaped, then weᵈ learned that the island was called Malta. ²The natives showed us uncommon kindness; for they kindled a fire, and received us all, because of the present rain, and because of the cold. ³But when Paul had gathered a bundle of sticks and placed them on the fire, a viper came out because of the heat, and fastened on his hand. ⁴When the natives saw the creature hanging from his hand, they said one to another, "No doubt this man is a murderer, whom, though he has escaped from the sea, yet Justice has not allowed to live." ⁵However he shook off the creature into the fire, and was not harmed. ⁶But they expected that he would have swollen or fallen down dead suddenly, but when they watched for a long time and saw nothing bad happen to him, they changed their minds, and said that he was a god.

⁷Now in the neighborhood of that place were lands belonging to the chief official of the island, named Publius, who received us, and courteously entertained us for three days. ⁸It happened that the father of Publius lay sick of fever and dysentery. Paul entered in to him, prayed, and laying his hands on him, healed him. ⁹Then when this was done, the rest also who had diseases in the island came, and were cured. ¹⁰They also honored us with many honors, and when we sailed, they put on board the things that we needed.

---

a   27:28 20 fathoms = 120 feet = 36.6 meters
b   27:28 15 fathoms = 90 feet = 27.4 meters
c   27:34 Some Mss read "fall"
d   28:1 Some Mss read "they"

[11]After three months, we set sail[a] in a ship of Alexandria which had wintered in the island, whose sign was "The Twin Brothers." [12]Touching at Syracuse, we stayed there three days. [13]From there we cast off[b] and arrived at Rhegium. After one day, a south wind sprang up, and on the second day we came to Puteoli, [14]where we found brothers, and were entreated to stay with them for seven days. So we came to Rome. [15]From there the brothers, when they heard of us, came to meet us as far as The Market of Appius and The Three Taverns. When Paul saw them, he thanked God, and took courage. [16]When we entered into Rome,[c] Paul was allowed to stay by himself with the soldier who guarded him.

[17]It happened that after three days Paul called together those who were the Jewish leaders. When they had come together, he said to them, "I, brothers, though I had done nothing against the people, or the customs of our fathers, still was delivered prisoner from Jerusalem into the hands of the Romans, [18]who, when they had examined me, desired to set me free, because there was no cause of death in me. [19]But when the Jews spoke against it, I was forced to appeal to Caesar, not that I had anything about which to accuse my nation. [20]For this cause therefore I asked to see you and to speak with you. For because of the hope of Israel I am bound with this chain."

[21]They said to him, "We neither received letters from Judea concerning you, nor did any of the brothers come here and report or speak any evil of you. [22]But we desire to hear from you what you think. For, as concerning this sect, it is known to us that everywhere it is spoken against."

[23]When they had appointed him a day, many people came to him at his lodging. He explained to them, testifying about the kingdom of God, and persuading them concerning Jesus, both from the Law of Moses and from the Prophets, from morning until evening. [24]Some believed the things which were spoken, and some disbelieved. [25]When they did not agree among themselves, they departed after Paul had spoken one word, "The Holy Spirit spoke rightly through Isaiah, the prophet, to your[d] fathers, [26]saying,

'Go to this people, and say,
in hearing, you will hear,
    but will in no way understand.
In seeing, you will see,
    but will in no way perceive.
[27]For this people's heart has grown
        callous.
    Their ears are dull of hearing.
    Their eyes they have closed.
Lest they should see with their eyes,
    hear with their ears,
    understand with their heart,
    and would turn again,
    and I would heal them.'[e]

[28]"Be it known therefore to you, that the salvation of God is sent to the nations. They will also listen."[29f]

[30]Paul stayed two whole years in his own rented house, and received all who were coming to him, [31]proclaiming the kingdom of God, and teaching the things concerning the Lord Jesus Christ with all boldness, without hindrance.

Romans

1 Paul, a servant of Christ Jesus, called[g] to be an apostle, set apart for the Good News of God, [2]which he promised before through his prophets in the holy Scriptures, [3]concerning his Son, who was born of the offspring of David according to the flesh, [4]who was declared to be the Son of God with power, according to the Spir-

---

a   28:11 Some Mss read "we were brought"
b   28:13 Some Mss read "circled around"
c   28:16 Some Mss add "the centurion delivered the prisoners to the captain of the guard, but"
d   28:25 Some Mss read "our"
e   28:27 Isaiah 6:9-10
f   28:28 Some Mss add "When he had said these words, the Jews departed, having a great dispute among themselves"
g   1:1 Some Mss have the order "Jesus Christ"

it of holiness, by the resurrection from the dead, Jesus Christ our Lord, [5]through whom we received grace and the office of apostle, for obedience of faith among all the nations, for his name's sake; [6]among whom you are also called to belong to Jesus Christ; [7]to all who are in Rome, loved by God, called to be saints: Grace to you and peace from God our Father and the Lord Jesus Christ.

[8]First, I thank my God through Jesus Christ for all of you, because your faith is proclaimed throughout the whole world.[a] [9]For God is my witness, whom I serve in my spirit in the Good News of his Son, how I constantly mention you [10]always in my prayers, requesting, if by any means now at last I may succeed by the will of God to come to you. [11]For I long to see you, that I may impart to you some spiritual gift to strengthen you; [12]that is, that you and I may be mutually encouraged by each other's faith, both yours and mine.

[13]Now I do not desire to have you unaware, brothers, that I often planned to come to you, and was hindered so far, that I might have some fruit among you also, even as among the rest of the non-Jewish people. [14]I have an obligation both to Greeks and to barbarians, both to the wise and to the foolish. [15]So, for my part, I am eager to preach the Good News to you also who are in Rome. [16]For I am not ashamed of the Good News,[b] for it is the power of God for salvation for everyone who believes; for the Jew first, and also for the Greek. [17]For in it is revealed God's righteousness from faith to faith. As it is written, "But the righteous will live by faith."[c] [18]For the wrath of God is revealed from heaven against all ungodliness and unrighteousness of people, who suppress the truth by unrighteousness, [19]because what can be known about God is plain to them, because God has shown it to them. [20]For since the creation of the world his invisible attributes, his eternal power and divine nature, have been clearly seen, being understood from what has been made. So they are without excuse. [21]Because, although they knew God, they did not glorify him as God or give him thanks, but their thinking became nonsense, and their foolish heart was darkened.

[22]Professing to be wise, they became fools, [23]and traded the glory of the incorruptible God for images resembling corruptible man, and of birds, and four-footed animals, and crawling creatures. [24]Therefore God also abandoned them in the lusts of their hearts to impurity, to the degrading of their bodies among themselves, [25]who exchanged the truth of God for a lie, and worshiped and served the creation rather than the Creator, who is blessed forever. Amen.

[26]For this reason, God abandoned them to their degrading passions. For their women exchanged natural relations for that which is contrary to nature. [27]Likewise also the men, giving up natural relations with women, burned in their lust toward one another, men doing what is inappropriate with men, and receiving in themselves the due penalty of their error. [28]Even as they refused to have God in their knowledge, God abandoned them to a reprobate mind, to do those things which are not right; [29]being filled with all unrighteousness, sexual immorality,[d] wickedness, covetousness, maliciousness; full of envy, murder, strife, deceit, evil habits, secret slanderers, [30]slanderers, haters of God, insolent, arrogant, boastful, inventors of evil things, disobedient to parents, [31]foolish, promise-breakers, heartless, unforgiving, unmerciful;[e] [32]who, knowing the ordinance of God, that those who practice such things are worthy of death, not only do the same, but also approve of those who practice them.

2 Therefore you are without excuse, everyone of you who passes judgment. For in that which you judge another, you condemn yourself. For you who judge practice the same things. [2]Now we know

---

a   1:8 E.g., throughout the Roman empire
b   1:16 Some Mss add "of Christ"
c   1:17 Habakkuk 2:4
d   1:29 Some Mss lack "sexual immorality"
e   1:31 Some Mss lack "unforgiving"

that the judgment of God is in accordance with truth against those who practice such things. ³And do you think this, you who judge those who practice such things, and do the same, that you will escape the judgment of God? ⁴Or do you despise the riches of his goodness, forbearance, and patience, not knowing that the goodness of God leads you to repentance? ⁵But according to your hardness and unrepentant heart you are storing up for yourself wrath in the day of wrath and revelation of the righteous judgment of God; ⁶who "will pay back to everyone according to their works:"[a] ⁷to those who by perseverance in good works seek glory and honor and immortality -- everlasting life. ⁸But to those who are self-seeking, and do not obey the truth, but obey wickedness -- wrath and anger, ⁹affliction and distress, on every human being who does evil, to the Jew first, and also to the Greek.

¹⁰But glory, honor, and peace for everyone who does good, to the Jew first, and also to the Greek. ¹¹For there is no partiality with God. ¹²For as many as have sinned without the law will also perish without the law. As many as have sinned under the law will be judged by the law. ¹³For it is not the hearers of the law who are righteous before God, but the doers of the law will be justified. ¹⁴For when non-Jews who do not have the law do by nature the things of the law, these, not having the law, are a law to themselves, ¹⁵since they show the work of the law written on their hearts, their conscience bearing witness, and their thoughts either accusing or defending them, ¹⁶in the day when God will judge the secrets of people, according to my Good News, by Christ Jesus.

¹⁷But if you call yourself a Jew, and rely on the law, and boast in God, ¹⁸and know his will, and approve the things that are excellent, being instructed out of the law, ¹⁹and are confident that you yourself are a guide of the blind, a light to those who are in darkness, ²⁰a corrector of the foolish, a teacher of children, having in the law the embodiment of knowledge and truth.

²¹You therefore who teach another, do you not teach yourself? You who preach against stealing, do you steal? ²²You who say that one should not commit adultery, do you commit adultery? You who detest idols, do you rob temples? ²³You who boast in the law, do you, by disobeying the law, dishonor God? ²⁴For "because of you the name of God is blasphemed among the nations,"[b] just as it is written. ²⁵For circumcision indeed profits, if you are a doer of the law, but if you are a transgressor of the law, your circumcision has become uncircumcision. ²⁶If therefore the uncircumcised keep the requirements of the law, won't his uncircumcision be counted as circumcision? ²⁷Won't the uncircumcision which is by nature, if it fulfills the law, judge you, who with the letter and circumcision are a transgressor of the law? ²⁸For he is not a Jew who is one outwardly, neither is that circumcision which is outward in the flesh; ²⁹but he is a Jew who is one inwardly, and circumcision is that of the heart, by the Spirit, not in the letter; whose praise is not from people, but from God.

3 Then what advantage does the Jew have? Or what is the profit of circumcision? ²Much in every way. Because first of all, they were entrusted with the oracles of God. ³For what if some were without faith? Will their lack of faith nullify the faithfulness of God? ⁴May it never be. Let God be found true, but every human being a liar. As it is written,

"That you may be justified in your words, and prevail when you judge."[c]

⁵But if our unrighteousness commends the righteousness of God, what will we say? Is God unrighteous who inflicts wrath? (I am speaking in human terms). ⁶May it never be. For then how will God judge the world? ⁷For if the truth of God through my lie abounded to his glory, why am I also still judged as a sinner? ⁸And why not (as

---

a   2:6 Psalm 62:12; Proverbs 24:12
b   2:24 Isaiah 52:5; Ezekiel 36:22
c   3:4 Psalm 51:4

we are slanderously reported, and as some affirm that we say), "Let us do evil, that good may come?" Their condemnation is just. ⁹What then? Are we better than they? No, in no way. For we previously warned both Jews and Greeks, that they are all under sin. ¹⁰As it is written,

"There is no one righteous,ᵃ
　　no, not one."ᵇ
¹¹"There is no one who understands.
　　There is no one who seeks after God.ᶜ
¹²They have all turned aside.
　　They have together become
　　　unprofitable.
There is no one who does good,
　　there is not even one."ᵈ

¹³"Their throat is an open tomb.
　　With their tongues they have used
　　　deceit."ᵉ

"Viper's poison is under their lips;"ᶠ
　¹⁴"Whose mouth is full of cursing
　　and bitterness."ᵍ

¹⁵"Their feet are swift to shed blood.
　¹⁶Destruction and calamity are in
　　their paths.
　¹⁷The way of peace, they have not
　　known."ʰ

¹⁸"There is no fear of God before their
　　eyes."ⁱ

¹⁹Now we know that whatever things the law says, it speaks to those who are under the law, that every mouth may be closed, and all the world may be brought under the judgment of God. ²⁰Because by the works of the law, no flesh will be justified in his sight. For through the law comes the knowledge of sin. ²¹But now apart from the law, a righteousness of God has been revealed, being testified by the Law and the Prophets; ²²even the righteousness of God through faith in Jesus Christ to all and upon allʲ who believe. For there is no distinction, ²³for all have sinned, and fall short of the glory of God; ²⁴being justified freely by his grace through the redemption that is in Christ Jesus; ²⁵whom God displayed

publicly as a mercy seat,ᵏ through faith in his blood, for a demonstration of his righteousness, because in God's forbearance he had passed over the sins previously committed; ²⁶to demonstrate his righteousness at this present time, so that he would be just, and the justifier of him who has faith in Jesus.

²⁷Where then is the boasting? It is excluded. By what manner of law? Of works? No, but by a law of faith. ²⁸For we maintainˡ that one is justified by faith apart from the works of the law. ²⁹Or is God for Jews only? Is he not the God of non-Jews also? Yes, of non-Jews also, ³⁰since indeed there is one God who will justify the circumcised by faith, and the uncircumcised through faith. ³¹Do we then nullify the law through faith? May it never be. No, we establish the law.

4 What then will we say that Abraham, our forefather,ᵐ has found according to the flesh? ²For if Abraham was justified by works, he has something to boast about, but not before God. ³For what does the Scripture say? "And Abraham believed God, and it was credited to him as righteousness."ⁿ ⁴Now to the one who works, the pay is not counted as a gift, but as an obligation. ⁵But to him who does not work, but believes in him who justifies the ungodly, his faith is credited as righteousness. ⁶Even as David also pronounces blessing on the one to whom God counts righteousness apart from works,

---

a　3:10 Ecclesiastes 7:20
b　3:10 A possible scripture combination of Ecclesiastes 7:20 and Psalm 14:3
c　3:11 Psalm 14:2; Psalm 53:2
d　3:12 Psalm 14:3; 53:3
e　3:13 Psalm 5:9
f　3:13 Psalm 140:3
g　3:14 Psalm 10:7
h　3:17 Isaiah 59:7-8
i　3:18 Psalm 36:1
j　3:22 Some Mss lack "and upon all"
k　3:25 Or, "publicly to be a propitiation." The mercy seat was the covering of the ark where the blood was sprinkled on the Day of Atonement
l　3:28 Some Mss read "We maintain therefore"
m　4:1 Some Mss read "father"
n　4:3 Genesis 15:6

[7]"Happy are those whose lawless deeds
        are forgiven,
    and whose sins are covered.
[8]Happy is the one whom the Lord will
        not charge with sin."[a]
[9]Is this blessing then pronounced on
the circumcised, or on the uncircumcised
also? For we say that faith was credited to
Abraham as righteousness. [10]How then was
it credited? When he was in circumcision,
or in uncircumcision? Not in circumcision,
but in uncircumcision. [11]He received the
sign of circumcision, a seal of the righteousness of the faith which he had while
he was in uncircumcision, that he might be
the father of all those who believe, though
they be in uncircumcision, that[b] righteousness might also be credited to them.
[12]The father of circumcision to those who
not only are of the circumcision, but who
also walk in the steps of that faith of our father Abraham, which he had in uncircumcision. [13]For the promise to Abraham and
to his descendants that he should be heir
of the world was not through the law, but
through the righteousness of faith. [14]For if
those who are of the law are heirs, faith is
made void, and the promise is made of no
effect. [15]For the law works wrath, for where
there is no law, neither is there disobedience. [16]For this cause it is of faith, that it
may be according to grace, to the end that
the promise may be sure to all the descendants, not to that only which is of the law,
but to that also which is of the faith of
Abraham, who is the father of us all. [17]As
it is written, "I have made you a father of
many nations."[c] This is in the presence of
him whom he believed: God, who gives life
to the dead, and calls the things that are
not, as though they were. [18]Who in hope
believed against hope, to the end that he
might become a father of many nations,
according to that which had been spoken,
"So will your descendants be."[d] [19]Without
being weakened in faith, he considered[e] his
own body, which was as good as[f] dead (he
being about a hundred years old), and the
deadness of Sarah's womb. [20]Yet, looking
to the promise of God, he did not waver

through unbelief, but grew strong through
faith, giving glory to God, [21]and being fully
assured that what he had promised, he was
able also to perform. [22]Therefore it also was
"credited to him as righteousness."[g] [23]Now
it was not written that it was credited to
him for his sake alone, [24]but for our sake
also, to whom it will be credited, who believe in him who raised Jesus our Lord
from the dead, [25]who was delivered up for
our trespasses, and was raised for our justification.

5 Being therefore justified by faith, we
    have peace with God through our Lord
Jesus Christ; [2]through whom we also have
our access by faith into this grace in which
we stand, and we rejoice in hope of the glory of God. [3]Not only this, but we also rejoice
in our sufferings, knowing that suffering
works perseverance; [4]and perseverance,
proven character; and proven character,
hope: [5]and hope does not disappoint us, because God's love has been poured out into
our hearts through the Holy Spirit who was
given to us. [6]For while we were yet weak, at
the right time Christ died for the ungodly.
[7]For rarely does one die for the righteous.
Yet perhaps for a good person someone
might dare to die. [8]But God commends his
own love toward us, in that while we were
yet sinners, Christ died for us.

[9]Much more then, being now justified
by his blood, we will be saved from God's
wrath through him. [10]For if, while we were
enemies, we were reconciled to God through
the death of his Son, much more, being reconciled, we will be saved by his life.

[11]Not only so, but we also rejoice in God
through our Lord Jesus Christ, through
whom we have now received the reconciliation. [12]Therefore, as sin entered into
the world through one man, and death

---

a   4:8 Psalm 32:1-2
b   4:11 Some Mss lack "that"
c   4:17 Genesis 17:5
d   4:18 Genesis 15:5
e   4:19 Some Mss read "did not consider"
f   4:19 Some Mss add "already"
g   4:22 Genesis 15:6

through sin; and so death passed to all people, because all sinned. [13]For until the law, sin was in the world; but sin is not charged when there is no law. [14]Nevertheless death reigned from Adam until Moses, even over those whose sins weren't like Adam's disobedience, who is a foreshadowing of him who was to come. [15]But the free gift is not like the trespass. For if by the trespass of the one the many died, much more did the grace of God, and the gift by the grace of the one man, Jesus Christ, abound to the many. [16]The gift is not as through one who sinned: for the judgment came by one to condemnation, but the free gift came of many trespasses to justification. [17]For if by the trespass of the one, death reigned through the one; so much more will those who receive the abundance of grace and of the gift of righteousness reign in life through the one, Jesus Christ. [18]So then as through one trespass, all people were condemned; even so through one act of righteousness, all people were justified to life. [19]For as through the one man's disobedience many were made sinners, even so through the obedience of the one, many will be made righteous. [20]The law came in besides, that the trespass might abound; but where sin abounded, grace abounded more exceedingly; [21]that as sin reigned in death, even so grace might reign through righteousness to everlasting life through Jesus Christ our Lord.

6 What should we say then? Should we continue in sin, that grace may abound? [2]May it never be. We who died to sin, how could we live in it any longer? [3]Or do you not know that all we who were baptized into Christ Jesus were baptized into his death? [4]We were buried therefore with him through baptism to death, that just like Christ was raised from the dead through the glory of the Father, so we also might walk in newness of life. [5]For if we have become united with him in the likeness of his death, we will also be part of his resurrection; [6]knowing this, that our old self was crucified with him, that the body

of sin might be done away with, so that we would no longer be in bondage to sin. [7]For he who has died has been freed from sin. [8]But if we died with Christ, we believe that we will also live with him; [9]knowing that Christ, being raised from the dead, dies no more. Death no more has dominion over him. [10]For the death that he died, he died to sin one time; but the life that he lives, he lives to God. [11]In the same way, consider yourselves dead to sin, but alive to God in Christ Jesus.[a]

[12]Therefore do not let sin reign in your mortal body, that you should obey it in its lusts. [13]Neither present your members to sin as instruments of unrighteousness, but present yourselves to God, as alive from the dead, and your members as instruments of righteousness to God. [14]For sin will not have dominion over you. For you are not under law, but under grace. [15]What then? Should we sin because we are not under law, but under grace? May it never be. [16]Do you not know that when you present yourselves to someone as obedient slaves, you are slaves of the one whom you obey, whether of sin, which leads to death, or of obedience, which leads to righteousness? [17]But thanks be to God, that, whereas you were servants of sin, you became obedient from the[b] heart to that form of teaching to which you were entrusted. [18]Being made free from sin, you became slaves of righteousness.

[19]I speak in human terms because of the weakness of your flesh, for as you presented your members as servants to uncleanness and to wickedness upon wickedness, even so now present your members as slaves to righteousness for sanctification. [20]For when you were slaves of sin, you were free in regard to righteousness. [21]What fruit then did you have at that time in the things of which you are now ashamed? For the end of those things is death. [22]But now, being made free from sin, and having become slaves of God, you have your fruit of

---

a   6:11 Some Mss add "our Lord"
b   6:17 One early Ms adds "pure"

sanctification, and the result of everlasting life. [23]For the wages of sin is death, but the free gift of God is everlasting life in Christ Jesus our Lord.

7 Or do you not know, brothers (for I speak to those who know the law), that the law has dominion over a person for as long as he lives? [2]For the woman that has a husband is bound by law to the husband while he lives, but if the husband dies, she is discharged from the law of the husband. [3]So then if, while the husband lives, she is joined to another man, she would be called an adulteress. But if the husband dies, she is free from the law, so that she is no adulteress, though she is joined to another man. [4]Therefore, my brothers, you also were made dead to the law through the body of Christ, that you would be joined to another, to him who was raised from the dead, that we might bring forth fruit to God. [5]For when we were in the flesh,[a] the sinful passions which were through the law, worked in our members to bring forth fruit for death. [6]But now we have been released from the law, having died to that which held us captive, so that we serve in newness of the Spirit, and not in oldness of the letter.

[7]What should we say then? Is[b] the law sin? May it never be. However, I would not have known sin, except through the law. For I would not have known coveting, unless the law had said, "Do not covet." [8]But sin, finding occasion through the commandment, produced in me all kinds of coveting. For apart from the law, sin is dead.[c] [9]I was alive apart from the law once, but when the commandment came, sin became alive, and I died. [10]The commandment, which was for life, this I found to be for death; [11]for sin, finding occasion through the commandment, deceived me, and through it killed me. [12]Therefore the law indeed is holy, and the commandment holy, and righteous, and good.

[13]Did that which is good, then, become death to me? May it never be. But sin, that it might be shown to be sin, by working death to me through that which is good; that through the commandment sin might become exceeding sinful. [14]For we know that the law is spiritual, but I am fleshly, sold under sin. [15]For I do not know what I am doing. For I do not practice what I desire to do; but what I hate, that I do. [16]But if what I do not desire, that I do, I consent to the law that it is good. [17]So now it is no more I that do it, but sin which dwells in me. [18]For I know that in me, that is, in my flesh,[d] dwells no good thing. For desire is present with me, but to do that which is good is not. [19]For the good which I desire, I do not do; but the evil which I do not desire, that I practice. [20]But if what I[e] do not desire, that I do, it is no more I that do it, but sin which dwells in me. [21]I find then the law, that, to me, while I desire to do good, evil is present. [22]For I delight in God's law in my inner being, [23]but I see a different law in my members, warring against the law of my mind, and bringing me into captivity under the law of sin which is in my members. [24]What a wretched man I am. Who will deliver me out of the body of this death? [25]Thanks be to[f] God through Jesus Christ, our Lord. So then with the mind, I myself serve God's law, but with the flesh, the sin's law.

8 There is therefore now no condemnation to those who are in Christ Jesus.[g] [2]For the law of the Spirit of life in Christ Jesus made you[h] free from the law of sin and of death. [3]For what the law could not do, in that it was weak through the flesh, God did, sending his own Son in the likeness of sinful flesh and for sin, he condemned sin in the flesh; [4]that the ordinance of the law might be fulfilled in us, who walk not after the flesh, but after the Spirit. [5]For those who live according to the flesh set their minds on the things

a   7:5 Or, "were living according to the sinful nature"
b   7:7 Some Mss lack "Is"
c   7:7 Exodus 20:17; Deuteronomy 5:21
d   7:18 Or, "in my sinful nature"
e   7:20 Some Mss lack "I"
f   7:25 Some Mss read "I thank God"
g   8:1 Some Mss add "who do not walk according to the flesh, but according to the Spirit." See verse 4
h   8:2 Some Mss read "me"

of the flesh, but those who live according to the Spirit, the things of the Spirit. [6]For the mind set on the flesh is death, but the mind set on the Spirit is life and peace; [7]because the mind set on the flesh is hostile towards God; for it is not subject to God's law, neither indeed can it be. [8]And those who are in the flesh cannot please God. [9]But you are not in the flesh but in the Spirit, if it is so that the Spirit of God dwells in you. But if anyone does not have the Spirit of Christ, he does not belong to him. [10]And if Christ is in you, the body is dead because of sin, but the Spirit gives life because of righteousness. [11]But if the Spirit of him who raised up Jesus from the dead dwells in you, he who raised up Christ[a] from the dead will also give life to your mortal bodies through his Spirit who dwells in you. [12]So then, brothers, we are debtors, not to the flesh, to live after the flesh. [13]For if you live after the flesh, you must die; but if by the Spirit you put to death the deeds of the body, you will live. [14]For as many as are led by the Spirit of God, these are children of God. [15]For you did not receive the spirit of bondage again to fear, but you received the Spirit of adoption, by whom we cry, "Abba.[b] Father."

[16]The Spirit himself testifies with our spirit that we are children of God; [17]and if children, then heirs; heirs of God, and joint heirs with Christ; if indeed we suffer with him, that we may also be glorified with him. [18]For I consider that the sufferings of this present time are not worthy to be compared with the glory which will be revealed to us. [19]For the creation waits with eager expectation for the children of God to be revealed. [20]For the creation was subjected to futility, not of its own will, but because of him who subjected it, in hope [21]that the creation itself also will be delivered from the bondage of decay into the glorious freedom of the children of God. [22]For we know that the whole creation groans and travails in pain together until now. [23]And not only this, but ourselves also, who have the first fruits of the Spirit, even we ourselves groan within ourselves, waiting for adoption, the redemption of our body.

[24]For we were saved in hope, but hope that is seen is not hope. For who hopes for that which he sees? [25]But if we hope for that which we do not see, we wait for it with patience. [26]In the same way, the Spirit helps us in our weakness, for we do not know how to pray as we ought. But the Spirit himself makes intercession for us with inexpressible groanings. [27]And he who searches the hearts knows what is on the Spirit's mind, because he makes intercession for the saints in accordance with God.

[28]And we know that all things work together for good[c] for those who love God, to those who are called according to his purpose. [29]For whom he foreknew, he also predestined to be conformed to the image of his Son, that he might be the firstborn among many brothers. [30]Whom he predestined, those he also called. Whom he called, those he also justified. Whom he justified, those he also glorified.

[31]What then are we to say about these things? If God is for us, who can be against us? [32]He who did not spare his own Son, but delivered him up for us all, how would he not also with him freely give us all things? [33]Who could bring a charge against God's chosen ones? It is God who justifies. [34]Who is he who condemns? It is Christ who died, yes rather, who was raised from the dead, who is at the right hand of God, who also makes intercession for us.

[35]Who will separate us from the love of Christ? Could oppression, or anguish, or persecution, or famine, or nakedness, or danger, or sword? [36]Even as it is written, "For your sake we are killed all day long. We were regarded as sheep for the slaughter."[d] [37]No, in all these things, we are more than conquerors through him who loved us. [38]For I am persuaded, that neither death, nor life, nor angels, nor rulers, nor things present, nor things to come, nor powers, [39]nor height,

---

a   8:11 Some Mss add "Jesus"

b   8:15 "Abba" is an Aramaic word for "father"

c   8:28 Or, "We know that he works all things together for good." Some Mss read "We know that God works all things together for good for those who love God"

d   8:36 Psalm 44:22

nor depth, nor any other created thing, will be able to separate us from the love of God, which is in Christ Jesus our Lord.

9 I tell the truth in Christ. I am not lying, my conscience testifying with me in the Holy Spirit, [2]that I have great sorrow and unceasing pain in my heart. [3]For I could wish that I myself were accursed from Christ for my brothers' sake, my relatives according to the flesh, [4]who are Israelites; whose is the adoption, and the glory, and the covenants, and the giving of the law, and the service, and the promises; [5]of whom are the patriarchs, and from whom is the Christ, as concerning the flesh, who is over all, God, blessed forever. Amen.

[6]But it is not as though the word of God has come to nothing. For they are not all Israel, that are of Israel. [7]Neither, because they are Abraham's descendants, are they all children. But, "In Isaac will your descendants be called."[a] [8]That is, it is not the children of the flesh who are children of God, but the children of the promise are counted as descendants. [9]For this is what the promise said, "At the appointed time I will come, and Sarah will have a son."[b] [10]And not only that, but Rebekah also had conceived by one, our father Isaac. [11]For being not yet born, neither having done anything good or bad, that the purpose of God according to election might stand, not of works, but of him who calls, [12]it was said to her, "The elder will serve the younger."[c] [13]Even as it is written, "Jacob I loved, but Esau I hated."[d]

[14]What should we say then? Is there unrighteousness with God? May it never be. [15]For he said to Moses, "I will have mercy on whom I have mercy, and I will have compassion on whom I have compassion."[e] [16]So then it is not of him who wills, nor of him who runs, but of God who has mercy. [17]For the Scripture says to Pharaoh, "For this very purpose I caused you to be raised up, that I might show in you my power, and that my name might be proclaimed in all the earth."[f] [18]So then, he has mercy on whom he desires, and he hardens whom he desires. [19]You will say then to me, "Why does he still find fault? For who withstands his will?" [20]But who indeed are you, a human being, to reply against God? Will the thing formed ask him who formed it, "Why did you make me like this?"[g] [21]Or hasn't the potter a right over the clay, from the same lump to make one part a vessel for honor, and another for dishonor? [22]What if God, willing to show his wrath, and to make his power known, endured with much patience vessels of wrath made for destruction, [23]and that he might make known the riches of his glory on vessels of mercy, which he prepared beforehand for glory, [24]us, whom he also called, not from the Jews only, but also from the non-Jews? [25]As he says also in Hosea,

> "I will call them which were not my
>   people 'my people,' and her who
>   was not loved, 'loved.'"[h]
> [26]"It will be that in the place where it
>   was said to them, 'You are not
>   my people,'
> There they will be called 'sons of the
>   living God.'"[i]

[27]And Isaiah cries out concerning Israel,

> "Though the number of the children of
>   Israel are as the sand of the sea,[j]
> the remnant will be kept safe.[k]
> [28]For he will fulfill the word and
>   decisively in righteousness;
>   because the Lord will carry
>   out the word decisively[l] on the
>   earth."[m]

---

a   9:7 Genesis 21:12
b   9:9 Genesis 18:10,14
c   9:12 Genesis 25:23
d   9:13 Malachi 1:2-3
e   9:15 Exodus 33:19
f   9:17 Exodus 9:16
g   9:20 Isaiah 29:16; 45:9
h   9:25 Hosea 2:23
i   9:26 Hosea 1:10
j   9:27 Hosea 1:10
k   9:27 Or, "be saved"
l   9:28 Lit. "For he will fulfill the word and decisively [in righteousness, because the word decisively] will the Lord carry out on the earth." Some Mss lack the bracketed
m   9:28 Isaiah 10:22-23, and Hosea 1:10. A scripture combination practice known as gezera shawa. For examples of composite quotes where the major prophet is named, see Matthew 27:9-10 and Mark 1:2-3

29 As Isaiah has said before,

"Unless the Lord of hosts had left us a
few survivors,
we would have become like Sodom,
and would have been made like
Gomorrah."[a]

30 What should we say then? That the non-Jews, who did not follow after righteousness, attained to righteousness, even the righteousness which is of faith; 31 but Israel, following after a law of righteousness, did not arrive at that law[b]. 32 Why? Because they did not seek it by faith, but as it were by works.[c] They stumbled over the stumbling stone; 33 even as it is written,

"Look, I lay in Zion[d] a stumbling stone
and a rock that will make them
fall;[e]
and whoever believes in him will not
be put to shame."[f]

10 Brothers, my heart's desire and my prayer to God is for them[g], that they may be saved. 2 For I testify about them that they have a zeal for God, but not according to knowledge. 3 For being ignorant of God's righteousness, and seeking to establish their own righteousness, they did not subject themselves to the righteousness of God. 4 For Christ is the end[h] of the law for righteousness to everyone who believes. 5 For Moses writes about the righteousness of the law, "The one who does them will live by them."[i] 6 But the righteousness which is of faith says this, "Do not say in your heart, 'Who will ascend into heaven?'[j] (that is, to bring Christ down); 7 or, 'Who will descend into the abyss?'[k] (that is, to bring Christ up from the dead.)" 8 But what does it say? "The word is near you, in your mouth, and in your heart;"[l] that is, the word of faith, which we proclaim: 9 that if you will confess with your mouth that Jesus is Lord, and believe in your heart that God raised him from the dead, you will be saved. 10 For with the heart one believes, resulting in righteousness, and with the mouth confession is made, resulting in salvation. 11 For the Scripture says, "Whoever believes in him will not be put to shame."[m] 12 For there is no distinction between Jew and Greek; for the same Lord of all is rich to all who call on him. 13 For, "Whoever will call on the name of the Lord will be saved."[n] 14 How then will they call on him in whom they have not believed? How will they believe in him whom they have not heard? And how will they hear without someone preaching? 15 And how will they preach unless they are sent? As it is written:

"How beautiful are the feet of those
who bring good news[o] of peace,
who bring good news of good
things."[p]

16 But they did not all listen to the Good News. For Isaiah says, "Lord, who has believed our report?"[q] 17 So faith comes by hearing, and hearing[r] by the word of Christ.[s] 18 But I say, did they not hear? Yes, truly,

"Their voice has gone out to all the earth,
their words to the farthest parts of
the world."[t]

19 But I ask, did not Israel know? First Moses says,

"I will provoke you to jealousy with that
which is not a people.
I will make you angry with a foolish
nation."[u]

20 Isaiah is very bold, and says,

"I was found by those who did not seek
me.

---

a 9:29 Isaiah 1:9
b 9:31 Some Mss add "of righteousness"
c 9:32 Some Mss add "of the law"
d 9:33 Isaiah 28:16
e 9:33 Isaiah 8:14
f 9:33 Isaiah 28:16
g 10:1 Some Mss read "Israel"
h 10:4 Or, "fulfillment," "goal," "aim," "completion"
i 10:5 Leviticus 18:5
j 10:6 Deuteronomy 30:12
k 10:7 Deuteronomy 30:13
l 10:8 Deuteronomy 30:14
m 10:11 Isaiah 28:16
n 10:13 Joel 2:32
o 10:15 Some Mss lack "of peace, who bring good news"
p 10:15 Isaiah 52:7
q 10:16 Isaiah 53:1
r 10:17 Gk. akoes: "hearing, message"
s 10:17 Some Mss read "God"
t 10:18 Psalm 19:4
u 10:19 Deuteronomy 32:21

I was revealed to those who did not ask for me."[a]

[21]But as to Israel he says, "All day long I have spread out my hands to a disobedient and obstinate people."[b]

11 I ask then, has God rejected his people?[c] May it never be. For I also am an Israelite, a descendant of Abraham, of the tribe of Benjamin. [2]God did not reject his people, which he foreknew. Or do you not know what the Scripture says about Elijah? How he pleads with God against Israel: [3]"Lord, they have killed your prophets, they have broken down your altars; and I am left alone, and they seek my life."[d] [4]But how does God answer him? "I have kept for myself seven thousand people, who have not bowed the knee to Baal."[e] [5]Even so then at this present time also there is a remnant according to the election of grace. [6]And if by grace, then it is no longer of works; otherwise grace is no longer grace.[f]

[7]What then? That which Israel seeks for, that he did not obtain, but the chosen ones obtained it, and the rest were hardened. [8]According as it is written, "God gave them a spirit of stupor, eyes that they should not see, and ears that they should not hear, to this very day."[g] [9]David says,

"Let their table be made a snare, and a trap,
   and a stumbling block, and a retribution to them.
[10]Let their eyes be darkened, so that they can't see,
   and their backs be bent continually."[h]

[11]I ask then, did they stumble that they might fall? May it never be. But by their fall salvation has come to the non-Jews, to provoke them to jealousy. [12]Now if their fall is the riches of the world, and their loss the riches of the non-Jews; how much more their fullness? [13]For I speak to you who are non-Jews. Since then as I am an apostle to non-Jews, I glorify my ministry; [14]if by any means I may provoke to jealousy those who are my flesh, and may save some of them. [15]For if the rejection of them is the reconciling of the world, what would their acceptance be, but life from the dead? [16]If the first fruit is holy, so is the lump. If the root is holy, so are the branches. [17]But if some of the branches were broken off, and you, being a wild olive, were grafted in among them, and became partaker with them of the rich root of the olive tree;[i] [18]do not boast over the branches. But if you boast, it is not you who support the root, but the root supports you. [19]You will say then, "Branches were broken off, that I might be grafted in." [20]True; by their unbelief they were broken off, and you stand by your faith. Do not be conceited, but fear; [21]for if God did not spare the natural branches, neither will he spare you. [22]See then the goodness and severity of God. Toward those who fell, severity; but toward you, goodness, if you continue in his goodness; otherwise you also will be cut off. [23]They also, if they do not continue in their unbelief, will be grafted in, for God is able to graft them in again. [24]For if you were cut out of that which is by nature a wild olive tree, and were grafted contrary to nature into a good olive tree, how much more will these, which are the natural branches, be grafted into their own olive tree? [25]For I do not desire you to be ignorant, brothers, of this mystery, so that you won't be wise in your own conceits, that a partial hardening has happened to Israel, until the fullness of the non-Jews has come in, [26]and so all Israel will be saved. Even as it is written,

"There will come out of Zion the Deliverer,
   and he will turn away ungodliness from Jacob.
[27]This is my covenant to them,
   when I will take away their sins."[j]

---

a   10:20 Isaiah 65:1
b   10:21 Isaiah 65:2
c   11:1 Some Mss read "did God reject his inheritance he foreknew"
d   11:3 1 Kings 19:10,14
e   11:4 1 Kings 19:18
f   11:6 Some Mss add "But if it is of works, it is no longer grace; otherwise work is no longer work"
g   11:8 Deuteronomy 29:4; Isaiah 29:10
h   11:10 Psalm 69:22, 23
i   11:17 Some Mss read "root and the richness"
j   11:27 Isaiah 59:20-21; 27:9; Jeremiah 31:33-34

[28]Concerning the Good News, they are enemies for your sake. But concerning the election, they are loved for the fathers' sake. [29]For the gifts and the calling of God are irrevocable. [30]For as you in time past were disobedient to God, but now have obtained mercy by their disobedience, [31]even so these also have now been disobedient, that by the mercy shown to you they may now[a] also obtain mercy. [32]For God has shut up all to disobedience, that he might have mercy on all. [33]Oh the depth of the riches both of the wisdom and the knowledge of God. How unsearchable are his judgments, and his ways past tracing out.

[34]For, "Who has known the mind of the Lord?
    Or who has been his counselor?"[b]
[35]Or, "Who has first given to him,
    and it will be repaid to him again?"[c]
[36]For from him and by him and in him are all things. To him be the glory for ever. Amen.

12 Therefore I urge you, brothers, by the mercies of God, to present your bodies a living sacrifice, holy, acceptable to God, which is your spiritual service. [2]And do not[d] be conformed to this world, but be transformed by the renewing of your mind, so that you may prove what is the good, well-pleasing, and perfect will of God. [3]For I say, through the grace that was given me, to everyone among you, not to think of himself more highly than he ought to think; but to think reasonably, as God has apportioned to each person a measure of faith. [4]For even as we have many members in one body, and all the members do not have the same function, [5]so we, who are many, are one body in Christ, and individually members one of another. [6]Having gifts differing according to the grace that was given to us, if prophecy, let us prophesy according to the proportion of our faith; [7]or service, let us give ourselves to service; or he who teaches, to his teaching; [8]or he who exhorts, to his exhorting: he who gives, let him do it with liberality; he who rules, with diligence; he

who shows mercy, with cheerfulness.

[9]Let love be without hypocrisy. Abhor that which is evil. Cling to that which is good. [10]In love of the brothers be tenderly affectionate one to another; outdo one another in showing honor; [11]not lagging in diligence; fervent in spirit; serving the Lord; [12]rejoicing in hope; enduring in troubles; continuing steadfastly in prayer; [13]contributing to the needs of the saints; given to hospitality. [14]Bless those who persecute you;[e] bless, and do not curse. [15]Rejoice with those who rejoice. Weep with those who weep. [16]Be of the same mind one toward another. Do not be arrogant, but associate with the humble. Do not be wise in your own conceits. [17]Repay no one evil for evil. Respect what is honorable in the sight of all people. [18]If it is possible, as much as it is up to you, be at peace with all people. [19]Do not seek revenge yourselves, beloved, but leave room for the wrath. For it is written, "Vengeance belongs to me; I will repay, says the Lord."[f] [20]Therefore

"If your enemy is hungry, feed him.
    If he is thirsty, give him a drink;
    for in doing so, you will heap coals of
        fire on his head."[g]

[21]Do not be overcome by evil, but overcome evil with good.

13 Let every person be subject to the governing authorities, for there is no authority except from God, and those[h] that exist are appointed by God. [2]Therefore he who resists the authority, withstands the ordinance of God; and those who withstand will receive to themselves judgment. [3]For rulers are not a terror to the good work, but to the evil. Do you desire to have no fear

a   11:31 Some Mss lack "now"
b   11:34 Isaiah 40:13
c   11:35 Job 41:11
d   12:2 Some Mss read "You are not to"
e   12:14 Some Mss read "you"
f   12:19 Deuteronomy 32:35
g   12:20 The extraordinary kindness bestowed upon an enemy is an attempt to stir within the person a response of remorse, to realize the wrong that they have been doing. Proverbs 25:21-22
h   13:1 Some Mss add "authorities"

of the authority? Do that which is good, and you will have praise from the same, [4]for he is a servant of God to you for good. But if you do that which is evil, be afraid, for he does not bear the sword in vain; for he is a servant of God, an avenger for wrath to him who does evil. [5]Therefore you need to be in subjection, not only because of the wrath, but also for conscience' sake. [6]For this reason you also pay taxes, for they are servants of God's service, attending continually on this very thing. [7]Give therefore to everyone what you owe: taxes to whom taxes are due; customs to whom customs; respect to whom respect; honor to whom honor. [8]Owe no one anything, except to love one another; for he who loves his neighbor has fulfilled the law.

[9]For the commandments, "Do not commit adultery," "Do not murder," "Do not steal," "Do not give false testimony,"[a] "Do not covet,"[b] and whatever other commandments there are, are all summed up in this saying, namely, "You are to love your neighbor as yourself."[c] [10]Love does not harm a neighbor. Love therefore is the fulfillment of the law. [11]Do this, knowing the time, that it is already time for you to awaken out of sleep, for salvation is now nearer to us than when we first believed. [12]The night is far gone, and the day is near. Let us therefore throw off the works of darkness, and let us put on the armor of light. [13]Let us walk decently, as in the daytime; not in carousing and drunkenness, not in sexual immorality and lustful acts, and not in dissension and jealousy. [14]But put on the Lord Jesus Christ, and make no provision for the flesh, for its lusts.

14 Now accept one who is weak in faith, but not for disputes over opinions. [2]One person has faith to eat all things, but the one who is weak eats only vegetables. [3]Do not let the one who eats despise the one who does not eat. Do not let the one who does not eat judge the one who eats, for God has accepted him. [4]Who are you who judge another's servant? To his own lord he stands or falls. Yes, he will be made

to stand, for the Lord[d] has power to make him stand.

[5]One esteems one day as more important; and another one esteems every day alike. Let each one be fully convinced in his own mind. [6]The one who observes the day, observes it to the Lord; and the one who does not observe the day, he does not observe it to the Lord.[e] The one who eats, he eats to the Lord; since he gives thanks to God. And the one who does not eat, he does not eat to the Lord, and gives thanks to God. [7]For none of us lives to himself, and none dies to himself. [8]For if we live, we live to the Lord. Or if we die, we die to the Lord. If therefore we live or die, we are the Lord's. [9]For to this end Christ died,[f] and lived again, that he might be Lord of both the dead and the living.

[10]But you, why do you judge your brother? Or you again, why do you despise your brother? For we will all stand before the judgment seat of God.[g] [11]For it is written,

" 'As I live,' says the Lord, 'to me every
knee will bow.

Every tongue will confess to God.' "[h]

[12]So then each one of us will give account of himself to God. [13]Therefore let us not judge one another any more, but judge this rather, not to put a stumbling block in a brother's way, or an occasion for falling. [14]I know, and am persuaded in the Lord Jesus, that nothing is unclean of itself; except that to him who considers anything to be unclean, to him it is unclean. [15]Yet if because of food your brother is grieved, you walk no longer in love. Do not destroy with your food him for whom Christ died. [16]Then do not let your good be slandered, [17]for the kingdom of God is not eating and drinking, but righteousness, peace, and joy in the Holy Spirit. [18]For he who

a 13:9 Some Mss lack "Do not give false testimony"
b 13:9 Exodus 20:13-15,17; Deuteronomy 5:17-19,21
c 13:9 Leviticus 19:18
d 14:4 Some Mss read "God"
e 14:6 Some Mss lack "and the one who does not
   observe the day, he does not observe it to the Lord"
f 14:9 Some Mss add "and rose"
g 14:10 Some Mss read "Christ"
h 14:11 Isaiah 45:23

serves Christ in these things is acceptable to God and approved by people. [19]So then, let us follow after things which make for peace, and things by which we may build one another up. [20]Do not overthrow God's work for food's sake. All things indeed are clean, however it is evil for anyone who creates a stumbling block by eating. [21]It is good to not eat meat, drink wine, or do anything by which your brother stumbles, or is offended, or is made weak.[a]

[22]Do you have faith? Have it to yourself before God. Happy is he who does not judge himself in that which he approves. [23]But he who doubts is condemned if he eats, because it is not of faith; and whatever is not of faith is sin.

15 Now we who are strong ought to bear the weaknesses of the weak, and not to please ourselves. [2]Let each one of us please his neighbor for that which is good, to be building him up. [3]For even Christ did not please himself. But, as it is written, "The reproaches of those who reproached you fell on me."[b] [4]For whatever things were written before were written for our instruction, that through patience and through encouragement of the Scriptures we might have hope. [5]Now the God of patience and of encouragement grant you to be of the same mind one with another according to Christ Jesus, [6]that with one accord you may with one mouth glorify the God and Father of our Lord Jesus Christ.

[7]Therefore accept one another, even as Christ also accepted you,[c] to the glory of God. [8]Now I say that Christ has been made a servant of the circumcision for the truth of God, that he might confirm the promises given to the fathers, [9]and that people who are not Jewish might glorify God for his mercy. As it is written,

"Therefore I will give praise to you
        among the nations,
    and sing to your name."[d]

[10]Again he says,

"Rejoice, you nations, with his people."[e]

[11]Again,

"Praise the Lord, all you nations.

Let all the peoples praise him."[f]

[12]Again, Isaiah says,

"There will be the root of Jesse,
    he who arises to rule over the
        peoples;[g]
    in him will the nations hope."[h]

[13]Now may the God of hope fill you with all joy and peace in believing, that you may abound in hope, in the power of the Holy Spirit. [14]I myself am also persuaded about you, my brothers, that you yourselves are full of goodness, filled with all knowledge,[i] able also to admonish others. [15]But I write the more boldly to you[j] in part, as reminding you, because of the grace that was given to me by God, [16]that I should be a servant of Christ Jesus to the non-Jews, serving as a priest the Good News of God, that the offering up of the non-Jews might be made acceptable, sanctified by the Holy Spirit. [17]I have therefore my[k] boasting in Christ Jesus in things pertaining to God. [18]For I will not dare to speak of any things except those which Christ worked through me, for the obedience of the non-Jews, by word and deed, [19]in the power of signs and wonders, in the power of the Spirit of God; so that from Jerusalem, and around as far as to Illyricum, I have fully preached the Good News of Christ; [20]yes, making it my aim to proclaim the Good News, not where Christ was already named, that I might not build on another's foundation. [21]But, as it is written,

"Those who were not told about him,
        they will see,
    and those who have not heard, they
        will understand."[i]

---

a   14:21 Some Mss lack "or is offended…weak"
b   15:3 Psalm 69:9
c   15:7 Some Mss read "us"
d   15:9 2 Samuel 22:50; Psalm 18:49
e   15:10 Deuteronomy 32:43
f   15:11 Psalm 117:1
g   15:12 Gk. ethnos: "peoples, nations, coastlands, gentiles"
h   15:12 Isaiah 11:10
i   15:14 Gk. "the knowledge." Some Mss lack "the"
j   15:15 Some Mss add "brothers"
k   15:17 Gk. "the boasting." Some Mss lack "the"
i   15:21 Isaiah 52:15

²²Therefore also I was hindered these many times from coming to you, ²³but now, no longer having any place in these regions, and having these many years a longing to come to you, ²⁴whenever I journey to Spain.ᵇ For I hope to see you on my journey, and to be helped on my way there by you, if first I may enjoy your company for a while. ²⁵But now, I say, I am going to Jerusalem, serving the saints. ²⁶For it has been the good pleasure of Macedonia and Achaia to make a certain contribution for the poor among the saints who are at Jerusalem. ²⁷Yes, it has been their good pleasure, and they are their debtors. For if the non-Jewish people have been made partakers of their spiritual things, they owe it to them also to serve them in fleshly things. ²⁸When therefore I have accomplished this, and have sealed to them this fruit, I will go on by way of you to Spain. ²⁹I know that, when I come to you, I will come in the fullness ofᶜ the blessing of Christ.

³⁰Now I appeal to you, brothers, by our Lord Jesus Christ, and by the love of the Spirit, that you strive together with me in your prayers to God for me, ³¹that I may be delivered from those who are disobedient in Judea, and that my service which I have for Jerusalem may be acceptable to the saints; ³²that I may come to you in joy through the will of God, and together with you, find rest. ³³Now the God of peace be with you all. Amen.

16 I commend to you Phoebe, our sister, who is a deaconess of the church that is at Cenchreae, ²that you receive her in the Lord, in a way worthy of the saints, and that you assist her in whatever matter she may need from you, for she herself also has been a helper of many, and of my own self.

³Greet Prisca and Aquila, my fellow workers in Christ Jesus, ⁴who for my life, laid down their own necks; to whom not only I give thanks, but also all the churches of the non-Jewish people. ⁵Greet the church that is in their house. Greet Epaenetus, my beloved, who is the first fruits of Asiaᵈ to Christ. ⁶Greet Mary, who labored much

for you.ᵉ ⁷Greet Andronicus and Junia, my relatives and my fellow prisoners, who are notable among the apostles, who also were in Christ before me. ⁸Greet Ampliatus,ᶠ my beloved in the Lord. ⁹Greet Urbanus, our fellow worker in Christ, and Stachys, my beloved. ¹⁰Greet Apelles, the approved in Christ. Greet those who are of the household of Aristobulus. ¹¹Greet Herodion, my kinsman. Greet them of the household of Narcissus, who are in the Lord. ¹²Greet Tryphaena and Tryphosa, who labor in the Lord. Greet Persis, the beloved, who labored much in the Lord. ¹³Greet Rufus, the chosen in the Lord, and his mother and mine. ¹⁴Greet Asyncritus, Phlegon, Hermes, Patrobas, Hermas, and the brothers who are with them. ¹⁵Greet Philologus and Julia, Nereus and his sister, and Olympas, and all the saints who are with them. ¹⁶Greet one another with a holy kiss. The churches of Christ greet you.

¹⁷Now I appeal to you, brothers, look out for those who are causing the divisions and occasions of stumbling, contrary to the doctrine which you learned, and turn away from them. ¹⁸For those who are such do not serve our Lordᵍ Christ, but their own belly; and by their smooth and flattering speech, they deceive the hearts of the innocent. ¹⁹For your obedience has become known to all. I rejoice therefore over you. But I desire to have you wise in that which is good, but innocent in that which is evil. ²⁰And the God of peace will quickly crush Satan under your feet. The grace of our Lord Jesus Christ be with you.

²¹Timothy, my fellow worker, greets you, as do Lucius, Jason, and Sosipater, my relatives. ²²I, Tertius, who write the letter, greet you in the Lord. ²³Gaius, my host and host of the whole church, greets you. Erastus, the treasurer of the city, greets you, as

---

b   15:24 Some Mss add "I will come to you"
c   15:29 Some Mss add "Good News of the"
d   16:5 Some Mss read "Achaia"
e   16:6 Some Mss read "us"
f   16:8 Some Mss read "Amplias"
g   16:18 Some Mss add "Jesus"

does Quartus, the brother.[24a] [25]Now to him who is able to establish you according to my Good News and the proclaiming of Jesus Christ, according to the revelation of the mystery which has been kept secret through long ages, [26]but now is revealed, and by the Scriptures of the prophets, according to the commandment of the eternal God, is made known for obedience of faith to all the nations; [27]to the only wise God, through Jesus Christ, to whom be the glory forever. Amen.[b]

1 Corinthians

1 Paul, called to be an apostle of Christ Jesus[c] by the will of God, and our brother Sosthenes, [2]to the church of God which is at Corinth; those who are sanctified in Christ Jesus, called to be saints, with all who call on the name of our Lord Jesus Christ in every place, both theirs and ours: [3]Grace to you and peace from God our Father and the Lord Jesus Christ.

[4]I always thank my God concerning you, for the grace of God which was given you in Christ Jesus; [5]that in everything you were enriched in him, in all speech and all knowledge; [6]even as the testimony of Christ was confirmed in you: [7]so that you are not lacking in any gift, as you wait for the revelation of our Lord Jesus Christ; [8]who will also confirm you until the end, blameless in the day of our Lord Jesus Christ. [9]God is faithful, through whom you were called into the fellowship of his Son, Jesus Christ, our Lord. [10]Now I appeal to you, brothers, through the name of our Lord, Jesus Christ, that you all speak the same thing and that there be no divisions among you, but that you be perfected together in the same mind and in the same judgment. [11]For it has been reported to me concerning you, my brothers, by those who are from Chloe's household, that there are contentions among you. [12]Now I mean this, that each one of you says, "I follow Paul," "I follow Apollos," "I follow Cephas," and, "I follow Christ." [13]Is[d] Christ divided? Was Paul crucified for you? Or were you baptized into the name of Paul? [14]I thank God[e] that I baptized none of you, except Crispus and Gaius, [15]so that no one should say that you had been baptized[f] into my own name. [16](Now I also baptized the household of Stephanas; beyond that, I do not know whether I baptized any other.) [17]For Christ sent me not to baptize, but to proclaim the Good News—not in wisdom of words, so that the cross of the Christ would not be made void. [18]For the message about the cross is foolishness to those who are perishing, but to us who are being saved it is the power of God. [19]For it is written,

"I will destroy the wisdom of the wise,
and the discernment of the
discerning I will nullify."[g]

[20]Where is the wise? Where is the scribe? Where is the debater of this age? Hasn't God made foolish the wisdom of this[h] world? [21]For seeing that in the wisdom of God, the world through its wisdom did not know God, it was God's good pleasure through the foolishness of the preaching to save those who believe. [22]For Jews ask for signs, and Greeks seek after wisdom, [23]but we preach Christ crucified, a stumbling block to Jews and foolishness to non-Jews[i], [24]but to those who are called, both Jews and Greeks, Christ is the power of God and the wisdom of God. [25]Because the foolishness of God is wiser than man's, and the weakness of God is stronger than man's. [26]For consider your calling, brothers, that not many were wise from a human perspective, not many

---

a   16:24 Some Mss add "The grace of our Lord Jesus Christ be with you all. Amen." Cf. v. 20

b   16:27 Some Mss place verses 25-27 after 14:23 as verses 24-26

c   1:1 Some Mss have the order "Jesus Christ"

d   1:13 Some Mss add "not"

e   1:14 Some Mss lack "God"

f   1:15 Some Mss read "that I had baptized you"

g   1:19 Isaiah 29:14

h   1:20 instead of "you had been baptized" lack "this"

i   1:23 Some Mss read "Greeks"

powerful, not many of noble birth. [27]But God chose the foolish of the world to shame the wise. And God chose the weak of the world to shame the strong. [28]And God chose the lowly of the world, and the despised, what is considered to be nothing, to bring to nothing what is considered to be something, [29]that no flesh might boast before God. [30]And because of him you are in Christ Jesus, who became for us wisdom from God, and righteousness and sanctification and redemption, [31]so that, as it is written, "Let him who boasts, boast in the Lord."[a]

2 When I came to you, brothers, I did not come with superiority of speech or wisdom, proclaiming to you the mystery[b] of God. [2]For I determined not to know anything among you, except Jesus Christ, and him crucified. [3]When I was with you, I was weak and afraid and I shook. [4]My speech and my preaching were not in persuasive words[c] of[d] wisdom, but in demonstration of the Spirit and of power, [5]that your faith would not rest on human wisdom, but on the power of God. [6]We speak wisdom, however, among those who are mature, but a wisdom not of this age or of the rulers of this age, who are passing away. [7]But we speak God's wisdom in a mystery, the wisdom that has been hidden, which God foreordained before the ages for our glory, [8]which none of the rulers of this age has understood. For had they known it, they would not have crucified the Lord of glory. [9]But as it is written, No eye has seen, and no ear has heard, and no mind has imagined the things which God has prepared for those who love him.[e]

[10]But to us God revealed it through the Spirit. For the Spirit searches all things, even the deep things of God. [11]For what person knows the things of a person except the spirit of the person that is in him? So also, no one knows the things of God except the Spirit of God. [12]But we received, not the spirit of the world, but the Spirit which is from God, that we might know the things that were freely given to us by God. [13]And we speak of these things, not with words taught by human wisdom, but with those taught by the[f] Spirit, comparing spiritual things with spiritual things. [14]Now the natural person does not receive the things of the Spirit of God, for they are foolishness to him, and he cannot understand them, because they are spiritually discerned. [15]But he who is spiritual discerns all things, and he himself is judged by no one. [16]For, "Who has known the mind of the Lord? Who will instruct him?"[g] But we have the mind of Christ.

3 And I, brothers, could not address you as spiritual, but as fleshly, as infants in Christ. [2]I fed you with milk, not solid food, for you weren't yet ready. And even now you are still not ready, [3]for you are still fleshly. For insofar as there is jealousy and strife[h] among you, are you not fleshly, and living by human standards? [4]For when one says, "I follow Paul," and another, "I follow Apollos," are you not merely human?[i] [5]What then is Apollos? And what is Paul? Servants through whom you believed, and each as the Lord gave to him. [6]I planted. Apollos watered. But God made it grow. [7]So then neither he who plants is anything, nor he who waters, but God who makes it grow. [8]Now he who plants and he who waters are the same, but each will receive his own reward according to his own labor. [9]For we are God's fellow workers. You are God's field, God's building. [10]According to the grace of God which was given to me, as a wise master builder I laid a foundation, and another builds on it. But let each one be careful how he builds on it. [11]For no one can lay any other foundation than that which has been laid, which is Jesus Christ. [12]But if anyone builds on this[j] foundation with gold, silver, costly stones, wood, hay, or

---

a   1:31 Jeremiah 9:24
b   2:1 Some Mss read "testimony"
c   2:4 Some Mss lack "words"
d   2:4 Some Mss add "human"
e   2:9 Isaiah 64:4; James 1:12
f   2:13 Some Mss add "Holy"
g   2:16 Isaiah 40:13
h   3:3 Some Mss add "and divisions"
i   3:4 Some Mss read "fleshly"
j   3:12 Some Mss lack "this"

straw; [13]each man's work will be revealed. For the Day will declare it, because it is revealed in fire; and the fire itself will test what sort of work each man's work is. [14]If any man's work remains which he built on it, he will receive a reward. [15]If any man's work is burned, he will suffer loss, but he himself will be saved, but as through fire.

[16]Do you not know that you are a temple of God, and that God's Spirit lives in you? [17]If anyone destroys the temple of God, God will destroy him; for God's temple is holy, which you are. [18]Let no one deceive himself. If anyone thinks that he is wise among you in this age, let him become a fool, that he may become wise. [19]For the wisdom of this world is foolishness with God. For it is written, "He traps the wise in their craftiness."[a] [20]And again, "The Lord knows the thoughts of the wise,[b] that they are futile."[c] [21]Therefore let no one boast about people. For all things are yours, [22]whether Paul, or Apollos, or Cephas, or the world, or life, or death, or things present, or things to come. All are yours, [23]and you are Christ's, and Christ is God's.

4 So a person should consider us as Christ's servants, and stewards of God's mysteries. [2]Here, moreover, it is required of stewards, that they be found faithful. [3]But with me it is a very small thing that I should be judged by you, or by man's judgment. Yes, I do not judge my own self. [4]For I know nothing against myself. Yet I am not justified by this, but he who judges me is the Lord. [5]Therefore judge nothing before the time, until the Lord comes, who will both bring to light the hidden things of darkness, and reveal the counsels of the hearts. Then each one will get his praise from God.

[6]Now these things, brothers, I have in a figure transferred to myself and Apollos for your sakes, that in us you might learn not to go[d] beyond the things which are written, that none of you be puffed up against one another. [7]For who makes you different? And what do you have that you did not receive? But if you did receive it, why do you boast as if you had not received it? [8]You are al-ready filled. You have already become rich. You have come to reign without us. Yes, and I wish that you did reign, that we also might reign with you. [9]For, I think that God has displayed us, the apostles, last of all, like men sentenced to death. For we are made a spectacle to the world, both to angels and people. [10]We are fools for Christ's sake, but you are wise in Christ. We are weak, but you are strong. You have honor, but we have dishonor. [11]Even to this present hour we hunger, thirst, are naked, are beaten, and have no certain dwelling place. [12]We toil, working with our own hands. When people curse us, we bless. Being persecuted, we endure. [13]Being defamed, we entreat. We are made as the filth of the world, the dirt wiped off by all, even until now. [14]I do not write these things to shame you, but to admonish you as my beloved children. [15]For though you have ten thousand tutors in Christ, yet not many fathers. For in Christ Jesus, I became your father through the Good News. [16]I appeal to you therefore, be imitators of me. [17]Because of this I[e] have sent Timothy to you, who is my beloved and faithful child in the Lord, who will remind you of my ways which are in Christ, even as I teach everywhere in every church. [18]Now some are puffed up, as though I were not coming to you. [19]But I will come to you shortly, if the Lord is willing. And I will know, not the word of those who are puffed up, but the power. [20]For the kingdom of God is not in word, but in power. [21]What do you want? Should I come to you with a rod, or in love and a spirit of gentleness?

5 It is actually reported that there is sexual immorality among you, and such sexual immorality as is not even[f] among the nations, that one has his father's wife. [2]You are puffed up, and did not rather mourn, that he who had done this deed

---

a   3:19 Job 5:13
b   3:20 Some Mss read "man"
c   3:20 Psalm 94:11
d   4:6 Some Mss read "think"
e   4:17 Some Mss add "he"
f   5:1 Some Mss add "named"

might be removed from among you. ³For I most certainly, as being absent in body but present in spirit, have already, as though I were present, judged him who has done this thing. ⁴In the name of our Lord Jesus,ᵃ you being gathered together, and my spirit, with the power of our Lord Jesus,ᵇ ⁵are to deliver such a one to Satan for the destruction of the flesh,ᶜ that the spirit may be saved in the day of the Lord.ᵈ

⁶Your boasting is not good. Do you not know that a little yeast leavens the whole lump? ⁷Purge out the old yeast, that you may be a new lump, even as you are unleavened. For indeed Christ, our Passover, has been sacrificed for us.ᵉ ⁸Therefore let us keep the feast, not with old yeast, neither with the yeast of malice and wickedness, but with the unleavened bread of sincerity and truth. ⁹I wrote to you in my letter to have no company with sexual sinners; ¹⁰yet not at all meaning with the sexual sinners of this world, or with the covetous and extortioners, or with idolaters; for then you would have to leave the world. ¹¹But as it is, I wrote to you not to associate with anyone who is called a brother who is a sexual sinner, or covetous, or an idolater, or a slanderer, or a drunkard, or an extortioner. Do not even eat with such a person. ¹²For what have I to do with also judging those who are outside? Do you not judge those who are within? ¹³But those who are outside, God judges. "Put away the wicked person from among yourselves."ᶠ

6 Dare any of you, having a matter against his neighbor, go to law before the unrighteous, and not before the saints? ²Do you not know that the saints will judge the world? And if the world is judged by you, are you unworthy to judge the smallest matters? ³Do you not know that we will judge angels? How much more, things that pertain to this life? ⁴If then, you have to judge things pertaining to this life, do you set them to judge who are of no account in the church? ⁵I say this to move you to shame. Is not there even one wise person among you who would be able to decide

between his brothers? ⁶But brother goes to law with brother, and that before unbelievers. ⁷Therefore it is already altogether a defect in you, that you have lawsuits one with another. Why not rather be wronged? Why not rather be defrauded? ⁸No, but you yourselves do wrong, and defraud, and that against your brothers. ⁹Or do you not know that the unrighteous will not inherit the kingdom of God? Do not be deceived. Neither the sexually immoral, nor idolaters, nor adulterers, nor effeminate,ᵍ nor men who have sexual relations with men,ʰ ¹⁰nor thieves, nor covetous, nor drunkards, nor slanderers, nor swindlers, will inherit the kingdom of God. ¹¹Such were some of you, but you were washed. But you were sanctified. But you were justified in the name of the Lord Jesus Christ,ⁱ and in the Spirit of our God. ¹²"All things are lawful for me," but not all things are expedient. "All things are lawful for me," but I will not be brought under the power of anything. ¹³"Foods for the belly, and the belly for foods," but God will bring to nothing both it and them. But the body is not for sexual immorality, but for the Lord; and the Lord for the body. ¹⁴Now God raised up the Lord, and will also raise us up by his power. ¹⁵Do you not know that your bodies are members of Christ? Should I then take the members of Christ, and make them members of a prostitute? May it never be. ¹⁶Or do you not know that he who is joined to a prostitute is one body? For he says, "The two will become one flesh."ʲ ¹⁷But he who is joined to the Lord is one spirit. ¹⁸Flee sexual immorality. "Every

---

a   5:4 Some Mss add "Christ"

b   5:4 Some Mss add "Christ"

c   5:5 Or, "destruction of the carnal nature"

d   5:5 Some Mss add "Jesus." Other Mss read "our Lord Jesus Christ"

e   5:7 Some Mss lack "for us"

f   5:13 Deuteronomy 13:5; 17:7; 19:19; 21:21; 22:21; 24:7

g   6:9 I.e., effeminate by perversion

h   6:9 Lit. "manlier." Gk arsenokoites. See Leviticus 18:22, 20:13 LXX where God forbids men (arsenos) to lie/have sex (koiten) as with a woman. See also Romans 1:26-27

i   6:11 Some Mss lack "Christ"

j   6:16 Genesis 2:24

sin that a person does is outside the body," but he who commits sexual immorality sins against his own body. [19]Or do you not know that your body is a temple of the Holy Spirit which is in you, which you have from God? You are not your own, [20]for you were bought with a price. Therefore glorify God in your body[a].

[7] Now concerning the things about which you wrote[b]: it is good for a man not to touch[c] a woman. [2]But, because of sexual immoralities, let each man have his own wife, and let each woman have her own husband. [3]Let the husband fulfill his marital duty[d] to his wife, and likewise also the wife to her husband. [4]The wife does not have authority over her own body, but the husband. Likewise also the husband does not have authority over his own body, but the wife. [5]Do not deprive one another, unless it is by consent for a season, that you may give yourselves to[e] prayer, and may be together again, that Satan does not tempt you because of your lack of self-control.

[6]But this I say by way of concession, not of commandment. [7]Yet I wish that all people were like me. However each one has his own gift from God, one of this kind, and another of that kind. [8]But I say to the unmarried and to widows, it is good for them if they remain even as I am. [9]But if they do not have self-control, let them marry. For it's better to marry than to burn. [10]But to the married I command—not I, but the Lord—that the wife not leave her husband [11](but if she departs, let her remain unmarried, or else be reconciled to her husband), and that the husband not leave his wife.

[12]But to the rest I—not the Lord—say, if any brother has an unbelieving wife, and she is content to live with him, let him not leave her. [13]The woman who has an unbelieving husband, and he is content to live with her, let her not leave her husband[f]. [14]For the unbelieving husband is sanctified in the wife, and the unbelieving wife is sanctified by the brother[g]. Otherwise your children would be unclean, but now they are holy. [15]Yet if the unbeliever departs, let there be separation. The brother or the sister is not under bondage in such cases, but God has called you[h] to peace. [16]For how do you know, wife, whether you will save your husband? Or how do you know, husband, whether you will save your wife? [17]Only, as the Lord has assigned to each one, as God[i] has called each, so let him walk. So I command in all the churches.

[18]Was anyone called having been circumcised? Let him not become uncircumcised. Has anyone been called in uncircumcision? Let him not be circumcised. [19]Circumcision is nothing, and uncircumcision is nothing, but the keeping of the commandments of God. [20]Let each person stay in that calling in which he was called. [21]Were you called being a slave? Do not let that bother you, but if you get an opportunity to become free, use it. [22]For he who was called in the Lord being a slave is the Lord's free person. Likewise he who was called being free is Christ's slave. [23]You were bought with a price. Do not become slaves of people. [24]Brothers, let each one, in whatever condition he was called, stay in that condition with God.

[25]Now concerning virgins, I have no commandment from the Lord, but I give my judgment as one who has obtained mercy from the Lord to be trustworthy. [26]I think that it is good therefore, because of the distress that is on us, that it is good for a person to remain as he is. [27]Are you bound to a wife? Do not seek to be freed. Are you free from a wife? Do not seek a wife. [28]But if you marry, you have not sinned. If a virgin marries, she has not sinned. Yet such

---

a   6:20 Some Mss add "and in your spirit, which are God's"
b   7:1 Some Mss add "to me"
c   7:1 A euphemism for sexual relations. See Genesis 20:6
d   7:3 Some Mss read "affection"
e   7:5 Some Mss read "fasting and"
f   7:13 Some Mss read "him"
g   7:14 Or, "believing husband." Some Mss read "in the husband"
h   7:15 Some Mss read "us"
i   7:17 Some Mss read "God…Lord" instead of "Lord…God"

will have trouble in this life,[a] and I want to spare you. [29]But I say this, brothers: the time is short, that from now on, those who have wives should be as though they had none; [30]and those who weep, as though they did not weep; and those who rejoice, as though they did not rejoice; and those who buy, as though they did not possess; [31]and those who use the[b] world, as not using it to the fullest. For the form of this world is passing away. [32]But I desire to have you to be free from cares. He who is unmarried is concerned for the things of the Lord, how he may please the Lord; [33]but he who is married is concerned about the things of the world, how he may please his wife, [34]and is divided. And the woman that is unmarried, or a virgin, is concerned about the things of the Lord, so that she may be holy both in body and in spirit. But the one that is married is concerned about the things of the world, how she may please her husband. [35]This I say for your own profit; not that I may ensnare you, but for that which is appropriate, and that you[c] may attend to the Lord without distraction. [36]But if anyone thinks that he is behaving inappropriately toward his virgin, if she is past the flower of her age, and if need so requires, let him do what he desires. He does not sin. Let them marry. [37]But he who stands steadfast in his heart, having no necessity, but has power over his own heart, to keep his own virgin, does well. [38]So then both he who gives his own virgin[d] in marriage does well, and he who does not give her in marriage does better. [39]A wife is bound[e] to her husband as long as he lives; but if the husband is dead, she is free to be married to whomever she desires, only in the Lord. [40]But she is happier if she stays as she is, in my judgment, and I think that I also have God's Spirit.

8 Now concerning things sacrificed to idols: We know that we all have knowledge. Knowledge puffs up, but love builds up. [2]But if anyone thinks that he knows anything, he does not yet know[f] as he ought to know. [3]But if anyone loves God, the same is known by him. [4]Therefore concerning the eating of things sacrificed to idols, we know that no idol is anything in the world, and that there is no[g] God but one. [5]For though there are things that are called "gods," whether in the heavens or on earth; as there are many "gods" and many "lords;" [6]yet to us there is one God, the Father, from whom are all things, and we for him; and one Lord, Jesus Christ, through whom are all things, and we live through him. [7]However, not all have this knowledge. But some, being so accustomed[h] to idols until now, eat as of a thing sacrificed to an idol, and their conscience, being weak, is defiled. [8]But food will not commend us to God. For neither, if we do not eat, are we the worse; nor, if we eat, are we the better. [9]But be careful that by no means does this liberty of yours become a stumbling block to the weak. [10]For if someone sees you who have knowledge sitting in an idol's temple, won't his conscience, if he is weak, be emboldened to eat things sacrificed to idols? [11]And through your knowledge, he who is weak perishes, the brother for whom the Christ died. [12]Thus, sinning against the brothers, and wounding their conscience when it is weak, you sin against Christ. [13]Therefore, if food causes my brother to stumble, I will eat no meat forevermore, that I do not cause my brother to stumble.

9 Am I not free? Am I not an apostle? Have I not seen Jesus[i] our Lord? Are you not my work in the Lord? [2]If to others I am not an apostle, yet at least I am to you; for you are the seal of my office of apostle in the Lord. [3]My defense to those who examine me is this. [4]Have we no right to eat and to drink? [5]Have we no right to take along a wife who is a believer, even as the rest of

---

a 7:28 Lit. "in the flesh"
b 7:31 Some Mss add "this"
c 7:35 One early Ms adds "you," making it explicit
d 7:38 Some Mss lack "his own virgin"
e 7:39 Some Mss add "by law"
f 8:2 Some Mss add "nothing"
g 8:4 Some Mss add "other"
h 8:7 Some Mss read "having consciousness"
i 9:1 Some Mss add "Christ"

the apostles, and the brothers of the Lord, and Cephas? [6]Or have only Barnabas and I no right to not work? [7]What soldier ever serves at his own expense? Who plants a vineyard, and does not eat of its fruit? Or who feeds a flock, and does not drink from the flock's milk? [8]Do I say these things according to human authority? Or does not the Law also say the same thing? [9]For it is written in the Law of Moses, "Do not muzzle an ox while it treads out the grain."[a] Is it for the oxen that God cares, [10]or does he say it assuredly for our sake? Yes, it was written for our sake, because he who plows ought to plow in hope, and he who threshes in the hope of having a share[b]. [11]If we sowed to you spiritual things, is it a great thing if we reap your fleshly things? [12]If others partake of this right over you, do not we yet more? Nevertheless we did not use this right, but we bear all things, that we may cause no hindrance to the Good News of Christ. [13]Do you not know that those who serve around sacred things eat from the things of the temple, and those who wait on the altar have their portion with the altar? [14]Even so the Lord ordained that those who proclaim the Good News should live from the Good News. [15]But I have used none of these things, and I do not write these things that it may be done so in my case; for I would rather die, than that anyone should make my boasting void. [16]For if I proclaim the Good News, I have nothing to boast about; for necessity is laid on me; but woe is to me, if I do not proclaim the Good News. [17]For if I do this of my own will, I have a reward. But if not of my own will, I have a stewardship entrusted to me. [18]What then is my reward? That, when I proclaim the Good News, I may present the Good News[c] without charge, so as not to abuse my authority in the Good News. [19]For though I was free from all, I brought myself under bondage to all, that I might gain the more. [20]To the Jews I became as a Jew, that I might gain Jews; to those who are under the law, as under the law, not being myself under the law,[d] that I might gain those who are under the law; [21]to those who are without law, as without law (not being without law toward God, but under law toward Christ), that I might win those who are without law. [22]To the weak I became as weak, that I might gain the weak. I have become all things to all people, that I may by all means save some. [23]Now I do all things[e] for the sake of the Good News, that I may be a joint partaker of it. [24]Do you not know that those who run in a race all run, but one receives the prize? Run like that, that you may win. [25]Now everyone who competes in the games exercises self-control in all things. Now they do it to receive a corruptible crown, but we an incorruptible. [26]I therefore run like that, as not uncertainly. I fight like that, as not beating the air, [27]but I beat my body and bring it into submission, lest by any means, after I have preached to others, I myself should be rejected.

10 Now I would not have you ignorant, brothers, that our fathers were all under the cloud, and all passed through the sea; [2]and were all baptized into Moses in the cloud and in the sea; [3]and all ate the same spiritual food; [4]and all drank the same spiritual drink. For they drank of a spiritual rock that followed them, and the rock was Christ. [5]However with most of them, God was not well pleased, for they were overthrown in the wilderness. [6]Now these things were our examples, to the intent we should not lust after evil things, as they also lusted. [7]Neither be idolaters, as some of them were. As it is written, "The people sat down to eat and drink, and rose up to play."[f] [8]Neither let us commit sexual immorality, as some of them committed, and in one day twenty-three thousand fell. [9]Neither let us test the Christ,[g] as some of them tested, and perished by the serpents. [10]Neither grumble, as some of them also

a   9:9 Deuteronomy 25:4
b   9:11 Some Mss add "of his hope"
c   9:18 Some Mss add "of Christ"
d   9:20 Some Mss lack "not being myself under the law"
e   9:23 Some Mss read "this"
f   10:7 Exodus 32:6
g   10:9 Some Mss read "Lord"

grumbled, and perished by the destroyer. [11]Now[a] these things happened to them by way of example, and they were written for our admonition, on whom the ends of the ages have come. [12]Therefore let him who thinks he stands be careful that he does not fall.

[13]No temptation has taken you except what is common to humanity. God is faithful, who will not allow you to be tempted above what you are able, but will with the temptation also make the way of escape, that you may be able to endure it. [14]Therefore, my beloved, flee from idolatry. [15]I speak as to wise people. Judge what I say. [16]The cup of blessing which we bless, is it not a sharing of the blood of Christ? The bread which we break, is it not a sharing of the body of Christ? [17]Because there is one loaf of bread, we, who are many, are one body; for we all partake of the one loaf of bread. [18]Consider Israel according to the flesh. Do not those who eat the sacrifices participate in the altar?

[19]What am I saying then? That a thing sacrificed to idols is anything, or that an idol is anything? [20]But I say that the things which they sacrifice, they sacrifice to demons, and not to God, and I do not desire that you would have fellowship with demons. [21]You cannot both drink the cup of the Lord and the cup of demons. You cannot both partake of the table of the Lord, and of the table of demons. [22]Or do we provoke the Lord to jealousy? Are we stronger than he? [23]"All things are lawful,[b]" but not all things are profitable. "All things are lawful," but not all things build up. [24]Let no one seek his own, but[c] his neighbor's good. [25]Whatever is sold in the butcher shop, eat, asking no question for the sake of conscience, [26]for "the earth is the Lord's, and its fullness."[d] [27]But if one of those who do not believe invites you to a meal, and you are inclined to go, eat whatever is set before you, asking no questions for the sake of conscience. [28]But if anyone says to you, "This was offered to idols," do not eat it for the sake of the one who told you, and for the sake of conscience.[e] [29]Conscience, I say, not your own, but the other's conscience. For why is my liberty judged by another conscience? [30]If I partake with thankfulness, why am I denounced for that for which I give thanks? [31]Whether therefore you eat, or drink, or whatever you do, do all to the glory of God. [32]Give no occasions for stumbling, either to Jews, or to Greeks, or to the church of God; [33]even as I also please all people in all things, not seeking my own profit, but the profit of the many, that they may be saved.

11 Be imitators of me, even as I also am of Christ. [2]Now I praise you,[f] that you remember me in all things, and hold firm the traditions, even as I delivered them to you. [3]But I would have you know that the head of every man is Christ, and the head of the woman is the man, and the head of Christ is God. [4]Every man praying or prophesying, having his head covered, dishonors his head. [5]But every woman praying or prophesying with her head unveiled dishonors her head. For it is one and the same thing as if she were shaved. [6]For if a woman is not covered, let her also be shorn. But if it is shameful for a woman to be shorn or shaved, let her be covered. [7]For a man indeed ought not to have his head covered, because he is the image and glory of God, but the woman is the glory of the man. [8]For man is not from woman, but woman from man; [9]for neither was man created for the woman, but woman for the man. [10]For this cause the woman ought to have authority on her head, because of the messengers.

[11]Nevertheless, neither is the woman independent of the man, nor the man independent of the woman, in the Lord. [12]For as woman came from man, so a man also comes through a woman; but all things

---

a   10:11 Some Mss add "all"
b   10:23 Some Mss add "for me"
c   10:24 Some Mss add "each"
d   10:26 Psalm 24:1
e   10:28 Some Mss add "For the earth is the Lord's, and all its fullness"
f   11:2 Some Mss add "brothers"

are from God. [13]Judge for yourselves. Is it appropriate that a woman pray to God unveiled? [14]Doesn't even nature itself teach you that if a man has long hair, it is a dishonor to him? [15]But if a woman has long hair, it is a glory to her, for her hair is given to her[a] for a covering. [16]But if anyone seems to be contentious, we have no such custom, neither do God's churches.

[17]But in giving you this command, I do not praise you, that you come together not for the better but for the worse. [18]For first of all, when you come together in the church, I hear that divisions exist among you, and I partly believe it. [19]For there also must be factions among you, that those who are approved may be revealed among you. [20]When therefore you assemble yourselves together, it is not the Lord's supper that you eat. [21]For in your eating each one takes his own supper first. One is hungry, and another is drunk. [22]What, do you not have houses to eat and to drink in? Or do you despise God's church, and put them to shame who do not have? What should I tell you? Should I praise you? In this I do not praise you.

[23]For I received from the Lord that which also I delivered to you, that the Lord Jesus on the night in which he was betrayed took bread. [24]When he had given thanks, he broke it, and said, "[b]This is my body, which is[c] for you. Do this in memory of me." [25]In the same way he also took the cup, after supper, saying, "This cup is the New Covenant in my blood. Do this, as often as you drink, in memory of me." [26]For as often as you eat this bread and drink this cup, you proclaim the Lord's death until he comes. [27]Therefore whoever eats this bread or drinks the Lord's cup in a manner unworthy[d] will be guilty of the body and the blood of the Lord. [28]But let a person examine himself, and so let him eat of the bread, and drink of the cup. [29]For he who eats and drinks eats and drinks[e] judgment to himself, if he does not discern the[f] body. [30]For this cause many among you are weak and sickly, and not a few sleep. [31]For if we discerned ourselves, we would not be judged. [32]But when we are

judged, we are punished by the[g] Lord, that we may not be condemned with the world. [33]Therefore, my brothers, when you come together to eat, wait one for another. [34]But if anyone is hungry, let him eat at home, lest your coming together be for judgment. The rest I will set in order whenever I come.

12 Now concerning spiritual things, brothers, I do not want you to be ignorant. [2]You know that when you were unbelievers, you were led away to those mute idols, however you might be led. [3]Therefore I make known to you that no one speaking by God's Spirit says, "Jesus is accursed." No one can say, "Jesus is Lord," but by the Holy Spirit. [4]Now there are various kinds of gifts[h], but the same Spirit.

[5]There are various kinds of service, and the same Lord. [6]There are various kinds of workings, but the same God, who works all things in all. [7]But to each one is given the manifestation of the Spirit for the profit of all. [8]For to one is given through the Spirit the word of wisdom, and to another the word of knowledge, according to the same Spirit; [9]to another faith, by the same Spirit; and to another gifts of healings, by the one Spirit;[i] [10]and to another workings of miracles; and to another prophecy; and to another discernings of spirits; to another different kinds of tongues; and to another the interpretation of tongues. [11]But the one and the same Spirit works all of these, distributing to each one separately as he desires.

[12]For as the body is one, and has many members, and all the members of the[j] body, being many, are one body; so also is Christ.

---

a 11:15 Some Mss lack "to her"
b 11:24 Some Mss add "Take, eat"
c 11:24 Some Mss add "broken"
d 11:27 Some Mss add "of the Lord"
e 11:29 Some Mss add "in an unworthy manner"
f 11:29 Some Mss add "Lord's"
g 11:32 Some Mss lack "the"
h 12:4 Or, "spiritual empowerments," "spiritual enablements"
i 12:9 Some Mss read "same"
j 12:12 Some Mss add "(the) one"

[13]For in one Spirit we were all baptized into one body, whether Jews or Greeks, whether bond or free; and were all given to drink of[a] one Spirit. [14]For the body is not one member, but many. [15]If the foot would say, "Because I'm not the hand, I'm not part of the body," it is not therefore not part of the body. [16]If the ear would say, "Because I'm not the eye, I'm not part of the body," it's not therefore not part of the body. [17]If the whole body were an eye, where would the hearing be? If the whole were hearing, where would the smelling be? [18]But now God has set the members, each one of them, in the body, just as he desired. [19]If they were all one member, where would the body be? [20]But now they are many members, but one body. [21]The eye cannot tell the hand, "I have no need for you," or again the head to the feet, "I have no need for you." [22]No, much rather, those members of the body which seem to be weaker are necessary. [23]Those parts of the body which we think to be less honorable, on those we bestow more abundant honor; and our unpresentable parts have more abundant propriety; [24]whereas our presentable parts have no such need. But God composed the body together, giving more abundant honor to the inferior part, [25]that there should be no division in the body, but that the members should have the same care for one another. [26]When one member suffers, all the members suffer with it. Or when one member is honored, all the members rejoice with it.

[27]Now you are the body of Christ, and members individually. [28]God has set some in the church: first apostles, second prophets, third teachers, then miracle workers, then gifts of healings, helps, governments, and various kinds of tongues. [29]Are all apostles? Are all prophets? Are all teachers? Are all miracle workers? [30]Do all have gifts of healings? Do all speak with tongues? Do all interpret? [31]But earnestly desire the greater[b] gifts. Moreover, I show a most excellent way to you.

13 If I speak with the tongues of humans and of angels, but do not have love, I have become sounding bronze, or a clanging cymbal. [2]If I have the gift of prophecy, and know all mysteries and all knowledge; and if I have all faith, so as to remove mountains, but do not have love, I am nothing. [3]If I dole out all my goods to feed the poor, and if I surrender my body so that I may boast,[c] but do not have love, it profits me nothing.

[4]Love is patient and is kind; love does not envy. Love does not brag, is not proud, [5]does not behave itself inappropriately, does not seek its own way, is not irritable, does not keep a record of wrongs; [6]does not rejoice in unrighteousness, but rejoices with the truth; [7]bears all things, believes all things, hopes all things, endures all things. [8]Love never fails. But where there are prophecies, they will be done away with. Where there are tongues, they will cease. Where there is knowledge, it will be done away with. [9]For we know in part, and we prophesy in part; [10]but when that which is complete has come,[d] that which is partial will be done away with. [11]When I was a child, I spoke as a child, I felt as a child, I thought as a child. Now that I have become an adult, I have put away childish things. [12]For now we see in a mirror, dimly, but then face to face. Now I know in part, but then I will know fully, even as I was also fully known. [13]But now faith, hope, and love remain—these three. The greatest of these is love.

14 Follow after love, and earnestly desire spiritual things, and especially that you may prophesy. [2]For the one who speaks in another language speaks not to people, but to God; for no one understands; but in the Spirit he speaks mysteries. [3]But he who prophesies speaks to people for their encouragement, strengthening, and comfort. [4]He who speaks in another language edifies himself, but he who prophesies edifies

---

a　12:13 Some Mss read "into"
b　12:31 Some Mss read "best"
c　13:3 Some Mss read "to be burned"
d　13:10 Some Mss add "then"

the church. [5]Now I would like you all to speak in tongues, but even more that you would prophesy, and[a] he is greater who prophesies than he who speaks with other tongues, unless he interprets, that the church may be built up.

[6]But now, brothers, if I come to you speaking with other languages, what would I profit you, unless I speak to you either by way of revelation, or of knowledge, or of prophesying, or of teaching? [7]Even things without life, giving a voice, whether pipe or harp, if they did not give a distinction in the sounds, how would it be known what is piped or harped? [8]For if the trumpet gave an uncertain sound, who would prepare himself for war? [9]So also you, unless you uttered by the tongue words easy to understand, how would it be known what is spoken? For you would be speaking into the air. [10]There are, it may be, so many kinds of sounds in the world, and none[b] is without meaning. [11]If then I do not know the meaning of the sound, I would be to him who speaks a foreigner; and he who speaks would be a foreigner to me. [12]So also you, since you are zealous for spiritual gifts, seek that you may abound to the building up of the church. [13]Therefore let him who speaks in another language pray that he may interpret. [14]For if I pray in another language, my spirit prays, but my understanding is unfruitful.

[15]What is it then? I will pray with the spirit, and I will pray with the understanding also. I will sing with the spirit, and I will sing with the understanding also. [16]Otherwise if you bless with the spirit, how will he who fills the place of the unlearned say the "Amen" at your giving of thanks, seeing he does not know what you say? [17]For you truly give thanks well, but the other person is not built up. [18]I thank[c] God I speak in tongues more than you all. [19]However in the church I would rather speak five words with my understanding, that I might instruct others also, than ten thousand words in another language.

[20]Brothers, do not be children in thoughts, yet in malice be babies, but in thoughts be mature. [21]In the law it is written, "By people of strange tongues and by the lips of strangers I will speak to this people; but even then they will not listen to me," says the Lord.[d] [22]Therefore tongues are for a sign, not to those who believe, but to the unbelieving; but prophesying is for a sign, not to the unbelieving, but to those who believe. [23]If therefore the whole church is assembled together and all speak in tongues, and unlearned or unbelieving people come in, won't they say that you are crazy? [24]But if all prophesy, and someone unbelieving or unlearned comes in, he is reproved by all, and he is judged by all. [25]And thus the secrets of his heart are revealed. So he will fall down on his face and worship God, declaring that God is among you indeed.

[26]What is it then, brothers? When you come together, each one[e] has a psalm, has a teaching, has a revelation, has another language, has an interpretation. Let all things be done to build each other up. [27]If anyone speaks in another language, let it be two, or at the most three, and in turn; and let one interpret. [28]But if there is no interpreter, let him keep silent in the church, and let him speak to himself, and to God. [29]Let the prophets speak, two or three, and let the others discern. [30]But if a revelation is made to another sitting by, let the first keep silent. [31]For you can all prophesy one by one, that all may learn and all may be encouraged. [32]The spirits of the prophets are subject to the prophets, [33]for God is not a God of confusion, but of peace.

As in all the churches of the saints, [34]let the women[f] keep silent in the churches, for it has not been permitted for them to speak; but let them be in subjection, as the Law also says. [35]If they desire to learn anything, let them ask their own husbands at home, for it is shameful for a woman to chatter in the church. [36]What? Was it from

---

a   14:5 Some Mss read "for"
b   14:10 Some Mss add "of them"
c   14:18 Some Mss add "my"
d   14:21 Isaiah 28:11-12
e   14:26 Some Mss add "of you"
f   14:34 Some Mss read "your"

you that the word of God went out? Or did it come to you alone? [37]If anyone thinks himself to be a prophet, or spiritual, let him recognize the things which I write to you, that they are the commandment of the Lord. [38]But if someone does not recognize this[a], he is not recognized. [39]Therefore, brothers, desire earnestly to prophesy, and do not forbid speaking in tongues. [40]Let all things be done decently and in order.

15 Now I declare to you, brothers, the Good News which I preached to you, which also you received, in which you also stand, [2]by which also you are saved, if you hold firmly the word which I preached to you—unless you believed in vain. [3]For I delivered to you first of all that which I also received:

that Christ died for our sins
according to the Scriptures,
[4]that he was buried,
that he was raised on the third day
according to the Scriptures,
[5]and that he appeared to Cephas,
then to the twelve.
[6]After that he appeared to over five
hundred brothers at once, most
of whom remain until now, but
some have also fallen asleep.
[7]After that he appeared to James,
then to all the apostles,
[8]and last of all, as to the child born
at the wrong time, he appeared
to me also.

[9]For I am the least of the apostles, who is not worthy to be called an apostle, because I persecuted the church of God. [10]But by the grace of God I am what I am. His grace which was bestowed on me was not futile, but I worked more than all of them; yet not I, but the grace of God which was with me. [11]Whether then it is I or they, so we proclaim, and so you believed.

[12]Now if Christ is preached, that he has been raised from the dead, how do some among you say that there is no resurrection of the dead? [13]But if there is no resurrection of the dead, neither has Christ been raised. [14]If Christ has not been raised, then our preaching is in vain, and your faith also is in vain. [15]Yes, we are found false witnesses of God, because we testified about God that he raised up Christ, whom he did not raise up, if it is so that the dead are not raised. [16]For if the dead are not raised, neither has Christ been raised. [17]If Christ has not been raised, your faith is vain; you are still in your sins. [18]Then they also who are fallen asleep in Christ have perished. [19]If we have only hoped in Christ in this life, we are of all people most to be pitied.

[20]But now Christ has been raised from the dead,[b] the first fruits of those who are asleep. [21]For since death came by a man, the resurrection of the dead also came by a man. [22]For as in Adam all die, so also in Christ all will be made alive. [23]But each in his own order: Christ the first fruits, then those who are Christ's, at his coming. [24]Then the end comes, when he will deliver up the kingdom to God, even the Father; when he will have abolished all rule and all authority and power. [25]For he must reign until he has put all his enemies under his feet. [26]The last enemy that will be abolished is death. [27]For, "He put[c] all things under his feet."[d] But when he says, "all things" are put, it is evident that he is excepted who put all things to him. [28]When all things have been subjected to him, then the Son will also himself be subjected to him who subjected all things to him, that God may be all[e] in all. [29]Or else what will they do who are baptized for the dead? If the dead are not raised at all, why then are they baptized for them[f]? [30]Why do we also stand in jeopardy every hour? [31]I affirm, by the boasting in you which I have in Christ Jesus our Lord, I die daily. [32]If I fought with animals at Ephesus for human purposes, what does it profit me? If the dead are not raised, then "let us eat and drink, for tomorrow we

---

a   14:38 Some Mss read "is ignorant"
b   15:20 Some Mss add "he became"
c   15:27 Or, "subjected"
d   15:27 Psalm 8:6
e   15:28 Gk. "the all." Some Mss lack "all"
f   15:29 Some Mss read "the dead"

die."ᵃ ³³Do not be deceived. "Evil companionships corrupt good morals." ³⁴Wake up righteously, and do not sin, for some have no knowledge of God. I say this to your shame. ³⁵But someone will say, "How are the dead raised?" and, "With what kind of body do they come?" ³⁶You foolish one, that which you yourself sow is not made alive unless it dies. ³⁷That which you sow, you do not sow the body that will be, but a bare grain, maybe of wheat, or of some other kind. ³⁸But God gives it a body even as it pleased him, and to each seed a body of its own. ³⁹All flesh is not the same flesh, but there is one flesh of humans, another flesh of animals, another of fish, and another of birds. ⁴⁰There are also celestial bodies, and terrestrial bodies; but the glory of the celestial differs from that of the terrestrial. ⁴¹There is one glory of the sun, another glory of the moon, and another glory of the stars; for one star differs from another star in glory. ⁴²So also is the resurrection of the dead. It is sown in corruption; it is raised in incorruption. ⁴³It is sown in dishonor; it is raised in glory. It is sown in weakness; it is raised in power. ⁴⁴It is sown a natural body; it is raised a spiritual body. There is a natural body and there is also a spiritual body.

⁴⁵So also it is written, "The first man, Adam, became a living soul."ᵇ The last Adam became a life-giving spirit. ⁴⁶However that which is spiritual is not first, but that which is natural, then that which is spiritual. ⁴⁷The first man isᶜ of the earth, made of dust. The second man is from heaven. ⁴⁸As is the one made of dust, such are those who are also made of dust; and as is the heavenly, such are they also that are heavenly. ⁴⁹As we have borne the image of those made of dust, we willᵈ also bear the image of the heavenly. ⁵⁰Now I say this, brothers, that flesh and blood cannot inherit the kingdom of God; neither does corruption inherit incorruption.

⁵¹Look, I tell you a mystery. We will not all sleep, but we will all be changed, ⁵²in a moment, in the twinkling of an eye, at the last trumpet. For the trumpet will sound, and the dead will be raised incorruptible, and we will be changed. ⁵³For this corruptible must put on incorruption, and this mortal must put on immortality. ⁵⁴But when this corruptible will have put on incorruption, and this mortal will have put on immortality, then what is written will happen: "Death is swallowed up in victory."ᵉ

⁵⁵"Death, where is your victory?
    Death,ᶠ where is your sting?"ᵍ

⁵⁶The sting of death is sin, and the power of sin is the law. ⁵⁷But thanks be to God, who gives us the victory through our Lord Jesus Christ. ⁵⁸Therefore, my beloved brothers, be steadfast, immovable, always abounding in the Lord's work, because you know that your labor is not in vain in the Lord.

16 Now concerning the collection for the saints, as I commanded the churches of Galatia, you do likewise. ²On the first day of the week, let each one of you save, as he may prosper, that no collections be made when I come. ³When I arrive, I will send whoever you approve with letters to carry your gracious gift to Jerusalem. ⁴If it is appropriate for me to go also, they will go with me. ⁵But I will come to you when I have passed through Macedonia, for I am passing through Macedonia. ⁶But with you it may be that I will stay, or even winter, that you may send me on my journey wherever I go. ⁷For I do not wish to see you now in passing, but I hope to stay a while with you, if the Lord permits. ⁸But I will stay at Ephesus until Pentecost,ʰ ⁹for a great and effective door has opened to me, and there are many adversaries. ¹⁰Now if Timothy comes, see that he is with you without fear, for he does the work of the Lord, as I also do. ¹¹Therefore let

a   15:32 Isaiah 22:13
b   15:45 Genesis 2:7
c   15:47 Some Mss add "the Lord"
d   15:49 Some Mss read "lets us"
e   15:54 Isaiah 25:8
f   15:55 Some Mss read "Hades" instead of "Death"
g   15:55 Hosea 13:14
h   16:8 For Heb. "Shavuot"

no one despise him. But set him forward on his journey in peace, that he may come to me; for I expect him with the brothers.

[12]Now concerning Apollos, the brother, I strongly urged him to come to you with the brothers; and it was not at all his desire to come now; but he will come when he has an opportunity.

[13]Watch. Stand firm in the faith. Be courageous. Be strong. [14]Let all that you do be done in love.

[15]Now I appeal to you, brothers (you know the house of Stephanas, that it is the first fruits of Achaia, and that they have set themselves to serve the saints), [16]that you also be in subjection to such, and to every-

one who helps in the work and labors. [17]I rejoice at the coming of Stephanas, Fortunatus, and Achaicus; for that which was lacking on your part, they supplied. [18]For they refreshed my spirit and yours. Therefore acknowledge those who are like that.

[19]The churches of Asia greet you. Aquila and Priscilla greet you much in the Lord, together with the church that is in their house. [20]All the brothers greet you. Greet one another with a holy kiss.

[21]This greeting is by me, Paul, with my own hand. [22]If anyone does not love the Lord,[a] a curse be on him.[b] Our Lord, come. [23]The grace of the Lord Jesus[c] be with you. [24]My love to all of you in Christ Jesus.[d]

2 Corinthians

1 Paul, an apostle of Christ Jesus through the will of God, and Timothy our brother, to the church of God which is at Corinth, with all the saints who are in the whole of Achaia: [2]Grace to you and peace from God our Father and the Lord Jesus Christ.

[3]Blessed be the God and Father of our Lord Jesus Christ, the Father of mercies and God of all comfort; [4]who comforts us in all our affliction, that we may be able to comfort those who are in any affliction, through the comfort with which we ourselves are comforted by God. [5]For as the sufferings of Christ abound to us, even so our comfort also abounds through Christ. [6]But if we are afflicted, it is for your comfort and salvation. If we are comforted, it is for your comfort, which produces in you the patient enduring of the same sufferings which we also suffer. [7]Our hope for you is steadfast, knowing that, since you are partakers of the sufferings, so also are you of the comfort. [8]For we do not desire to have you uninformed, brothers, concerning our affliction which happened[e] in Asia, that we were weighed down exceedingly, beyond our power, so much that we despaired even of life. [9]Yes, we ourselves have had the sentence of death within ourselves,

that we should not trust in ourselves, but in God who raises the dead, [10]who delivered us out of so great a death, and he will deliver us. On him we have set our hope that he will also deliver us again; [11]you also helping together on our behalf by your petition; that, for the gift bestowed on us by means of many, thanks may be given by many persons on our[f] behalf. [12]For our boasting is this: the testimony of our conscience, that with pure motives[g] and sincerity of God, not in fleshly wisdom but in the grace of God we conducted ourselves in the world, and more abundantly toward you. [13]For we write no other things to you, than what you read or even acknowledge, and I hope you will fully acknowledge; [14]as also you acknowledged us in part, that we are your boasting, even as you also are ours, in the day of our Lord Jesus. [15]In this confidence, I was determined to come first to you, that you might have a second benefit; [16]and by you to pass into Macedonia,

---

a   16:22 Some Mss add "Jesus Christ"
b   16:22 Gk. anathema
c   16:23 Some Mss add "Christ"
d   16:24 Some Mss add "Amen"
e   1:8 Some Mss add "to us"
f   1:11 Some Mss read "your"
g   1:12 Some Mss read "holiness"

and again from Macedonia to come to you, and to be sent forward by you on my journey to Judea. [17]When I therefore was planning this, did I do it lightly? Or the things that I purpose, do I purpose according to the flesh, that with me there should be the "Yes, yes" and the "No, no?" [18]But as God is faithful, our word toward you is[a] not "Yes and no." [19]For the Son of God, Jesus Christ, who was preached among you by us, by me, Silvanus, and Timothy, was not "Yes and no," but in him is "Yes." [20]For however many are the promises of God, in him they are "Yes." Therefore also through him they are "Amen," to the glory of God through us.

[21]Now he who establishes us with you in Christ, and anointed us, is God; [22]who also sealed us, and gave us the down payment of the Spirit in our hearts. [23]But I call God as a witness to my soul, that to spare you I did not come again to Corinth. [24]Not that we rule over your faith, but are fellow workers with you for your joy. For you stand firm in faith.

2 For[b] I determined this for myself, that I would not come to you again in sorrow. [2]For if I make you sorry, then who will make me glad but he who is made sorry by me? [3]And I wrote this very thing,[c] so that, when I came, I would not have sorrow from them of whom I ought to rejoice; having confidence in you all, that my joy would be shared by all of you. [4]For out of much affliction and anguish of heart I wrote to you with many tears, not that you should be made sorry, but that you might know the love that I have so abundantly for you. [5]But if any has caused sorrow, he has caused sorrow, not to me, but in part (that I not press too heavily) to you all. [6]Sufficient to such a one is this punishment which was inflicted by the many; [7]so that on the contrary you should rather[d] forgive him and comfort him, lest by any means such a one should be swallowed up with his excessive sorrow. [8]Therefore I urge you to confirm your love toward him. [9]For to this end I also wrote, that I might know the proof of you, whether you are obedient in all things.

[10]Now I also forgive whomever you forgive anything. For if indeed I have forgiven anything, I have forgiven that one for your sakes in the presence of Christ, [11]that no advantage may be gained over us by Satan; for we are not ignorant of his schemes.

[12]Now when I came to Troas for the Good News of Christ, and when a door was opened to me in the Lord, [13]I had no relief for my spirit, because I did not find Titus, my brother, but taking my leave of them, I went out into Macedonia. [14]Now thanks be to God, who always leads us in triumph in Christ, and reveals through us the sweet aroma of his knowledge in every place. [15]For we are a sweet aroma of Christ to God, in those who are saved, and in those who perish; [16]to the one a stench from death to death; to the other a sweet aroma from life to life. Who is sufficient for these things? [17]For we are not, like so many, peddling the word of God. But as of sincerity, but as of God, in the sight of God, we speak in Christ.

3 Are we beginning again to commend ourselves? We do not need, as do some, letters of commendation to you or[e] from you, do we? [2]You are our letter, written in our hearts, known and read by everyone; [3]being revealed that you are a letter of Christ, served by us, written not with ink, but with the Spirit of the living God; not in tablets of stone, but in tablets that are hearts of flesh. [4]Such confidence we have through Christ toward God; [5]not that we are sufficient of ourselves, to account anything as from ourselves; but our sufficiency is from God; [6]who also made us sufficient as servants of a New Covenant; not of the letter, but of the Spirit. For the letter kills, but the Spirit gives life. [7]But if the service of death, written engraved on stones, came with glory, so that the children of Israel could not look steadfastly on the face of

---

a   1:18 Some Mss read "was"
b   2:1 Some Mss read "But"
c   2:3 Some Mss add "to you"
d   2:7 Some Mss lack "rather"
e   3:1 Some Mss add "of recommendation"

Moses for the glory of his face; which was passing away: [8]won't service of the Spirit be with much more glory? [9]For if the service of condemnation has glory, the service of righteousness exceeds much more in glory. [10]For truly that which has been made glorious has not been made glorious in this respect, by reason of the glory that surpasses. [11]For if that which passes away was with glory, much more that which remains is in glory.

[12]Having therefore such a hope, we use great boldness of speech, [13]and not as Moses, who put a veil on his face, that the children of Israel would not look steadfastly on the end of that which was passing away. [14]But their minds were hardened, for until this very day at the reading of the old covenant the same veil remains, because in Christ it passes away. [15]But to this day, when Moses is read, a veil lies on their heart. [16]But whenever one turns to the Lord, the veil is taken away. [17]Now the Lord is the Spirit and where the Spirit of the Lord is, there is liberty. [18]But we all, with unveiled face beholding as in a mirror the glory of the Lord, are transformed into the same image from glory to glory, even as from the Lord, the Spirit.

4 Therefore seeing we have this ministry, even as we obtained mercy, we do not faint. [2]But we have renounced the hidden things of shame, not walking in craftiness, nor handling the word of God deceitfully; but by the manifestation of the truth commending ourselves to every man's conscience in the sight of God. [3]Even if our Good News is veiled, it is veiled to those who are perishing; [4]in whom the god of this world has blinded the minds of the unbelieving, to prevent the light shining from the Good News of the glory of Christ, who is the image of God. [5]For we do not preach ourselves, but Christ Jesus as Lord, and ourselves as your slaves because of Jesus. [6]For it is God, who spoke for light to shine out of darkness,[a] who has shone in our hearts to give the light of the knowledge of the glory of God in the face of Christ.[b]

[7]But we have this treasure in clay vessels, that the exceeding greatness of the power may be of God, and not from ourselves. [8]We are pressed on every side, yet not crushed; perplexed, yet not to despair; [9]pursued, yet not forsaken; struck down, yet not destroyed; [10]always carrying in the body the death of[c] Jesus, that the life of Jesus may also be revealed in our body. [11]For we who live are always delivered to death for Jesus' sake, that the life also of Jesus may be revealed in our mortal flesh. [12]So then death works in us, but life in you. [13]But having the same spirit of faith, according to that which is written, "I believed, and therefore I spoke."[d] We also believe, and therefore also we speak; [14]knowing that he who raised the Lord[e] Jesus will raise us also with Jesus, and will present us with you. [15]For all things are for your sakes, that the grace, being multiplied through the many, may cause the thanksgiving to abound to the glory of God. [16]Therefore we do not lose heart, but though our outer nature is wearing away, yet our inner nature is being renewed day by day. [17]For this momentary light affliction is working for us a far more exceeding and everlasting weight of glory; [18]while we do not look at the things which are seen, but at the things which are not seen. For the things which are seen are temporal, but the things which are not seen are everlasting.

5 For we know that if the earthly house of our tent is dissolved, we have a building from God, a house not made with hands, everlasting, in the heavens. [2]For truly in this we groan, longing to be clothed with our habitation which is from heaven, [3]since, after we have put it on, we will not be found naked. [4]For indeed we who are in this tent do groan, being burdened; not that we desire to be unclothed, but that we desire to be clothed, that what is mortal

---

a   4:6 An allusion to Genesis 1:3
b   4:6 Some Mss read "Jesus Christ"
c   4:10 Some Mss add "the Lord"
d   4:13 Psalm 116:10
e   4:14 Some Mss lack "Lord"

may be swallowed up by life. ⁵Now he who made us for this very thing is God, who also gave to us the down payment of the Spirit.

⁶Therefore, we are always confident and know that while we are at home in the body, we are absent from the Lord; ⁷for we walk by faith, not by sight. ⁸We are of good courage, I say, and are willing rather to be absent from the body, and to be at home with the Lord. ⁹Therefore also we make it our aim, whether at home or absent, to be well pleasing to him. ¹⁰For we must all appear before the judgment seat of Christ; that each one may receive the things in the body, according to what he has done, whether good or bad. ¹¹Knowing therefore the fear of the Lord, we persuade people, but we are revealed to God; and I hope that we are revealed also in your consciences. ¹²For we are not commending ourselves to you again, but speak as giving you occasion of boasting on our behalf, that you may have something to answer those who boast in appearance, and not in heart. ¹³For if we are beside ourselves, it is for God. Or if we are of sound mind, it is for you. ¹⁴For the love of Christ constrains us; because we judge thus, that one died for all, therefore all died. ¹⁵He died for all, that those who live should no longer live to themselves, but to him who for their sakes died and rose again. ¹⁶Therefore we know no one after the flesh from now on. Even though we have known Christ after the flesh, yet now we know him so no more. ¹⁷Therefore if anyone is in Christ, he is a new creation. The old things have passed away. Look, new things have come.ᵃ ¹⁸But all things are of God, who reconciled us to himself through Jesus Christ, and gave to us the ministry of reconciliation; ¹⁹namely, that God was in Christ reconciling the world to himself, not counting their trespasses against them, and having committed to us the word of reconciliation. ²⁰We are therefore ambassadors on behalf of Christ, as though God were making his appeal through us. We implore you on behalf of Christ, be reconciled to God. ²¹For him who knew no sin he made to be sin on our

behalf; so that in him we might become the righteousness of God.

6 Working together, we entreat also that you not receive the grace of God in vain, ²for he says,

"At an acceptable time I listened to you, and in a day of salvation I helped you."ᵇ

Look, now is the "acceptable time." Look, now is the "day of salvation." ³We give no occasion of stumbling in anything, that our service may not be blamed, ⁴but in everything commending ourselves, as servants of God, in great endurance, in afflictions, in hardships, in distresses, ⁵in beatings, in imprisonments, in riots, in labors, in watchings, in fastings; ⁶in pureness, in knowledge, in patience, in kindness, in the Holy Spirit, in sincere love, ⁷in the word of truth, in the power of God; by the armor of righteousness on the right hand and on the left, ⁸by glory and dishonor, by evil report and good report; as deceivers, and yet true; ⁹as unknown, and yet well known; as dying, and look, we live; as punished, and not killed; ¹⁰as sorrowful, yet always rejoicing; as poor, yet making many rich; as having nothing, and yet possessing all things.

¹¹Our mouth is open to you, Corinthians. Our heart is enlarged. ¹²You are not restricted by us, but you are restricted by your own affections. ¹³Now in return, I speak as to my children, you also be open wide. ¹⁴Do not be unequally yoked with unbelievers, for what fellowship have righteousness and iniquity? Or what fellowship has light with darkness? ¹⁵What agreement has Christ with Belial? Or what portion has a believer with an unbeliever? ¹⁶What agreement has a temple of God with idols? For weᶜ are a temple of the living God. Even as God said, "I will dwell in them, and walk in them; and I will be their God, and they will be my people."ᵈ ¹⁷Therefore,

" 'Go out from their midst,
     and be separate,' says the Lord,

---

a   5:17 Some Mss read "all things have become new"
b   6:2 Isaiah 49:8
c   6:16 Some Mss read "you"
d   6:16 Leviticus 26:12; Jeremiah 32:38; Ezekiel 37:27

'and touch no unclean thing,'
and I will receive you.[a]

[18]And I will be a Father to you,
and you will be my sons and
daughters,"[b]
says the Lord of hosts.[c]

7 Having therefore these promises, beloved, let us cleanse ourselves from all defilement of flesh and spirit, perfecting holiness in the fear of God. [2]Open your hearts to us. We wronged no one. We corrupted no one. We took advantage of no one. [3]I say this not to condemn you, for I have said before, that you are in our hearts to die together and live together. [4]Great is my boldness of speech toward you. Great is my boasting on your behalf. I am filled with comfort. I overflow with joy in all our affliction. [5]For even when we had come into Macedonia, our flesh had no relief, but we were afflicted on every side. Fightings were outside. Fear was inside. [6]Nevertheless, he who comforts the lowly, God, comforted us by the coming of Titus; [7]and not by his coming only, but also by the comfort with which he was comforted in you, while he told us of your longing, your mourning, and your zeal for me; so that I rejoiced still more.

[8]For though I made you sorry with my letter, I do not regret it, though I did regret it. For I see that my letter made you sorry, though just for a while. [9]I now rejoice, not that you were made sorry, but that you were made sorry to repentance. For you were made sorry in a godly way, that you might suffer loss by us in nothing. [10]For godly sorrow works repentance to salvation, which brings no regret. But the sorrow of the world works death. [11]For look at this very thing, that you were made sorry in a godly way. What diligence it produced in you, what clearing of yourselves, what indignation, what fear, what longing, what zeal, what vindication. In everything you proved yourselves to be innocent in the matter. [12]So although I wrote to you, I wrote not for his cause that did the wrong, nor for his cause that suffered the wrong, but that

your earnest care for us might be revealed in you in the sight of God. [13]Therefore we have been comforted. In our[d] comfort we rejoiced the more exceedingly for the joy of Titus, because his spirit has been refreshed by you all. [14]For if in anything I have boasted to him on your behalf, I was not disappointed. But as we spoke all things to you in truth, so our glorying also which I made before Titus was found to be truth. [15]His affection is more abundantly toward you, while he remembers all of your obedience, how with fear and trembling you received him. [16]I rejoice that in everything I am of good courage concerning you.

8 Moreover, brothers, we make known to you the grace of God which has been given in the churches of Macedonia; [2]how that in much proof of affliction the abundance of their joy and their deep poverty abounded to the riches of their liberality. [3]For according to their power, I testify, yes and beyond their power, they gave of their own accord, [4]begging us with much entreaty to receive this grace and the fellowship in the service to the saints. [5]This was not as we had hoped, but first they gave their own selves to the Lord, and to us through the will of God. [6]So we urged Titus, that as he made a beginning before, so he would also complete in you this grace. [7]But as you abound in everything, in faith, utterance, knowledge, all earnestness, and in the love from us that is in you,[e] see that you also abound in this grace. [8]I speak not by way of commandment, but as proving through the earnestness of others the sincerity also of your love. [9]For you know the grace of our Lord Jesus Christ, that, though he was rich, yet for your sakes he became poor, that you through his poverty might become rich. [10]I give a judgment in

---

a   6:17 Isaiah 52:11; Ezekiel 20:34,41
b   6:18 2 Samuel 7:14; Isaiah 43:6
c   6:18 Or, "Lord Almighty." Gk kurios pantokrator
     is used in the LXX for "LORD of hosts." In Job LXX,
     without kurios, it is used for "Shaddai"
d   7:13 Some Mss read "your"
e   8:7 Some Mss read "your love to us"

this: for this is expedient for you, who were the first to start a year ago, not only to do, but also to be willing. [11]But now complete the doing also, that as there was the readiness to be willing, so there may be the completion also out of your ability. [12]For if the readiness is there, it is acceptable according to what you have, not according to what you do not have. [13]For this is not that others may be eased and you distressed, [14]but for equality. Your abundance at this present time supplies their lack, that their abundance also may become a supply for your lack; that there may be equality. [15]As it is written, "He who gathered much had nothing left over, and he who gathered little had no lack."[a]

[16]But thanks be to God, who puts the same earnest care for you into the heart of Titus. [17]For he indeed accepted our exhortation, but being himself very earnest, he went out to you of his own accord. [18]We have sent together with him the brother whose praise in the Good News is known through all the churches. [19]Not only so, but who was also appointed by the churches to travel with us in this grace, which is served by us to the glory of the Lord himself, and to show our readiness. [20]We are avoiding this, that no one should blame us concerning this abundance which is administered by us. [21]Having regard for honorable things, not only in the sight of the Lord, but also in the sight of others.[b] [22]We have sent with them our brother, whom we have many times proved earnest in many things, but now much more earnest, by reason of the great confidence which he has in you. [23]As for Titus, he is my partner and fellow worker for you. As for our brothers, they are the apostles of the churches, the glory of Christ. [24]Therefore show the proof of your love to them in front of the churches, and of our boasting on your behalf.

9 It is indeed unnecessary for me to write to you concerning the service to the saints, [2]for I know your readiness, of which I boast on your behalf to them of Macedonia, that Achaia has been pre-

pared for a year past. Your zeal has stirred up very many of them. [3]But I have sent the brothers that our boasting on your behalf may not be in vain in this respect, that, just as I said, you may be prepared, [4]so that I won't by any means, if there come with me any of Macedonia and find you unprepared, we (to say nothing of you) should be disappointed in this confidence.[c] [5]I thought it necessary therefore to entreat the brothers that they would go before to you, and arrange ahead of time the generous gift that you promised before, that the same might be ready as a matter of generosity, and not of greediness. [6]Remember this: he who sows sparingly will also reap sparingly. He who sows bountifully will also reap bountifully. [7]Each person should give according as he has determined in his heart; not grudgingly, or under compulsion; for God loves a cheerful giver. [8]And God is able to make all grace abound to you, that you, always having all sufficiency in everything, may abound to every good work. [9]As it is written,

"He has scattered, he has given to the poor;

his righteousness endures forever."[d]

[10]Now[e] he who supplies seed to the sower and bread for food, will supply and multiply your seed for sowing, and increase the fruits of your righteousness; [11]you being enriched in everything to all liberality, which works through us thanksgiving to God. [12]For this service of giving that you perform not only makes up for lack among the saints, but abounds also through many thanksgivings to God; [13]seeing that through the proof given by this service, they glorify God for the obedience of your confession to the Good News of Christ, and for the liberality of your contribution to them and to all; [14]while they themselves also, with petition on your behalf, yearn for you by reason of the exceeding grace

a   8:15 Exodus 16:18
b   8:22 An allusion to Proverbs 3:4
c   9:4 Some Mss add "of boasting"
d   9:9 Psalm 112:9
e   9:10 Some Mss add "may"

of God in you. [15]Thanks[a] be to God for his inexpressible gift.

10 Now I Paul, myself, entreat you by the humility and gentleness of Christ; I who in your presence am lowly among you, but being absent am of good courage toward you. [2]But I implore you that when I am present I may not have to be bold with the confidence with which I intend on showing against some, who consider us to be walking according to the flesh. [3]For though we walk in the flesh, we do not wage war according to the flesh; [4]for the weapons of our warfare are not of the flesh, but mighty in God for the tearing down of strongholds, [5]throwing down imaginations and every high thing that is exalted against the knowledge of God, and bringing every thought into captivity to the obedience of Christ; [6]and being in readiness to avenge all disobedience, when your obedience will be made full. [7]Do you look at things only as they appear in front of your face? If anyone trusts in himself that he is Christ's, let him consider this again with himself, that, even as he is Christ's, so also we are Christ's. [8]For though I should boast somewhat abundantly concerning our authority, (which the Lord gave for building you up, and not for casting you down) I will not be disappointed, [9]that I may not seem as if I desire to terrify you by my letters. [10]For, "His letters," they say, "are weighty and strong, but his bodily presence is weak, and his speech is despised." [11]Let such a person consider this, that what we are in word by letters when we are absent, such are we also in deed when we are present. [12]For we are not bold to number or compare ourselves with some of those who commend themselves. But they themselves, measuring themselves by themselves, and comparing themselves with themselves, are without understanding. [13]But we will not boast beyond proper limits, but within the boundaries with which God appointed to us, which reach even to you. [14]For we do not stretch ourselves too much, as

though we did not reach to you. For we came even as far as to you with the Good News of Christ, [15]not boasting beyond proper limits in other men's labors, but having hope that as your faith grows, we will be abundantly enlarged by you in our sphere of influence, [16]so as to proclaim the Good News even to the regions beyond you, not to boast in what someone else has already done. [17]But "he who boasts, let him boast in the Lord."[b] [18]For it is not he who commends himself who is approved, but whom the Lord commends.

11 I wish that you would bear with me in a little foolishness, but indeed you do bear with me. [2]For I am jealous over you with a godly jealousy. For I married you to one husband, that I might present you as a pure virgin to Christ. [3]But I am afraid that somehow, as the serpent deceived Eve[c] in his craftiness, so your minds might be corrupted from the sincerity and purity[d] that is in Christ. [4]For if he who comes preaches another Jesus, whom we did not preach, or if you receive a different spirit, which you did not receive, or a different "good news", which you did not accept, you put up with that well enough. [5]For I reckon that I am not at all behind the very best apostles. [6]Even though I am unskilled in speech, I am not unskilled in knowledge. But in every way we have made this known[e] to you in all things. [7]Or did I commit a sin in humbling myself that you might be exalted, because I preached to you God's Good News free of charge? [8]I robbed other churches, taking wages from them that I might serve you. [9]When I was present with you and was in need, I was not a burden on anyone, for the brothers, when they came from Macedonia, supplied the measure of my need. In everything I kept myself from being burdensome to you, and I will continue to do so. [10]As the truth of Christ

---

a   9:15 Some Mss add "And/But"
b   10:17 Jeremiah 9:24
c   11:3 Greek for Hebrew "Havah"
d   11:3 Some Mss lack "and purity"
e   11:6 Some Mss read "we have been made known"

is in me, no one will stop me from this boasting in the regions of Achaia. ¹¹Why? Because I do not love you? God knows. ¹²But what I do, that I will do, that I may cut off occasion from them that desire an occasion, that in which they boast, they may be found even as we. ¹³For such people are false apostles, deceitful workers, masquerading as Christ's apostles. ¹⁴And no wonder, for even Satan masquerades as an angel of light. ¹⁵It is no great thing therefore if his servants also masquerade as servants of righteousness, whose end will be according to their works.

¹⁶I say again, let no one think me foolish. But if so, yet receive me as foolish, that I also may boast a little. ¹⁷That which I speak, I do not speak according to the Lord, but as in foolishness, in this confidence of boasting. ¹⁸Seeing that many boast after the flesh, I will also boast. ¹⁹For you bear with the foolish gladly, being wise. ²⁰For you put up with it if someone makes slaves of you, if someone exploits you, if someone takes advantage of you, if someone exalts himself, if someone strikes you on the face. ²¹I speak by way of disparagement, as though we had been weak. Yet however any is bold (I speak in foolishness), I am bold also. ²²Are they Hebrews? So am I. Are they Israelites? So am I. Are they descendants of Abraham? So am I. ²³Are they servants of Christ? (I speak as one beside himself) I am more so; in labors more abundantly, in prisons more abundantly, in stripes above measure, in deaths often. ²⁴Five times from the Jews I received forty stripes minus one. ²⁵Three times I was beaten with rods. Once I was stoned. Three times I suffered shipwreck. I have been a night and a day in the deep. ²⁶I have been in travels often, perils of rivers, perils of robbers, perils from my countrymen, perils from those who are not Jews, perils in the city, perils in the wilderness, perils in the sea, perils among false brothers; ²⁷in labor and travail, in watchings often, in hunger and thirst, in fastings often, and in cold and nakedness.

²⁸Besides those things that are outside, there is that which presses on me daily, anxiety for all the churches. ²⁹Who is weak, and I am not weak? Who is caused to stumble, and I do not burn with indignation? ³⁰If I must boast, I will boast of the things that concern my weakness. ³¹The God and Father of the Lord Jesus,[a] he who is blessed forevermore, knows that I do not lie. ³²In Damascus the governor under Aretas the king guarded the city of the Damascenes[b] to arrest me. ³³Through a window I was let down in a basket by the wall, and escaped his hands.

12 It is necessary to boast[c], though it is not profitable. But I will come to visions and revelations of the Lord. ²I know a man in Christ, fourteen years ago (whether in the body, I do not know, or whether out of the body, I do not know; God knows), such a one was caught up into the third heaven. ³I know such a man (whether in the body, or apart[d] from the body, I do not know; God knows), ⁴how he was caught up into Paradise, and heard unspeakable words, which it is not lawful for a human to utter. ⁵On behalf of such a one I will boast, but on my own behalf I will not boast, except in my weaknesses. ⁶For if I would desire to boast, I will not be foolish; for I will speak the truth. But I refrain, so that no one may think more of me than that which he sees in me, or hears from me. ⁷And because of the surpassing greatness of the revelations, therefore, to keep me from exalting myself, there was given to me a thorn in the flesh, a messenger of Satan to pound away at me, to keep me from exalting myself. ⁸Concerning this thing, I begged the Lord three times that it might depart from me. ⁹He has said to me, "My grace is sufficient for you, for[e] power is made perfect in weakness." Most gladly

---

a   11:31 Some Mss add "Christ"
b   11:32 Some Mss add "desiring"
c   12:1 Some Mss read "It is doubtless not profitable for me to boast"
d   12:3 Some Mss read "outside of"
e   12:9 Some Mss add "my"

therefore I will rather glory in my weaknesses, that the power of Christ may rest on me.

[10]Therefore I take pleasure in weaknesses, in injuries, in necessities, in persecutions, in distresses, for Christ's sake. For when I am weak, then am I strong. [11]I have become foolish[a]. You compelled me, for I ought to have been commended by you, for in nothing was I inferior to the very best apostles, though I am nothing. [12]Truly the signs of an apostle were worked among you in all patience, in signs and wonders and mighty works. [13]For what is there in which you were made inferior to the rest of the churches, unless it is that I myself was not a burden to you? Forgive me this wrong.

[14]Look, for the third time I am ready to come to you, and I will not be a burden to you; for I seek not what is yours, but you. For the children ought not to save up for the parents, but the parents for the children. [15]I will most gladly spend and be spent for your souls. If I love you more abundantly, am I loved the less? [16]But be it so, I did not myself burden you. But, being crafty, I caught you with deception. [17]Did I take advantage of you by anyone of them whom I have sent to you? [18]I exhorted Titus, and I sent the brother with him. Did Titus take any advantage of you? Did not we walk in the same spirit? Did not we walk in the same steps? [19]Have you been thinking all this time[b] that we have been defending ourselves before you? In the sight of God we speak in Christ; and all things, beloved, are for your edifying. [20]For I am afraid that by any means, when I come, I might find you not the way I want to, and that I might be found by you as you do not desire; that by any means there would be strife, jealousy, outbursts of anger, factions, slander, whisperings, proud thoughts, riots; [21]that again when I come my God would humble me before you, and I would mourn for many of those who have sinned before now, and not repented of the uncleanness and sexual immorality and lustfulness which they committed.

13 This is the third time I am coming to you. "At the mouth of two or three witnesses will every word be established."[c] [2]I have said beforehand, and I do say beforehand, as when I was present the second time, so now, being absent,[d] to those who have sinned before now, and to all the rest, that, if I come again, I will not spare; [3]seeing that you seek a proof of Christ who speaks in me; who toward you is not weak, but is powerful in you. [4]For indeed[e] he was crucified through weakness, yet he lives through the power of God. For we also are weak in him, but we will live with him through the power of God toward you. [5]Test your own selves, whether you are in the faith. Test your own selves. Or do you not know as to your own selves, that Jesus Christ is in[f] you?—unless indeed you are disqualified. [6]But I hope that you will know that we are not disqualified.

[7]Now we[g] pray to God that you do no evil; not that we may appear approved, but that you may do that which is honorable, though we are as reprobate. [8]For we can do nothing against the truth, but for the truth. [9]For we rejoice when we are weak and you are strong. And this we also pray for, even your perfecting. [10]For this cause I write these things while absent, that I may not deal sharply when present, according to the authority which the Lord gave me for building up, and not for tearing down.

[11]Finally, brothers, rejoice. Be perfected, be comforted, be of the same mind, live in peace, and the God of love and peace will be with you. [12]Greet one another with a holy kiss. [13]All the saints greet you. [14]The grace of the Lord Jesus Christ, the love of God, and the fellowship of the Holy Spirit, be with you all.[h]

---

a　12:11 Some Mss add "in boasting"
b　12:19 Some Mss read "Again"
c　13:1 Deuteronomy 19:15
d　13:2 Some Mss add "I write"
e　13:4 Some Mss read "even since"
f　13:5 Some Mss lack "is"
g　13:7 Some Mss read "I"
h　13:14 Some Mss add "Amen"

Galatians

1 Paul, an apostle (not from humans, nor through humans, but through Jesus Christ, and God the Father, who raised him from the dead), ²and all the brothers who are with me, to the churches of Galatia: ³Grace to you and peace from God our Father, and the[a] Lord Jesus Christ, ⁴who gave himself for our sins, that he might deliver us out of this present evil age, according to the will of our God and Father—⁵to whom be the glory forever and ever. Amen.

⁶I marvel that you are so quickly deserting him who called you by the grace of Christ[b] to a different "good news"; ⁷and there is not another "good news." Only there are some who trouble you, and want to pervert the Good News of Christ. ⁸But even though we, or an angel from heaven, should proclaim to you a "good news" other than that which we preached to you, let him be cursed. ⁹As we have said before, so I now say again: if anyone preaches to you a "good news" other than that which you received, let him be cursed. ¹⁰For am I now seeking the favor of people, or of God? Or am I striving to please people? For if I were still pleasing people, I would not be a servant of Christ. ¹¹But I make known to you, brothers, concerning the Good News which was preached by me, that it is not of human origin. ¹²For neither did I receive it from a human source, nor was I taught it, but it came to me through revelation of Jesus Christ. ¹³For you have heard of my former way of life in Judaism,[c] how I severely persecuted the church of God, and tried to destroy it. ¹⁴I advanced in Judaism beyond many of my own age among my countrymen, being more exceedingly zealous for the traditions of my fathers. ¹⁵But when God,[d] who had set me apart from my mother's womb and called me through his grace, was pleased ¹⁶to reveal his Son to me, that I might proclaim him among those who are not Jewish, I did not immediately confer with flesh and blood, ¹⁷nor did I go up to Jerusalem to those who were apostles before me, but

I went away into Arabia. Then I returned to Damascus. ¹⁸Then after three years I went up to Jerusalem to visit Cephas,[e] and stayed with him fifteen days. ¹⁹But of the other apostles I saw no one, except James, the Lord's brother. ²⁰Now about the things which I write to you, look, before God, I'm not lying. ²¹Then I came to the regions of Syria and Cilicia. ²²I was still unknown by face to the churches of Judea which were in Christ, ²³but they only heard: "He who once persecuted us now preaches the faith that he once tried to destroy." ²⁴And they glorified God because of me.

2 Then after a period of fourteen years I went up again to Jerusalem with Barnabas, taking Titus also with me. ²I went up by revelation, and I explained to them the Good News which I proclaim among those who are not Jewish, but privately before those who were respected, for fear that I might be running, or had run, in vain. ³But not even Titus, who was with me, being a Greek, was compelled to be circumcised. ⁴This was because of the false brothers secretly brought in, who stole in to spy out our liberty which we have in Christ Jesus, that they might bring us into bondage; ⁵to whom we gave no place in the way of subjection, not for an hour, that the truth of the Good News might continue with you. ⁶But from those who were reputed to be important (whatever they were, it makes no difference to me; God shows no favoritism between people)—they, I say, who were respected imparted nothing to me, ⁷but to the contrary, when they saw that I had been entrusted with the Good News for the uncircumcision, even as Peter with the Good News for the circumcision ⁸(for he who appointed Peter to be an apostle of

---

a   1:3 Some Mss read "the Father and our"
b   1:6 Some Mss lack "Christ"
c   1:13 Or, "traditional Judaism"
d   1:15 Some Mss lack "God"
e   1:18 Some Mss read "Peter"

the circumcision appointed me also to non-Jews); ⁹and when they perceived the grace that was given to me, James and Cephas and John, they who were reputed to be pillars, gave to me and Barnabas the right hand of fellowship, that we should go to the non-Jews, and they to the circumcised. ¹⁰They only asked us to remember the poor—which very thing I was also zealous to do.

¹¹But when Cephasᵃ came to Antioch, I resisted him to his face, because he stood condemned. ¹²For before some people came from James, he ate with those who were not Jewish. But when they came, he drew back and separated himself, fearing those who were of the circumcision. ¹³And the rest of the Jewish believers joined him in his hypocrisy; so that even Barnabas was carried away with their hypocrisy. ¹⁴But when I saw that they did not walk uprightly according to the truth of the Good News, I said to Cephas before them all, "If you, being a Jew, live as the non-Jews do, and not as the Jews do, how can you compel the non-Jews to live as the Jews do?

¹⁵"We, being Jews by birth, and not non-Jewish sinners, ¹⁶yet knowing that no one is justified by the works of the law but through faith in Jesus Christ, even we believed in Christ Jesus, that we might be justified by faith in Christ, and not by the works of the law, because no flesh will be justified by the works of the law. ¹⁷But if, while we sought to be justified in Christ, we ourselves also were found sinners, is Christ a servant of sin? Certainly not. ¹⁸For if I build up again those things which I destroyed, I prove myself a law-breaker. ¹⁹For I, through the law, died to the law, that I might live to God. ²⁰I have been crucified with Christ, and it is no longer I that live, but Christ living in me. That life which I now live in the flesh, I live by faith in the Son of God, who loved me, and gave himself up for me. ²¹I do not make void the grace of God. For if righteousness is through the law, then Christ died for nothing."

3 Foolish Galatians, who has cunningly deceivedᵇ you,ᶜ before whose eyes Jesus Christ was openly set forthᵈ as crucified? ²I just want to learn this from you. Did you receive the Spirit by the works of the law, or by hearing of faith? ³Are you so foolish? Having begun in the Spirit, are you now completed in the flesh? ⁴Did you suffer so many things in vain, if it is indeed in vain? ⁵He therefore who supplies the Spirit to you, and works miracles among you, does he do it by the works of the law, or by hearing of faith? ⁶Even as Abraham "believed God, and it was credited to him as righteousness." ⁷Know therefore that those who are of faith, the same are children of Abraham. ⁸The Scripture, foreseeing that God would justify the non-Jews by faith, preached the Good News beforehand to Abraham, saying, "In you all the nations will be blessed."ᵉ ⁹So then, those who are of faith are blessed with the faithful Abraham. ¹⁰For as many as are of the works of the law are under a curse. For it is written, "Cursed is everyone who does not continue in all things that are written in the book of the law, to do them."ᶠ ¹¹Now it is evident that no one is justified by the law before God, for, "The righteous will live by faith."ᵍ ¹²The law is not of faith, but, "The one who does them will live by them."ʰ

¹³Christ redeemed us from the curse of the law, having become a curse for us. For it is written, "Cursed is everyone who hangs on a tree,"ⁱ ¹⁴that the blessing of Abraham might come on the non-Jews through Christ Jesus; that we might receive the promise of the Spirit through faith. ¹⁵Brothers, I am speaking in human terms. Though it is only a human covenant, once it has been ratified, no one annuls it or adds to it. ¹⁶Now the promises were spoken to Abraham and to his offspring.ʲ He does not say, "And to

---

a   2:11 Some Mss read "Peter"
b   3:1 Or, "bewitched." See L&N 88.159.
c   3:1 Some Mss add "not to obey the truth"
d   3:1 Some Mss add "among you"
e   3:8 Genesis 12:3; 18:18; 22:18
f   3:10 Deuteronomy 27:26
g   3:11 Habakkuk 2:4
h   3:12 Leviticus 18:5
i   3:13 Deuteronomy 21:23
j   3:16 Lit., "seed"

offsprings," as of many, but as of one, "And to your offspring,"[a] which is Christ. [17]Now I say this: the law which came four hundred thirty years later, does not annul a covenant previously ratified by God,[b] so as to cancel the promise. [18]For if the inheritance is of the law, it is no more of promise; but God has granted it to Abraham by promise.

[19]What then is the law? It was added because of transgressions, until the offspring should come to whom the promise has been made. It was ordained through angels by the hand of a mediator. [20]Now a mediator is not between one, but God is one. [21]Is the law then against the promises of God? Certainly not. For if there had been a law given which could give life, most certainly righteousness would have been of the law. [22]But the Scriptures imprisoned all things under sin, that the promise by faith in Jesus Christ might be given to those who believe. [23]But before faith came, we were kept in custody under the law, confined for the faith which should afterwards be revealed. [24]So that the law has become our tutor to bring us to Christ, that we might be justified by faith. [25]But now that faith has come, we are no longer under a tutor. [26]For you are all children of God, through faith in Christ Jesus. [27]For as many of you as were baptized into Christ have put on Christ. [28]There is neither Jew nor Greek, there is neither slave nor free, there is neither male nor female; for you are all one in Christ Jesus. [29]If you are Christ's, then you are Abraham's offspring and heirs according to promise.

4 But I say that so long as the heir is a child, he is no different from a slave, though he is lord of all; [2]but is under guardians and stewards until the day appointed by the father. [3]So we also, when we were children, were held in bondage under the elemental principles of the world. [4]But when the fullness of the time came, God sent out his Son, born to a woman, born under the law, [5]that he might redeem those who were under the law, that we might receive the adoption of children. [6]And because you are children, God sent out the Spirit of his Son

into our[c] hearts, crying, "Abba, Father." [7]So you are no longer a slave, but a son; and if a son, then an heir of God.[d] [8]However at that time, not knowing God, you were in bondage to those who by nature are not gods. [9]But now that you have come to know God, or rather to be known by God, why do you turn back again to the weak and miserable elemental principles, to which you desire to be in bondage all over again? [10]You observe days, months, seasons, and years. [11]I am afraid for you, that I might have wasted my labor for you. [12]I beg you, brothers, become as I am, for I also have become as you are. You did me no wrong, [13]but you know that in physical weakness I preached the Good News to you the first time; [14]and though my condition was a trial to you, you did not despise nor reject; but you received me as an angel of God, even as Christ Jesus.

[15]Where was the blessing you enjoyed? For I testify to you that, if possible, you would have plucked out your eyes and given them to me. [16]So then, have I become your enemy by telling you the truth? [17]They zealously seek you, but for no good purpose; they desire to alienate you, that you may be zealous for them. [18]But it is always good to be zealous in a good cause, and not only when I am present with you.

[19]My[e] children, of whom I am again in travail until Christ is formed in you—[20]but I could wish to be present with you now, and to change my tone, for I am perplexed about you. [21]Tell me, you that desire to be under the law, do you not listen to the law? [22]For it is written that Abraham had two sons, one by the handmaid, and one by the free woman. [23]However, the son by the handmaid was born according to the flesh, but the son by the free woman was born through promise. [24]These things contain an allegory, for these are two covenants. One is from Mount Sinai, bearing children to slavery, which is Hagar. [25]For this Hagar

---

a   3:16 Genesis 12:7; 13:15; 24:7
b   3:17 Some Mss add "in Christ"
c   4:6 Some Mss read "your"
d   4:7 Some Mss add "through Christ"
e   4:19 Some Mss add "little"

is Mount Sinai in Arabia and represents Jerusalem that exists now, for she is in slavery with her children. ²⁶But the Jerusalem that is above is free, and she is our mother.^a ²⁷For it is written,

"Rejoice, you barren who do not bear.
Break forth and shout, you that do
    not travail.
For more are the children of the
    desolate than of her who has a
    husband."^b

²⁸Now you,^c brothers, as Isaac was, are children of promise. ²⁹But as then, he who was born according to the flesh persecuted him who was born according to the Spirit, so also it is now. ³⁰However what does the Scripture say? "Throw out the handmaid and her son, for the son of the handmaid will not inherit with the son" of the free woman.^d ³¹So then, brothers, we are not children of a handmaid, but of the free woman.

5 Stand firm therefore in the liberty by which Christ has made us free, and do not be entangled again with a yoke of bondage. ²Listen, I, Paul, tell you that if you receive circumcision, Christ will profit you nothing. ³Yes, I testify again to every man who receives circumcision, that he is a debtor to do the whole law. ⁴You are alienated from Christ, you who desire to be justified by the law. You have fallen away from grace. ⁵For we, through the Spirit, by faith wait for the hope of righteousness. ⁶For in Christ Jesus neither circumcision amounts to anything, nor uncircumcision, but faith working through love. ⁷You were running well. Who interfered with you that you should not obey the truth? ⁸This persuasion is not from him who calls you. ⁹A little yeast grows through the whole lump. ¹⁰I have confidence toward you in the Lord that you will think no other way. But he who troubles you will bear his judgment, whoever he is.

¹¹But I, brothers, if I still proclaim circumcision, why am I still persecuted? Then the stumbling block of the cross has been removed. ¹²I wish that those who disturb

you would cut themselves off. ¹³For you, brothers, were called for freedom. Only do not use your freedom for gain to the flesh, but through love be servants to one another. ¹⁴For the whole law is fulfilled in one word, in this: "You are to love your neighbor as yourself."^e ¹⁵But if you bite and devour one another, be careful that you do not consume one another. ¹⁶But I say, walk by the Spirit, and you will not carry out the desires of the flesh. ¹⁷For the flesh lusts against the Spirit, and the Spirit against the flesh; and these are contrary to one another, that you may not do the things that you desire. ¹⁸But if you are led by the Spirit, you are not under the law. ¹⁹Now the works of the flesh are obvious, which are:^f sexual immorality, uncleanness, lustfulness, ²⁰idolatry, sorcery, hatred, strife, jealousies, outbursts of anger, rivalries, divisions, heresies, ²¹envyings, murders,^g drunkenness, orgies, and things like these; of which I forewarn you, even as I also forewarned you, that those who practice such things will not inherit the kingdom of God.

²²But the fruit of the Spirit is love, joy, peace, patience, kindness, goodness, faithfulness, ²³gentleness, and self-control. Against such things there is no law. ²⁴Those who belong to Christ have crucified the flesh with its passions and lusts. ²⁵If we live by the Spirit, let us also walk by the Spirit. ²⁶Let us not become conceited, provoking one another, and envying one another.

6 Brothers, even if someone is caught in some fault, you who are spiritual must restore such a one in a spirit of gentleness; looking to yourself so that you also are not tempted. ²Bear one another's burdens, and so you will fulfill the law of Christ. ³For if anyone thinks himself to be something when he is nothing, he deceives

---

a 4:26 Some Mss read "the mother of us all"
b 4:27 Isaiah 54:1
c 4:28 Some Mss read "we"
d 4:30 Genesis 21:10
e 5:14 Leviticus 19:18
f 5:19 Some Mss add "adultery"
g 5:21 Some Mss lack "murders"

himself. [4]But let each one test his own work, and then he will take pride in himself and not in his neighbor. [5]For every person will bear his own load. [6]But let him who is taught in the word share all good things with him who teaches. [7]Do not be deceived. God is not mocked, for whatever a person sows, that he will also reap. [8]For he who sows to his own flesh will from the flesh reap corruption. But he who sows to the Spirit will from the Spirit reap everlasting life. [9]Let us not be weary in doing good, for we will reap in due season, if we do not give up. [10]So then, as we have opportunity, let us do what is good toward all people, and especially toward those who are of the household of the faith.

[11]See with what large letters I write to you with my own hand. [12]As many as desire to make a good showing in the flesh, they compel you to be circumcised; only that they may not be persecuted for the cross of Christ. [13]For even they who receive circumcision do not keep the law themselves, but they desire to have you circumcised, that they may boast in your flesh. [14]But far be it from me to boast, except in the cross of our Lord Jesus Christ, through which the world has been crucified to me, and I to the world. [15]For neither[a] is circumcision anything, nor uncircumcision, but a new creation. [16]As many as walk by this rule, peace and mercy be on them, and on God's Israel. [17]From now on, let no one cause me any trouble, for I bear the marks of[b] Jesus branded on my body.

[18]The grace of our Lord Jesus Christ be with your spirit, brothers. Amen.

Ephesians

1 Paul, an apostle of Christ Jesus through the will of God, to the saints in Ephesus[c] who are faithful in Christ Jesus: [2]Grace to you and peace from God our Father and the Lord Jesus Christ.

[3]Blessed be the God and Father of our Lord Jesus Christ, who has blessed us with every spiritual blessing in the heavenly places in Christ; [4]even as he chose us in him before the foundation of the world, that we would be holy and without blemish before him in love; [5]having predestined us for adoption as children through Jesus Christ to himself, according to the good pleasure of his desire, [6]to the praise of the glory of his grace,[d] which he freely bestowed on us in the Beloved One, [7]in whom we have our redemption through his blood, the forgiveness of our trespasses, according to the riches of his grace, [8]which he made to abound toward us in all wisdom and prudence, [9]making known to us the mystery of his will, according to his good pleasure which he purposed in him [10]to an administration of the fullness of the times, to sum up all things in Christ, the things in the heavens, and the things on the earth, in him; [11]in whom also we were assigned an inheritance, having been foreordained according to the purpose of him[e] who works all things after the counsel of his will; [12]to the end that we should be to the praise of his glory, we who had before hoped in Christ: [13]in whom you also, having heard the word of the truth, the Good News of your salvation,—in whom, having also believed, you were sealed with the Holy Spirit of promise, [14]who is a pledge of our inheritance, to the redemption of God's own possession, to the praise of his glory. [15]For this cause I also, having heard of the faith in the Lord Jesus which is among you, and the love which you have toward all the saints, [16]do not cease to give thanks for you, making mention of you in my prayers, [17]that the God of our Lord Jesus Christ, the Father of glory, may give to you a spirit of wisdom and revelation in the knowledge of him; [18]having the eyes of your heart

---

a   6:15 Some Mss add "in Christ Jesus"
b   6:17 Some Mss add "the Lord"
c   1:1 Some Mss lack "in Ephesus"
d   1:6 Some Mss add "by"
e   1:11 Some Mss add God"

enlightened, that you may know what is the hope of his calling, and what are the riches of the glory of his inheritance in the saints, [19]and what is the exceeding greatness of his power toward us who believe, according to that working of the strength of his might [20]which he worked in Christ, when he raised him from the dead, and made him to sit at his right hand in the heavenly places, [21]far above all rule, and authority, and power, and dominion, and every name that is named, not only in this age, but also in that which is to come. [22]He put[a] all things under his feet, and gave him to be head over all things for the church, [23]which is his body, the fullness of him who fills all in all.

2 You were made alive when you were dead in your[b] transgressions and sins, [2]in which you once walked according to the course of this world, according to the prince of the power of the air, the spirit who now works in the children of disobedience; [3]among whom we also all once lived in the lust of our flesh, doing the desires of the flesh and of the mind, and were by nature children of wrath, even as the rest. [4]But God, being rich in mercy, for his great love with which he loved us, [5]even when we were dead through our trespasses, made us alive together with Christ[c] (by grace you have been saved), [6]and raised us up with him, and made us to sit with him in the heavenly places in Christ Jesus, [7]that in the ages to come he might show the exceeding riches of his grace in kindness toward us in Christ Jesus; [8]for by grace you have been saved through faith, and that not of yourselves; it is the gift of God, [9]not of works, that no one would boast. [10]For we are his workmanship, created in Christ Jesus for good works, which God prepared before that we would walk in them.

[11]Therefore remember that once you, the non-Jews in the flesh, who are called "uncircumcision" by that which is called "circumcision," (in the flesh, made by hands); [12]that you were at that time separate from Christ, alienated from the commonwealth of Israel, and strangers from the covenants of the promise, having no hope and without God in the world. [13]But now in Christ Jesus you who formerly were far away have been brought near by the blood of Christ. [14]For he is our peace, who made both one, and broke down the middle wall of partition, [15]having abolished in the flesh the hostility, the law of commandments contained in ordinances, that he might create in himself one new man of the two, making peace; [16]and might reconcile them both in one body to God through the cross, by which he put to death their enmity. [17]He came and preached peace to you who were far off and peace[d] to those who were near. [18]For through him we both have our access in one Spirit to the Father. [19]So then you are no longer strangers and foreigners, but you[e] are fellow citizens with the saints, and of the household of God, [20]being built on the foundation of the apostles and prophets, Christ Jesus himself being the chief cornerstone; [21]in whom the whole building, fitted together, grows into a holy temple in the Lord; [22]in whom you also are built together for a habitation of God in the Spirit.

3 For this cause I, Paul, am the prisoner of Christ Jesus on behalf of you non-Jews, [2]if it is so that you have heard of the administration of that grace of God which was given me toward you; [3]how that by revelation the mystery was made known to me, as I wrote before in few words, [4]by which, when you read, you can perceive my understanding in the mystery of Christ; [5]which in other generations was not made known to people,[f] as it has now been revealed to his holy apostles and prophets in the Spirit; [6]that the non-Jews are fellow heirs, and fellow members of the body, and fellow partakers of the[g] promise in Christ

---

a   1:22 Or, "subjected"
b   2:1 Some Mss lack "your"
c   2:5 Some Mss read "in the Christ"
d   2:17 Some Mss lack "peace"
e   2:19 Some Mss lack "you"
f   3:5 Lit. "the sons of men," a Semitic idiom referring to people
g   3:6 Some Mss read "his"

Jesus through the Good News, [7]of which I was made a servant, according to the gift of that grace of God which was given me according to the working of his power. [8]To me, the very least of all saints, was this grace given, to proclaim to the non-Jews the unsearchable riches of Christ, [9]and to bring to light for all what is the administration[a] of the mystery which for ages has been hidden in God, who created all things[b]; [10]to the intent that now through the church the manifold wisdom of God might be made known to the rulers and the authorities in the heavenly places, [11]according to the purpose of the ages which he purposed in Christ Jesus our Lord; [12]in whom we have boldness and access in confidence through our faith in him. [13]Therefore I ask that you may not lose heart at my troubles for you, which are your glory.

[14]For this cause, I bow my knees before the Father,[c] [15]from whom every family in heaven and on earth is named, [16]that he would grant you, according to the riches of his glory, that you may be strengthened with power through his Spirit in the inner person; [17]that Christ may dwell in your hearts through faith; to the end that you, being rooted and grounded in love, [18]may be strengthened to comprehend with all the saints what is the breadth and length and height and depth, [19]and to know Christ's love which surpasses knowledge, that you may be filled with all the fullness of God. [20]Now to him who is able to do exceedingly abundantly above all that we ask or think, according to the power that works in us, [21]to him be the glory in the church and in Christ Jesus to all generations forever and ever. Amen.

4 I therefore, the prisoner in the Lord, urge you to walk worthily of the calling with which you were called, [2]with all lowliness and humility, with patience, bearing with one another in love; [3]being eager to keep the unity of the Spirit in the bond of peace. [4]There is one body, and one Spirit, even as you also were called in one hope of your calling; [5]one Lord, one faith, one baptism, [6]one God and Father of all, who is over all, and through all, and in[d] all. [7]But to each one of us was the grace given according to the measure of the gift of Christ. [8]Therefore he says, "When he ascended on high, he led captivity captive, and[e] gave gifts to people."[f] [9]Now this, "He ascended," what is it but that he also[g] descended into the lower parts of the earth? [10]He who descended is the one who also ascended far above all the heavens, that he might fill all things.

[11]He gave some to be apostles; and some, prophets; and some, evangelists; and some, pastors and teachers; [12]for the perfecting of the saints, to the work of serving, to the building up of the body of Christ; [13]until we all attain to the unity of the faith, and of the knowledge of the Son of God, to a mature person, to the measure of the stature of the fullness of Christ; [14]that we may no longer be children, tossed back and forth and carried about with every wind of doctrine, by the trickery of people, by cleverness in deceitful schemes; [15]but speaking truth in love, we may grow up in all things into him, who is the head, Christ; [16]from whom all the body, being fitted and knit together through that which every joint supplies, according to the proper working of each individual part, makes the body increase to the building up of itself in love.

[17]This I say therefore, and testify in the Lord, that you no longer walk as the rest of the nations also walk, in the futility of their mind, [18]being darkened in their understanding, alienated from the life of God, because of the ignorance that is in them, because of the hardening of their hearts; [19]who having become callous gave themselves up to lust, to work all uncleanness with greediness. [20]But you did not learn Christ that way; [21]if indeed you heard him, and were taught in him, even as truth is in

---

a   3:9 Some Mss read "fellowship"
b   3:9 Some Mss add "through Jesus Christ"
c   3:14 Some Mss add "of our Lord Jesus Christ"
d   4:6 Some Mss add "us"
e   4:8 Some Mss lack "and"
f   4:8 Psalm 68:18
g   4:9 Some Mss add "first"

Jesus: [22]that you put away, as concerning your former way of life, the old self, that grows corrupt after the lusts of deceit; [23]and that you be renewed in the spirit of your mind, [24]and put on the new self, who in the likeness of God has been created in righteousness and holiness of truth.

[25]Therefore, putting away falsehood, speak truth each one with his neighbor. For we are members of one another. [26]"Be angry, but do not sin."[a] Do not let the sun go down on your anger, [27]neither give place to the devil. [28]Let him who stole steal no more; but rather let him labor, working with his hands the thing that is good, that he may have something to give to him who has need. [29]Let no corrupt speech proceed out of your mouth, but such as is good for building up as the need may be, that it may give grace to those who hear. [30]Do not grieve the Holy Spirit of God, in whom you were sealed for the day of redemption. [31]Let all bitterness, wrath, anger, outcry,[b] and slander, be put away from you, with all malice. [32]And be kind to one another, tenderhearted, forgiving each other, just as God also in Christ forgave you.[c]

5 Be therefore imitators of God, as beloved children. [2]And walk in love, even as Christ also loved us,[d] and gave himself up for us, an offering and a sacrifice to God for a sweet-smelling fragrance. [3]But sexual immorality, and all uncleanness, or covetousness, let it not even be mentioned among you, as becomes saints; [4]nor filthiness, nor foolish talking, nor jesting, which are not appropriate; but rather giving of thanks.

[5]Know this for sure, that no sexually immoral or impure or greedy person, that is, an idolater, has any inheritance in the kingdom of Christ and God.

[6]Let no one deceive you with empty words. For because of these things, the wrath of God comes on the children of disobedience. [7]Therefore do not be partakers with them. [8]For you were once darkness, but are now light in the Lord. Walk as children of light, [9]for the fruit of the light[e] is in all goodness and righteousness and truth,

[10]proving what is well pleasing to the Lord. [11]Have no fellowship with the unfruitful works of darkness, but rather even reprove them. [12]For the things which are done by them in secret, it is a shame even to speak of. [13]But all things, when they are reproved, are revealed by the light, for everything that reveals is light. [14]Therefore he says, "Awake, you who sleep, and rise from the dead, and Christ will shine on you."

[15]Therefore watch carefully how you walk, not as unwise, but as wise; [16]redeeming the time, because the days are evil. [17]Therefore do not be foolish, but understand what the will of the Lord is. [18]Do not get drunk with wine, which is debauchery, but be filled with the Spirit, [19]speaking to one another in psalms, hymns, and spiritual songs; singing, and singing praises in your heart to the Lord; [20]giving thanks always concerning all things in the name of our Lord Jesus Christ to God the Father; [21]subjecting yourselves one to another in the fear of Christ.[f]

[22]Wives, be subject to your own husbands, as to the Lord. [23]For the husband is the head of the wife, and Christ also is the head of the church, being himself the savior of the body. [24]But as the church is subject to Christ, so let the wives also be to their own husbands in everything.

[25]Husbands, love your wives, even as Christ also loved the church, and gave himself up for it; [26]that he might sanctify it, having cleansed it by the washing of water with the word, [27]that he might present the church to himself gloriously, not having spot or wrinkle or any such thing; but that it should be holy and without blemish. [28]Even so husbands also ought to love their own wives as their own bodies. He who loves his own wife loves himself. [29]For no one ever hated his own flesh; but nourishes and cherishes it, even as Christ[h]

---

a   4:26 Psalm 4:4
b   4:31 Or, shouting, violent assertiveness
c   4:32 Some Mss read "us"
d   5:2 Some Mss read "you"
e   5:9 Some Mss read "Spirit"
f   5:21 Some Mss read "of God"
h   5:29 Some Mss read "the Lord"

also does the church; [30]because we are members of his body, of his flesh and of his bones.[a] [31]"For this cause a man will leave his father and mother, and will be joined to his wife, and the two will become one flesh."[b] [32]This mystery is great, but I speak concerning Christ and of the church. [33]Nevertheless each of you must also love his own wife even as himself; and let the wife see that she respects her husband.

6 Children, obey your parents in the Lord, for this is right. [2]"Honor your father and mother," which is the first commandment with a promise: [3]"that it may be well with you, and that you may live long in the land."[c]

[4]And fathers, do not provoke your children to anger, but nurture them in the discipline and instruction of the Lord.

[5]Servants, be obedient to those who according to the flesh are your masters, with fear and trembling, in singleness of your heart, as to Christ; [6]not in the way of service only when eyes are on you, as people-pleasers; but as servants of Christ, doing the will of God from the heart; [7]with good will doing service, as to the Lord, and not to people; [8]knowing that whatever good thing each one does, he will receive the same again from the Lord, whether he is bound or free.

[9]You masters, do the same things to them, and give up threatening, knowing that he who is both their Master and yours[d] is in heaven, and there is no partiality with him.

[10]Finally,[e] be strong in the Lord, and in the strength of his might. [11]Put on the whole armor of God, that you may be able to stand against the schemes of the devil. [12]For our wrestling is not against flesh and blood, but against the rulers, against the powers, against the world's rulers of this darkness,[f] and against the spiritual forces of wickedness in the heavenly places. [13]Therefore, put on the whole armor of God, that you may be able to withstand in the evil day, and, having done all, to stand. [14]Stand therefore, having the utility belt of truth buckled around your waist, and having put on the breastplate of righteousness, [15]and having fitted your feet with the preparation of the Good News of peace; [16]above all, taking up the shield of faith, with which you will be able to quench all the fiery darts of the evil one. [17]And take the helmet of salvation, and the sword of the Spirit, which is the spoken word of God; [18]with all prayer and requests, praying at all times in the Spirit, and being watchful to this end in all perseverance and requests for all the saints: [19]on my behalf, that utterance may be given to me in opening my mouth, to make known with boldness the mystery of the Good News, [20]for which I am an ambassador in chains; that in it I may speak boldly, as I ought to speak.

[21]But that you also may know my affairs, how I am doing, Tychicus, the beloved brother and faithful servant in the Lord, will make known to you all things; [22]whom I have sent to you for this very purpose, that you may know our state, and that he may comfort your hearts.

[23]Peace be to the brothers, and love with faith, from God the Father and the Lord Jesus Christ. [24]Grace be with all those who love our Lord Jesus Christ with incorruptible love.[g]

Philippians

1 Paul and Timothy, servants of Christ Jesus;[h] To all the saints in Christ Jesus who are at Philippi, with the overseers and deacons: [2]Grace to you, and peace from God, our Father, and the Lord Jesus Christ. [3]I thank my God whenever I remember you, [4]always in every request of mine on

---

a   5:30 Some Mss lack "of his flesh and of his bones"
b   5:31 Genesis 2:24
c   6:3 Exodus 20:12
d   6:9 Some Mss read "your own master"
e   6:10 Some Mss add "my brothers"
f   6:12 Some Mss add "of this age"
g   6:24 Some Mss add "Amen"
h   1:1 Some Mss read "Jesus Christ"

behalf of you all making my requests with joy, [5]for your partnership[a] in furtherance of the Good News from the first day until now; [6]being confident of this very thing, that he who began a good work in you will complete it until the day of Christ Jesus. [7]It is even right for me to think this way on behalf of all of you, because I have you in my heart, because, both in my bonds and in the defense and confirmation of the Good News, you all are partakers with me of grace. [8]For God is my witness, how I long after all of you in the tender mercies of Christ Jesus.

[9]This I pray, that your love may abound yet more and more in knowledge and all discernment; [10]so that you may approve the things that are excellent; that you may be sincere and without offense to the day of Christ; [11]being filled with the fruit[b] of righteousness, which are through Jesus Christ, to the glory and praise of God.

[12]Now I desire to have you know, brothers, that the things which happened to me have turned out rather to the progress of the Good News; [13]so that it became evident to the whole praetorian guard, and to all the rest, that my bonds are in Christ; [14]and that most of the brothers in the Lord, being confident through my bonds, are more abundantly bold to speak the word[c] without fear. [15]Some indeed proclaim Christ even out of envy and strife, and some also out of good will. [16]The latter out of love, knowing that I am appointed for the defense of the Good News. [17]The former insincerely proclaim Christ from selfish ambition, thinking that they add affliction to my chains.

[18]What does it matter? Only that in every way, whether out of false motives or in truth, Christ is proclaimed. I rejoice in this, yes, and will rejoice. [19]For I know that this will turn out for my deliverance, through your petition and the supply of the Spirit of Jesus Christ, [20]according to my earnest expectation and hope, that I will in no way be disappointed, but with all boldness, as always, now also Christ will be magnified in my body, whether by life, or by death. [21]For to me to live is Christ, and to die is gain. [22]But if I live on in the flesh, this will bring fruit from my work; yet I do not make known what I will choose. [23]But I am in a dilemma between the two, having the desire to depart and be with Christ, which is far better. [24]Yet, to remain in the flesh is more needful for your sake. [25]Having this confidence, I know that I will remain, yes, and remain with you all, for your progress and joy in the faith, [26]that your rejoicing may abound in Christ Jesus in me through my presence with you again.

[27]Only let your manner of life be worthy of the Good News of Christ, that, whether I come and see you or am absent, I may hear of your state, that you stand firm in one spirit, with one soul striving for the faith of the Good News; [28]and in nothing frightened by the adversaries, which is for them a proof of destruction, but to you of salvation, and that from God. [29]Because it has been granted to you on behalf of Christ, not only to believe in him, but also to suffer on his behalf, [30]having the same conflict which you saw in me, and now hear is in me.

2 If there is therefore any exhortation in Christ, if any consolation of love, if any fellowship of the Spirit, if any tender mercies and compassion, [2]make my joy full, by being like-minded, having the same love, being of one accord, of one mind; [3]doing nothing through rivalry or through conceit, but in humility, each counting others better than himself; [4]each of you not just looking to his own things, but each of you also to the things of others.

[5]Have this in your mind, which was also in Christ Jesus, [6]who, existing in the form of God, did not consider equality with God a thing to be grasped, [7]but emptied himself, taking the form of a servant,

---

a   1:5 Gk. koinonia. It also means "fellowship" and "sharing"

b   1:11 Some Mss read "fruits"

c   1:14 Some Mss add "of God"

being made in the likeness of men. [8]And being found in human form, he humbled himself, becoming obedient to death, yes, the death of the cross. [9]Therefore God also highly exalted him, and gave to him the name which is above every name; [10]that at the name of Jesus every knee should bow, of those in heaven, those on earth, and those under the earth, [11]and that every tongue should confess that Jesus Christ is Lord[a], to the glory of God the Father.

[12]So then, my beloved, even as you have always obeyed, not only in my presence, but now much more in my absence, work out your own salvation with fear and trembling. [13]For it is God who works in you both to will and to work, for his good pleasure. [14]Do all things without murmurings and disputes, [15]that you may be blameless and pure, children of God without blemish in the midst of a crooked and perverse generation, among whom you are seen as lights in the world, [16]holding up the word of life; that I may have something to boast in the day of Christ, that I did not run in vain nor labor in vain. [17]Yes, and if I am poured out on the sacrifice and service of your faith, I rejoice, and rejoice with you all. [18]In the same way, you also rejoice, and rejoice with me.

[19]But I hope in the Lord Jesus to send Timothy to you soon, that I also may be cheered up when I know how you are doing. [20]For I have no one else like-minded, who will truly care about you. [21]For they all seek their own, not the things of Jesus Christ. [22]But you know the proof of him, that, as a child serves a father, so he served with me in furtherance of the Good News. [23]Therefore I hope to send him at once, as soon as I see how it will go with me. [24]But I trust in the Lord that I myself also will come shortly. [25]But I counted it necessary to send to you Epaphroditus, my brother, fellow worker, fellow soldier, and your apostle and servant of my need; [26]since he longed for you all, and was very troubled, because you had heard that he was sick. [27]For indeed he was sick, nearly to death, but God had mercy on him; and not on

him only, but on me also, that I might not have sorrow upon sorrow. [28]I have sent him all the more eagerly, therefore, so that when you see him again you may rejoice, and that I may be less anxious. [29]Receive him therefore in the Lord with all joy, and hold such in honor, [30]because for the work of Christ he came near to death, risking[b] his life to supply that which was lacking in your service toward me.

3 Finally, my brothers, rejoice in the Lord. To write the same things to you, to me indeed is not tiresome, but for you it is safe. [2]Beware of the dogs, beware of the evil workers, beware of the false circumcision. [3]For we are the circumcision, who worship God in the Spirit, and rejoice in Christ Jesus, and have no confidence in the flesh; [4]though I myself might have confidence even in the flesh. If anyone else thinks that he has confidence in the flesh, I yet more: [5]circumcised the eighth day, of the stock of Israel, of the tribe of Benjamin, a Hebrew of Hebrews; concerning the law, a Pharisee; [6]concerning zeal, persecuting the church; concerning the righteousness which is in the law, found blameless.

[7]However, what things were gain to me, these have I counted loss for Christ. [8]More than that, I count all things to be loss for the excellency of the knowledge of Christ Jesus, my Lord, for whom I suffered the loss of all things, and count them nothing but refuse, that I may gain Christ [9]and be found in him, not having a righteousness of my own, that which is of the law, but that which is through faith in Christ, the righteousness which is from God by faith; [10]that I may know him, and the power of his resurrection, and the fellowship of his sufferings, becoming conformed to his death; [11]if by any means I may attain to the resurrection from the dead. [12]Not that I have already obtained, or am already made perfect; but I press on, if it is so that

---

a 2:11 See Isaiah 45:23
b 2:30 Some Mss read "disregarding"

I may take hold of that for which also I was taken hold of by Christ Jesus.[a]

[13]Brothers, I do not regard myself as having taken hold of it, but one thing I do. Forgetting the things which are behind, and reaching forward to the things which are ahead, [14]I press on toward the goal for the prize of the high calling of God in Christ Jesus. [15]Let us therefore, as many as are perfect, think this way. If in anything you think otherwise, God will also reveal that to you. [16]Nevertheless, to what we have attained, let us walk by the same rule, being of the same mind.[b] [17]Brothers, be imitators together of me, and note those who walk this way, even as you have us for an example. [18]For many walk, of whom I told you often, and now tell you even weeping, as the enemies of the cross of Christ, [19]whose end is destruction, whose god is the belly, and whose glory is in their shame, who think about earthly things. [20]For our citizenship is in heaven, from where we also wait for a Savior, the Lord Jesus Christ; [21]who will transform our lowly body into the likeness of his glorious body, according to the power by which he is able even to subject all things to himself.

4 Therefore, my brothers, beloved and longed for, my joy and crown, so stand firm in the Lord, my beloved. [2]I exhort Euodia, and I exhort Syntyche, to think the same way in the Lord. [3]Yes, I ask you also, true companion, help these women, for they labored with me in the Good News, with Clement also, and the rest of my fellow workers, whose names are in the book of life. [4]Rejoice in the Lord always. Again I will say, Rejoice. [5]Let your gentleness be known to all people. The Lord is near. [6]Do not be anxious about anything, but in everything, by prayer and petition with thanksgiving, let your requests be made known to God. [7]And the peace of God, which surpasses all understanding, will guard your hearts and your thoughts in Christ Jesus.

[8]Finally, brothers, whatever things are true, whatever things are honest, whatever things are just, whatever things are pure, whatever things are lovely, whatever things are of good report; if there is any virtue, and if there is any praise, think on these things. [9]And the things you learned and received and heard and saw in me, do these things. And the God of peace will be with you. [10]But I rejoice in the Lord greatly, that now at length you have revived your thought for me; in which you did indeed take thought, but you lacked opportunity. [11]Not that I speak in respect to lack, for I have learned in whatever state I am, to be content in it. [12]I know how to be humbled, and I know also how to abound. In everything and in all things I have learned the secret both to be filled and to be hungry, both to abound and to be in need. [13]I can do all things through him[c] who strengthens me. [14]However you did well that you shared in my affliction. [15]You yourselves also know, you Philippians, that in the beginning of the Good News, when I departed from Macedonia, no church shared with me in the matter of giving and receiving but you only. [16]For even in Thessalonica you sent once and again to my need. [17]Not that I seek for the gift, but I seek for the fruit that increases to your account. [18]But I have all things, and abound. I am filled, having received from Epaphroditus the things that came from you, a sweet-smelling fragrance, an acceptable and well-pleasing sacrifice to God. [19]My God will supply every need of yours according to his riches in glory in Christ Jesus. [20]Now to our God and Father be the glory forever and ever. Amen.

[21]Greet every saint in Christ Jesus. The brothers who are with me greet you. [22]All the saints greet you, especially those who are of Caesar's household. [23]The grace of the Lord Jesus Christ be with your spirit[d].[e]

a   3:12 Some Mss lack "Jesus"
b   3:16 Some Mss lack "rule, being of the same mind"
c   4:13 Some Mss read "Christ"
d   4:23 Some Mss read "with you all"
e   4:23 Some Mss add "Amen"

Colossians

1 Paul, an apostle of Christ Jesus through the will of God, and Timothy our brother, [2]to the saints and faithful brothers in Christ at Colossae: Grace to you and peace from God our Father.[a]

[3]We give thanks to God the Father of our Lord Jesus Christ, praying always for you, [4]having heard of your faith in Christ Jesus, and of the love which you have toward all the saints, [5]because of the hope which is laid up for you in the heavens, of which you heard before in the word of the truth of the Good News, [6]which has come to you; even as it is in all the world and is bearing fruit and growing, as it does in you also, since the day you heard and knew the grace of God in truth; [7]even as you learned of Epaphras our beloved fellow servant, who is a faithful servant of Christ on our[b] behalf, [8]who also declared to us your love in the Spirit. [9]For this cause, we also, since the day we heard this, do not cease praying and making requests for you, that you may be filled with the knowledge of his will in all spiritual wisdom and understanding, [10]that you may walk worthily of the Lord,[c] to please him in all respects, bearing fruit in every good work, and increasing in the knowledge of God; [11]strengthened with all power, according to the might of his glory, for all endurance and perseverance with joy; [12]giving thanks to the Father, who made you[d] fit to be partakers of the inheritance of the saints in the light; [13]who delivered us out of the power of darkness, and transferred us into the kingdom of the Son of his love; [14]in whom we have our redemption,[e] the forgiveness of our sins; [15]who is the image of the invisible God, preeminent[f] over all creation. [16]For by him all things were created, in the heavens and on the earth, things visible and things invisible, whether thrones or dominions or rulers or powers; all things have been created by him and for[g] him. [17]He is before all things, and in him all things are held together. [18]He is the head of the body, the church, who is the beginning, the firstborn from the dead;[h] that in all things he might have the preeminence. [19]For all the fullness was pleased to dwell in him, [20]and through him to reconcile all things to himself, making peace through the blood of his cross through him,[i] whether things on the earth or things in heaven.

[21]You, being in past times alienated and enemies in your mind in your evil works, [22]yet now he has reconciled in the body of his flesh through death, to present you holy and without blemish and blameless before him, [23]if it is so that you continue in the faith, grounded and steadfast, and not moved away from the hope of the Good News which you heard, which is being proclaimed[j] in all creation under heaven; of which I, Paul, was made a servant.

[24]Now I rejoice in my sufferings for your sake, and fill up on my part that which is lacking of the afflictions of Christ in my flesh for his body's sake, which is the church; [25]of which I was made a servant, according to the stewardship of God which was given me toward you, to fulfill the word of God, [26]the mystery which has been hidden for ages and generations. But now it has been revealed to his saints, [27]to them God was pleased to make known what are the riches of the glory of this mystery among the non-Jews, which is Christ in you, the hope of glory; [28]whom we proclaim, admonishing everyone and teaching everyone all wisdom, that we may present everyone perfect in Christ Jesus; [29]for which I also labor, struggling according to his power, which works in me mightily.

---

a 1:2 Some Mss add "and the Lord Jesus Christ"
b 1:7 Some Mss read "your"
c 1:10 Some Mss read "God" instead of "Lord"
d 1:12 Some Mss read "us"
e 1:14 Some Mss add "through his blood"
f 1:15 Or, "supreme." Gk. prototokos
g 1:16 Or, "in him"
h 1:18 Or, "preeminent over all who rise from the dead"
i 1:20 Some Mss lack "through him"
j 1:23 The word for "is being" (rather than "has") is an aorist in substantival participles

2 For I desire to have you know how greatly I struggle for you, and for those at Laodicea, and for as many as have not seen my face in the flesh; [2]that their hearts may be comforted, they being knit together in love, and gaining all riches of the full assurance of understanding, that they may know the mystery of God,[a] namely, Christ, [3]in whom are all the treasures of wisdom and knowledge hidden. [4]Now this I say that no one may delude you with persuasiveness of speech. [5]For though I am absent in the flesh, yet am I with you in the spirit, rejoicing and seeing your order, and the steadfastness of your faith in Christ. [6]As therefore you received Christ Jesus, the Lord, walk in him, [7]rooted and built up in him, and established in the faith, even as you were taught, abounding in it[b] with thanksgiving. [8]Be careful not to allow anyone to captivate you through an empty and deceptive philosophy, according to human tradition, according to the elementary principles of the world, and not according to Christ. [9]For in him all the fullness of Deity dwells in bodily form, [10]and in him you are made full, who is the head of all principality and power; [11]in whom you were also circumcised with a circumcision not made with hands, in the putting off of the body of[c] the flesh, in the circumcision of Christ; [12]having been buried with him in baptism, in which you were also raised with him through faith in the working of God, who raised him from the dead. [13]You were dead through your trespasses and the uncircumcision of your flesh. He made you alive together with him, having forgiven us all our trespasses, [14]wiping out the handwriting in ordinances which was against us; and he has taken it out of the way, nailing it to the cross; [15]having disarmed the rulers and authorities, he made a show of them openly, triumphing over them in it.

[16]Therefore do not let anyone judge you in eating, or in drinking, or with respect to a feast day or a new moon or a Sabbath day, [17]which are a shadow of the things to come; but the body is Christ's. [18]Let no one rob you of your prize by a voluntary humility and worshipping of the angels, dwelling in the things which he has[d] seen, vainly puffed up by his fleshly mind, [19]and not holding firmly to the Head, from whom all the body, being supplied and knit together through the joints and ligaments, grows with God's growth. [20]If you died with Christ from the elementary principles of the world, why, as though living in the world, do you subject yourselves to regulations, [21]"Do not handle, nor taste, nor touch" [22](all of which perish with use), according to human commandments and teachings? [23]Which things indeed appear like wisdom in self-imposed worship, and humility, and severity to the body; but are not of any value against the indulgence of the flesh.

3 If then you were raised together with Christ, seek the things that are above, where Christ is, seated on the right hand of God. [2]Set your mind on the things that are above, not on the things that are on the earth. [3]For you died, and your life is hidden with Christ in God. [4]When Christ, your[e] life, is revealed, then you will also be revealed with him in glory. [5]Put to death, therefore, whatever is worldly in you: sexual immorality, impurity, lust, evil desire, and covetousness, which is idolatry. [6]Because of these, the wrath of God is coming on the sons of disobedience.[f] [7]You also once walked in those, when you lived in them; [8]but now you also put them all away: anger, wrath, malice, slander, and shameful speaking out of your mouth. [9]Do not lie to one another, seeing that you have put off the old self with its practices, [10]and have put on the new self, who is being renewed in knowledge after the image of his Creator, [11]where there cannot be Greek and Jew, circumcision and uncircumcision, barbarian, Scythian, slave, freeman; but Christ is all, and in all.

---

a　2:2 Some Mss add "both of the Father and of"
b　2:7 Some Mss lack "it in"
c　2:11 Some Mss add "the sins of"
d　2:18 Some Mss add "not"
e　3:4 Some Mss read "our"
f　3:6 Some Mss lack "sons of disobedience"

¹²Put on therefore, as God's chosen ones, holy and beloved, a heart of compassion, kindness, lowliness, humility, and perseverance; ¹³bearing with one another, and forgiving each other, if anyone has a complaint against another; even as the Lord[a] forgave you, so you also do. ¹⁴Above all these things, walk in love, which is the bond of perfection. ¹⁵And let the peace of Christ[b] rule in your hearts, to which also you were called in one body; and be thankful. ¹⁶Let the word of Christ dwell in you richly; in all wisdom teaching and admonishing one another with psalms, hymns, and spiritual songs, singing with grace in your heart to God[c].

¹⁷Whatever you do, in word or in deed, do all in the name of the Lord Jesus, giving thanks to God the Father, through him.

¹⁸Wives, be in subjection to your husbands, as is fitting in the Lord.

¹⁹Husbands, love your wives, and do not be bitter against them.

²⁰Children, obey your parents in all things, for this pleases the Lord.

²¹Fathers, do not provoke your children, so that they won't be discouraged.

²²Servants, obey in all things those who are your masters according to the flesh, not just when they are looking, as people-pleasers, but in singleness of heart, fearing the Lord[d]. ²³And whatever you do, work heartily, as for the Lord, and not for people, ²⁴knowing that from the Lord you will receive the reward of the inheritance; for you serve the Lord Christ. ²⁵But he who does wrong will receive again for the wrong that he has done, and there is no partiality.

4 Masters, give to your servants that which is just and equal, knowing that you also have a Master in heaven.

²Continue steadfastly in prayer, watching in it with thanksgiving; ³praying together for us also, that God may open to us a door for the word, to speak the mystery of Christ, for which I am also in bonds; ⁴that I may reveal it as I ought to speak. ⁵Walk in wisdom toward those who are outside, redeeming the time. ⁶Let your speech always be with grace, seasoned with salt, that you may know how you ought to answer each one.

⁷All my affairs will be made known to you by Tychicus, the beloved brother, faithful servant, and fellow slave in the Lord. ⁸I am sending him to you for this very purpose, that you[e] may know our[f] circumstances and that he may encourage your hearts, ⁹together with Onesimus, the faithful and beloved brother, who is one of you. They will make known to you everything that is going on here. ¹⁰Aristarchus, my fellow prisoner greets you, and Mark, the cousin of Barnabas (concerning whom you received commandments, "if he comes to you, receive him"), ¹¹and Jesus who is called Justus, who are of the circumcision. These are my only fellow workers for the kingdom of God, and they have been a comfort to me.

¹²Epaphras, who is one of you, a servant of Christ, salutes you, always striving for you in his prayers, that you may stand perfect and fully assured[g] in all the will of God. ¹³For I testify about him, that he has worked hard[h] for you, and for those in Laodicea, and for those in Hierapolis. ¹⁴Luke, the beloved physician, and Demas greet you. ¹⁵Greet the brothers who are in Laodicea, and to Nympha[i] and the church that is in her[j] house. ¹⁶When this letter has been read among you, cause it to be read also in the church of the Laodiceans; and that you also read the letter from Laodicea. ¹⁷Tell Archippus, "Take heed to the ministry which you have received in the Lord, that you fulfill it."

¹⁸The salutation of me, Paul, with my own hand: remember my bonds. Grace be with you.[k]

---

a   3:13 Some Mss read "Christ"
b   3:15 Some Mss read "God"
c   3:16 Some Mss read "the Lord"
d   3:22 Some Mss read "God"
e   4:8 Some Mss read "he"
f   4:8 Some Mss read "your"
g   4:12 Some Mss read "complete"
h   4:13 Some Mss read "great zeal"
i   4:15 Some Mss read Nymphas"
j   4:15 Some Mss read "his"
k   4:18 Some Mss add "Amen"

1 Thessalonians

1 Paul, Silvanus, and Timothy, to the church of the Thessalonians in God the Father and the Lord Jesus Christ: Grace to you and peace[a].

[2] We always give thanks to God for all of you, mentioning you in our prayers, [3] remembering without ceasing your work of faith and labor of love and patience of hope in our Lord Jesus Christ, before our God and Father. [4] We know, brothers loved by God, that you are chosen, [5] and that our Good News came to you not in word only, but also in power, and in the Holy Spirit, and with much assurance. You know what kind of persons we showed ourselves to be among you for your sake. [6] You became imitators of us, and of the Lord, having received the word in much affliction, with joy of the Holy Spirit, [7] so that you became an example to all who believe in Macedonia and in Achaia. [8] For from you the word of the Lord has been declared, not only in Macedonia and Achaia, but also in every place your faith toward God has gone out; so that we do not need to say anything. [9] For they themselves report concerning us what kind of a reception we had from you; and how you turned to God from idols, to serve a living and true God, [10] and to wait for his Son from heaven, whom he raised from the dead—Jesus, who delivers us from the wrath to come.

2 For you yourselves know, brothers, our visit to you was not in vain, [2] but having suffered before and been shamefully treated, as you know, at Philippi, we grew bold in our God to tell you the Good News of God in much conflict. [3] For our exhortation is not of error, nor of uncleanness, nor in deception. [4] But even as we have been approved by God to be entrusted with the Good News, so we speak; not as pleasing people, but God, who tests our hearts. [5] For neither were we at any time found using words of flattery, as you know, nor a cloak of covetousness (God is witness), [6] nor seeking glory from people (neither from you nor from others), when we might have claimed authority as apostles of Christ. [7] But we were like little children[b] among you, like a nursing mother cherishes her own children.

[8] Even so, affectionately longing for you, we were well pleased to impart to you, not the Good News of God only, but also our own souls, because you had become very dear to us. [9] For you remember, brothers, our labor and travail; for working night and day, that we might not burden any of you, we preached to you the Good News of God. [10] You are witnesses with God, how holy, righteously, and blamelessly we behaved ourselves toward you who believe. [11] As you know, as a father with his own children, [12] we exhorted, comforted, and implored every one of you to lead a life worthy of God, who calls you into his own kingdom and glory. [13] For this cause we also thank God without ceasing, that, when you received from us the word of the message of God, you accepted it not as a human word, but, as it is in truth, the word of God, which also works in you who believe. [14] For you, brothers, became imitators of the churches of God which are in Judea in Christ Jesus; for you also suffered the same things from your own countrymen, even as they did from the Jews; [15] who killed both the Lord Jesus and the[c] prophets, and drove us out, and did not please God, and are hostile to all people; [16] forbidding us to speak to those who are not Jewish that they may be saved; to fill up their sins always. But wrath has come on them to the uttermost.

[17] But we, brothers, being bereaved of you for a short season, in presence, not in heart, tried even harder to see your face with great

---

a   1:1 Some Mss add "from God our Father and the Lord Jesus Christ"

b   2:7 Some Mss read "gentle"

c   2:15 Some Mss read "their own"

desire, [18]because we wanted to come to you—indeed, I, Paul, once and again—but Satan hindered us. [19]For what is our hope, or joy, or crown of rejoicing? Is it not even you, before our Lord Jesus[a] at his coming? [20]For you are our glory and our joy.

3 Therefore, when we could not stand it any longer, we thought it good to be left behind at Athens alone, [2]and sent Timothy, our brother and God's fellow worker[b] in the Good News of Christ, to establish you, and to comfort you concerning your faith; [3]that no one be moved by these afflictions. For you know that we are appointed to this task. [4]For truly, when we were with you, we told you beforehand that we are to suffer affliction, even as it happened, and you know. [5]For this cause I also, when I could not stand it any longer, sent that I might know your faith, for fear that by any means the tempter had tempted you, and our labor would have been in vain. [6]But when Timothy came just now to us from you, and brought us glad news of your faith and love, and that you have good memories of us always, longing to see us, even as we also long to see you; [7]for this cause, brothers, we were comforted over you in all our distress and affliction through your faith. [8]For now we live, since you stand firm[c] in the Lord. [9]For what thanksgiving can we render again to God for you, for all the joy with which we rejoice for your sakes before our God; [10]night and day praying exceedingly that we may see your face, and may perfect that which is lacking in your faith? [11]Now may our God and Father himself, and our Lord Jesus,[d] direct our way to you; [12]and the Lord make you to increase and abound in love for one another and for all,, even as we also do toward you, [13]to the end he may establish your hearts blameless in holiness before our God and Father, at the coming of our Lord Jesus with all his saints.

4 Finally then, brothers, we ask and urge you in the Lord Jesus, that as you received from us how you ought to live and to please God, even as you are living,[e] that

you excel more and more. [2]For you know what instructions we gave you through the Lord Jesus. [3]For this is the will of God: your sanctification, that you abstain from sexual immorality, [4]that each one of you know how to possess himself of his own vessel in sanctification and honor, [5]not in the passion of lust, even as the nations who do not know God; [6]that no one should take advantage of and wrong a brother or sister in this matter; because the Lord is an avenger in all these things, as also we forewarned you and testified. [7]For God called us not for uncleanness, but in sanctification. [8]Therefore he who rejects this does not reject man, but God, who has also given his Holy Spirit to you.

[9]But concerning brotherly love, you have no need that one write to you. For you yourselves are taught by God to love one another, [10]for indeed you do it toward all the brothers who are in all Macedonia. But we exhort you, brothers, that you abound more and more; [11]and that you make it your ambition to lead a quiet life, and to do your own business, and to work with your own hands, even as we instructed you; [12]that you may walk properly toward those who are outside, and may have need of nothing.

[13]But we do not want you to be ignorant, brothers, concerning those who have fallen asleep, so that you do not grieve like the rest, who have no hope. [14]For if we believe that Jesus died and rose again, even so God will bring with him those who have fallen asleep in Jesus. [15]For this we tell you by the word of the Lord, that we who are alive, who are left to the coming of the Lord, will in no way precede those who have fallen asleep. [16]For the Lord himself will descend from heaven with a shout, with the voice of the archangel, and with God's trumpet. The dead in Christ will rise first, [17]then we who are alive, who are left, will be caught

---

a   2:19 Some Mss add "Christ"
b   3:2 Some Mss read "servant"
c   3:8 Some Mss read "if you stand firm"
d   3:11 Some Mss add "Christ"
e   4:1 Some Mss lack "even as you are living"

up together[a] with them in the clouds, to meet the Lord in the air. So we will be with the Lord forever. [18]Therefore comfort one another with these words.

5 But concerning the times and the seasons, brothers, you have no need that anything be written to you. [2]For you yourselves know well that the day of the Lord comes like a thief in the night. [3]For when they are saying, "Peace and safety," then sudden destruction will come on them, like birth pains on a pregnant woman; and they will in no way escape. [4]But you, brothers, are not in darkness, that the day should overtake you like a thief. [5]You are all children of light, and children of the day. We do not belong to the night, nor to darkness, [6]so then let us not sleep, as the rest do, but let us watch and be sober. [7]For those who sleep, sleep in the night, and those who are drunk are drunk in the night. [8]But let us, since we belong to the day, be sober, putting on the breastplate of faith and love, and, for a helmet, the hope of salvation. [9]For God did not appoint us to wrath, but to the obtaining of salvation through our Lord Jesus Christ, [10]who died for us, that, whether we wake or sleep, we should live together with him. [11]Therefore exhort one another, and build each other up, even as you also do. [12]But we ask you, brothers, to recognize those who labor among you, and are over you in the Lord, and admonish you, [13]and to respect and honor them in love for their work's sake.

Be at peace among yourselves. [14]We exhort you, brothers, admonish the disorderly, encourage the fainthearted, support the weak, be patient toward all. [15]See that no one returns evil for evil to anyone, but always follow after that which is good, for one another, and for all.

[16]Rejoice always. [17]Pray without ceasing. [18]In everything give thanks, for this is the will of God in Christ Jesus toward you. [19]Do not quench the Spirit. [20]Do not treat prophecies with contempt, [21]but[b] test all things; hold firmly that which is good. [22]Abstain from every form of evil.

[23]May the God of peace himself sanctify you completely. May your whole spirit, soul, and body be preserved blameless at the coming of our Lord Jesus Christ. [24]He who calls you is faithful, who will also do it. [25]Brothers, pray for us also.[c] [26]Greet all the brothers with a holy kiss. [27]I solemnly command you by the Lord that this letter be read to all the holy[d] brothers.

[28]The grace of our Lord Jesus Christ be with you.[e]

2 Thessalonians

1 Paul, Silvanus, and Timothy, to the church of the Thessalonians in God our Father, and the Lord Jesus Christ: [2]Grace to you and peace from God our Father and the Lord Jesus Christ.

[3]We are bound to always give thanks to God for you, brothers, even as it is appropriate, because your faith grows exceedingly, and the love of each and every one of you towards one another abounds; [4]so that we ourselves boast about you in the churches of God for your patience and faith in all your persecutions and in the afflictions which you endure. [5]This is an obvious sign of the righteous judgment of God, to the end that you may be counted worthy of the kingdom of God, for which you also suffer. [6]Since it is a righteous thing with God to repay affliction to those who afflict you, [7]and to give relief to you who are afflicted with us, when the Lord Jesus is revealed from heaven with his

---

a   4:17 Gk. harpazo. The word "rapture" comes from the Latin word rapturo, meaning "caught up." Cf. Daniel 7:13; Acts 1:9, 8:39; 1 Co 15:51ff; 2 Co 12:2; Revelation 11:12, 12:5
b   5:21 Some Mss lack "but"
d   5:25 Some Mss lack "also"
d   5:27 Some Mss lack "holy"
e   5:28 Some Mss add "Amen"

mighty angels in flaming fire, [8]giving vengeance to those who do not know God, and to those who do not obey the Good News of our Lord Jesus, [9]who will pay the penalty: everlasting destruction from the face of the Lord and from the glory of his might, [10]when he comes to be glorified in his saints, and to be admired among all those who have believed (because our testimony to you was believed) in that day.

[11]To this end we also pray always for you, that our God may count you worthy of your calling, and fulfill every desire of goodness and work of faith, with power; [12]that the name of our Lord Jesus[a] may be glorified in you, and you in him, according to the grace of our God and the Lord Jesus Christ.

2 Now, brothers, concerning the coming of our Lord Jesus Christ, and our gathering together to him, we ask you [2]not to be quickly shaken in your mind, nor yet to be troubled, either by spirit, or by word, or by letter as from us, saying that the day of the Lord[b] had come. [3]Let no one deceive you in any way. For it will not be, unless the departure comes first, and the man of lawlessness[c] is revealed, the son of destruction, [4]he who opposes and exalts himself against all that is called God or that is worshiped; so that he sits[d] in the temple of God, setting himself up as God. [5]Do you not remember that, when I was still with you, I told you these things? [6]Now you know what is restraining him, to the end that he may be revealed in his own season. [7]For the mystery of lawlessness already works. Only there is one who restrains now, until he is taken out of the way. [8]Then the lawless one will be revealed, whom the Lord Jesus [e]will kill with the breath of his mouth, and destroy by the manifestation of his coming; [9]even he whose coming is according to the working of Satan with all power and signs and lying wonders, [10]and with all deception of wickedness for those who are being lost, because they did not receive the love of the truth, that they might be saved. [11]And because of this, God sends them a strong delusion,[f] that they should believe the lie, [12]in order that all might be judged who did not believe the truth, but had pleasure in unrighteousness. [13]But we are bound to always give thanks to God for you, brothers loved by the Lord, because God chose you from the beginning[g] for salvation through sanctification of the Spirit and belief in the truth; [14]to which he called you through our Good News, for the obtaining of the glory of our Lord Jesus Christ. [15]So then, brothers, stand firm, and hold the traditions which you were taught by us, whether by word, or by letter.

[16]Now our Lord Jesus Christ himself, and God our Father, who loved us and gave us everlasting comfort and good hope through grace, [17]comfort your hearts and establish you in every good work and word.

3 Finally, brothers, pray for us, that the word of the Lord may spread rapidly and be glorified, even as also with you; [2]and that we may be delivered from unreasonable and evil people; for not all have faith. [3]But the Lord is faithful, who will establish you, and guard you from the evil one. [4]We have confidence in the Lord concerning you, that you both do and will do the things we command. [5]May the Lord direct your hearts into the love of God, and into the patience of Christ.

[6]Now we command you, brothers, in the name of our Lord Jesus Christ, that you withdraw yourselves from every brother who walks in rebellion, and not after the tradition which they received from us. [7]For you know how you ought to imitate us. For we did not behave ourselves rebelliously among you, [8]neither did we eat bread

a 1:12 Some Mss add "Christ"
b 2:2 Some Mss read "Christ"
c 2:3 Some Mss read "sin"
d 2:4 Some Mss add "as God"
e 2:8 Some Mss lack "Jesus"
f 2:11 Gk. "a working of error"
g 2:13 Other Mss read "as first fruits"

from anyone's hand without paying for it, but in labor and travail worked night and day, that we might not burden any of you; [9]not because we do not have the right, but to make ourselves an example to you, that you should imitate us. [10]For even when we were with you, we commanded you this: "If anyone will not work, neither let him eat." [11]For we hear of some who walk among you in rebellion, who do not work at all, but are busybodies. [12]Now those who are that way, we command and exhort in the[a] Lord Jesus Christ, that with quietness they work, and eat their own bread.

[13]But you, brothers, do not be weary in doing well. [14]If anyone does not obey our word in this letter, note that person, that you have no company with him, to the end that he may be ashamed. [15]Do not count him as an enemy, but admonish him as a brother.

[16]Now may the Lord of peace himself give you peace at all times in all ways. The Lord be with you all.

[17]The greeting of me, Paul, with my own hand, which is the sign in every letter: this is how I write. [18]The grace of our Lord Jesus Christ be with you all.[b]

1 Timothy

1 Paul, an apostle of Christ Jesus according to the commandment of God our Savior, and Christ Jesus our hope; [2]to Timothy, my true child in faith: Grace, mercy, and peace, from God the[c] Father and Christ Jesus our Lord.

[3]As I urged you when I was going into Macedonia, stay at Ephesus that you might command certain people not to teach a different doctrine, [4]neither to pay attention to myths and endless genealogies, which cause speculation,[d] rather than God's stewardship, which is in faith— [5]but the goal of this command is love, out of a pure heart and a good conscience and unfeigned faith; [6]from which things some, having missed the mark, have turned aside to vain talking; [7]desiring to be teachers of the law, though they understand neither what they say, nor about what they strongly affirm. [8]But we know that the law is good, if one uses it lawfully, [9]as knowing this, that law is not made for a righteous person, but for the lawless and insubordinate, for the ungodly and sinners, for the unholy and profane, for those who kill their father or mother, for murderers, [10]for the sexually immoral, for men who have sexual relations with men,[e] for kidnappers, for liars, for perjurers, and for any other thing contrary to the sound doctrine; [11]according to the Good News of the glory of the blessed God,

which was committed to my trust. [12]And I thank him who enabled me, Christ Jesus our Lord, because he counted me faithful, appointing me to service; [13]although I was before a blasphemer, a persecutor, and insolent. However, I obtained mercy, because I did it ignorantly in unbelief. [14]The grace of our Lord abounded exceedingly with faith and love which is in Christ Jesus. [15]The saying is faithful and worthy of all acceptance, that Christ Jesus came into the world to save sinners; of whom I am chief. [16]However, for this cause I obtained mercy, that in me first, Jesus Christ might display all his patience, for an example of those who were going to believe in him for everlasting life. [17]Now to the King eternal, immortal, invisible, the only God[f], be honor and glory forever and ever. Amen.

[18]This instruction I commit to you, my child Timothy, according to the prophecies which led the way to you, that by them you may wage the good warfare; [19]holding faith and a good conscience; which some having thrust away made a shipwreck concerning the faith; [20]of whom is Hymenaeus and

---

a   3:12 Some Mss read "by our"
b   3:18 Some Mss add "Amen"
c   1:2 Some Mss read "our"
d   1:4 Some Mss read "disputes"
e   1:10 Leviticus 18:22, 20:13
f   1:17 Some Mss add "who alone is wise"

Alexander; whom I delivered to Satan, that they might be taught not to blaspheme.

2 I exhort therefore, first of all, that petitions, prayers, intercessions, and thanksgivings, be made for all people: ²for kings and all who are in high places; that we may lead a tranquil and quiet life in all godliness and reverence. ³For this is good and acceptable in the sight of God our Savior; ⁴who desires all people to be saved and come to full knowledge of the truth. ⁵For there is one God, and one mediator between God and humanity, a human, Christ Jesus, ⁶who gave himself as a ransom for all; the testimony in its own times; ⁷to which I was appointed a preacher and an apostle (I am telling the truthᵃ, I am not lying), a teacher of the non-Jews in faith and truth.

⁸I desire therefore that the men in every place pray, lifting up holy hands without anger and doubting. ⁹In the same way, that women also adorn themselves in decent clothing, with modesty and propriety; not just with braided hair, gold, pearls, or expensive clothing; ¹⁰but (which becomes women professing godliness) with good works. ¹¹Let a woman learn in quietness with all subjection. ¹²But I do not permit a woman to teach or to exercise authority over a man, but to be in quietness. ¹³For Adam was first formed, then Eveᵇ. ¹⁴Adam was not deceived, but the woman, being deceived, has fallen into disobedience; ¹⁵but she will be deliveredᶜ through the childbirth, if they continue in faith and love and holiness, with good judgment.

3 This is a faithful saying: If someone aspires to the office of overseer, he desires a good work. ²The overseer, therefore must be without reproach, the husband of one wife, temperate, sensible, modest, hospitable, good at teaching; ³not a drunkard, not violent,ᵈ but gentle, not quarrelsome, not a lover of money; ⁴one who rules his own house well, having children in subjection with all reverence; ⁵(but if someone does not know how to manage his own

house, how will he take care of the church of God?) ⁶not a new convert, lest being puffed up he fall into the same condemnation as the devil. ⁷Moreover he must have good testimony from those who are outside, to avoid falling into reproach and the snare of the devil.

⁸Deacons, in the same way, must be reverent, not double-tongued, not devoted to a lot of wine, not greedy for money; ⁹holding the mystery of the faith in a pure conscience. ¹⁰Let them also first be tested; then let them serve as deacons, if they are blameless. ¹¹Their wives in the same way must be reverent, not slanderers, temperate, faithful in all things. ¹²Let deacons be husbands of one wife, ruling their children and their own houses well. ¹³For those who have served well as deacons gain for themselves a good standing, and great boldness in the faith which is in Christ Jesus.

¹⁴These things I write to you, hoping to come to you shortly; ¹⁵but if I wait long, that you may know how people ought to behave themselves in the house of God, which is the church of the living God, the pillar and ground of the truth. ¹⁶Without controversy, the mystery of godliness is great:

Heᵉ was revealed in the flesh,
    justified by the Spirit,
    seen by angels,
    preached among the nations,
    believed on in the world,
    and received up in glory.

4 But the Spirit says expressly that in later times some will fall away from the faith, paying attention to seducing spirits and doctrines of demons, ²through the hypocrisy of liars, branded in their own conscience as with a hot iron; ³forbidding marriage and commanding to abstain from foods which God created to be received with thanksgiving by those who believe and know the truth. ⁴For every creature of

---

a 2:7 Some Mss add "in Christ"
b 2:13 Gk. for Heb. "Havah"
c 2:15 Or, "preserved," "rescued," "saved." Gk. sothesetai
d 3:3 Some Mss add "not greedy for dishonest gain"
e 3:16 Some Mss read "God"

God is good, and nothing is to be rejected, if it is received with thanksgiving. ⁵For it is sanctified through the word of God and prayer. ⁶If you instruct the brothers of these things, you will be a good servant of Christ Jesus, nourished in the words of the faith, and of the good doctrine which you have followed. ⁷But refuse profane and old wives' tales. Exercise yourself toward godliness. ⁸For bodily exercise has some value, but godliness has value in all things, having the promise of the life which is now, and of that which is to come. ⁹This saying is faithful and worthy of all acceptance. ¹⁰For to this end we both labor and strive,ᵃ because we have set our trust in the living God, who is the Savior of all people, especially of those who believe. ¹¹Command and teach these things.

¹²Let no one despise your youth; but be an example to those who believe, in word, in your way of life, in love,ᵇ in faith, and in purity. ¹³Until I come, pay attention to reading, to exhortation, and to teaching. ¹⁴Do not neglect the gift that is in you, which was given to you by prophecy, with the laying on of the hands of the elders. ¹⁵Be diligent in these things. Give yourself wholly to them, that your progress may be revealed to all. ¹⁶Pay attention to yourself, and to your teaching. Continue in these things, for in doing this you will save both yourself and those who hear you.

5 Do not rebuke an older man, but exhort him as a father; the younger men as brothers; ²the older women as mothers; the younger as sisters, in all purity. ³Honor widows who are widows indeed. ⁴But if any widow has children or grandchildren, let them learn first to show piety towards their own family, and to repay their parents, for this isᶜ acceptable in the sight of God. ⁵Now she who is a widow indeed, and desolate, has her hope set on God, and continues in petitions and prayers night and day. ⁶But she who gives herself to pleasure is dead while she lives. ⁷Also command these things, that they may be without reproach. ⁸But if anyone does not provide for his own, and especially his own household, he has denied the faith, and is worse than an unbeliever. ⁹Let no one be enrolled as a widow under sixty years old, having been the wife of one man, ¹⁰being approved by good works, if she has brought up children, if she has been hospitable to strangers, if she has washed the saints' feet, if she has relieved the afflicted, and if she has diligently followed every good work.

¹¹But refuse younger widows, for whenever their passions lead them away from Christ, they desire to marry; ¹²having condemnation, because they have rejected their first pledge. ¹³Besides, they also learn to be idle, going about from house to house. Not only idle, but also gossips and busybodies, saying things which they ought not. ¹⁴I desire therefore that the younger widows marry, bear children, rule the household, and give no occasion to the adversary for reviling. ¹⁵For already some have turned aside after Satan. ¹⁶If any believing man orᵈ believing woman has widows, let them assist them, and do not let the church be burdened; that it might help those widows who are truly in need.

¹⁷Let the elders who rule well be counted worthy of double honor, especially those who labor in the word and in teaching. ¹⁸For the Scripture says, "Do not muzzle the ox when it treads out the grain."ᵉ And, "The laborer is worthy of his wages."ᶠ

¹⁹Do not receive an accusation against an elder, except at the word of two or three witnesses. ²⁰Those who sin, reprove in the sight of all, that the rest also may be in fear. ²¹I command you in the sight of God, and Christ Jesus, and the chosen angels, that you observe these things without prejudice, doing nothing by partiality. ²²Lay hands hastily on no one, neither be a participant in other men's sins. Keep yourself pure. ²³Be no longer a drinker of water only, but use a little wine for your stomach's sake and your frequent infirmities.

---

a   4:10 Some Mss read "suffer reproach"
b   4:12 Some Mss add "in spirit"
c   5:4 Some Mss add "good and"
d   5:16 Some Mss lack "believing man or"
e   5:18 Deuteronomy 25:4
f   5:18 Luke 10:7; Leviticus 19:13

[24]Some men's sins are evident, preceding them to judgment, and some also follow later. [25]In the same way also there are good works that are obvious, and those that are otherwise cannot be hidden.

6 Let as many as are slaves under the yoke count their own masters worthy of all honor, that the name of God and the doctrine not be blasphemed. [2]Those who have believing masters, let them not despise them, because they are brothers, but rather let them serve them, because those who partake of the benefit are believing and beloved. Teach and exhort these things.

[3]If anyone teaches a different doctrine, and does not consent to sound words, the words of our Lord Jesus Christ, and to the doctrine which is according to godliness, [4]he is conceited, knowing nothing, but obsessed with arguments, disputes, and word battles, from which come envy, strife, reviling, evil suspicions, [5]constant friction of people of corrupt minds and destitute of the truth, who suppose that godliness is a means of gain.[a]

[6]But godliness with contentment is great gain. [7]For we brought nothing into the world, so[b] neither can we carry anything out. [8]But having food and clothing, we will be content with that. [9]But those who are determined to be rich fall into a temptation and a snare and many foolish and harmful lusts, such as plunge people into ruin and destruction. [10]For the love of money is a root of all kinds of evil. Some have been led astray from the faith in their greed, and have pierced themselves through with many sorrows.

[11]But you, man of God, flee these things, and follow after righteousness, godliness, faith, love, patience, and gentleness. [12]Fight the good fight of faith. Lay hold of the everlasting life to which you were called, and you confessed the good confession in the sight of many witnesses. [13]I command you before God, who gives life to all things, and before Christ Jesus, who before Pontius Pilate testified the good confession,[c] [14]that you keep the commandment without spot, blameless, until the appearing of our Lord Jesus Christ; [15]which in its own times he will show, who is the blessed and only Ruler, the King of kings, and Lord of lords; [16]who alone has immortality, dwelling in unapproachable light; whom no human has seen, nor can see: to whom be honor and eternal power. Amen.

[17]Charge those who are rich in this present world that they not be haughty, nor have their hope set on the uncertainty of riches, but on [d]God, who richly provides us with everything to enjoy; [18]that they do good, that they be rich in good works, that they be ready to distribute, willing to communicate; [19]laying up in store for themselves a good foundation against the time to come, that they may lay hold of that which is truly life.[e]

[20]Timothy, guard that which is committed to you, turning away from the empty chatter and oppositions of the knowledge which is falsely so called; [21]which some professing have erred concerning the faith. Grace be with you.[f]

2 Timothy

1 Paul, an apostle of Christ Jesus[g] through the will of God, according to the promise of the life which is in Christ Jesus, [2]to Timothy, my beloved child: Grace, mercy, and peace, from God the Father and Christ Jesus our Lord.

[3]I thank God, whom I serve as my forefathers did, with a pure conscience. How unceasing is my memory of you in my petitions, night and day [4]longing to see you, remembering your tears, that I may

---

a   6:5 Some Mss add "Withdraw yourself from such."
b   6:7 Some Mss add "certainly"
c   6:13 John 18:34-37
d   6:17 Some Mss add "the living"
e   6:19 Some Mss read "everlasting"
f   6:21 Some Mss add "Amen"
g   1:1 Some Mss read "Jesus Christ"

be filled with joy; ⁵having been reminded of the unfeigned faith that is in you; which lived first in your grandmother Lois, and your mother Eunice,ᵃ and, I am persuaded, in you also.

⁶For this cause, I remind you that you should stir up the gift of God which is in you through the laying on of my hands. ⁷For God did not give us a spirit of fear, but of power and love and of a sound mind. ⁸Therefore do not be ashamed of the testimony of our Lord, nor of me his prisoner; but endure hardship for the Good News according to the power of God, ⁹who saved us and called us with a holy calling, not according to our works, but according to his own purpose and grace, which was given to us in Christ Jesus before time began, ¹⁰but has now been revealed by the appearing of our Savior, Christ Jesus, who abolished death, and brought life and immortality to light through the Good News. ¹¹For this, I was appointed a preacher, an apostle, and a teacherᵇ. ¹²For this cause I also suffer these things.

Yet I am not ashamed, for I know him whom I have believed, and I am persuaded that he is able to guard that which I have committed to him against that day.

¹³Hold the pattern of sound words which you have heard from me, in faith and love which is in Christ Jesus. ¹⁴That good thing which was committed to you, guard through the Holy Spirit who dwells in us.

¹⁵This you know, that all who are in Asia turned away from me; of whom are Phygelus and Hermogenes. ¹⁶May the Lord grant mercy to the house of Onesiphorus, for he often refreshed me, and was not ashamed of my chain, ¹⁷but when he was in Rome, he sought me diligently, and found me ¹⁸(the Lord grant to him to find the Lord's mercy in that day); and in how many things he served at Ephesus, you know very well.

2 You therefore, my child, be strengthened in the grace that is in Christ Jesus. ²The things which you have heard from me among many witnesses, commit the same to faithful people, who will be able to teach others also. ³You therefore must share in hardship, as a good soldier of Christ Jesus. ⁴No soldier on duty entangles himself in the affairs of life, that he may please him who enrolled him as a soldier. ⁵Also, if anyone competes in athletics, he is not crowned unless he has competed by the rules. ⁶The farmers who labor must be the first to get a share of the crops. ⁷Consider what I say, for the Lord will giveᶜ you understanding in all things.

⁸Remember Jesus Christ, risen from the dead, a descendant of David, according to my Good News, ⁹in which I suffer hardship to the point of chains as a criminal. But God's word is not chained. ¹⁰Therefore I endure all things for the chosen ones' sake, that they also may obtain the salvation which is in Christ Jesus with everlasting glory. ¹¹This saying is faithful:

"For if we died with him,
    we will also live with him.
¹²If we endure,
    we will also reign with him.
If we deny him,
    he also will deny us.
¹³If we are faithless,
    he remains faithful,
    for he cannot deny himself."

¹⁴Remind them of these things, charging them in the presence of God,ᵈ not to wrangle about words, to no profit, to the subverting of those who hear.

¹⁵Do your best to present yourself approved by God, a worker who does not need to be ashamed, properly handling the word of truth. ¹⁶But shun empty chatter, for they will proceed further in ungodliness, ¹⁷and their word will consume like gangrene, of whom is Hymenaeus and Philetus; ¹⁸who have erred concerning the truth, saying that the resurrection is already past, and overthrowing the faith of some. ¹⁹However God's firm foundation stands, having

---

a   1:5 Gk. "Eunikay"
b   1:11 Some Mss add "of the non-Jews"
c   2:7 Some Mss read "and may the Lord give"
d   2:14 Some Mss read "the Lord"

this seal, "The Lord knows those who are his,"[a] and, "Let every one who names the name of the Lord[b] depart from unrighteousness." 20Now in a large house there are not only vessels of gold and of silver, but also of wood and of clay. Some are for honor, and some for dishonor. 21If anyone therefore purges himself from these, he will be a vessel for honor, sanctified, and suitable for the master's use, prepared for every good work.

22Flee from youthful lusts; but pursue righteousness, faith, love, and peace with those who call on the Lord out of a pure heart. 23But refuse foolish and ignorant questionings, knowing that they generate strife. 24The Lord's servant must not quarrel, but be gentle towards all, able to teach, patient, 25in gentleness correcting those who oppose him: perhaps God may give them repentance leading to a full knowledge of the truth, 26and they may recover themselves out of the devil's snare, having been taken captive by him to his will.

3 But know this, that in the last days, grievous times will come. 2For people will be lovers of self, lovers of money, boastful, arrogant, blasphemers, disobedient to parents, unthankful, unholy, 3unloving, unforgiving, slanderers, without self-control, brutal, hateful of good, 4traitors, headstrong, conceited, lovers of pleasure rather than lovers of God; 5holding a form of godliness, but having denied the power thereof. Turn away from these, also. 6For among them are those who creep into households and take captive weak-willed women weighed down with sins, led away by various passions and pleasures,[c] 7always learning, and never able to come to the knowledge of the truth. 8Even as Jannes and Jambres opposed Moses, so do these also oppose the truth; people corrupted in mind, disapproved concerning the faith. 9But they will proceed no further. For their folly will be evident to all, as theirs also was. 10But you did follow my teaching, conduct, purpose, faith, patience, love, steadfastness, 11persecutions, and sufferings: those things

that happened to me at Antioch, Iconium, and Lystra. I endured those persecutions. Out of them all the Lord delivered me. 12Yes, and all who desire to live godly in Christ Jesus will suffer persecution. 13But evil people and impostors will grow worse and worse, deceiving and being deceived. 14But you remain in the things which you have learned and have been assured of, knowing from whom you have learned them. 15From infancy, you have known the holy Scriptures which are able to make you wise for salvation through faith, which is in Christ Jesus. 16All Scripture is God-breathed and profitable for teaching, for reproof, for correction, and for training in righteousness, 17that the person of God may be complete, thoroughly equipped for every good work.

4 I command you therefore before God and of Christ Jesus,[d] who will judge the living and the dead, and by[e] his appearing and his kingdom: 2proclaim the word; be urgent in season and out of season; reprove, rebuke, and exhort, with all patience and teaching. 3For the time will come when they will not listen to the sound doctrine, but, having itching ears, will heap up for themselves teachers after their own lusts; 4and will turn away their ears from the truth, and turn aside to myths. 5But you be sober in all things, endure hardship,[f] do the work of an evangelist, fulfill your ministry.

6For I am already being offered, and the time of my departure has come. 7I have fought the good fight. I have finished the course. I have kept the faith. 8From now on, there is stored up for me the crown of righteousness, which the Lord, the righteous judge, will give to me on that day; and not to me only, but also to all those who have loved his appearing. 9Be diligent to come to me soon, 10for Demas left me, having

---

a   2:19 Numbers 16:5

b   2:19 Some Mss read "Christ"

c   3:6 Some Mss lack "and pleasures"

d   4:1 Some Mss read "Lord Jesus Christ"

e   4:1 Some Mss read "at"

f   4:5 One early Ms adds "as a good soldier of Christ Jesus." See also 2:3

loved this present world, and went to Thessalonica; Crescens to Galatia, and Titus to Dalmatia. [11]Only Luke is with me. Take Mark, and bring him with you, for he is useful to me for service. [12]But I sent Tychicus to Ephesus. [13]Bring the cloak that I left at Troas with Carpus when you come, and the books, especially the parchments. [14]Alexander, the coppersmith, did much evil to me. The Lord will[a] repay him according to his works, [15]of whom you also must beware; for he greatly opposed our words.

[16]At my first defense, no one came to help me, but all left me. May it not be held against them. [17]But the Lord stood by me, and strengthened me, that through me the message might be fully proclaimed, and that all the non-Jewish people might hear; and I was delivered out of the mouth of the lion. [18]And the Lord will deliver me from every evil work, and will preserve me for his heavenly kingdom; to whom be the glory forever and ever. Amen.

[19]Greet Prisca and Aquila, and the house of Onesiphorus. [20]Erastus remained at Corinth, and I left Trophimus at Miletus, ill. [21]Be diligent to come before winter. Eubulus salutes you, as do Pudens, Linus, Claudia, and all the brothers. [22]The Lord[b] be with your spirit. Grace be with you.[c]

Titus

1 Paul, a servant of God, and an apostle of Jesus Christ, according to the faith of God's chosen ones, and the knowledge of the truth which is according to godliness, [2]in hope of everlasting life, which God, who cannot lie, promised before time began; [3]but in his own time revealed his word in the message with which I was entrusted according to the commandment of God our Savior; [4]to Titus, my true child according to a common faith: Grace[d] and peace from God the Father and Christ Jesus[e] our Savior.

[5]I left you in Crete for this reason, that you would set in order the things that were lacking, and appoint elders in every city, as I directed you; [6]if anyone is blameless, the husband of one wife, having children who believe, who are not accused of loose or unruly behavior. [7]For the overseer must be blameless, as God's steward; not self-pleasing, not easily angered, not given to wine, not violent, not greedy for dishonest gain;[f] [8]but given to hospitality, as a lover of good, sober minded, fair, holy, self-controlled; [9]holding to the faithful word which is according to the teaching, that he may be able to exhort in the sound doctrine, and to convict those who contradict him. [10]For there are also many rebellious people, empty talkers and deceivers, especially those of the circumcision, [11]whose mouths must be silenced; who are upsetting whole families, teaching things which they should not, for the sake of dishonest gain. [12]One of them, a prophet of their own, said, "Cretans are always liars, evil beasts, and idle gluttons." [13]This testimony is true. For this cause, reprove them sharply, that they may be sound in the faith, [14]not paying attention to Jewish myths and commandments of people who reject the truth. [15]To the pure, all things are pure; but to those who are defiled and unbelieving, nothing is pure; but both their mind and their conscience are defiled. [16]They profess that they know God, but by their works they deny him, being abominable, disobedient, and unfit for any good work.

2 But say the things which fit sound doctrine, [2]that older men should be temperate, sensible, sober minded, sound in faith, in love, and in patience: [3]and that older women likewise be reverent in behavior, not slanderers nor enslaved to much wine, teachers of that which is good; [4]that they

---

a   4:14 Some Mss read "May the Lord"
b   4:22 Some Mss add "Jesus Christ"
c   4:22 Some Mss add "Amen"
d   1:4 Some Mss add "mercy"
e   1:4 Some Mss read "Lord Jesus Christ"
f   2:7 Some Mss add "incorruptibility"

may train the young women to love their husbands, to love their children, [5]to be sober minded, chaste, workers at home, kind, being in subjection to their own husbands, that God's word may not be blasphemed. [6]Likewise, exhort the younger men to be sober minded; [7]in all things showing yourself an example of good works. In your teaching show integrity, seriousness, [8]and a sound message that cannot be condemned; that he who opposes you may be ashamed, having no evil thing to say about us[a]. [9]Exhort servants to be in subjection to their own masters, and to be well-pleasing in all things; not contradicting; [10]not stealing, but showing all good fidelity; that they may adorn the doctrine of God, our Savior, in all things. [11]For the grace of God has appeared, bringing salvation to all people, [12]instructing us to say "No" to ungodliness and worldly desires, and to live soberly, righteously, and godly in this present age; [13]looking for the blessed hope and appearing of the glory of our great God and Savior, Jesus Christ; [14]who gave himself for us, that he might redeem us from all iniquity, and purify for himself a people for his own possession, zealous for good works. [15]Say these things and exhort and reprove with all authority. Let no one despise you.

3 Remind them to be in subjection to rulers and to authorities, to be obedient, to be ready for every good work, [2]to speak evil of no one, not to be contentious, to be gentle, showing courtesy to all people. [3]For we were also once foolish, disobedient, deceived, serving various lusts and pleasures, living in malice and envy, hateful, and hating one another. [4]But when the kindness and love of God our Savior appeared, [5]not by works of righteousness, which we did ourselves, but according to his mercy, he saved us, through the washing of rebirth and renewing by the Holy Spirit, [6]whom he poured out on us richly, through Jesus Christ our Savior; [7]that, being justified by his grace, we might be made heirs according to the hope of everlasting life. [8]This saying is faithful, and concerning these things I desire that you affirm confidently, so that those who have believed God may be careful to maintain good works. These things are good and profitable for people; [9]but shun foolish questionings, genealogies, strife, and disputes about the law; for they are unprofitable and vain. [10]Reject a divisive person after a first and second warning; [11]knowing that such a one is perverted, and sins, being self-condemned.

[12]When I send Artemas to you, or Tychicus, be diligent to come to me to Nicopolis, for I have determined to winter there. [13]Send Zenas, the Law scholar, and Apollos on their journey speedily, that nothing may be lacking for them. [14]Let our people also learn to maintain good works for necessary uses, that they may not be unfruitful.

[15]All who are with me greet you. Greet those who love us in faith. Grace be with you all.[b]

Philemon

1 Paul, a prisoner of Christ Jesus, and Timothy our brother, to Philemon, our beloved fellow worker, [2]and to Apphia our sister[c], to Archippus, our fellow soldier, and to the church in your house: [3]Grace to you and peace from God our Father and the Lord Jesus Christ.

[4]I thank my God always, making mention of you in my prayers, [5]hearing of your love, and of the faith which you have toward the Lord Jesus, and toward all the saints; [6]that the fellowship of your faith may become effective, in the knowledge of every good thing which is in you[d] in Christ.[e] [7]For I have much joy[f] and comfort in your love, because the hearts of the

---

a   2:8 Some Mss read "you"
b   3:15 Some Mss add "Amen"
c   1:2 Some Mss read "to the beloved Apphia"
d   1:6 Some Mss read "us"
e   1:6 Some Mss add "Jesus"
f   1:7 Some Mss read "thankfulness"

saints have been refreshed through you, brother.

⁸Therefore, though I have all boldness in Christ to command you that which is appropriate, ⁹yet on the basis of love I rather appeal, being such a one as Paul, the aged, but also a prisoner of Jesus Christ. ¹⁰I appeal to you for my child, whom I have become the father of in my chains, Onesimus,ᵃ ¹¹who once was useless to you, but now is useful to you and to me. ¹²I am sending back to you,ᵇ him who is my very heart, ¹³whom I desired to keep with me, that on your behalf he might serve me in my chains for the Good News. ¹⁴But I was willing to do nothing without your consent, that your goodness would not be as of necessity, but of free will. ¹⁵For perhaps he was therefore separated from you for a while, that you would have him forever, ¹⁶no longer as a slave, but more than a slave, a beloved brother, especially to me, but how much rather to you, both in the flesh and in the Lord.

¹⁷If then you count me a partner, receive him as you would receive me. ¹⁸But if he has wronged you at all, or owes you anything, put that to my account. ¹⁹I, Paul, write this with my own hand: I will repay it (not to mention to you that you owe to me even your own self besides). ²⁰Yes, brother, let me have joy from you in the Lord. Refresh my heart in Christ.ᶜ ²¹Having confidence in your obedience, I write to you, knowing that you will do even beyond what I say.

²²Also, prepare a guest room for me, for I hope that through your prayers I will be restored to you.

²³Epaphras, my fellow prisoner in Christ Jesus, greets you, ²⁴as do Mark, Aristarchus, Demas, and Luke, my fellow workers. ²⁵The grace of theᵈ Lord Jesus Christ be with your spirit.ᵉ

Hebrews

1 God, having in the past spoken to the fathers through the prophets at many times and in various ways, ²in these last days has spoken to us by a Son, whom he appointed heir of all things, through whom also he made the ages.ᶠ ³He is the radiance of his glory, the very image of his substance, and upholding all things by the word of his power, when he had madeᵍ purification forʰ sins, sat down on the right hand of the Majesty on high; ⁴having become so much better than the angels, as he has inherited a more excellent name than they have. ⁵For to which of the angels did he say at any time,

"You are my Son.
    Today have I become your father?"ⁱ

And again,

"I will be to him a Father,
    and he will be to me a Son?"ʲ

⁶And again, when he brings in the firstborn into the world he says, "Let all the angels of God worship him."ᵏ ⁷Of the angels he says,

"Who makes his angels winds,
    and his servants a flame of fire."ˡ

⁸But of the Son he says,

"Your throne, O God, is forever and ever,
    and the scepter of equity is the
        scepter of yourᵐ kingdom.
⁹You have loved righteousness, and
        hated iniquity;
    therefore God, your God, has
        anointed you with the oil
        of gladness above your
        companions."ⁿ

¹⁰And,

"In the beginning, Lord, you established
        the foundation of the earth.

---

a   1:10 Onesimus means "useful"
b   1:12 Some Mss lack "to you"
c   1:20 Some Mss read "the Lord"
d   1:25 Some Mss read "our"
e   1:25 Some Mss add "Amen"
f   1:2 Or, "worlds," or "universe." Gk. aiwn
g   1:3 Some Mss add "of himself"
h   1:3 Some Mss add "our"
i   1:5 Psalm 2:7
j   1:5 2 Samuel 7:14; 1 Chronicles 17:13
k   1:6 Deuteronomy 32:43
l   1:7 Psalm 104:4
m   1:8 Some Mss read "his"
n   1:9 Psalm 45:6-7

The heavens are the works of your
hands.
[11]They will perish, but you remain;
and they will all wear out like a
garment.
[12]As a cloak, you will roll them up,
and like a garment[a] they will be
changed.
But you remain the same, and
your years will have no end."[b]
[13]But which of the angels has he told at
any time,
"Sit at my right hand,
until I make your enemies the
footstool of your feet?"[c]
[14]Are they not all ministering spirits, sent
forth to serve for the sake of those who will
inherit salvation?

2 Therefore we ought to pay greater attention to the things that were heard,
so that we will not drift away. [2]For if the
word spoken through angels proved steadfast, and every transgression and disobedience received a just recompense; [3]how
will we escape if we neglect so great a
salvation—which at the first having been
spoken through the Lord, was confirmed to
us by those who heard; [4]God also testifying with them, both by signs and wonders,
by various works of power, and by gifts of
the Holy Spirit, according to his own will?
[5]For he did not subject the world to come,
of which we speak, to angels. [6]But one has
somewhere testified, saying,
"What is man, that you think of him?
Or the son of man, that you care for
him?
[7]You made him a little lower than the
angels.
You crowned him with glory and
honor.[d]
[8]You have put[e] all things under his
feet."[f]
For in that he put all things under him,
he left nothing that is not under him.[g]
But now we do not yet see that all things
are under him. [9]But we see him who has
been made a little lower than the angels,
Jesus, because of the suffering of death

crowned with glory and honor, that by the
grace of God he should taste of death for
everyone. [10]For it became him, for whom
are all things, and through whom are all
things, in bringing many children to glory,
to make the author of their salvation perfect through sufferings. [11]For both he who
sanctifies and those who are sanctified
are all from one, for which cause he is not
ashamed to call them brothers, [12]saying,
"I will declare your name to my brothers.
In the midst of the assembly I will
praise you."[h]
[13]And again, "I will put my trust in
him."[i] And again, "Look, I and the children
whom God has given me."[j] [14]Since then the
children have shared in flesh and blood, he
also himself in like manner partook of the
same, that through death he might bring to
nothing him who had the power of death,
that is, the devil, [15]and might deliver all of
them who through fear of death were all
their lifetime subject to bondage. [16]For, truly, he did not come to help the angels, but to
help the offspring of Abraham. [17]Therefore
he was obligated in all things to be made
like his brothers, that he might become a
merciful and faithful high priest in things
pertaining to God, to make atonement[k] for
the sins of the people. [18]For in that he himself has suffered being tempted, he is able
to help those who are tempted.

3 Therefore, holy brothers, partakers of
a heavenly calling, consider the Apostle and High Priest of our confession,
Jesus; [2]who was faithful to him who appointed him, as also was Moses in all[l] his
house. [3]For he has been counted worthy

---

a   1:12 Some Mss lack "like a garment"
b   1:12 Psalm 102:25-27
c   1:13 Psalm 110:1
d   2:7 Some Mss add "and set him over the works of
    your hands"
e   2:8 Or, "subjected"
f   22:8 Psalm 8:4-6
g   2:8 Or, "under his control"
h   2:12 Psalm 22:22
i   2:13 Isaiah 8:17
j   2:13 Isaiah 8:18
k   2:17 Gk. hilaskomai
l   3:2 Some Mss lack "all"

of more glory than Moses, inasmuch as he who built the house has more honor than the house. ⁴For every house is built by someone; but he who built all things is God. ⁵Moses indeed was faithful in all his house as a servant, for a testimony of those things which were afterward to be spoken, ⁶but Christ is faithful as a Son over his house; whose house we are, if we hold fast our confidence and the boast of our hope.ᵃ ⁷Therefore, even as the Holy Spirit says,

"Today if you will hear his voice,
⁸do not harden your hearts, as in the provocation,ᵇ
like as in the day of the trialᶜ in the wilderness,
⁹where your fathers tested me and challenged me,
and saw my works for forty years.
¹⁰Therefore I was displeased with thisᵈ generation,
and said, 'They always err in their heart,
but they did not know my ways;'
¹¹as I swore in my wrath,
'They will not enter into my rest.' "ᵉ

¹²Beware, brothers, lest perhaps there be in any one of you an evil heart of unbelief, in falling away from the living God; ¹³but exhort one another day by day, so long as it is called "today;" lest any one of you be hardened by the deceitfulness of sin. ¹⁴For we have become partakers of Christ, if we hold fast the beginning of our confidence firm to the end: ¹⁵while it is said,

"Today if you will hear his voice,
do not harden your hearts, as in the rebellion."ᶠ

¹⁶For who, when they heard, rebelled? No, did not all those who came out of Egypt by Moses? ¹⁷With whom was he displeased forty years? Was not it with those who sinned, whose bodies fell in the wilderness? ¹⁸To whom did he swear that they would not enter into his rest, but to those who were disobedient? ¹⁹We see that they were not able to enter in because of unbelief.

4 Let us fear therefore, lest perhaps anyone of you should seem to have come short of a promise of entering into his rest. ²For indeed we have had good news preached to us, even as they also did, but the word they heard did not profit them, because theyᵍ were not united by faith with those who heard. ³For we who have believed do enter into that rest, even as he has said, "As I swore in my wrath, they will not enter into my rest;"ʰ although the works were finished from the foundation of the world. ⁴For he has said this somewhere about the seventh day, "And God rested on the seventh day from all his works;"ⁱ ⁵and in this place again, "They will not enter into my rest."ʲ

⁶Since therefore it remains for some to enter it, and they to whom the good news was before preached failed to enter in because of disobedience, ⁷he again appoints a certain day, "Today," saying through David so long a time afterward (just as has been said),

"Today if you will hear his voice,
do not harden your hearts."ᵏ

⁸For if Joshua had given them rest, he would not have spoken afterward of another day. ⁹There remains therefore a Sabbath rest for the people of God. ¹⁰For he who has entered into his rest has himself also rested from his works, as God did from his. ¹¹Let us therefore give diligence to enter into that rest, lest anyone fall after the same example of disobedience. ¹²For the word of God is living, and active, and sharper than any two-edged sword, and piercing even to the dividing of soul and spirit, of both joints and marrow, and is able to discern the thoughts and intentions of the heart.

¹³There is no creature that is hidden from his sight, but all things are naked

---

a   3:6 Some Mss add "firm to the end"
b   3:9 I.e., "as in Meribah." See Psalm 95:8
c   3:9 I.e., "of Massah." See Psalm 95:8
d   3:10 Some Mss read "that"
e   3:11 Psalm 95:7-11
f   3:15 Psalm 95:7-8
g   4:2 Some Mss read "it was not"
h   4:3 Psalm 95:11
i   4:4 Genesis 2:2
j   4:5 Psalm 95:11
k   4:7 Psalm 95:7-8

and laid open before the eyes of him with whom we have to do. [14]Having then a great high priest, who has passed through the heavens, Jesus, the Son of God, let us hold tightly to our confession. [15]For we do not have a high priest who cannot be touched with the feeling of our infirmities, but one who has been in all points tempted[a] like we are, yet without sin. [16]Let us therefore draw near with boldness to the throne of grace, that we may receive mercy, and may find grace for help in time of need.

5 For every high priest, being taken from among men, is appointed for people in things pertaining to God, that he may offer both gifts and sacrifices for sins. [2]The high priest can deal gently with those who are ignorant and going astray, because he himself is also surrounded with weakness. [3]Because of this, he must offer sacrifices for sins for the people, as well as for himself. [4]Nobody takes this honor on himself, but he is called by God, just like Aaron was. [5]So also Christ did not glorify himself to be made a high priest, but it was he who said to him,

"You are my Son.

Today I have become your father."[b]

[6]As he says also in another place,

"You are a priest forever,

after the order of Melchizedek."[c]

[7]In the days of his flesh, he offered up prayers and petitions with loud cries and tears to him who was able to save him from death, and he was heard because of his reverence. [8]Although he was a Son, he learned obedience by the things which he suffered. [9]Having been made perfect, he became to all of those who obey him the author of everlasting salvation, [10]named by God a high priest after the order of Melchizedek. [11]About him we have many words to say, and hard to interpret, seeing you have become dull of hearing. [12]For when by reason of the time you ought to be teachers, you again need to have someone teach you the rudiments of the first principles of the oracles of God. You have come to need milk, and not solid food.

[13]For everyone who lives on milk is not experienced in the word of righteousness, for he is a baby. [14]But solid food is for those who are full grown, who by reason of use have their senses exercised to discern good and evil.

6 Therefore leaving the doctrine of the first principles of Christ, let us press on to perfection—not laying again a foundation of repentance from dead works, of faith toward God, [2]of the teaching of washings, of laying on of hands, of resurrection of the dead, and of everlasting judgment. [3]And this we will do if God permits. [4]For concerning those who were once enlightened and tasted of the heavenly gift, and were made partakers of the Holy Spirit, [5]and tasted the good word of God, and the powers of the age to come, [6]and then fell away, it is impossible to renew them again to repentance; seeing they crucify the Son of God for themselves again, and put him to open shame. [7]For the land which has drunk the rain that comes often on it, and brings forth a crop suitable for them for whose sake it is also tilled, receives blessing from God; [8]but if it bears thorns and thistles, it is rejected and near being cursed, whose end is to be burned.

[9]But, beloved, we are persuaded of better things for you, and things that accompany salvation, even though we speak like this. [10]For God is not unrighteous, so as to forget your work and the[d] love which you showed toward his name, in that you served the saints, and still do serve them. [11]We desire that each one of you may show the same diligence to the fullness of hope even to the end, [12]that you won't be sluggish, but imitators of those who through faith and patience inherited the promises. [13]For when God made a promise to Abraham, since he could swear by none greater, he swore by himself, [14]saying, "Surely in blessing I will bless you, and in multiplying I will

a   4:15 Some Mss read "tried"
b   5:5 Psalm 2:7
c   5:6 Psalm 110:4
d   6:10 Some Mss add "labor of"

multiply you."[a] [15]Thus, having patiently endured, he obtained the promise. [16]For people[b] swear oaths by something greater, and in every dispute of theirs the oath is final for confirmation. [17]In this way God, being determined to show more abundantly to the heirs of the promise the immutability of his counsel, interposed with an oath; [18]that by two immutable things, in which it is impossible for God to lie, we may have a strong encouragement, who have fled for refuge to take hold of the hope set before us. [19]This hope we have as an anchor of the soul, a hope both sure and steadfast and entering into that which is within the veil; [20]where as a forerunner Jesus entered for us, having become a high priest forever after the order of Melchizedek.

7 For this Melchizedek, king of Salem, priest of God Most High, who met Abraham returning from the slaughter of the kings and blessed him, [2]to whom also Abraham divided a tenth part of all (being first, by interpretation, king of righteousness, and then also king of Salem, which is king of peace; [3]without father, without mother, without genealogy, having neither beginning of days nor end of life, but made like the Son of God), remains a priest continually. [4]Now consider how great this man was, to whom even Abraham, the patriarch, gave a tenth out of the most valuable plunder. [5]They indeed of the sons of Levi who receive the priest's office have a commandment to take tithes of the people according to the Law, that is, of their brothers, though these have come out of the body of Abraham, [6]but he whose genealogy is not counted from them has accepted tithes from Abraham, and has blessed him who has the promises. [7]But without any dispute the lesser is blessed by the greater. [8]Here people who die receive tithes, but there one receives tithes of whom it is testified that he lives. [9]We can say that through Abraham even Levi, who receives tithes, has paid tithes, [10]for he was yet in the body of his father when Melchizedek met him. [11]Now if there was perfection through the Levitical priesthood (for under

it the people have received the law), what further need was there for another priest to arise after the order of Melchizedek, and not be called after the order of Aaron? [12]For the priesthood being changed, there is of necessity a change made also in the law. [13]For he of whom these things are said belongs to another tribe, from which no one has officiated at the altar. [14]For it is evident that our Lord has sprung out of Judah, about which tribe Moses spoke nothing concerning priests[c]. [15]This is yet more abundantly evident, if after the likeness of Melchizedek there arises another priest, [16]who has been made, not after the law of a fleshly commandment, but after the power of an endless life: [17]for it is testified,[d]

"You are a priest forever,
  according to the order of
    Melchizedek."[e]

[18]For there is an annulling of a foregoing commandment because of its weakness and uselessness [19](for the law made nothing perfect), and a bringing in of a better hope, through which we draw near to God. [20]Inasmuch as he was not made priest without the taking of an oath, [21]for they indeed have been made priests without an oath, but he with an oath by him that says of him,

"The Lord swore and will not change
  his mind,
'You are a priest forever, according to
  the order of Melchizedek.'"[g]

[22]Accordingly Jesus has become the guarantor of a better covenant. [23]Many, indeed, have been made priests, because they are hindered from continuing by death. [24]But he, because he lives forever, has his priesthood unchangeable. [25]Therefore he is also able to save completely those who draw near to God through him, seeing that he lives forever to make intercession for them.

---

a 6:14 Genesis 22:17
b 6:16 Some Mss add "indeed"
c 7:14 Some Mss read "priesthood"
d 7:17 Some Mss read "He testifies"
e 7:17 Psalm 110:4
f 7:21 Some Mss lack "according to the order of Melchizedek"
g 7:21 Psalm 110:4

[26]For such a high priest was fitting for us: holy, guiltless, undefiled, separated from sinners, and made higher than the heavens; [27]who does not need, like those high priests, to offer up sacrifices daily, first for his own sins, and then for the sins of the people. For he did this once for all, when he offered up himself. [28]For the Law appoints men as high priests who have weakness, but the word of the oath which came after the Law appoints a Son forever who has been perfected.

8 Now in the things which we are saying, the main point is this. We have such a high priest, who sat down on the right hand of the throne of the Majesty in the heavens, [2]a servant of the sanctuary, and of the true tabernacle, which the Lord set up, and not man. [3]For every high priest is appointed to offer both gifts and sacrifices. Therefore it is necessary that this high priest also have something to offer. [4]Now if he were on earth, he would not be a priest at all, seeing there are priests who offer the gifts according to the Law; [5]who serve a copy and shadow of the heavenly things, even as Moses was warned when he was about to make the tabernacle, for he said, "See that you make everything according to the pattern that was shown to you on the mountain."[a] [6]But now he has obtained a more excellent ministry, by so much as he is also the mediator of a better covenant, which on better promises has been given as Law. [7]For if that first covenant had been faultless, then no place would have been sought for a second. [8]For finding fault with them, he said,

"Look, the days are coming," says the Lord,

"when I will make a new covenant with the house of Israel and with the house of Judah;
[9]not according to the covenant that I made with their fathers,
in the day that I took them by the hand to lead them out of the land of Egypt;
for they did not continue in my covenant,

and I disregarded them," says the Lord.
[10]"For this is the covenant that I will make with the house of Israel.
After those days," says the Lord;
"I will put my laws into their mind,
I will also write them on their heart.
I will be their God,
and they will be my people.
[11]They will not teach each one his fellow citizen,[b]
and each one his brother, saying, 'Know the Lord,'
for all will know me,
from the least of them to the greatest of them.
[12]For I will be merciful to their unrighteousness,
and I will remember their sins[c] no more."[d]

[13]In that he says, "new," he has made first old. But that which is becoming old and grows aged is near to vanishing away.

9 Now indeed even the first covenant had ordinances of divine service, and an earthly sanctuary. [2]For a tabernacle was prepared. In the first part were the lampstand, the table, and the show bread; which is called the Holy Place. [3]After the second veil was the tabernacle which is called the Holy of Holies, [4]having a golden censer, and the ark of the covenant overlaid on all sides with gold, in which was a gold jar containing the manna, Aaron's rod that budded, and the tablets of the covenant; [5]and above it cherubim of glory overshadowing the mercy seat, of which things we cannot speak now in detail. [6]Now these things having been thus prepared, the priests go in continually into the first tabernacle, performing their duties. [7]But into the second the high priest alone, once in the year, not without blood, which he offers for himself, and for the sins of the people committed in ignorance. [8]The Holy Spirit is indicating

a   8:5 Exodus 25:40
b   8:11 Some Mss read "neighbor"
c   8:12 Some Mss add "and lawless deeds"
d   8:12 Jeremiah 31:31-34

this, that the way into the Holy Place was not yet revealed while the first tabernacle was still standing; [9]which is a symbol of the present age, where gifts and sacrifices are offered that are incapable, concerning the conscience, of making the worshipper perfect, [10]but deal only with foods and drinks and various washings; they are regulations for the flesh imposed until the time of setting things right.

[11]But Christ having come as a high priest of the good things that have come,[a] through the greater and more perfect tabernacle, not made with hands, that is to say, not of this creation, [12]nor yet through the blood of goats and calves, but through his own blood, entered in once for all into the Holy Place, having obtained everlasting redemption. [13]For if the blood of goats and bulls, and the ashes of a heifer sprinkling those who have been defiled, sanctify to the cleanness of the flesh: [14]how much more will the blood of Christ, who through the eternal Spirit offered himself without blemish to God, cleanse our[b] conscience from dead works to serve the living God? [15]For this reason he is the mediator of a New Covenant, since a death has occurred for the redemption of the transgressions that were under the first covenant, that those who have been called may receive the promise of the everlasting inheritance. [16]For where a last will and testament is, there must of necessity be the death of him who made it. [17]For a will is in force where there has been death, for it is never in force while he who made it lives. [18]Therefore even the first covenant has not been dedicated without blood. [19]For when every commandment had been spoken by Moses to all the people according to the Law, he took the blood of the calves and the goats,[c] with water and scarlet wool and hyssop, and sprinkled both the scroll itself and all the people, [20]saying, "This is the blood of the covenant which God has commanded you."[d]

[21]Moreover he sprinkled the tabernacle and all the vessels of the ministry in like manner with the blood. [22]According to the Law, nearly everything is cleansed with blood, and apart from shedding of blood there is no remission. [23]It was necessary therefore that the copies of the things in the heavens should be cleansed with these; but the heavenly things themselves with better sacrifices than these. [24]For Christ hasn't entered into holy places made with hands, which are representations of the true, but into heaven itself, now to appear in the presence of God for us; [25]nor yet that he should offer himself often, as the high priest enters into the holy place year by year with blood not his own, [26]or else he must have suffered often since the foundation of the world. But now once at the end of the ages, he has been revealed to put away sin by the sacrifice of himself. [27]Inasmuch as it is appointed for people to die once, and after this, judgment, [28]so Christ also, having been offered once to bear the sins of many,[e] will appear a second time, without sin, to those who are eagerly waiting for him for salvation.

10 For the Law, having a shadow of the good to come, not the very image of the things, [f]can never with the same sacrifices year by year, which they offer continually, make perfect those who draw near. [2]Or else would not they have ceased to be offered, because the worshippers, having been once cleansed[g], would have had no more consciousness of sins? [3]But in those sacrifices there is yearly reminder of sins. [4]For it is impossible that the blood of bulls and goats should take away sins. [5]Therefore when he comes into the world, he says,

"Sacrifice and offering you did not
　　desire,
　but a body you prepared for me.
[6]Whole burnt offerings and sin-offerings
　　you took no pleasure in.

---

a   9:11 Some Mss read "things to come"
b   9:14 Some Mss read "your" instead of "our"
c   9:19 Some Mss lack "and the goats"
d   9:20 Exodus 24:8
e   9:28 Isaiah 53:12
f   10:1 Some Mss add "they"
g   10:2 Some Mss read "purified"

⁷Then I said, 'Look, I have come. It is written about me in the scroll of a book; to do your will, O God.'"ᵃ

⁸Previously saying, "Sacrifices and offerings and whole burnt offerings and sin-offerings you did not desire, nor took pleasure in" (which are offered according to the Law), ⁹then he said, "Look, I have come to do your will.ᵇ" He takes away the first, that he may establish the second, ¹⁰by which will we have been sanctifiedᶜ through the offering of the body of Jesus Christ once for all. ¹¹Every priest indeed stands day by day serving and often offering the same sacrifices, which can never take away sins, ¹²but this oneᵈ, when he had offered one sacrifice for sins forever, sat down on the right hand of God; ¹³from that time waiting until his enemies are made the footstool of his feet. ¹⁴For by one offering he has perfected forever those who are being sanctified. ¹⁵The Holy Spirit also testifies to us, for after saying,

¹⁶"This is the covenant that I will make with them:

'After those days,' says the Lord,

'I will put my laws on their hearts,

I will also write them on their minds.'"ᵉ

¹⁷"And I will remember their sins and their iniquities no more."ᶠ

¹⁸Now where remission of these is, there is no more offering for sin. ¹⁹Having therefore, brothers, boldness to enter into the holy place by the blood of Jesus, ²⁰by the way which he dedicated for us, a new and living way, through the veil, that is to say, his flesh; ²¹and having a great priest over the house of God, ²²let us draw near with a true heart in fullness of faith, having our hearts sprinkled from an evil conscience, and having our body washed with pure water, ²³let us hold fast the confession of our hope without wavering; for he who promised is faithful.

²⁴Let us consider how to provoke one another to love and good works, ²⁵not forsaking our own assembling together, as the custom of some is, but exhorting one another; and so much the more, as you see

the Day approaching. ²⁶For if we sin willfully after we have received the knowledge of the truth, there remains no more a sacrifice for sins, ²⁷but a certain fearful expectation of judgment, and a fierceness of fire which will devour the adversaries. ²⁸Anyone who disregards the Law of Moses dies without compassion on the word of two or three witnesses. ²⁹How much worse punishment, do you think, will he be judged worthy of, who has trodden under foot the Son of God, and has counted the blood of the covenant with which he was sanctified an unholy thing, and has insulted the Spirit of grace? ³⁰For we know him who said, "Vengeance belongs to me; I will repayᵍ."ʰ Again, "The Lord will judge his people."ⁱ ³¹It is a fearful thing to fall into the hands of the living God. ³²But remember the former days, in which, after you were enlightened, you endured a great struggle with sufferings; ³³partly, being exposed to both reproaches and oppressions; and partly, becoming partakers with those who were treated so. ³⁴For you both had compassion on them that were inʲ chains, and joyfully accepted the plundering of your possessions, since you knew that you yourselves had a betterᵏ possession and an enduring oneˡ. ³⁵Therefore do not throw away your boldness, which has a great reward. ³⁶For you need patient endurance so that, having done the will of God, you may receive the promise.

³⁷"For in just a little while,

he who is coming will come and will not delay.

³⁸But theᵐ righteous will live by faith,

---

a   10:7 Psalm 40:6-8
b   10:9 Some Mss add "O God"
c   10:10 Some Mss add "those"
d   10:12 Some Mss read "he"
e   10:16 Jeremiah 31:33; Hebrews 8:10
f   10:17 Jeremiah 31:34
g   10:30 Some Mss add "says the Lord"
h   10:30 Deuteronomy 32:35
i   10:30 Deuteronomy 32:36; Psalm 135:14
j   10:34 Some Mss read "me in my"
k   10:34 Some Mss read "since you know that you had for yourselves better"
l   10:34 Some Mss add "in the heavens"
m   10:38 Some Mss add "my"

and if he holds back,[a] my soul has no pleasure in him."[b] [39]But we are not of those who shrink back[c] to destruction, but of those who have faith to the saving of the soul.

11 Now faith is being confident of what we hope for, convinced about things we do not see. [2]For by this, the people of old were attested. [3]By faith, we understand that the ages[d] were prepared by the word of God, so that what is seen has not been made out of things which are visible. [4]By faith, Abel offered to God a better sacrifice than Cain,[e] through which he was attested as righteous, God testifying with respect to his gifts; and though he died he still speaks through it. [5]By faith, Enoch was taken away, so that he would not see death, "and he was not found, because God took him away."[f] For before he was taken he was attested as having pleased God. [6]Now without faith it is impossible to be well pleasing to him, for he who comes to God must believe that he exists, and that he is a rewarder of those who seek him. [7]By faith, Noah, being warned about things not yet seen, in reverence prepared a box-shaped vessel[g] for the salvation of his household,[h] through which he condemned the world, and became heir of the righteousness which is according to faith. [8]By faith, Abraham, when he was called, obeyed to go out to a[i] place which he was to receive for an inheritance.[j] He went out, not knowing where he was going. [9]By faith, he sojourned in a land of promise, as a foreigner, living in tents with Isaac and Jacob, the heirs with him of the same promise. [10]For he looked for the city which has foundations, whose architect and builder is God. [11]By faith, even barren[k] Sarah herself received power to conceive when she was past age, and gave birth, since she considered him faithful who had promised. [12]Therefore as many as the stars of the sky in multitude, and as innumerable as the sand which is by the sea shore, were fathered by one man, and him as good as dead. [13]These all died in faith, not having received the promises, but having seen them[l] and embraced them from afar, and having acknowledged that they were strangers and

temporary residents on the earth. [14]For those who say such things make it clear that they are seeking a country of their own. [15]If indeed they had been thinking of that country from which they went out, they would have had enough time to return. [16]But now they desire a better country, that is, a heavenly one. Therefore God is not ashamed of them, to be called their God, for he has prepared a city for them.

[17]By faith, Abraham, being tested, offered up Isaac; and he who had gladly received the promises was offering up his one and only son;[m] [18]even he to whom it was said, "In Isaac will your descendants be called;"[n] [19]concluding that God is able to raise up even from the dead. Figuratively speaking, he also did receive him back from the dead. [20]By faith, Isaac blessed Jacob and Esau, even concerning things to come.[o] [21]By faith, Jacob, when he was dying, blessed each of the sons of Joseph, and worshiped, leaning on the top of his staff.[p] [22]By faith, Joseph, when his end was near, made mention of the departure of the children of Israel; and gave instructions concerning his bones.[q] [23]By faith, Moses, when he was born, was hidden for three months by his parents, because they saw that he was a beautiful child, and they were not afraid of

---

a   10:38 Gk. hupostello. L&N 13.160: "to hold oneself back from doing something…Acts 20:27"
b   10:38 Habakkuk 2:3-4
c   10:39 Gk. hupostole. Gingrich 6641 shrinking, timidity"; Strong's 5289: "a shrinking, drawing back"
d   11:3 Or, "worlds," "universe." Gk. aiwn
e   11:4 Genesis 4:4-8
f   11:5 Genesis 5:24
g   11:7 Or, "ship." Gk. kibotos "box-shaped." Traditionally "ark," from Latin arca "box, chest." The vessel, according to the Hebrew royal cubit of 52.5 centimeters, was 517 feet in length x 86 feet in width x 52 feet in height, or 157.5 meters x 26.3 meters x 15.8 meters. See Genesis 6:15
h   11:7 Genesis 6:13-7:1
i   11:8 Some Mss read "the"
j   11:8 Genesis 12:1-7
k   11:11 Some Mss lack "barren"
l   11:13 Some Mss add "and being persuaded"
m   11:17 Genesis 22:1-10
n   11:18 Genesis 21:12
o   11:20 Genesis 27:28-29, 39-40
p   11:21 Genesis 47:31
q   11:22 Genesis 50:24-25
r   11:23 Exodus 1:16, 22

the king's commandment.[r] 24By faith, Moses, when he had grown up, refused to be called the son of Pharaoh's daughter,[a] 25choosing rather to share ill treatment with God's people, than to enjoy the pleasures of sin for a time; 26considering the reproach of the Messiah[b] greater riches than the treasures of Egypt; for he looked to the reward. 27By faith he left Egypt, not fearing the anger of the king; for he endured as seeing him who is invisible.[c] 28By faith, he kept the Passover, and the sprinkling of the blood, that the destroyer of the firstborn should not touch them.[d] 29By faith, they passed through the Red Sea as on dry land. When the Egyptians tried to do so, they were swallowed up.[e] 30By faith, the walls of Jericho fell down, after they had been encircled for seven days.[f] 31By faith, Rahab the prostitute, did not perish with those who were disobedient,[g] having received the spies in peace.[h] 32And what more should I say? For the time would fail me if I told of Gideon, Barak, Samson, Jephthah, David, Samuel, and the prophets; 33who, through faith subdued kingdoms, worked out righteousness, obtained promises, stopped the mouths of lions,[i] 34quenched the power of fire,[j] escaped the edge of the sword, [k]from weakness were made strong, grew mighty in war, and caused foreign armies to flee. 35Women received their dead by resurrection.[l] And others were tortured, not accepting the payment for release,[m] that they might obtain a better resurrection. 36Others were tried by mocking and scourging, yes, moreover by bonds and imprisonment. 37They were stoned,[n] they were sawed apart, they were put to the test,[o] they were killed with the sword.[p] They went around in sheepskins[q] and in goatskins,[r] being destitute, afflicted, mistreated 38(of whom the world was not worthy), wandering in deserts, mountains, caves, and the holes of the earth. 39These all, having had testimony given to them through their faith, did not receive the promise, 40God having provided some better thing concerning us, so that apart from us they should not be made perfect.

12 Therefore let us also, seeing we are surrounded by so great a cloud of witnesses, lay aside every weight and the sin which so easily entangles us, and let us run with patience the race that is set before us, 2looking to Jesus, the author and finisher of our faith, who for the joy that was set before him endured the cross, disregarding its shame, and has sat down at the right hand of the throne of God. 3For consider him who has endured such hostility from sinners against himself, so that you do not grow weary in your souls and lose heart. 4You have not yet resisted to the point of shedding blood in your struggle against sin; 5and you have forgotten the exhortation which reasons with you as with children,

"My son, do not take lightly the
discipline of the Lord,
nor lose heart when you are
corrected by him.
6For whom the Lord loves he disciplines,
and punishes every son he accepts."[s]

7If you are enduring discipline, God is dealing with you as sons. For what son is there whom his father does not discipline? 8But if you are without discipline, of which all have been made partakers, then you are illegitimate, and not sons. 9Furthermore, we had earthly fathers who disciplined us, and we paid them respect. Should we not much rather be subject to the Father of spirits, and live? 10For they indeed, for a few days, disciplined us as

---

a 11:24 Exodus 2:10, 11
b 11:26 Or, "the Anointed One." Deuteronomy 18:15; John 5:46
c 11:27 1 Timothy 1:17
d 11:28 Exodus 12:21-30
e 11:29 Exodus 14:21-30
f 11:30 Joshua 6:15, 16, 20
g 11:31 Joshua 6:23-25
h 11:31 Joshua 2:9 ff
i 11:33 Daniel 6:22-23
j 11:34 Daniel 3:1-30 cf. Isaiah 43:2
k 11:34 1 Kings 19:1-3; 2 Kings 6:31-7:20
l 11:35 1Kings 17:22; 2Kings 4:35
m 11:35 Gk. apolutrosis. Thayer 653: "to redeem one by paying the price." E.g., a release offered on the terms of recanting ones faith
n 11:37 2 Chronicles 24:20-21
o 11:37 Some Mss lack "they were put to the test"
p 11:37 Jeremiah 26:20-23; 1 Kings 19:10
q 11:37 1Kings 19:13, 19 LXX;
r 11:37 Possibly Zechariah 13:4
s 12:6 Proverbs 3:11-12

seemed good to them; but he for our profit, that we may be partakers of his holiness. [11]All discipline seems for the moment painful, not joyful; yet afterward it yields the peaceful fruit of righteousness to those who have been trained by it. [12]Therefore, lift up the hands that hang down and the feeble knees,[a] [13]and make straight paths for your feet,[b] so that which is lame may not be dislocated, but rather be healed. [14]Pursue peace with everyone, and the sanctification without which no one will see the Lord, [15]looking carefully lest there be anyone who falls short of the grace of God; that no root of bitterness springing up cause trouble, and by it many become defiled; [16]that there be no sexually immoral or profane person like Esau, who sold his own[c] birthright for one meal. [17]For you know that even when he afterward desired to inherit the blessing, he was rejected, for he found no place for a change of mind though he sought it diligently with tears. [18]For you have not come to something[d] that might be touched, and that burned with fire, and darkness, gloom, and storm, [19]the sound of a trumpet, and the voice of words; which those who heard it begged that not one more word should be spoken to them, [20]for they could not stand that which was commanded, "If even an animal touches the mountain, it must be stoned[e];"[f] [21]and so fearful was the appearance, that Moses said, "I am terrified and trembling."

[22]But you have come to Mount Zion, and to the city of the living God, the heavenly Jerusalem, and to innumerable multitudes of angels, [23]to the assembly of the firstborn who are enrolled in heaven, to God the Judge of all, to the spirits of righteous people made perfect, [24]to Jesus, the mediator of a New Covenant,[g] and to the blood of sprinkling that speaks better than that of Abel.

[25]See that you do not refuse him who speaks. For if they did not escape when they refused him who warned on the earth, how much more will we not escape who turn away from him who warns from heaven, [26]whose voice shook the earth then, but now he has promised, saying, "Yet once more I will shake[h] not only the earth, but also the heavens."[i] [27]This phrase, "Yet once more," signifies the removing of those things that are shaken, as of things that have been made, that those things which are not shaken may remain. [28]So since we are receiving a kingdom that cannot be shaken, let us give thanks,[j] through which we may offer service pleasing to God, with reverence and awe, [29]for our God is a consuming fire.[k]

13 Let brotherly love continue. [2]Do not forget to show hospitality to strangers, for in doing so, some have entertained angels without knowing it. [3]Remember those who are in bonds, as bound with them; and those who are ill-treated, since you are also in the body. [4]Let marriage be held in honor among all, and let the bed be undefiled: for[l] God will judge the sexually immoral and adulterers.

[5]Be free from the love of money, content with such things as you have, for he has said, "I will never leave you or forsake you."[m] [6]So we can say with confidence,

"The Lord is my helper;[n] I will not fear.
    What can man do to me?"[o]

[7]Remember your leaders, who spoke to you the word of God, and considering the results of their conduct, imitate their faith. [8]Jesus Christ is the same yesterday, today, and forever. [9]Do not be carried away by all kinds of strange teachings, for it is good that the heart be established by grace, not by food, through which those who were so occupied were not benefited.

---

a   12:12 Isaiah 35:3
b   12:13 Proverbs 4:26
c   12:16 Some Mss lack "own"
d   12:18 Some Mss add "a mountain"
e   12:20 Some Mss add "or shot with an arrow"
f   12:20 Exodus 19:12-13
g   12:24 Jeremiah 31:31
h   12:26 Some Mss read "I am shaking"
i   12:26 Haggai 2:6
j   12:26 Or, "let us have grace"
k   12:29 Deuteronomy 4:24
l   13:4 Some Mss read "but"
m   13:5 Deuteronomy 31:6
n   13:6 Some Mss add "and"
o   13:6 Psalm 118:6-7

¹⁰We have an altar from which those who serve the holy tabernacle have no right to eat. ¹¹For the bodies of those animals, whose blood is brought into the holy place by the high priest as an offering for sin, are burned outside of the camp.ᵃ ¹²Therefore Jesus also, that he might sanctify the people through his own blood, suffered outside of the gate. ¹³Let us therefore go out to him outside of the camp, bearing his reproach. ¹⁴For we do not have here an enduring city, but we seek that which is to come. ¹⁵Through him, then, let us offer up a sacrifice of praise to God continually, that is, the fruit of lips that confess his name.ᵇ ¹⁶But do not forget to be doing good and sharing, for with such sacrifices God is well pleased.

¹⁷Obey your leaders and submit to them, for they watch on behalf of your souls, as those who will give account, that they may do this with joy, and not with groaning, for that would be unprofitable for you.

¹⁸Pray for us, for we are persuadedᶜ that we have a good conscience, desiring to live honorably in all things. ¹⁹I strongly urge you to do this, that I may be restored to you sooner.

²⁰Now may the God of peace, who brought again from the dead the great Shepherd of the sheep with the blood of an everlasting covenant, our Lord Jesus, ²¹make you complete in every good thingᵈ to do his will, working in usᵉ that which is well pleasing in his sight, through Jesus Christ, to whom be the glory foreverᶠ. Amen.

²²But I exhort you, brothers, endure the word of exhortation, for I have written to you in few words. ²³Know that our brother Timothy has been freed, with whom, if he comes shortly, I will see you. ²⁴Greet all of your leaders and all the saints. Those from Italy send you greetings. ²⁵Grace be with you all.ᵍ

James

1 James,ʰ a servant of God and of the Lord Jesus Christ, to the twelve tribes which are in the Diaspora: Greetings. ²Count it all joy, my brothers, when you encounter various trials, ³knowing that the testing of your faith produces endurance. ⁴Let endurance have its perfect work, that you may be perfect and complete, lacking in nothing. ⁵But if any of you lacks wisdom, let him ask of God, who gives to all liberally and without reproach; and it will be given to him. ⁶But let him ask in faith, without any doubting, for the one who doubts is like a wave of the sea, driven and tossed by the wind. ⁷For let that person not think that he will receive anything from the Lord. ⁸He is a double-minded person, unstable in all his ways.

⁹But let the brother in humble circumstances glory in his high position; ¹⁰and the rich, in that he is made humble, because like the flower in the grass, he will pass away. ¹¹For the sun arises with the scorching wind, and withers the grass, and the flower in it falls, and the beauty of its appearance perishes. So also will the rich person fade away in his pursuits.

¹²Blessed is the one who perseveres under trial, for when he has been approved, he will receive the crown of life, which heⁱ promised to those who love him. ¹³Let no one say when he is tempted, "I am tempted by God," for God cannot be tempted by evil, and he himself tempts no one. ¹⁴But each one is tempted, when he is drawn away by his own lust, and enticed. ¹⁵Then the lust, when it has conceived, bears sin; and the sin, when it is full grown, brings forth death. ¹⁶Do not be deceived, my beloved brothers. ¹⁷All generous giving and

---

a   13:11 Leviticus 16:27
b   13:15 An allusion to Hosea 14:2
c   13:18 Some Mss read "confident"
d   13:21 Some Mss read "work"
e   13:21 Some Mss read "in you"
f   13:21 Some Mss add "and ever"
g   13:24 Some Mss add "Amen"
h   1:1 Or "Jacob." Gk. "Iakobos"
i   1:12 Some Mss read "the Lord"

every perfect gift is from above, coming down from the Father of lights, with whom can be no variation, nor turning shadow. [18]Of his own will he brought us forth by the word of truth, that we should be a kind of first fruits of his creatures.

[19]This you know[a], my beloved brothers. But let every person be swift to hear, slow to speak, and slow to anger; [20]for human anger does not accomplish[b] the righteousness of God. [21]Therefore, putting away all filthiness and overflowing of wickedness, receive with humility the implanted word, which is able to save your souls[c]. [22]But be doers of the word, and not only hearers, deluding your own selves. [23]For if anyone is a hearer of the word and not a doer, he is like someone looking at his natural face in a mirror; [24]for he sees himself, and goes away, and immediately forgets what kind of person he was. [25]But he who looks into the perfect Law of freedom, and continues, not being a hearer who forgets, but a doer of the work, this person will be blessed in what he does.

[26]If anyone[d] thinks himself to be religious while he does not bridle his tongue, but deceives his heart, this man's religion is worthless. [27]Pure religion and undefiled before our God and Father is this: to visit the fatherless and widows in their affliction, and to keep oneself unstained by the world.

2 My brothers, do not hold the faith of our Lord Jesus Christ of glory with partiality. [2]For if someone with a gold ring, in fine clothing, comes into your synagogue, and a poor person in filthy clothing also comes in; [3]and you pay special attention to the one who wears the fine clothing, and say[e], "Sit here in a good place;" but you tell the poor person, "Stand there," or "Sit by my footstool;" [4]haven't you shown partiality among yourselves, and become judges with evil thoughts? [5]Listen, my beloved brothers. Did not God choose those who are poor in this world to be rich in faith, and heirs of the kingdom which he promised to those who love him? [6]But you have

dishonored the poor person. Do not the rich oppress you, and personally drag you before the courts? [7]Do not they blaspheme the honorable name by which you are called? [8]However, if you fulfill the royal law, according to the Scripture, "You are to love your neighbor as yourself,"[f] you do well. [9]But if you show partiality, you commit sin, being convicted by the law as transgressors. [10]For whoever keeps the whole law, and yet stumbles in one point, he has become guilty of all. [11]For he who said, "Do not commit adultery,"[g] also said, "Do not commit murder."[h] Now if you do not commit adultery, but murder, you have become a transgressor of the law. [12]So speak, and so do, as those who are to be judged by a law of freedom. [13]For judgment is without mercy to him who has shown no mercy. Mercy triumphs over judgment.

[14]What good is it, my brothers, if someone says he has faith, but has no works? Can faith save him? [15]And if a brother or sister is naked and in lack of daily food, [16]and one of you tells them, "Go in peace, be warmed and filled;" and yet you did not give them the things the body needs, what good is it? [17]Even so faith, if it has no works, is dead in itself. [18]But someone will say, "You have faith, and I have works." Show me your faith without works, and I by my works will show you my faith.

[19]You believe that God is one. You do well. The demons also believe, and shudder. [20]But do you want to know, foolish person, that faith apart from works is useless?[i] [21]Wasn't Abraham our father justified by works, in that he offered up Isaac his son on the altar? [22]You see that faith worked with his works, and by works faith was perfected; [23]and the Scripture was fulfilled which says, "And Abraham believed God,

---

a   1:19 Some Mss read "So then"
b   1:20 Some Mss read "produce"
c   1:21 Or, "preserve your life"
d   1:26 Some Mss add "among you"
e   2:3 Some Mss add "to him"
f   2:8 Leviticus 19:18
g   2:11 Exodus 20:14; Deuteronomy 5:18
h   2:11 Exodus 10:13; Deuteronomy 5:17
i   2:20 Some Mss read "dead"

and it was credited to him as righteousness;"[a] and he was called the friend of God.[b] 24You see[c] that a person is justified[d] by works and not by faith alone. 25In like manner was not Rahab the prostitute also justified by works, in that she received the messengers, and sent them out another way? 26For as the body apart from the spirit is dead, even so faith apart from works is dead.

3 Let not many of you be teachers, my brothers, knowing that we will receive heavier judgment. 2For in many things we all stumble. If anyone does not stumble in word, this one is a perfect person, able to bridle the whole body also. 3Now if[e] we put bits into the horses' mouths so that they may obey us, we guide their whole body. 4And look at the ships also, though they are so big and are driven by fierce winds, are yet guided by a very small rudder, wherever the pilot desires. 5So the tongue is also a little member, and boasts great things. See how a small fire can spread to a large forest. 6And the tongue is a fire. The world of iniquity among our members is the tongue, which defiles the whole body, and sets on fire the course of nature, and is set on fire by hell.[f] 7For all kinds of animals, and birds, of reptiles and sea creatures, are being tamed and have been tamed by humankind. 8But nobody can tame the tongue. It is a restless[g] evil, full of deadly poison. 9With it we bless our Lord[h] and Father, and with it we curse people, who are made in the image of God. 10Out of the same mouth comes forth blessing and cursing. My brothers, these things ought not to be so. 11Does a spring send out from the same opening fresh and bitter water? 12Can a fig tree, my brothers, yield olives, or a vine figs? Nor is salt water able to produce sweet[i].

13Who is wise and understanding among you? Let him show by his good conduct that his deeds are done in gentleness of wisdom. 14But if you have bitter jealousy and selfish ambition in your heart, do not boast and do not lie against the truth. 15This wisdom is not that which comes down from above, but is earthly, sensual, and demonic. 16For where jealousy and selfish ambition are, there is confusion and every evil deed. 17But the wisdom that is from above is first pure, then peaceful, gentle, reasonable, full of mercy and good fruits, without partiality, [j]without hypocrisy. 18Now the fruit of righteousness is sown in peace by those who make peace.

4 Where do conflicts and quarrels among you come from? Do they not come from your passions that war in your members? 2You lust, and do not have. You kill, covet, and cannot obtain. You fight and make war. You do not have, because you do not ask. 3You ask, and do not receive, because you ask with wrong motives, so that you may spend it for your pleasures. 4You adulterers and adulteresses,[k] do you not know that friendship with the world is hostility toward God? Therefore whoever wants to be a friend of the world makes himself an enemy of God. 5Or do you think that the Scripture says in vain, "The Spirit which he made to dwell[l] in us yearns jealously"? 6But he gives more grace. Therefore it says, "God resists the proud, but gives grace to the humble."[m] 7Be subject therefore to God. But resist the devil, and he will flee from you. 8Draw near to God, and he will draw near to you. Cleanse your hands, you sinners; and purify your hearts, you doubleminded. 9Lament, mourn, and weep. Let your laughter be turned to mourning,

---

a   2:23 Genesis 15:6
b   2:23 2 Chronicles 20:7; Isaiah 41:8
c   2:24 Some Mss add "then/therefore"
d   2:24 Or, "declared righteous"
e   3:3 Some Mss read "Look"
f   3:6 Gk. "Gehenna"
g   3:8 Some Mss read "uncontrollable"
h   3:9 Some Mss read "God"
i   3:12 Some Mss read "Thus no spring yields both salt water and fresh water"
j   3:17 Some Mss add "and"
k   4:4 Some Mss lack "adulterers and"
l   4:5 Some Mss read "who dwells"
m   4:6 Proverbs 3:34

and your joy to gloom. [10]Humble yourselves in the sight of the Lord, and he will exalt you.

[11]Do not speak against one another, brothers. He who speaks against a brother or[a] judges his brother, speaks against the law and judges the law. But if you judge the law, you are not a doer of the law, but a judge. [12]Only one is the lawgiver and judge,[b] who is able to save and to destroy. But who are you to judge your neighbor[c]?

[13]Come now, you who say, "Today or tomorrow let us go into this city, and spend a year there, trade, and make a profit." [14]Whereas you do not know what tomorrow will be like. What is your life? For you are[d] a vapor that appears for a little time and then vanishes away.

[15]For you ought to say, "If the Lord wills, we will both live, and do this or that." [16]But now you glory in your boasting. All such boasting is evil. [17]To him therefore who knows to do good, and does not do it, to him it is sin.

5 Come now, you rich, weep and cry aloud for your miseries that are coming on you. [2]Your riches are corrupted and your garments are moth-eaten. [3]Your gold and your silver are corroded, and their corrosion will be for a testimony against you, and will eat your flesh like fire. You have laid up your treasure in the last days. [4]Look, the wages of the laborers who mowed your fields, which you have kept back by fraud, cry out, and the cries of those who reaped have entered into the ears of the Lord of hosts. [5]You have lived delicately on the earth, and taken your pleasure. You have nourished your hearts[e] in a day of slaughter. [6]You have condemned, you have murdered the righteous one. He does not resist you.

[7]Be patient therefore, brothers, until the coming of the Lord. Look, the farmer waits for the precious fruit of the earth, being patient over it, until it receives the early and late rain. [8]You also be patient. Establish your hearts, for the coming of the Lord is near.

[9]Do not grumble, brothers, against one another, so that you won't be judged.[f] Look, the judge stands at the door. [10]Take,[g] brothers, for an example of suffering and of patience, the prophets who spoke in the name of the Lord. [11]Look, we call them blessed who endured. You have heard of the patience of Job, and have seen the Lord in the outcome, and how the Lord[h] is full of compassion and mercy. [12]But above all things, my brothers, do not swear, neither by heaven, nor by the earth, nor by any other oath; but let your "yes" be "yes," and your "no," "no;" so that you do not fall under judgment.[i]

[13]Is any among you suffering? Let him pray. Is any cheerful? Let him sing praises. [14]Is any among you sick? Let him call for the elders of the church, and let them pray over him, anointing him with oil in the name of the Lord, [15]and the prayer of faith will save the one who is sick, and the Lord will raise him up. If he has committed sins, he will be forgiven. [16]Therefore[j] confess your sins[k] to one another, and pray for one another, that you may be healed. The prayer of the righteous person is powerfully effective. [17]Elijah was a human being with a nature like ours, and he prayed earnestly that it might not rain, and it did not rain on the land for three years and six months. [18]He prayed again, and the sky gave rain, and the earth brought forth its fruit.

[19]My[l] brothers, if any among you wanders from the truth, and someone turns him back, [20]let him know that he who turns a sinner from the error of his way will save his[m] soul from death, and will cover a multitude of sins.

---

a   4:11 Some Mss read "and"
b   4:12 Some Mss lack "and judge"
c   4:12 Some Mss read "another"
d   4:14 Some Mss read "it will be"
e   5:5 Some Mss add "as"
f   5:9 Some Mss read "condemned"
g   5:11 Some Mss add "my"
h   5:11 Some Mss lack "the Lord"
i   5:12 Some Mss read "into hypocrisy"
j   5:16 Some Mss lack "Therefore"
k   5:16 Some Mss read "transgressions"
l   5:19 Some Mss lack "My"
m   5:20 Some Mss read "a"

1 Peter

1 Peter, an apostle of Jesus Christ, to the chosen ones who are living as foreigners in the Diaspora in Pontus, Galatia, Cappadocia, Asia, and Bithynia, ²according to the foreknowledge of God the Father, in sanctification of the Spirit, that you may obey Jesus Christ and be sprinkled with his blood: Grace to you and peace be multiplied. ³Blessed be the God and Father of our Lord Jesus Christ, who according to his great mercy became our father again to a living hope through the resurrection of Jesus Christ from the dead, ⁴to an incorruptible and undefiled inheritance that does not fade away, reserved in Heaven for you, ⁵who by the power of God are guarded through faith for a salvation ready to be revealed in the last time. ⁶Wherein you greatly rejoice, though now for a little while, if necessary, you have been grieved by various trials, ⁷that the genuineness of your faith, which is more precious than gold that perishes even though it is tested by fire, may be found to result in praise, glory, and honor at the revelation of Jesus Christ—⁸whom not having seen[a] you love; in whom, though now you do not see him, yet believing, you rejoice greatly with joy inexpressible and full of glory—⁹receiving the result of your faith, the salvation of your souls. ¹⁰Concerning this salvation, the prophets sought and searched diligently, who prophesied of the grace that would come to you, ¹¹searching for who or what kind of time the Spirit of Christ, which was in them, pointed to, when he predicted the sufferings of Christ, and the glories that would follow them. ¹²To them it was revealed, that not to themselves, but to you, they ministered these things, which now have been announced to you through those who preached the Good News to you by the Holy Spirit sent out from heaven; which things angels desire to look into.

¹³Therefore, prepare your minds for action,[b] be sober and set your hope fully on the grace that will be brought to you at the revelation of Jesus Christ. ¹⁴As obedient children, do not be conformed to the desires as in your ignorance, ¹⁵but just as he who called you is holy, you yourselves also be holy in all of your behavior; ¹⁶because it is written, "Be holy, for I am holy."[c] ¹⁷If you call on him as Father, who without respect of persons judges according to each man's work, pass the time of your living as foreigners here in reverent fear: ¹⁸knowing that you were redeemed, not with corruptible things, with silver or gold, from the useless way of life handed down from your fathers, ¹⁹but with precious blood, as of a faultless and pure lamb, namely Christ; ²⁰who was foreknown indeed before the foundation of the world, but was revealed in these last times for your sake, ²¹who through Him are believers in God, who raised him from the dead, and gave him glory; so that your faith and hope might be in God.

²²Seeing you have purified your souls in your obedience to the truth[d] in sincere brotherly affection, love one another from a pure[e] heart fervently: ²³having been born again, not of corruptible seed, but of incorruptible, through the living and abiding word of God.[f] ²⁴For,

"All flesh is like grass,
    and all it's[g] glory like the flower in
        the grass.
The grass withers, and its flower falls;
    ²⁵but the word of the Lord endures
        forever."[h]

This is the word of Good News which was preached to you.

2 Putting away therefore all wickedness, and all deceit, and hypocrisy, and envy, and all slander, ²as newborn babies, long

---

a 1:8 Some Mss read "known"
b 1:13 Lit., "gird up the waist of your mind"
c 1:16 Some Mss read "Be becoming holy." Leviticus 11:44-45
d 1:22 Some Mss add "through the Spirit"
e 1:22 Some Mss lack "pure"
f 1:23 Some Mss add "forever," reading "through the Word of God, which lives and remains forever"
g 1:24 Some Mss read "of man's"
h 1:25 Isaiah 40:6-8

for the pure milk of the word, that you may grow thereby to salvation, ³if indeed you have tasted that the Lord is gracious: ⁴coming to him, a living stone, rejected indeed by men, but chosen by God, precious. ⁵You also, as living stones, are built up as a spiritual house, to be a holy priesthood, to offer up spiritual sacrifices, acceptable to God through Jesus Christ. ⁶Because it is contained in[a] Scripture,

"Look, I lay in Zion a stone, a chosen precious cornerstone,
and whoever believes in him will not be put to shame."[b]

⁷For you who believe therefore is the honor, but for those who do not believe,[c]

"The stone which the builders rejected, has become the chief cornerstone,"[d]

⁸and,

"a stone of stumbling, and a rock of offense."[e]

For they stumble at the word, being disobedient, to which also they were appointed. ⁹But you are a chosen race, a royal priesthood, a holy nation, a people for his own possession, that you may proclaim the excellence of him who called you out of darkness into his marvelous light: ¹⁰who once were not a people, but now are God's people, who had not obtained mercy, but now have obtained mercy. ¹¹Beloved, I urge you as foreigners and temporary residents, to abstain from fleshly lusts, which war against the soul; ¹²having good behavior among the nations, so in that of which they speak against you as evildoers, they may by your good works, which they see, glorify God in the day of visitation. ¹³[f]Subject yourselves to every human institution for the Lord's sake: whether to the king, as supreme; ¹⁴or to governors, as sent by him for vengeance on evildoers and for praise to those who do well. ¹⁵For this is the will of God, that by well-doing you should put to silence the ignorance of foolish people: ¹⁶as free, and not using your freedom for a cloak of wickedness, but as slaves of God.

¹⁷Honor all people. Love the brotherhood. Fear God. Honor the king. ¹⁸Servants, be in subjection to your masters with all fear; not only to the good and gentle, but also to the wicked. ¹⁹For it is commendable if someone endures pain, suffering unjustly, because of conscience toward God. ²⁰For what glory is it if, when you sin, you patiently endure beating? But if, when you do well, you patiently endure suffering, this is commendable with God. ²¹For to this you were called, because Christ also suffered for you[g], leaving you an example, that you should follow his steps, ²²who committed no sin, nor was deceit found in his mouth.[h] ²³Who, when he was cursed, did not curse back. When he suffered, did not threaten, but committed himself to him who judges righteously; ²⁴who his own self bore our sins in his body on the tree, that we, having died to sins, might live to righteousness; by his stripes you were healed.[i] ²⁵For you were going astray like sheep; but now have returned to the Shepherd and Overseer of your souls.

3 In like manner, wives, be in subjection to your own husbands; so that, even if any do not obey the word, they may be won by the behavior of their wives without a word; ²seeing your pure behavior in fear. ³Let your beauty be not just the outward adorning of braiding the hair, and of wearing jewels of gold, or of putting on fine clothing; ⁴but in the hidden person of the heart, in the incorruptible adornment of a gentle and quiet spirit, which is in the sight of God very precious. ⁵For this is how the holy women before, who hoped in God also adorned themselves, being in subjection to their own husbands: ⁶as Sarah obeyed Abraham, calling him lord, whose children you now are, if you do well, and are not put in fear by any terror.

⁷You husbands, in like manner, live with your wives according to knowledge, giving honor to the woman, as to the weaker ves-

---

a   2:6 Some Mss add "the"
b   2:6 Isaiah 28:16
c   2:7 Some Mss read "are disobedient"
d   2:7 Psalm 118:22
e   2:8 Isaiah 8:14
f   2:13 Some Mss add "Therefore"
g   2:21 Some Mss read "us"
h   2:22 Isaiah 53:9
i   Isaiah 53:5

sel, as being also joint heirs of the grace of life; that your prayers may not be hindered.

⁸Finally, be all like-minded, compassionate, loving as brothers, tenderhearted, humble[a], ⁹not rendering evil for evil, or reviling for reviling; but instead blessing; because[b] to this were you called, that you may inherit a blessing. ¹⁰For,

"He who would love life,
and see good days,
let him keep his tongue from evil,
and his lips from speaking deceit.
¹¹Let him turn away from evil, and do good.
Let him seek peace, and pursue it.
¹²For the eyes of the Lord are on the righteous,
and his ears open to their prayer;
but the face of the Lord is against those who do evil."[c]

¹³Now who is he who will harm you, if you become zealous[d] of that which is good? ¹⁴But even if you should suffer for righteousness' sake, you are blessed. "And do not fear what they fear,[e] nor be troubled."[f] ¹⁵But sanctify in your hearts Christ as Lord;[g] and always be ready to give an answer to everyone who asks you a reason concerning the hope that is in you, yet[h] with humility and fear: ¹⁶having a good conscience; so that when they speak evil against you, they may be put to shame who slander your good manner of life in Christ.

¹⁷For it is better, if it is God's will, that you suffer for doing well than for doing evil. ¹⁸Because Christ also suffered for sins once, the righteous for the unrighteous, that he might bring you to God; being put to death in the flesh, but made alive in the spirit; ¹⁹in which he also went and made a proclamation to the spirits in prison, ²⁰who before were disobedient, when God waited patiently in the days of Noah, while the box-shaped vessel[i] was being built. In it, few, that is, eight souls, were saved by means of water. ²¹This is a symbol of baptism, which now saves you—not the removal of dirt from the body, but an appeal to God for a good conscience, through the resurrection of Jesus Christ, ²²who is at the right hand of God, having gone into heaven, angels and authorities and powers being made subject to him.

4 Forasmuch then as Christ suffered[j] in the flesh, arm yourselves also with the same mind; for he who has suffered in the flesh has ceased from sin; ²that you no longer should live the rest of your time in the flesh for human desires, but for the will of God. ³For enough time in the past has been spent[k] doing the will of the unbelievers, and having walked in lewdness, lusts, drunkenness, orgies, carousings, and abominable idolatries. ⁴They think it is strange that you do not run with them into the same flood of debauchery, blaspheming: ⁵who will give account to him who is ready to judge the living and the dead. ⁶For this reason also the Good News was preached[l] to those who are now dead,[m] that they might be judged according to man in the flesh, but might live according to God in the Spirit.[n] ⁷But the end of all things is near. Therefore be of sound mind, self-controlled, and sober in[o] prayer. ⁸Above all things be earnest in your love[q] among yourselves, for love covers a multitude of sins. ⁹Be hospitable to one another without grumbling. ¹⁰As each has received a gift, employ it in serving one another, as good managers of the grace of God in its various forms. ¹¹If anyone speaks, let it be as it were the very words of God. If anyone serves, let it be as of the strength which[r] God supplies, that in all

---

a 3:8 Some Mss read "courteous"
b 3:9 Some Mss read "knowing that"
c 3:12 Psalm 34:12-16
d 3:13 Some Mss read "imitators"
e 3:14 Lit. "do not fear their fear"
f 3:14 Isaiah 8:12
g 3:15 Some Mss read "the Lord God in your hearts"
h 3:15 Some Mss lack "yet"
i 3:20 Or, "ship." Gk. kibotos "box-shaped." Traditionally "ark," from Latin arca "box, chest." The vessel, according to the Hebrew royal cubit of 52.5 centimeters, was 517 feet in length x 86 feet in width x 52 feet in height, or 157.5 meters x 26.3 meters x 15.8 meters. See Genesis 6:15
j 4:1 Some Mss add "for you"
k 4:3 Some Mss read "lifetime"
l 4:6 The Gk. is passive: "Good News was preached"
m 4:6 Gk. "preached to the dead"
n 4:6 Or, "spirit"
o 4:7 Some Mss add "your"
p 4:8 Some Mss add "And"
q 4:8 Some Mss add "will"
r 4:11 Some Mss read "as"

things God may be glorified through Jesus Christ, to whom belong the glory and the dominion forever and ever. Amen.

[12]Beloved, do not be astonished at the fiery trial which has come upon you, to test you, as though a strange thing happened to you. [13]But because you are partakers of Christ's sufferings, rejoice; that at the revelation of his glory you also may rejoice with exceeding joy. [14]If you are insulted for the name of Christ, you are blessed; because the Spirit of glory[a] and of God rests on you. On their part he is blasphemed, but on your part he is glorified.[b] [15]For let none of you suffer as a murderer, or a thief, or an evil doer, or a meddler in other men's matters. [16]But if one of you suffers for being a Christian, let him not be ashamed; but let him glorify God in this name[c]. [17]For the time has come for judgment to begin with the household of God; and if it begins first with us, what will happen to those who do not obey the Good News of God? [18]And "If the righteous is delivered with difficulty, where will the ungodly and the sinner appear?"[d] [19]Therefore let them also who suffer according to the will of God in doing good entrust their souls to him, as to a faithful Creator.

5 Therefore[e], I exhort the elders among you, as a fellow elder, and a witness of the sufferings of Christ, and who will also share in the glory that will be revealed. [2]Shepherd the flock of God which is among you, exercising the oversight, not under compulsion, but voluntarily, as God wants;[f] not for dishonest gain, but willingly; [3]neither as lording it over those entrusted to you, but making yourselves examples to the flock. [4]When the chief Shepherd is revealed, you will receive the crown of glory that does not fade away.

[5]Likewise, you younger ones, be subject to the elder. Yes, all of you[g] clothe yourselves with humility, towards one another; for God resists the proud, but gives grace to the humble.[h] [6]Humble yourselves therefore under the mighty hand of God, that he may exalt you in due time; [7]casting all your worries on him, because he cares for you.

[8]Be sober and self-controlled. Be watchful. Your adversary the devil, walks around like a roaring lion, seeking whom he may devour. [9]Withstand him steadfast in your faith, knowing that your brothers who are in the world are undergoing the same sufferings. [10]And the God of all grace, who called you to his eternal glory in Christ,[i] after you have suffered a little while, will himself restore, confirm, strengthen and establish you. [11]To him be the[j] power forever[k]. Amen.

[12]Through Silvanus, our faithful brother, as I consider him, I have written to you briefly, exhorting, and testifying that this is the true grace of God. Stand firm in it.[l] [13]She who is in Babylon, chosen together with you, greets you; and so does Mark, my son. [14]Greet one another with a kiss of love. Peace be to you all who are in Christ.[m]

2 Peter

1 Simeon[n] Peter, a servant and apostle of Jesus Christ, to those who have obtained a like precious faith with us in the righteousness of our God and Savior, Jesus Christ: [2]Grace to you and peace be multiplied in the knowledge of God and of Jesus our Lord, [3]seeing that his divine power has granted to us all things that pertain to life and godliness, through the knowledge of him who called us by his own[o] glory and virtue; [4]by which he has granted to us his precious and exceed-

---

a 4:14 Some Mss add "and of power"
b 4:14 Some Mss lack "On their part...glorified"
c 4:16 Some Mss read "matter"
d 4:18 Proverbs 11:31
e 5:1 Some Mss lack "Therefore"
f 5:2 Some Mss lack "as God wants"
g 5:5 Some Mss add "be subjected to one another"
h 5:5 Proverbs 3:34
i 5:10 Some Mss add "Jesus"
j 5:11 Some Mss add "glory and the"
k 5:11 Some Mss add "and ever"
l 5:12 Some Mss read "in which you stand"
m 5:14 Some Mss add "Jesus. Amen"
n 1:1 Some Mss read "Simon." See Acts 15:14
o 1:3 Some Mss lack "his own"

ingly great promises; that through these you may become partakers of the divine nature, having escaped from the corruption that is in the world by lust. ⁵Yes, and for this very cause adding on your part all diligence, in your faith supply moral excellence; and in moral excellence, knowledge; ⁶and in knowledge, self-control; and in self-control patience; and in patience godliness; ⁷and in godliness brotherly affection; and in brotherly affection, love. ⁸For if these things are yours and abound, they make you to be not idle nor unfruitful to the knowledge of our Lord Jesus Christ. ⁹For he who lacks these things is blind, seeing only what is near, having forgotten the cleansing from his old sins. ¹⁰Therefore, brothers, be more diligent to make your calling and election sure. For if you do these things, you will never stumble. ¹¹For thus you will be richly supplied with the entrance into the everlasting kingdom of our Lord and Savior, Jesus Christ.

¹²Therefore I will be ready always[a] to remind you of these things, though you know them, and are established in the present truth. ¹³I think it right, as long as I am in this tent, to stir you up by reminding you; ¹⁴knowing that the putting off of my tent comes swiftly, even as our Lord Jesus Christ made clear to me. ¹⁵Yes, I will make every effort that you may always be able to remember these things even after my departure. ¹⁶For we did not follow cunningly devised tales, when we made known to you the power and coming of our Lord Jesus Christ, but we were eyewitnesses of his majesty. ¹⁷For he received from God the Father honor and glory, when the voice came to him from the Majestic Glory, "This is my beloved Son, in whom I am well pleased."[b] ¹⁸We heard this voice come out of heaven when we were with him on the holy mountain.

¹⁹We have the more sure word of prophecy; and you do well that you heed it, as to a lamp shining in a dark place, until the day dawns, and the morning star arises in your hearts; ²⁰knowing this first, that no prophecy of Scripture is of private interpretation. ²¹For no prophecy ever came by human will, but people spoke from[c] God, being moved by the Holy Spirit.

2 But false prophets also arose among the people, as false teachers will also be among you, who will secretly bring in destructive heresies, denying even the Master who bought them, bringing on themselves swift destruction. ²Many will follow their immoral[d] ways, and as a result, the way of the truth will be maligned. ³In covetousness they will exploit you with deceptive words: whose sentence now from of old does not linger, and their destruction is not asleep[e]. ⁴For if God did not spare angels when they sinned, but cast them down to the lower parts of hell,[f] and committed them to chains[g] of darkness, to be reserved for judgment; ⁵and did not spare the ancient world, but preserved Noah with seven others, a proclaimer of righteousness, when he brought a flood on the world of the ungodly; ⁶and turning the cities of Sodom and Gomorrah into ashes, condemned them to destruction, having made them an example of what is going to happen to the ungodly; ⁷and delivered righteous Lot, who was very distressed by the lustful life of the wicked ⁸(for that righteous man dwelling among them, was tormented in his righteous soul from day to day with seeing and hearing lawless deeds): ⁹the Lord knows how to deliver the godly out of temptation and to keep the unrighteous under punishment for the day of judgment; ¹⁰but chiefly those who walk after the flesh in the lust of defilement, and despise authority. Daring, self-willed, they are not afraid to speak evil of dignitaries; ¹¹whereas angels, though greater in might and power, do not bring a railing judgment against them before the Lord. ¹²But these, as unreasoning creatures, born natural animals to be taken

---

a   1:12 Some Mss read "not be negligent"
b   1:17 Matthew 17:5; Mark 9:7; Luke 9:35
c   1:21 Some Mss read "holy"
d   2:2 Some Mss read "destructive"
e   2:3 Some Mss read "will not sleep"
f   2:4 Gk. Tartarus. The lowest parts, or below Sheol
g   2:4 Other Mss read "pits/caverns"

and destroyed, speaking evil in matters about which they are ignorant, will in their destroying surely be destroyed, [13]suffering the penalty as the wages of evil; people who count it pleasure to revel in the daytime, spots and blemishes, reveling in their deceit while they feast with you; [14]having eyes full of adultery, and who cannot cease from sin; enticing unsettled souls; having a heart trained in greed; children of cursing; [15]forsaking the right way, they went astray, having followed the way of Balaam the son of Bosor, who loved the wages of wrongdoing; [16]but he was rebuked for his own disobedience. A mute donkey spoke with a man's voice and stopped the madness of the prophet. [17]These are wells without water, and mists driven by a storm; for whom the blackness of darkness has been reserved[a]. [18]For, uttering great swelling words of emptiness, they entice in the lusts of the flesh, by licentiousness, those who actually[b] escape from those who live in error; [19]promising them liberty, while they themselves are slaves of corruption; for a person is brought into bondage by whoever overcomes him.

[20]For if, after they have escaped the defilement of the world through the knowledge of our[c] Lord and Savior Jesus Christ, they are again entangled in it and overcome, the last state has become worse for them than the first. [21]For it would be better for them not to have known the way of righteousness, than, after knowing it, to turn back from the holy commandment delivered to them. [22]It[d] has happened to them according to the true proverb, "The dog turns to his own vomit again,"[e] and "the sow that has washed to wallowing in the mire."

3 This is now, beloved, the second letter that I have written to you; and in both of them I stir up your sincere mind by reminding you; [2]that you should remember the words which were spoken before by the holy prophets, and the commandment of the Lord and Savior through your apostles: [3]knowing this first, that in the last days scoffers will come, mocking[f] and walking after their own lusts, [4]and saying, "Where is the promise of his coming? For, from the day that the fathers fell asleep, all things continue as they were from the beginning of the creation." [5]For this they willfully forget, that there were heavens from of old, and an earth formed out of water and amid water, by the word of God; [6]by which means the world that then was, being overflowed with water, perished. [7]But the heavens that now are, and the earth, by the same[g] word have been stored up for fire, being reserved against the day of judgment and destruction of ungodly people. [8]But do not forget this one thing, beloved, that one day is with the Lord as a thousand years, and a thousand years as one day. [9]The Lord is not slow concerning his promise, as some count slowness; but is patient toward[h] you[i], not wishing that any should perish, but that all should come to repentance. [10]But the day of the Lord will come as a thief[j]; in which the heavens will pass away with a great noise, and the elements will be dissolved with fervent heat, and the earth and the works that are in it will be disclosed.[k] [11]Therefore since all these things will be destroyed like this, what kind of people ought you to be in holy living and godliness, [12]looking for and earnestly desiring the coming of the day of God, which will cause the burning heavens to be dissolved, and the elements will melt with fervent heat? [13]But, according to his promise, we look for new heavens and a new earth, in which righteousness dwells.

[14]Therefore, beloved, seeing that you look for these things, be diligent to be found in peace, without blemish and blameless in his sight. [15]Regard the patience of our Lord as salvation; even as our beloved brother

---

a   2:17 Some Mss add "forever"
b   2:18 Some Mss read "barely"
c   2:20 Some Mss read "the"
d   2:22 Some Mss read "But it"
e   2:22 Proverbs 26:11
f   3:3 Some Mss lack "mocking"
g   3:7 Some Mss read "His"
h   3:9 Some Mss read "because"
i   3:9 Some Mss read "us"
j   3:10 Some Mss add "in the night"
k   3:10 Some Mss read "burned up"

Paul also, according to the wisdom given to him, wrote to you; [16]as also in all of his letters, speaking in them of these things. In those, there are some things that are hard to understand, which the ignorant and unsettled twist, as they also do to the other Scriptures, to their own destruction. [17]You therefore, beloved, knowing these things beforehand, beware, lest being carried away with the error of the wicked, you fall from your own steadfastness. [18]But grow in the grace and knowledge of our Lord and Savior Jesus Christ. To him be the glory both now and forever. Amen.[a]

1 John

1 That which was from the beginning, that which we have heard, that which we have seen with our eyes, that which we saw, and our hands touched, concerning the Word of life [2](and the life was revealed, and we have seen, and testify, and declare to you the life, the eternal life, which was with the Father, and was revealed to us); [3]that which we have seen and heard we declare to you also,[b] that you also may have fellowship with us. Yes, and our fellowship is with the Father, and with his Son, Jesus Christ. [4]And we write these things[c], that our joy may be fulfilled.

[5]This is the message which we have heard from him and announce to you, that God is light, and in him is no darkness at all. [6]If we say that we have fellowship with him and walk in the darkness, we lie, and do not tell the truth. [7]But if we walk in the light, as he is in the light, we have fellowship with one another, and the blood of Jesus[d], his Son, cleanses us from all sin. [8]If we say that we have no sin, we deceive ourselves, and the truth is not in us. [9]If we confess our sins, he is faithful and righteous to forgive us the sins, and to cleanse us from all unrighteousness. [10]If we say that we have not sinned, we make him a liar, and his word is not in us.

2 My little children, I write these things to you so that you may not sin. If anyone sins, we have an advocate[e] with the Father, Jesus Christ, the righteous. [2]And he is the atoning sacrifice for our sins, and not for ours only, but also for the whole world. [3]This is how we know that we know him: if we keep his commandments. [4]One who says, "I know him," and does not keep his commandments, is a liar, and the truth is not in him. [5]But whoever keeps his word, God's love has truly been perfected in him. This is how we know that we are in him: [6]he who says he remains in him ought himself also to walk just like he walked.

[7]Beloved[f], I write no new commandment to you, but an old commandment which you had from the beginning. The old commandment is the word which you heard[g]. [8]Again, I write a new commandment to you, which is true in him and in you; because the darkness is passing away, and the true light already shines. [9]He who says he is in the light and hates his brother, is in the darkness even until now. [10]He who loves his brother remains in the light, and there is no occasion for stumbling in him. [11]But he who hates his brother is in the darkness, and walks in the darkness, and does not know where he is going, because the darkness has blinded his eyes.

[12]I write to you, little children, because your sins are forgiven you for his name's sake.

[13]I am writing[h] to you, fathers, because you know him who is from the beginning.

I write to you, young people, because you have overcome the evil one.

I write to you, little children, because you know the Father.

---

a 3:18 Some Mss lack "Amen"
b 1:3 Some Mss lack "also"
c 1:4 Some Mss add "to you"
d 1:7 Some Mss add "Christ"
e 2:1 Gk. Parakleton
f 2:7 Some Mss read "Brothers"
g 2:7 Some Mss add "from the beginning"
h 2:13 Some Mss read "I write"

[14]I have written to you, fathers, because you know him who is from the beginning.

I have written to you, young people, because you are strong, and the word of God remains in you, and you have overcome the evil one.

[15]Do not love the world, neither the things that are in the world. If anyone loves the world, the Father's love is not in him. [16]For all that is in the world, the lust of the flesh, the lust of the eyes, and the pride of life, is not the Father's, but is the world's. [17]The world is passing away with its lusts, but he who does God's will remains forever.

[18]Little children, these are the end times, and as you heard that the antichrist is coming, even now many antichrists have arisen. By this we know that it is the final hour. [19]They went out from us, but they did not belong to us; for if they had belonged to us, they would have continued with us. But they left, that they might be revealed that none of them belong to us. [20]You have an anointing from the Holy One, and you all have knowledge.[a] [21]I have not written to you because you do not know the truth, but because you know it, and because no lie is of the truth. [22]Who is the liar but he who denies that Jesus is the Christ? This is the antichrist, he who denies the Father and the Son. [23]Whoever denies the Son, the same does not have the Father. He who confesses the Son has the Father also.[b]

[24]As for you, let that remain in you which you heard from the beginning. If that which you heard from the beginning remains in you, you also will remain in the Son, and in the Father. [25]This is the promise which he promised us, the everlasting life. [26]These things I have written to you concerning those who would lead you astray. [27]As for you, the anointing which you received from him remains in you, and you do not need for anyone to teach you. But as his[d] anointing teaches you concerning all things, and is true, and is no lie, and even as it taught you, you[e] remain in him. [28]Now, little children, remain in him, that when he appears, we may have boldness, and not be ashamed before him at his coming. [29]If you know that he is righteous, you know that everyone also[f] who practices righteousness is born of him.

3 See what kind of love the Father has bestowed on us, that we should be called children of God; and we are. [g]For this reason the world does not know us,[h] because it did not know him. [2]Beloved, now we are children of God, and it is not yet revealed what we will be. [i]We know that, when he is revealed, we will be like him; for we will see him just as he is. [3]Everyone who has this hope set on him purifies himself, even as he is pure. [4]Everyone who sins also commits lawlessness. Sin is lawlessness. [5]You know that he was revealed to take away[j] sins, and in him is no sin. [6]Whoever remains in him does not sin. Whoever sins hasn't seen him, neither knows him.

[7]Little children, let no one lead you astray. He who does righteousness is righteous, even as he is righteous. [8]He who sins is of the devil, for the devil has been sinning from the beginning. To this end the Son of God was revealed, to destroy the works of the devil. [9]Whoever is born of God does not commit sin, because his seed remains in him; and he cannot sin, because he is born of God. [10]In this the children of God are revealed, and the children of the devil. Whoever does not do righteousness is not of God, neither is he who does not love his brother. [11]For this is the message which you heard from the beginning, that we should love one another; [12]unlike Cain, who was of the evil one, and killed his brother. Why did he kill him? Because his works were evil, and his brother's righteous. [13]Do not be surprised,[k] brothers, if the world hates you.

---

a   2:20 Or, "know what is true," "know all things"
b   2:23 Some Mss lack "He who confesses the Son has the Father also"
c   2:24 Some Mss add "Therefore"
d   2:27 Some Mss read "the same"
e   2:27 Some Mss add "will"
f   2:29 Some Mss lack "also"
g   3:1 Some Mss lack "and we are"
h   3:1 Some Mss read "you"
i   3:2 Some Mss add "But"
j   3:5 Some Mss add "our"
k   3:13 Some Mss add "my"

[14]We know that we have passed out of death into life, because we love the brothers. He who does not love[a] remains in death. [15]Whoever hates his brother is a murderer, and you know that no murderer has everlasting life remaining in him.[b]

[16]By this we know love, because he laid down his life for us. And we ought to lay down our lives for the brothers. [17]But whoever has the world's goods, and sees his brother in need, and closes his heart of compassion against him, how does the love of God remain in him? [18]Little children, let us not love in word only, neither with the tongue only, but in deed and truth. [19]And by this we will know that we are of the truth, and persuade our heart before him, [20]because if our heart condemns us, God is greater than our heart, and knows all things. [21]Beloved, if our hearts do not condemn us, we have confidence before God; [22]and whatever we ask, we receive from him, because we keep his commandments and do the things that are pleasing in his sight. [23]This is his commandment, that we should believe in the name of his Son, Jesus Christ, and love one another, even as he commanded us[c]. [24]He who keeps his commandments remains in him, and he in him. By this we know that he remains in us, by the Spirit which he gave us.

4 Beloved, do not believe every spirit, but test the spirits, whether they are of God, because many false prophets have gone out into the world. [2]By this you know the Spirit of God: every spirit who confesses that Jesus Christ has come in the flesh is of God, [3]and every spirit who does not confess[d] Jesus is not of God; and this is that of the antichrist, of whom you have heard that it comes. Now it is in the world already. [4]You are of God, little children, and have overcome them; because greater is he who is in you than he who is in the world. [5]They are of the world. Therefore they speak of the world, and the world hears them. [6]We are of God. He who knows God listens to us. He who is not of God does not listen to us. By this we know the spirit of truth, and the spirit of error.

[7]Beloved, let us love one another, for love is of God; and everyone who loves is born of God, and knows God. [8]He who does not love does not know God, for God is love. [9]By this God's love was revealed in us, that God has sent his one and only Son into the world that we might live through him. [10]In this is love, not that we have loved God, but that he loved us, and sent his Son as the atoning sacrifice for our sins. [11]Beloved, if God loved us in this way, we also ought to love one another. [12]No one has seen God at any time. If we love one another, God remains in us, and his love has been perfected in us.

[13]By this we know that we remain in him and he in us, because he has given us of his Spirit. [14]We have seen and testify that the Father has sent the Son as the Savior of the world. [15]Whoever confesses that Jesus is the Son of God, God remains in him, and he in God. [16]We know and have believed the love which God has for us. God is love, and he who remains in love remains in God, and God remains in him. [17]In this love has been made perfect among us, that we may have boldness in the day of judgment, because as he is, even so are we in this world. [18]There is no fear in love; but perfect love casts out fear, because fear has punishment. He who fears is not made perfect in love. [19]We love[e], because he first loved us. [20]If anyone says, "I love God," and hates his brother, he is a liar; for he who does not love his brother whom he has seen, cannot love God whom he has not seen. [21]This commandment we have from him, that he who loves God should also love his brother.

5 Whoever believes that Jesus is the Christ is born of God. Whoever loves the Father also loves the child who is born of him. [2]By this we know that we love the children of God, when we love God and do

---

a   3:14 Some Mss add "his brother"
b   3:15 Some Mss read "himself"
c   3:23 Some Mss lack "us"
d   4:3 Some Mss add "the Christ has come in the flesh"
e   4:19 Some Mss add "him"

his commandments. ³For this is the love of God, that we keep his commandments. His commandments are not grievous. ⁴For whatever is born of God overcomes the world. This is the victory that has overcome the world: our^a faith. ⁵Who is he who overcomes the world, but he who believes that Jesus is the Son of God? ⁶This is he who came by water and blood, Jesus Christ; not with the water only, but with the water and the blood. It is the Spirit who testifies, because the Spirit is the truth. ⁷For there are three who testify^b: ⁸the Spirit, the water, and the blood; and the three agree as one. ⁹If we accept human testimony, the witness of God is greater; for this is God's testimony that he has testified concerning his Son. ¹⁰He who believes in the Son of God has the testimony in himself. He who does not believe God has made him a liar, because he has not believed in the testimony that God has given concerning his Son. ¹¹The testimony is this, that God gave to us everlasting life, and this life is in his Son. ¹²He who has the Son has the life. He who does not have God's Son does not have the life. ¹³These things I have written to you who believe in the name of the Son of God, that you may know that you have everlasting life^c.

¹⁴This is the boldness which we have toward him, that, if we ask anything according to his will, he listens to us. ¹⁵And if we know that he listens to us, whatever we ask, we know that we have the petitions which we have asked of him.

¹⁶If anyone sees his brother sinning a sin not leading to death, he should ask, and he will give him life for those who sin not leading to death. There is a sin leading to death. I do not say that he should make a request concerning this. ¹⁷All unrighteousness is sin, and there is a sin not leading to death. ¹⁸We know that whoever is born of God does not sin, but he who was born of God protects him, and the evil one does not touch him. ¹⁹We know that we are of God, and the whole world lies in the power of the evil one. ²⁰We know that the Son of God has come, and has given us an understanding, that we know him who is true, and we are in him who is true, in his Son Jesus Christ. He is the true God and eternal life.

²¹Little children, keep yourselves from idols.^d

2 John

1 The elder, to the chosen lady and her children, whom I love in truth; and not I only, but also all those who know the truth; ²for the truth's sake, which remains in us, and it will be with us forever: ³Grace, mercy, and peace will be with us, from God the Father, and from^e Jesus Christ, the Son of the Father, in truth and love.

⁴I rejoice greatly that I have found some of your children walking in truth, even as we have been commanded by the Father. ⁵And now I ask you, dear lady, not as though I wrote to you a new commandment, but that which we had from the beginning, that we love one another. ⁶And this is love, that we should walk according to his commandments. This is the commandment, even as you heard from the beginning, that you should walk in it.

⁷For many deceivers have gone out into the world, those who do not confess that Jesus Christ came in the flesh. This is the deceiver and the antichrist. ⁸Watch yourselves, that you^f do not lose the things which we have accomplished, but that you^g receive a full reward. ⁹Whoever goes on and does not remain in the teaching of Christ, does not have God. He who remains in the teaching, the same has both the Father and

---

a   5:4 Some Mss read "your"
b   5:7 Some Mss add "in heaven: the Father, the Word, and the Holy Spirit; and these three are one. And there are three that testify on earth"
c   5:13 Some Mss add "and that you may continue to believe in the name of the Son of God"
d   5:21 Some Mss add "Amen"
e   1:3 Some Mss add "the Lord"
f   1:8 Some Mss read "we" Ibid
g   1:9 Some Mss read "transgresses"

the Son. [10]If anyone comes to you, and does not bring this teaching, do not receive him into your house, and do not welcome him, [11]for he who welcomes him participates in his evil works.

[12]Having many things to write to you, I do not want to do so with paper and ink, but I hope to come to you, and to speak face to face, that our joy may be made full. [13]The children of your chosen sister greet you. [a]

3 John

1 The elder to Gaius the beloved, whom I love in truth.

[2]Beloved, I pray that you may prosper in all things and be in good health, even as your soul prospers. [3]For I rejoiced greatly, when brothers came and testified about your truth, even as you walk in truth. [4]I have no greater joy than this, to hear about my children walking in truth.

[5]Beloved, you do a faithful work in whatever you accomplish for those who are brothers and strangers. [6]They have testified about your love before the church. You will do well to send them forward on their journey in a manner worthy of God, [7]because for the sake of the Name they went out, taking nothing from the non-believers[b]. [8]We therefore ought to receive such, that we may be fellow workers for the truth.

[9]I wrote something to the church, but Diotrephes, who loves to be first among them, does not accept what we say. [10]Therefore, if I come, I will call attention to his deeds which he does, unjustly accusing us with wicked words. Not content with this, neither does he himself receive the brothers, and those who would, he forbids and throws out of the church. [11]Beloved, do not imitate that which is evil, but that which is good. He who does good is of God. He who does evil hasn't seen God. [12]Demetrius has the testimony of all, and of the truth itself; yes, we also testify, and you know that our testimony is true.

[13]I had many things to write to you[b], but I am unwilling to write to you with ink and pen; [14]but I hope to see you soon, and we will speak face to face. Peace be to you. The friends greet you. Greet the friends by name.

Jude

1 Jude,[c] a servant of Jesus Christ, and brother of James, to those who are called, loved[d] by God the Father, and kept for Jesus Christ: [2]Mercy to you and peace and love be multiplied.

[3]Beloved, while I was very eager to write to you about our[e] common salvation, I was constrained to write to you exhorting you to contend earnestly for the faith which was once for all delivered to the saints. [4]For there are certain men who crept in secretly, even those who were long ago written about for this condemnation: ungodly men, turning the grace of our God into sensuality, and denying our only Master[f] and Lord, Jesus Christ.

[5]Now I desire to remind you, though you already know this, that the Lord,[g] having

saved a people out of the land of Egypt, afterward destroyed those who did not believe. [6]Angels who did not keep their first domain, but deserted their own dwelling place, he has kept in everlasting bonds under darkness for the judgment of the great day. [7]Even as Sodom and Gomorrah, and the cities around them, having, in the same way as these, given themselves over to

---

a   1:13 Some Mss add "Amen"
b   1:13 Some Mss lack "to you"
c   1:1 Gk. "Ioudas" for Hebrew "Judah." "Jude" has been traditionally used to distinguish him from the one who betrayed Jesus
d   1:1 Some Mss read "sanctified"
e   1:3 Some Mss read "the
f   1:4 Some Mss add "God"
g   1:5 Some Mss read "Jesus." Other Mss read "God"

sexual immorality and gone after strange flesh, are set forth as an example, suffering the punishment of everlasting fire.

8Yet in like manner these also in their dreaming defile the flesh, despise authority, and slander celestial beings. **9**But Michael, the archangel, when contending with the devil and arguing about the body of Moses, dared not bring against him an abusive condemnation, but said, "May the Lord rebuke you." **10**But these speak evil of whatever things they do not know. What they understand naturally, like the creatures without reason, they are destroyed in these things. **11**Woe to them. For they went in the way of Cain, and ran riotously in the error of Balaam for profit, and perished in Korah's rebellion.

12These are hidden rocky reefs in your love feasts when they feast with you, shepherds who without fear feed themselves; clouds without water, carried along by winds; autumn leaves without fruit, twice dead, plucked up by the roots; **13**wild waves of the sea, foaming out their own shame; wandering stars, for whom the blackness of darkness has been reserved forever. **14**About these also Enoch, the seventh from Adam, prophesied, saying, "Look, the Lord comes with ten thousands of his saints, **15**to execute judgment on all, and to convict all

the ungodly of all their works of ungodliness which they have done in an ungodly way, and of all the hard things which ungodly sinners have spoken against him."

16These are murmurers and complainers, walking after their lusts (and their mouth speaks proud things), showing respect of persons to gain advantage.

17But you, beloved, remember the words which have been spoken before by the apostles of our Lord Jesus Christ. **18**They said to you that "In the last time there will be mockers, walking after their own ungodly lusts." **19**These are they who cause divisions, and are sensual, not having the Spirit. **20**But you, beloved, keep building yourselves up in your most holy faith, praying in the Holy Spirit. **21**Keep yourselves in the love of God, looking for the mercy of our Lord Jesus Christ to everlasting life. **22**On some have compassion, who are in doubt,^a **23**and some save,^b snatching them out of the fire, and on some have mercy with fear^c; hating even the clothing stained by the flesh.

24Now to him who is able to keep you^d from stumbling, and to present you faultless before the presence of his glory in great joy, **25**to the only^e God our Savior, through Jesus Christ our Lord,^f be glory and majesty, dominion and power, both now and forever. Amen.

Revelation

1 This is the Revelation of Jesus Christ, which God gave him to show to his servants the things which must happen soon, which he sent and made known by his angel^g to his servant, John, **2**who testified to God's word, and of the testimony of Jesus Christ, about everything that he saw.

3Blessed is he who reads and those who hear the words of the prophecy, and keep the things that are written in it, for the time is near.

4John, to the seven churches that are in Asia: Grace to you and peace, from him^h who is and who was and who is to come;

and from the seven Spirits who are before his throne; **5**and from Jesus Christ, the faithful witness, the firstborn of the dead, and the ruler of the kings of the earth. To him who loves us, and freedⁱ us from our sins by his blood; **6**and he made us to be a

---

a   1:22 Some Mss read "making a distinction"
b   1:23 Some Mss add "with fear"
c   1:23 Some Mss lack "and on some have mercy"
d   1:24 Some Mss read "them"
e   1:25 Some Mss add "wise"
f   1:25 Some Mss lack "through Jesus Christ our Lord"
g   1:1 Or, "messenger" (here and wherever angel is mentioned)
h   1:4 Some Mss read "God"
i   1:5 Some Mss read "washed"

kingdom,[a] priests[b] to his God and Father; to him be the glory and the dominion forever and ever.[c] Amen.

[7]Look, he is coming with the clouds, and every eye will see him, including those who pierced him. And all the tribes of the earth will mourn over him. Even so, Amen.

[8]"I am the Alpha and the Omega,[d]" says the Lord God,[e] "who is and who was and who is to come, the Almighty."

[9]I John, your brother and fellow-partner with you in persecution, kingdom, and patient endurance in Jesus,[f] was on the island that is called Patmos because of the word of God and the testimony of Jesus.[g] [10]I was in the Spirit on the Lord's day, and I heard behind me a loud voice, like a trumpet[h] [11]saying, "[i]What you see, write on a scroll and send to the seven churches[j]: to Ephesus, Smyrna, Pergamum, Thyatira, Sardis, Philadelphia, and to Laodicea."

[12]I turned to see the voice that spoke with me. Having turned, I saw seven golden lampstands. [13]And among the[k] lampstands was one like a son of man,[l] clothed with a robe reaching down to his feet, and with a golden sash around his chest. [14]His head and his hair were white as white wool, like snow. His eyes were like a flame of fire. [15]His feet were like burnished bronze, as if it had been refined in a furnace. His voice was like the voice of many waters. [16]He had seven stars in his right hand. Out of his mouth proceeded a sharp two-edged sword. His face was like the sun shining at its brightest. [17]When I saw him, I fell at his feet like a dead man.

He laid his right hand on me, saying, "Do not be afraid. I am the first and the last, [18]and the Living one. I was dead, but look, I am alive forevermore.[m] I have the keys of Death and of hell[n]. [19]Write therefore the things which you have seen, and the things which are, and the things which will happen hereafter; [20]the mystery of the seven stars which you saw in my right hand, and the seven golden lampstands. The seven stars are the angels of the seven churches. The seven lampstands are seven churches.

2 "To the angel of the church in Ephesus write:

"He who holds the seven stars in his right hand, he who walks among the seven golden lampstands says these things:

[2]"I know your works, and your toil and perseverance, and that you cannot tolerate those who are evil, and have tested those who call themselves apostles, and they are not, and found them false. [3]You have perseverance and have endured for my name's sake, and have[o] not grown weary. [4]But I have this against you, that you left your first love. [5]Remember therefore from where you have fallen, and repent and do the first works; or else I am coming to you,[p] and will move your lampstand[q] out of its place, unless you repent. [6]But this you have, that you hate the works of the Nicolaitans, which I also hate. [7]He who has an ear, let him hear what the Spirit says to the churches. To him who overcomes I will give to eat of the tree of life, which is in the[r] Paradise of[s] God.

[8]"To the angel of the church in Smyrna write:

"The first and the last, who was dead, and has come to life says these things:

[9]"I know your[t] tribulation and your poverty (but you are rich), and the blasphemy

---

a   1:6 Some Mss read "kings"
b   1:6 Exodus 19:6; Isaiah 61:6
c   1:6 Lit. "to the ages of ages." Some Mss lack "of ages"
d   1:8 Some Mss add "the Beginning and the End"
e   1:8 Some Mss lack "God"
f   1:9 Some Mss add "Christ"
g   1:9 Some Mss add "Christ"
h   1:9 Or, "shofar" (here and wherever trumpet is mentioned)
i   1:11 Some Mss add "I am the Alpha and the Omega, the First and the Last"
j   1:11 Some Mss add "which are in Asia"
k   1:13 Some Mss add "seven"
l   1:13 Daniel 7:13
m   1:18 Some Mss add "Amen"
n   1:18 Gk. Hades, Heb. Sheol
o   2:3 Some Mss add "have labored and"
p   2:5 Some Mss add "quickly"
q   2:5 Or, "Menorah" (here and wherever lampstand is mentioned)
r   2:7 Some Mss add "midst of the"
s   2:7 Some Mss add "my"
t   2:9 Some Mss add "works, and"

of those who say they are Jews, and they are not, but are a synagogue of Satan. ¹⁰Do not be afraid of the things which you are about to suffer. Look, the devil is about to throw some of you into prison, that you may be tested; and you will have oppression for ten days. Be faithful until death, and I will give you the crown of life. ¹¹He who has an ear, let him hear what the Spirit says to the churches. He who overcomes won't be harmed by the second death.

¹²"To the angel of the church in Pergamum write:

"He who has the sharp two-edged sword says these things:

¹³"I know[a] where you dwell, where Satan's throne is. You hold firmly to my name, and did not deny my faith even[b] in the days in which[c] Antipas was my witness, my[d] faithful one, who was killed among you, where Satan dwells. ¹⁴But I have a few things against you, because you have there some who hold the teaching of Balaam, who taught Balak to throw a stumbling block before the children of Israel, to eat things sacrificed to idols, and to commit sexual immorality. ¹⁵So you also have some who hold to the teaching of the Nicolaitans likewise[e]. ¹⁶Repent therefore,[f] or else I am coming to you quickly, and I will make war against them with the sword of my mouth. ¹⁷He who has an ear, let him hear what the Spirit says to the churches. To him who overcomes, to him I will give[g] of the hidden manna, and I will give him a white stone, and on the stone a new name written, which no one knows but he who receives it.

¹⁸"To the angel of the church in Thyatira write:

"The Son of God, who has his eyes like a flame of fire, and his feet are like burnished bronze, says these things:

¹⁹"I know your works, your love, faith, service, patient endurance, and that your last works are more than the first. ²⁰But I have this against you, that you tolerate the[h] woman, Jezebel, who calls herself a prophetess. She teaches and seduces my servants to commit sexual immorality, and to eat things sacrificed to idols. ²¹I gave her time to repent, but she refuses to repent of her sexual immorality. ²²Look, I will throw her into a sickbed,[i] and those who commit adultery with her into great oppression, unless they repent of her[j] works. ²³I will kill her children with Death, and all the churches will know that I am he who searches the minds and hearts. I will give to each one of you according to your deeds. ²⁴But to you I say, to the rest who are in Thyatira, as many as do not have this teaching, who do not know what some call 'the deep things of Satan,' to you I say, I am not putting any other burden on you. ²⁵Nevertheless, hold that which you have firmly until I come. ²⁶He who overcomes, and he who keeps my works to the end, to him I will give authority over the nations. ²⁷He will rule them with an iron scepter, shattering them like clay pots;[k] as I also have received of my Father: ²⁸and I will give him the morning star. ²⁹He who has an ear, let him hear what the Spirit says to the churches.

3 "And to the angel of the church in Sardis write:

"He who has the seven Spirits of God,[l] and the seven stars says these things:

"I know your works, that you have a reputation of being alive, but you are dead. ²Wake up, and keep the things that remain, which were about to die[m], for I have found

---

a   2:13 Some Mss add "your works and"
b   2:13 Some Mss lack "even"
c   2:13 Some Mss lack "in which"
d   2:13 Some Mss lack "my"
e   2:15 Some Mss read "which I hate"
f   2:16 Some Mss lack "therefore"
g   2:17 Some Mss add "to eat"
h   2:20 Some Mss read "your"
i   2:22 Gk. "into a bed." In the context, a possible idiom for illness
j   2:22 Some Mss read "their"
k   2:27 Psalm 2:9
l   3:1 Possibly the seven different expressions of the One God: Spirit of the Lᴏʀᴅ, Spirit of Wisdom, Spirit of Understanding, Spirit of Counsel, Spirit of Strength, Spirit of Knowledge and the Spirit of the Reverence of the Lᴏʀᴅ. See Isaiah 11:2; Revelation 4:5, 5:6
m   3:2 Some Mss read "which you were about to throw away"

no works of yours perfected before my God. ³Remember therefore how you have received and heard. Keep it, and repent. If therefore you do not wake up, I will come as a thief, and you won't know what hour I will come to you. ⁴Nevertheless you have a few names in Sardis that did not defile their garments. They will walk with me in white, for they are worthy. ⁵He who overcomes will be arrayed in white garments, and I will in no way blot his name out of the book of life, and I will confess his name before my Father, and before his angels. ⁶He who has an ear, let him hear what the Spirit says to the churches.

⁷"To the angel of the church in Philadelphia write:

"These are the words of the Holy One, the True One, he who has the key of David, he who opens and no one can shut, and who shuts and no one opens:

⁸"I know your works. Look, I have set before you an open door, which no one can shut. For you have a little power, and have kept my word, and did not deny my name. ⁹Look, I give of the synagogue of Satan, of those who say they are Jews, and they are not, but lie; look, I will make them to come and worship before your feet, and to know that I have loved you. ¹⁰Because you kept my command to endure, I also will keep you from the hour of testing, which is to come on the whole world, to test those who dwell on the earth. ¹¹I am coming quickly. Hold firmly that which you have, so that no one takes your crown. ¹²He who overcomes, I will make him a pillar in the temple of my God, and he will go out from there no more. I will write on him the name of my God, and the name of the city of my God, the new Jerusalem, which comes down out of heaven from my God, and my own new name. ¹³He who has an ear, let him hear what the Spirit says to the churches.

¹⁴"To the angel of the church in Laodicea write:

"The Amen, the Faithful and True Witness, the Head of God's creation, says these things:

¹⁵"I know your works, that you are neither cold nor hot. I wish you were cold or hot. ¹⁶So, because you are lukewarm, and neither hot nor cold, I will vomit you out of my mouth. ¹⁷Because you say, 'I am rich, and have gotten riches, and have need of nothing;' and do not know that you are wretched[a], miserable, poor, blind, and naked; ¹⁸I counsel you to buy from me gold refined by fire, that you may become rich; and white garments, that you may clothe yourself, and that the shame of your nakedness may not be revealed; and eye salve to put on your eyes, that you may see. ¹⁹As many as I love, I rebuke and discipline. Be zealous therefore, and repent. ²⁰Look, I stand at the door and knock. If anyone hears my voice and opens the door, I will come in to him, and will dine with him, and he with me. ²¹He who overcomes, I will give to him to sit down with me on my throne, as I also overcame, and sat down with my Father on his throne. ²²He who has an ear, let him hear what the Spirit says to the churches."

4 After these things I looked and saw a door opened in heaven, and the first voice that I heard, like a trumpet speaking with me, was one saying, "Come up here, and I will show you the things which must happen after this."

²Immediately I was in the Spirit; and look, there was a throne set in heaven, and one sitting on the throne. ³And the one who sat there[b] looked like a jasper stone and a sardius. There was a rainbow around the throne, like an emerald to look at. ⁴Around the throne were twenty-four thrones. On the thrones were twenty-four elders sitting, dressed in white garments, with crowns of gold on their heads. ⁵And from the throne came flashes of lightning and sounds and peals of thunder. And there were seven torches of fire burning before the[c] throne, which are the seven

---

a   3:17 Some Mss read "the wretched one"

b   4:3 Some Mss lack "And the one who sat there"

c   4:5 Some Mss read "his"

Spirits of God. [6]Before the throne was something like a sea of glass, similar to crystal. In the midst of the throne, and around the throne were four living creatures full of eyes before and behind. [7]The first living creature was like a lion, and the second living creature like a calf, and the third living creature had a face like a man, and the fourth living creature[a] was like a flying eagle. [8]The four living creatures, each one of them having six wings, are full of eyes around and within. They have no rest day and night, saying, "Holy, holy, holy is the Lord God of hosts,[b] who was and who is and who is to come."

[9]And when the living creatures give glory and honor and thanks to him who sits on the throne, to him who lives forever and ever, [10]the twenty-four elders fall down before him who sits on the throne, and worship him who lives forever and ever, and throw their crowns before the throne, saying, [11]"Worthy are you, our Lord and God,[c] to receive the glory, the honor, and the power, for you created all things, and because of your desire they existed, and were created."

5 I saw, in the right hand of him who sat on the throne, a scroll written inside and on the back[d], sealed shut with seven seals. [2]I saw a mighty angel proclaiming with a loud voice, "Who is worthy to open the scroll, and to break its seals?" [3]No one in heaven above,[e] or on the earth, or under the earth, was able to open the scroll, or to look in it. [4]And I wept much, because no one was found worthy to open the scroll, or to look in it. [5]One of the elders said to me, "Do not weep. Look, the Lion who is of the tribe of Judah, the Root of David, has overcome so that he can open the scroll and loose[f] its seven seals." [6]I saw in the midst of the throne and of the four living creatures, and in the midst of the elders, a Lamb standing, as though it had been slain, having seven horns, and seven eyes, which are the seven[g] Spirits of God, sent out into all the earth. [7]Then he came, and he took it out of the right hand of him who

sat on the throne. [8]Now when he had taken the scroll, the four living creatures and the twenty-four elders fell down before the Lamb, each one having a harp, and golden bowls full of incense, which are the prayers of the saints. [9]They sang a new song, saying,

"You are worthy to take the scroll,
    and to open its seals:
for you were killed,
    and redeemed us[h] for God with your
      blood,
    out of every tribe, language, people,
      and nation,
[10]and made them a kingdom[i] and
      priests to our God,
    and they[j] will reign on earth."

[11]I saw, and I heard[k] the voice of many angels around the throne, the living creatures, and the elders; and the number of them was ten thousands of ten thousands, and thousands of thousands; [12]saying with a loud voice, "Worthy is the Lamb who has been killed to receive the power, wealth, wisdom, strength, honor, glory, and blessing."

[13]I heard every created thing which is in heaven, on the earth, under the earth, on the sea, and everything in them, saying, "To him who sits on the throne, and to the Lamb be the blessing, the honor, the glory, and the dominion, forever and ever."[l]

[14]The four living creatures were saying, "Amen." The[m] elders fell down and worshiped.[n]

---

a 4:7 Some Mss lack "living creature"
b 4:8 Or, "the Lord God Almighty." Gk kurios o theos o pantokrator is used in Hosea, Amos and Nahum LXX for "Lord God of hosts"
c 4:11 Some Mss add "the Holy One." Some Mss lack "and God"
d 5:1 Some Mss read "outside"
e 5:3 Some Mss lack "above"
f 5:5 Some Mss lack "loose"
g 5:6 Some Mss lack "seven"
h 5:9 Some Mss lack "us"
i 5:10 Some Mss read "made us kings"
j 5:10 Some Mss read "we" instead of "they"
k 5:11 Some Mss add "as it were"
l 5:13 Some Mss add "Amen"
m 5:14 Some Mss add "twenty-four"
n 5:14 Some Mss add "the one living forever and ever"

6 I saw when[a] the Lamb opened one of the seven[b] seals, and I heard one of the four living creatures saying, as with a voice of thunder, "Come." [2]And I looked,[c] and suddenly there was a white horse, and he who sat on it had a bow; and a crown was given to him, and he came forth conquering, and to conquer.

[3]When he opened the second seal, I heard the second living creature saying, "Come.[d]" [4]Another came forth, a fiery red[e] horse. To him who sat on it was given power to take peace from the earth, and that they should kill one another. There was given to him a great sword.

[5]When he opened the third seal, I heard the third living creature saying, "Come."[f] And I looked, and suddenly there was a black horse, and he who sat on it had a balance in his hand. [6]I heard something like a voice in the midst of the four living creatures saying, "A choenix[g] of wheat for a denarius, and three choenixes of barley for a denarius. Do not damage the oil and the wine."

[7]When he opened the fourth seal, I heard the fourth living creature saying, "Come."[h] [8]And I looked, and suddenly there was a pale horse, and he who sat on it had the name Death. Hell[i] followed with him. Authority over one fourth of the earth, to kill with the sword, with famine, with death, and by the wild animals of the earth was given to him.

[9]When he opened the fifth seal, I saw underneath the altar the souls of people[j] who had been killed for the Word of God, and for the testimony[k] which they had. [10]They called out with a loud voice, saying, "How long, Master, the holy and true, until you judge and avenge our blood on those who dwell on the earth?" [11]A long white robe was given to each of them. They were told that they should rest yet for a little longer, until their fellow servants and their brothers, who would also be killed even as they were, should complete their course.

[12]I saw when he opened the sixth seal, and there was a great earthquake. The sun became black as sackcloth made of hair, and the whole moon became as blood. [13]The stars of the sky fell to the earth, like a fig tree dropping its unripe figs when it is shaken by a great wind. [14]The sky was removed like a scroll when it is rolled up. Every mountain and island were moved out of their places. [15]The kings of the earth, the princes, the commanding officers, the rich, the strong, and every slave and free person, hid themselves in the caves and in the rocks of the mountains. [16]They told the mountains and the rocks, "Fall on us, and hide us from the face of him who sits on the throne, and from the wrath of the Lamb, [17]for the great day of their[l] wrath has come; and who is able to stand?"

7 And[m] after this, I saw four angels standing on the four quarters[n] of the earth, holding the four winds of the earth, so that no wind would blow on the earth, or on the sea, or on any tree. [2]I saw another angel ascend from the sunrise, having the seal of the living God. He called out with a loud voice to the four angels to whom it was given to harm the earth and the sea, [3]saying, "Do not harm the earth, neither the sea, nor the trees, until we have sealed the servants of our God on their foreheads." [4]I heard the number of those who were sealed, one hundred forty-four thousand, sealed out of every tribe of the children of Israel:

a 6:1 Some Mss read "that"
b 6:1 Some Mss lack "seven"
c 6:2 Some Mss lack "And I looked"
d 6:3 Some Mss add "and see"
e 6:4 Some Mss read "fiery"
f 6:5 Some Mss add "and see"
g 6:6 A choenix is a dry volume measure that is a little more than a liter (a little more than a quart)
h 6:7 Some Mss add "and see"
i 6:8 Gk. Hades, Heb. Sheol
j 6:9 Some Mss lack "people"
k 6:9 Some Mss add "of the Lamb"
l 6:17 Some Mss read "his"
m 7:1 Some Mss lack "And"
n 7:1 Gk. gonia: angle, corner, quarter, chief, secret place. Figuratively, speaking of the entire earth into four quadrants, quarters, divisions or directions (of north, south, east, west), or meaning "throughout." See 2 Chronicles 28:24 LXX where Ahaz made altars in every corner (gonia) of Jerusalem, i.e. figuratively throughout

⁵of the tribe of Judah were sealed twelve thousand,
of the tribe of Reuben twelve thousand,
of the tribe of Gad twelve thousand,
⁶of the tribe of Asher twelve thousand,
of the tribe of Naphtali twelve thousand,
of the tribe of Manasseh twelve thousand,
⁷of the tribe of Simeon twelve thousand,
of the tribe of Levi twelve thousand,
of the tribe of Issachar twelve thousand,
⁸of the tribe of Zebulun twelve thousand,
of the tribe of Joseph twelve thousandᵃ,
of the tribe of Benjamin were sealed twelve thousand.

⁹After these things I looked, and suddenly there was a great multitude, which no one could number, out of every nation and of all tribes, peoples, and languages, standing before the throne and before the Lamb, dressed in white robes, with palm branches in their hands. ¹⁰They shouted with a loud voice, saying, "Salvation be to our God, who sits on the throne, and to the Lamb."

¹¹All the angels were standing around the throne, the elders, and the four living creatures; and they fell on their faces before theᵇ throne, and worshiped God, ¹²saying, "Amen. Blessing, glory, wisdom, thanksgiving, honor, power, and might, be to our God forever and ever. Amen."

¹³One of the elders answered, saying to me, "These who are arrayed in white robes, who are they, and from where did they come?"

¹⁴So I said to him, "My lord, you know."

He said to me, "These are the ones who came out of the great tribulation. They washed their robes, and made them white in the Lamb's blood. ¹⁵Therefore they are before the throne of God, they serve him day and night in his temple. He who sits on the throne will spread his tabernacle over them. ¹⁶They will hunger no more, neither thirst any more; neither will the sun beat on them, nor any heat; ¹⁷for the Lamb who is in the midst of the throne shepherds them, and leads them to springs of waters

of life. And God will wipe away every tear from their eyes."

8 When he opened the seventh seal, there was silence in heaven for about half an hour. ²I saw the seven angels who stand before God, and seven trumpets were given to them. ³Another angel came and stood over the altar, having a golden censer. Much incense was given to him to offer up, with the prayers of all the saints, on the golden altar which was before the throne. ⁴The smoke of the incense, with the prayers of the saints, went up before God out of the angel's hand. ⁵The angel took the censer, and he filled it with the fire of the altar, and threw it on the earth. There followed thunders, sounds, lightnings, and an earthquake.

⁶The seven angels who had the seven trumpets prepared themselves to sound. ⁷And the first angelᶜ sounded, and there followed hail and fire, mixed with blood, and they were thrown to the earth. One third of the earth was burnt up,ᵈ and one third of the trees were burnt up, and all green grass was burnt up.

⁸The second angel sounded, and something like a great mountain burning with fireᵉ was thrown into the sea. One third of the sea became blood, ⁹and one third of the living creatures which were in the sea died. One third of the ships were destroyed.

¹⁰The third angel sounded, and a great star fell from the sky, burning like a torch, and it fell on one third of the rivers, and on the springs of the waters. ¹¹The name of the star is called "Wormwood." One third of the waters became wormwood. Many people died from the waters, because they were made bitter.

¹²The fourth angel sounded, and one third of the sun was struck, and one third of the moon, and one third of the stars; so that one third of them would be darkened,

---

a   7:8 Some Mss add "sealed" after each tribe from Reuben to Joseph

b   7:11 Some Mss read "his"

c   8:7 Some Mss lack "angel"

d   8:7 Some Mss lack "One third of the earth was burnt up"

e   8:8 Some Mss read "a great burning mountain"

and the day would not shine for one third of it, and the night in the same way. [13]I saw, and I heard an eagle,[a] flying in mid heaven, saying with a loud voice, "Woe. Woe. Woe for those who dwell on the earth, because of the other voices of the trumpets of the three angels, who are yet to sound."

9 The fifth angel sounded, and I saw a star from the sky which had fallen to the earth. The key to the pit of the abyss was given to him. [2]He opened the shaft of the bottomless pit, and smoke went up out of the shaft, like the smoke from a great[b] furnace. The sun and the air were darkened because of the smoke from the pit. [3]Then out of the smoke came forth locusts on the earth, and power was given to them, as the scorpions of the earth have power. [4]They were told that they should not hurt the grass of the earth, neither any green thing, neither any tree, but only those people who do not have God's seal on their[c] foreheads. [5]They were given power not to kill them, but to torment them for five months. Their torment was like the torment of a scorpion, when it strikes a person.[6]In those days people will seek death, and will in no way find it. They will desire to die, and death will flee from them. [7]The shapes of the locusts were like horses prepared for war. On their heads were something like golden crowns, and their faces were like people's faces. [8]They had hair like women's hair, and their teeth were like those of lions. [9]They had breastplates, like breastplates of iron. The sound of their wings was like the sound of chariots, or of many horses rushing to war. [10]They have tails like those of scorpions, and stings. In their tails is their[d] power to harm people for five months. [11]They have over them as king the angel of the abyss. His name in Hebrew is "Abaddon,"[e] and in Greek, he has the name "Apollyon."[f] [12]The first woe is past. Look, there are still two woes coming after this.

[13]The sixth angel sounded. I heard a voice from the four[g] horns of the golden altar which is before God, [14]saying to the sixth angel who had one trumpet, "Free the four angels who are bound at the great river Euphrates.[h]"

[15]The four angels were freed who had been prepared for this hour and day and month and year, so that they might kill one third of humanity. [16]The number of the armies of the horsemen[i] was two[j] hundred million[k]. I heard the number of them. [17]Thus I saw the horses in the vision, and those who sat on them, having breastplates of fiery red, hyacinth blue, and sulfur yellow; and the heads of lions. Out of their mouths proceed fire, smoke, and sulfur. [18]By these three plagues were one third of humanity killed: from the fire, the smoke, and the sulfur, which proceeded out of their mouths. [19]For the power of the horses[l] is in their mouths, and in their tails. For their tails are like serpents, and have heads, and with them they harm. [20]The rest of humanity, who were not killed with these plagues, did not repent of the works of their hands, that they would not worship demons, and the idols of gold, and of silver, and of bronze, and of stone, and of wood; which can neither see, nor hear, nor walk. [21]They did not repent of their murders, nor of their sorceries, nor of their sexual immorality, nor of their thefts.

10 I saw another[m] mighty angel coming down out of the sky, clothed with a cloud. A rainbow was on his head. His face was like the sun, and his legs[n] like pillars of fire. [2]He had in his hand a little[o] open

---

a   8:13 Some Mss read "angel"
b   9:2 Some Mss read "a burning furnace"
c   9:4 Some Mss lack "their"
d   9:10 Some Mss read "they have"
e   9:11 "Abaddon" is a Hebrew word that means ruin, destruction, or the place of destruction
f   9:11 "Apollyon" means "Destroyer"
g   9:13 Some Mss lack "four"
h   9:14 Also known as the Perath
i   9:16 Some Mss read "horse"
j   9:16 Some Mss read "one" (ten thousand ten thousand) instead of "two" (twenty thousand ten thousand)
k   9:16 Lit., "ten thousands of ten thousands"
l   9:19 Some Mss lack "of the horses"
m   10:1 Some Mss read "a"
n   10:1 Or, "feet." See Exodus 25:26
o   10:2 Some Mss lack "little"

scroll. He set his right foot on the sea, and his left on the land. [3]He shouted with a loud voice, as a lion roars. When he shouted, the seven thunders uttered their voices. [4]When the seven thunders sounded, I was about to write; but I heard a voice from the sky saying, "Seal up the things which the seven thunders said, and do not write them."

[5]The angel whom I saw standing on the sea and on the land lifted up his right[a] hand to the sky, [6]and swore by him who lives forever and ever, who created heaven and the things that are in it, the earth and the things that are in it, and the sea and the things that are in it, that there will no longer be delay, [7]but in the days of the voice of the seventh angel, when he is about to sound, then the mystery of God is finished, as he declared to his servants, the prophets. [8]The voice which I heard from heaven, again speaking with me, said, "Go, take the[b] scroll which is open in the hand of the angel who stands on the sea and on the land."

[9]I went to the angel, telling him to give me the little scroll.

He said to me, "Take it, and eat it up. It will make your stomach bitter, but in your mouth it will be as sweet as honey."

[10]I took the little[c] scroll out of the angel's hand, and ate it up. It was as sweet as honey in my mouth. When I had eaten it, my stomach was made bitter. [11]They[d] told me, "You must prophesy again about many peoples, nations, languages, and kings."

11 A reed like a rod was given to me. Someone said[e], "Rise and measure God's temple, and the altar, and those who worship in it. [2]Leave out the court which is outside of the temple, and do not measure it, for it has been given to the nations. They will tread the holy city under foot for forty-two months. [3]I will give power to my two witnesses, and they will prophesy one thousand two hundred sixty days, clothed in sackcloth." [4]These are the two olive trees and the two lampstands, standing before the Lord[f] of the earth. [5]If anyone desires to harm them, fire proceeds out of

their mouth and devours their enemies. If anyone desires to harm them, he must be killed in this way.

[6]These have the power to shut up the sky, that it may not rain during the days of their prophecy. They have power over the waters, to turn them into blood, and to strike the earth with every plague, as often as they desire. [7]When they have finished their testimony,[g] the beast that comes up out of the abyss will make war with them, and overcome them, and kill them. [8]Their dead bodies will be in the street of the great city, which spiritually is called Sodom and Egypt, where also their[h] Lord was crucified.

[9]From among the peoples, tribes, languages, and nations people will look at their dead bodies for three and a half days, and will not allow their dead bodies to be placed in a tomb[i]. [10]Those who dwell on the earth rejoice over them, and they will be glad. They will give gifts to one another, because these two prophets tormented those who dwell on the earth. [11]After the three and a half days, the breath of life from God entered into them, and they stood on their feet. Great fear fell on those who saw them.

[12]I heard a loud voice from heaven saying to them, "Come up here." They went up into heaven in the cloud, and their enemies saw them. [13]In that hour[j] there was a great earthquake, and a tenth of the city fell. Seven thousand people were killed in the earthquake, and the rest were terrified, and gave glory to the God of heaven. [14]The second woe is past. Look, the third woe comes quickly.

[15]The seventh angel sounded, and great voices in heaven followed, saying, "The

---

a   10:5 Some Mss lack "right"
b   10:8 Some Mss add "little"
c   10:10 Some Mss lack "little"
d   10:11 Some Mss read "He"
e   11:1 Some Mss read "And the angel stood, saying"
f   11:4 Some Mss read "God"
g   11:7 Some Mss add "then"
h   11:8 Some Mss read "our"
i   11:9 Some Mss read "in tombs"
j   11:13 Some Mss read "day"

kingdom of the world now belongs to our Lord and to his Messiah, and he will reign forever and ever.[a]"

[16]The twenty-four elders, who sit on their thrones before God's throne, fell on their faces and worshiped God, [17]saying: "We give you thanks, Lord God of hosts,[b] the one who is and who was[c]; because you have taken your great power, and reigned. [18]The nations were angry, and your wrath came, as did the time for the dead to be judged, and to give your servants the prophets, their reward, as well as to the saints, and those who fear your name, to the small and the great; and to destroy those who destroy the earth."

[19]God's temple that is in heaven was opened, and the ark of his[d] covenant was seen in his temple. Lightnings, sounds, thunders, an earthquake, and great hail followed.

12 A great sign was seen in heaven: a woman clothed with the sun, and the moon under her feet, and on her head a crown of twelve stars. [2]She was with child. She screamed out in pain, laboring to give birth. [3]Another sign was seen in heaven. Look, a great fiery red serpent,[e] having seven heads and ten horns, and on his heads seven crowns. [4]His tail drew one third of the stars of the sky, and threw them to the earth. The serpent stood before the woman who was about to give birth, so that when she gave birth he might devour her child. [5]She gave birth to a son, a male child, who is to rule all the nations with an iron scepter. Her child was caught up to God, and to his throne. [6]The woman fled into the wilderness, where she has a place prepared by God, that there they may nourish her one thousand two hundred sixty days.

[7]There was war in the sky. Michael and his angels made war on the serpent. The serpent and his angels made war. [8]They did not prevail, neither was a place found for them[f] any more in heaven. [9]The great serpent was thrown down, the ancient serpent, he who is called the devil and Satan, the deceiver of the whole world. He was thrown down to the earth, and his angels were thrown down with him. [10]I heard a loud voice in heaven, saying, "Now is come the salvation, the power, and the kingdom of our God, and the authority of his Christ; for the accuser of our brothers has been thrown down, who accuses them before our God day and night. [11]They overcame him by the blood of the Lamb, and by the word of their testimony. They did not love their life, even to death. [12]Therefore rejoice, heavens, and you who dwell in them. Woe to the land and the sea, because the devil has gone down to you, having great wrath, knowing that he has but a short time."

[13]When the serpent saw that he was thrown down to the earth, he persecuted the woman who gave birth to the male child. [14]Two wings of the great eagle were given to the woman, that she might fly into the wilderness to her place, so that she might be nourished for a time, and times, and half a time, from the face of the serpent. [15]The serpent spewed water out of his mouth after the woman like a river, that he might cause her to be carried away by the stream. [16]The earth helped the woman, and the earth opened its mouth and swallowed up the river which the serpent spewed out of his mouth. [17]The serpent grew angry with the woman, and went away to make war with the rest of her offspring, who keep God's commandments and hold to the testimony of Jesus.[g] [18]And he[h] stood on the sand of the sea.

---

a   11:15 Some Mss add "amen"

b   4:8 Or, "Lord God Almighty." Gk. kurios o theos o pantokrator is used in Hosea, Amos and Nahum LXX for "Lᴏʀᴅ God of hosts"

c   11:17 Some Mss add "and who is coming"

d   11:19 Some Mss read "the Lord's"

e   12:3 Gk. drakon, which is used in the LXX for Heb tannin "serpent/snake" (Deuteronomy 32:33) or "sea-monster" (Job 7:12) for Heb. "Leviathan" (Psalm 74:14), and Heb. nachash "serpent/snake" (Amos 9:3). In Revelation Gk. drakon is used metaphorically as a designation for the devil, and is usually transliterated in Revelation as "dragon"

f   12:8 Some Mss read "him"

g   12:17 Some Mss add "Christ"

h   12:18 Some Mss read "I"

13 And I saw a beast coming up out of the sea, having ten horns and seven heads. On his horns were ten crowns, and on his heads, blasphemous names.[a] [2]The beast which I saw was like a leopard, and his feet were like those of a bear, and his mouth like the mouth of a lion. The serpent gave him his power, his throne, and great authority. [3]One of his heads looked like it had been wounded fatally. His fatal wound was healed, and the whole earth was amazed and followed the beast. [4]They worshiped the serpent, because he gave his authority to the beast, and they worshiped the beast, saying, "Who is like the beast? Who is able to make war with him?" [5]A mouth was given to him speaking proud words and blasphemies. There was given to him authority to act[b] for forty-two months. [6]He opened his mouth for blasphemies against God, to blaspheme his name, and his dwelling, those who dwell in heaven. [7]It was given to him to make war with the saints,[c] and to overcome them. Authority over every tribe, people, language, and nation was given to him. [8]All who dwell on the earth will worship him, everyone whose name has not been written from the foundation of the world in the book of life of the Lamb who has been killed. [9]If anyone has an ear, let him hear. [10]If anyone is to go into[d] captivity,[e] he will go into captivity. If anyone is to be killed with the sword, he must[f] be killed with the sword. Here is the endurance and the faith of the saints.

[11]I saw another beast coming up out of the earth. He had two horns like a lamb, and he spoke like a serpent. [12]He exercises all the authority of the first beast in his presence. He makes the earth and those who dwell in it to worship the first beast, whose fatal wound was healed. [13]He performs great signs, even making fire come down out of heaven to the earth in the sight of people. [14]He deceives those[g] who dwell on the earth because of the signs he was granted to do in front of the beast; saying to those who dwell on the earth, that they should make an image to the beast who had been wounded by the sword and yet lived. [15]It was given to him to give breath to it, to the image of the beast, that the image of the beast could both speak and cause those who would not worship the image of the beast to be killed. [16]He causes all, the small and the great, the rich and the poor, and the free and the slave, to be given a mark[h] on their right hand, or on their forehead[i]; [17]and that no one could be able to buy or to sell, unless he has that mark, the name of the beast or the number of his name. [18]Here is wisdom. He who has understanding, let him calculate the number of the beast, for it is the number of a man. His number is six hundred sixty-six.

14 And I looked, and suddenly on Mount Zion stood the Lamb, and with him[j] one hundred forty-four thousand, having his name, and the name of his Father, written on their foreheads. [2]I heard a sound from heaven, like the sound of many waters, and like the sound of a great thunder. The sound which I heard was like that of harpists playing on their harps. [3]They sing a new song before the throne, and before the four living creatures and the elders. No one could learn the song except the one hundred forty-four thousand, those who had been redeemed out of the earth. [4]These are those who were not defiled with women, for they are virgins. These are those who follow the Lamb wherever he goes. These were redeemed[k] from among humanity, the first fruits to God and to the Lamb. [5]In their mouth was found no lie; they are blameless.[l]

---

a 13:1 Some Mss read "name"
b 13:5 Some Mss read "make war"
c 13:7 The first eleven Greek words in this verse dropped out in many Mss from haplography
d 13:10 Some Mss lack "into"
e 13:10 Lit., "If anyone into captivity"
f 13:10 Some Mss lack "must"
g 13:14 Some Mss add "my own," i.e. "deceives my own who"
h 13:16 Some Mss read "marks"
i 13:16 Some Mss read "foreheads"
j 14:1 Some Mss add "a number"
k 14:4 Some Mss add "by Jesus"
l 14:5 Some Mss add "before the throne of God"

⁶I saw another^a angel flying in mid heaven, having an everlasting Good News to proclaim to those who dwell on the earth, and to every nation, tribe, language, and people. ⁷He said with a loud voice, "Fear God^b, and give him glory; for the hour of his judgment has come. Worship him who made the heaven, the earth, the sea, and the springs of waters."

⁸Another, a second^c angel, followed, saying, "Babylon the great has fallen, which has made all the nations to drink of the wine of the wrath of her sexual immorality."

⁹Another angel, a third, followed them, saying with a great voice, "If anyone worships the beast and his image, and receives a mark on his forehead, or on his hand, ¹⁰he also will drink of the wine of the wrath of God, which is prepared unmixed in the cup of his anger. He will be tormented with fire and sulfur in the presence of the holy angels, and in the presence of the Lamb. ¹¹The smoke of their torment goes up forever and ever. They have no rest day and night, those who worship the beast and his image, and whoever receives the mark of his name. ¹²Here is the patience of the saints, those who keep the commandments of God, and the faith of Jesus."

¹³I heard the voice from heaven saying^d, "Write, 'Blessed are the dead who die in the Lord from now on.'"

"Yes," says the Spirit, "that they may rest from their labors; for their works follow with them."

¹⁴And I looked, and suddenly there was a white cloud, and on the cloud one sitting like a son of man,^e having on his head a golden crown, and in his hand a sharp sickle. ¹⁵Another angel came out from the temple, crying with a loud voice to him who sat on the cloud, "Send forth your sickle, and reap; for the hour to reap has come; for the harvest of the earth is ripe." ¹⁶He who sat on the cloud thrust his sickle on the earth, and the earth was reaped.

¹⁷Another angel came out from the temple which is in heaven. He also had a sharp sickle. ¹⁸Another angel came out from the altar, he who has power over fire, and he

called with a loud voice to him who had the sharp sickle, saying, "Send forth your sharp sickle, and gather the clusters of the vine of the earth, for its grapes are fully ripe." ¹⁹The angel thrust his sickle into the earth, and gathered the vintage of the earth, and threw it into the great winepress of the wrath of God. ²⁰The winepress was trodden outside of the city, and blood came out from the winepress, even to the bridles of the horses, as far as one hundred eighty four miles.^f

15 I saw another great and marvelous sign in the sky: seven angels having the seven last plagues, for in them God's wrath is finished. ²I saw something like a sea of glass mixed with fire, and those who overcame the beast, his image,^g and the number of his name, standing on the sea of glass, having harps of God. ³They sang the song of Moses, the servant of God, and the song of the Lamb, saying,

"Great and marvelous are your works,
    Lord God of hosts.^h
Righteous and true are your ways, O
    King eternal.^i
⁴Who would not fear you, Lord,
    and glorify your name?
For you only are holy.
    For all the nations will come and
        worship before you.
    For your righteous acts have been
        revealed."

⁵After these things I looked, and the temple of the tabernacle of the testimony in heaven was opened. ⁶The seven angels came out of the temple^j who had the seven plagues, clothed with pure, bright linen,

a   14:6 Some Mss read "an angel"
b   14:7 Some Mss read "Lord"
c   14:8 Some Mss lack "a second"
d   14:13 Some Mss add "to me"
e   14:14 Daniel 7:13
f   14:20 Or, 296 kilometers. Lit. 1600 stadia
g   15:2 Some Mss add "his mark"
h   15:3 Or, "Lord God Almighty." Gk. kurios o theos o pantokrator is used in Hosea, Amos and Nahum LXX for "Lord God of hosts"
i   15:3 Some Mss read "King of the nations." Jeremiah 10:7. Other Mss read "King of the holy ones"
j   15:6 Some Mss lack "out of the temple"

and wearing golden sashes around their chests.

⁷One of the four living creatures gave to the seven angels seven golden bowls full of the wrath of God, who lives forever and ever. ⁸The temple was filled with smoke from the glory of God, and from his power. No one was able to enter into the temple, until the seven plagues of the seven angels would be finished.

16 I heard a loud voice out of the temple, saying to the seven angels, "Go and pour out the sevenª bowls of the wrath of God on the earth."

²The first went, and poured out his bowl into the earth, and it became a harmful and evil sore on the people who had the mark of the beast, and who worshiped his image.

³The second one poured out his bowl into the sea, and it became blood as of a corpse. And every living thing in the sea died.

⁴The third poured out his bowl into the rivers and springs of water, and they became blood. ⁵I heard the angel of the waters saying, "You are righteous,ᵇ who is and who was, the Holy One,ᶜ because you have judged these things. ⁶For they poured out the blood of the saints and the prophets, and you have given them blood to drink. They deserve this." ⁷I heard the altar saying, "Yes, Lord God of hosts,ᵈ true and righteous are your judgments."

⁸The fourth poured out his bowl on the sun, and it was given to him to scorch people with fire. ⁹People were scorched with great heat, and theyᵉ blasphemed the name of God who has the power over these plagues. They did not repent and give him glory.

¹⁰The fifth poured out his bowl on the throne of the beast, and his kingdom was darkened. They gnawed their tongues because of the pain, ¹¹and they blasphemed the God of heaven because of their pains and their sores. They did not repent of their works.

¹²The sixth poured out his bowl on the great river, the Euphrates.ᶠ Its water was dried up, that the way might be made ready for the kings that come from the sunrise. ¹³I saw coming out of the mouth of the serpent, and out of the mouth of the beast, and out of the mouth of the false prophet, three unclean spirits, something like frogs; ¹⁴for they are spirits of demons, performing signs; which go forth to the kings of the whole inhabited earth, to gather them together for the war of the great day of God, the Almighty.

¹⁵"Look, I am coming like a thief. Blessed is he who watches, and keeps his clothes, so that he does not walk naked, and they see his shame." ¹⁶He gathered them together into the place which is called in Hebrew, Har Megiddo.ᵍ

¹⁷The seventh poured out his bowl into the air. A loud voice came forth out of the temple,ʰ from the throne, saying, "It is done." ¹⁸There were lightnings, voices, and peals of thunder; and there was a great earthquake, such as was not since man was on the earth, so great an earthquake, so mighty. ¹⁹The great city was divided into three parts, and the cities of the nations fell. Babylon the great was remembered in the sight of God, to give to her the cup of the wine of the fierceness of his wrath. ²⁰Every island fled away, and the mountains were not found. ²¹Great hailstones, about one hundred pounds each,ⁱ came down out of the sky on people. People blasphemed God because of the plague of the hail, for this plague is exceedingly severe.

17 One of the seven angels who had the seven bowls came and spoke with me, saying, "Come here. I will show you

---

a   16:1 Some Mss lack "seven"

b   16:5 Some Mss add "O Lord"

c   16:5 Some Mss read "and shall be"

d   16:7 Or, "Lord God Almighty." Gk. kurios o theos o pantokrator is used in Hosea, Amos and Nahum LXX for "LORD God of hosts"

e   16:9 Some Mss read "people"

f   16:12 Also known by its earlier name as the "Perath"

g   16:16 Gk. Harmagedon. The Gk. word Har is a transliteration of the Heb. word for "mountain," and Gk. Magedon is translated in the LXX for Heb. Megiddo. Megiddo comes from the verb gadad: "to cut, or invade"

h   16:17 Some Mss add "of/the heaven" i   16:21 Or, 40 kg. Lit. a talent the judgment of the great prostitute who sits on many waters, [2]with whom the kings of the earth committed sexual immorality, and those who dwell in the earth were made drunk with the wine of her sexual immorality." [3]He carried me away in the Spirit into a wilderness. I saw a woman sitting on a scarlet-colored animal, full of blasphemous names, having seven heads and ten horns. [4]The woman was dressed in purple and scarlet, and decked with gold and precious stones and pearls, having in her hand a golden cup full of abominations and the impurities of her sexual immorality. [5]And on her forehead a name was written, "MYSTERY, BABYLON THE GREAT, THE MOTHER OF THE PROSTITUTES AND OF THE ABOMINATIONS OF THE EARTH." [6]I saw the woman drunk with the blood of the saints, and with the blood of the martyrs of Jesus. When I saw her, I wondered with great amazement. [7]The angel said to me, "Why do you wonder? I will tell you the mystery of the woman, and of the beast that carries her, which has the seven heads and the ten horns. [8]The beast that you saw was, and is not; and is about to come up out of the abyss and is going[a] to destruction. Those who dwell on the earth and whose names have not been written in the book of life from the foundation of the world will marvel when they see that the beast was, and is not, but is to come. [9]Here is the mind that has wisdom. The seven heads are seven mountains, on which the woman sits. [10]They are seven kings. Five have fallen, the one is, the other has not yet come. When he comes, he must continue a little while. [11]The beast that was, and is not, is himself also an eighth, and is of the seven; and he goes to destruction. [12]The ten horns that you saw are ten kings who have received no kingdom as yet, but they receive authority as kings, with the beast, for one hour. [13]These have one mind, and they give their power and authority to the beast. [14]These will war against the Lamb, and the Lamb will overcome them, for he is Lord of lords, and King of kings. They also will overcome who are with him,

called and chosen and faithful." [15]He said to me, "The waters which you saw, where the prostitute sits, are peoples, multitudes, nations, and languages. [16]The ten horns which you saw, and the beast, these will hate the prostitute, and will make her desolate and[b] naked, and will eat her flesh, and will burn her utterly with fire. [17]For God has put in their hearts to do what he has in mind, and to be of one mind, and to give their kingdom to the beast, until the words of God should be accomplished. [18]The woman whom you saw is the great city, which reigns over the kings of the earth."

18 After these things, I saw another angel coming down out of the sky, having great authority. The earth was illuminated with his glory. [2]He shouted with a mighty voice, saying, "Fallen, fallen is Babylon the great, and she has become a habitation of demons, a prison of every unclean spirit, and a prison of every unclean bird, and a prison of every unclean and detestable beast.[c] [3]For all the nations have drunk of the wine of the wrath of her sexual immorality, the kings of the earth committed sexual immorality with her, and the merchants of the earth grew rich from the abundance of her luxury."

[4]I heard another voice from heaven, saying, "Come out of her, my people, that you have no participation in her sins, and that you do not receive of her plagues, [5]for her sins have reached to the sky, and God has remembered her iniquities. [6]Return to her just as she returned, and repay her double as she did, and according to her works. In the cup which she mixed, mix to her double. [7]However much she glorified herself, and grew wanton, so much give her of torment and mourning. For she says in her heart, 'I sit a queen, and am no widow, and will in no way see mourning.' [8]Therefore in one day her plagues will come: death, mourn-

---

a 17:8 Some Mss read "and to go"
b 17:16 Some Mss add "will make her"
c 18:2 Some Mss lack "and a prison of every unclean (and detestable) beast"

ing, and famine; and she will be utterly burned with fire; for the Lord God who has judged her is strong. ⁹The kings of the earth, who committed sexual immorality and lived wantonly with her, will weep and wail over her, when they look at the smoke of her burning, ¹⁰standing far away for the fear of her torment, saying, 'Woe, woe, the great city, Babylon, the strong city. For your judgment has come in one hour.' ¹¹The merchants of the earth weep and mourn over her, for no one buys their merchandise any more; ¹²merchandise of gold, silver, precious stones, pearls, fine linen, purple, silk, scarlet, all expensive wood, every vessel of ivory, every vessel made of most precious wood, and of bronze, and iron, and marble; ¹³and cinnamon, spice, incense, perfume, frankincense, wine, olive oil, fine flour, wheat, cattle, sheep, horses, chariots, slaves and human lives. ¹⁴The fruits which your soul lusted after have been lost to you, and all things that were luxury and splendor have perished from you, and you will never ever find them again. ¹⁵The merchants of these things, who were made rich by her, will stand far away for the fear of her torment, weeping and mourning; ¹⁶saying, 'Woe, woe, the great city, she who was dressed in fine linen, purple, and scarlet, and decked with gold and precious stones and pearls. ¹⁷For in an hour such great riches are made desolate.' Every shipmaster, and everyone who sails anywhere, and mariners, and as many as gain their living by sea, stood far away, ¹⁸and exclaimed as they looked at the smoke of her burning, saying, 'What is like the great city?' ¹⁹They cast dust on their heads, and shouting, weeping and mourning, saying, 'Woe, woe, the great city, in which all who had their ships in the sea were made rich by reason of her great wealth.' For in one hour is she made desolate.

²⁰"Rejoice over her, O heaven, you saints, apostles, and prophets; for God has judged your judgment on her." ²¹A mighty angel took up a stone like a great millstone and cast it into the sea, saying, "Thus with violence will Babylon, the great city, be thrown down, and will be found no more

at all. ²²The voice of harpists, minstrels, flute players, and trumpeters will be heard no more at all in you. No craftsman, of whatever craft, will be found any more at all in you. The sound of a mill will be heard no more at all in you. ²³The light of a lamp will shine no more at all in you. The voice of the bridegroom and of the bride will be heard no more at all in you; for your merchants were the princes of the earth; for with your sorcery all the nations were deceived. ²⁴In her was found the blood of prophets and of saints, and of all who have been slain on the earth."

19 After these things I heard something like a loud voice of a great multitude in heaven, saying, "Hallelujah. Salvation, glory, and power belong to ᵃour God: ²for true and righteous are his judgments. For he has judged the great prostitute, who corrupted the earth with her sexual immorality, and he has avenged the blood of his servants at her hand."

³A second said, "Hallelujah. Her smoke goes up forever and ever." ⁴The twenty-four elders and the four living creatures fell down and worshiped God who sits on the throne, saying, "Amen. Hallelujah."

⁵A voice came forth from the throne, saying, "Give praise to our God, all you his servants, you who fear him, the small and the great."

⁶I heard something like the voice of a great multitude, and like the voice of many waters, and like the voice of mighty thunders, saying, "Hallelujah. For the Lord our God of hosts^b reigns. ⁷Let us rejoice and be exceedingly glad, and let us give the glory to him. For the marriage of the Lamb has come, and his wife has made herself ready." ⁸It was given to her that she would array herself in bright, pure, fine linen: for the fine linen is the righteous acts of the saints.

⁹He said to me, "Write, 'Blessed are those who are invited to the marriage supper of

---

a 19:1 Some Mss add "the Lord"
b 19:6 Or, "God, the Almighty,"

the Lamb.'" He said to me, "These are true words of God."

¹⁰I fell down before his feet to worship him. He said to me, "Look. Do not do it. I am a fellow servant with you and with your brothers who hold the testimony of Jesus. Worship God, for the testimony of Jesus is the Spirit of Prophecy."

¹¹And I saw heaven opened, and suddenly there was a white horse, and he who sat on it is called Faithful and True. In righteousness he judges and makes war. ¹²His eyes are a flame of fire, and on his head are many crowns. He had[a] a name written which no one knows but he himself. ¹³He is clothed in a garment dipped[b] in blood. His name is called "The Word of God." ¹⁴The armies which are in heaven followed him on white horses, clothed in white, pure, fine linen. ¹⁵Out of his mouth proceeds a sharp[c] sword, that with it he should strike the nations. He will rule them with an iron scepter.[d] He treads the winepress of the fierceness of the wrath of God, the Almighty. ¹⁶He has on his garment and on his thigh a name written, "King of kings, and Lord of lords."

¹⁷I saw an angel standing in the sun. He shouted with a loud voice, saying to all the birds that fly in the sky, "Come. Be gathered together to the great supper of God,[e] ¹⁸that you may eat the flesh of kings, the flesh of captains, the flesh of mighty people, and the flesh of horses and of those who sit on them, and the flesh of all people, both free and slave, and small and great." ¹⁹I saw the beast, and the kings of the earth, and their armies, gathered together to make war against him who sat on the horse, and against his army. ²⁰The beast was taken, and with him the false prophet who worked the signs in his sight, with which he deceived those who had received the mark of the beast and those who worshiped his image. These two were thrown alive into the lake of fire that burns with sulfur. ²¹The rest were killed with the sword of him who sat on the horse, the sword which came forth out of his mouth. All the birds were filled with their flesh.

20 I saw an[f] angel coming down out of heaven, having the key of the abyss and a great chain in his hand. ²He seized the serpent, the ancient snake,[g] which is the devil and Satan,[h] and bound him for a thousand years, ³and cast him into the abyss, and shut it, and sealed it over him, that he should deceive the nations no more, until the thousand years were finished. After this, he must be freed for a short time. ⁴I saw thrones, and they sat on them, and judgment was given to them. I saw the souls of those who had been beheaded for the testimony of Jesus, and for the word of God, and such as did not worship the beast nor his image, and did not receive the mark on their forehead and on their hand. They lived, and reigned with Christ for a thousand years. ⁵The rest of the dead did not live until the thousand years were finished. This is the first resurrection. ⁶Blessed and holy is he who has part in the first resurrection. Over these, the second death has no power, but they will be priests of God and of Christ, and will reign with him one thousand years.

⁷And after the thousand years, Satan will be released from his prison, ⁸and he will come out to deceive the nations which are in the four quarters of the earth, Gog and Magog, to gather them together to the war; the number of whom is as the sand of the sea. ⁹They went up over the breadth of the earth, and surrounded the camp of the saints, and the beloved city, and fire came down out of heaven[i] and devoured them. ¹⁰The devil who deceived them was thrown into the lake of fire and sulfur, where the beast and the false prophet are also. They will be tormented day and night forever and ever.

a   19:12 Some Mss add "names written and"
b   19:13 Other Mss read "sprinkled"
c   19:15 Some Mss add "double edged"
d   19:15 Psalm 2:9
e   19:17 Some Mss read "supper of the great God"
f   20:1 Some Mss add "another"
g   20:2 Gk. ophis "snake," used in Genesis 3:1 LXX for the devil, Heb. nachash "snake"
h   20:2 Some Mss add "who deceives the whole inhabited earth"
i   20:9 Some Mss add "from God"

[11]I saw a great white throne, and him who sat on it, from whose face the earth and the heaven fled away. There was found no place for them. [12]I saw the dead, the great and the small, standing before the throne[a], and they opened books. Another book was opened, which is the book of life. The dead were judged out of the things which were written in the books, according to their works. [13]The sea gave up the dead who were in it. Death and hell[b] gave up the dead who were in them. They were judged, each one according to his works. [14]Death and hell were thrown into the lake of fire. This is the second death, the lake of fire. [15]If anyone was not found written in the book of life, he was cast into the lake of fire.

21 I saw a new heaven and a new earth: for the first heaven and the first earth have passed away, and the sea is no more. [2]I[c] saw the holy city, New Jerusalem, coming down out of heaven from God, made ready like a bride adorned for her husband. [3]I heard a loud voice from the throne[d] saying, "Look, the tabernacle of God is with humans, and he will dwell with them, and they will be his people,[e] and God himself will be with them and be their God.[f] [4]And he will wipe away every tear from their eyes, and death will be no more, nor will there be mourning, nor crying, nor pain, anymore, for[g] the first things have passed away."

[5]He who sits on the throne said, "Look, I am making all things new." He said[h], "Write, for these words are faithful and true." [6]He said to me, "It is done. I am the Alpha and the Omega, the Beginning and the End. I will give freely to him who is thirsty from the spring of the water of life. [7]He who overcomes, I will give him these things. I will be his God, and he will be my son. [8]But for the cowardly, unbelieving,[i] abominable, murderers, sexually immoral, sorcerers, idolaters, and all liars, their part is in the lake that burns with fire and sulfur, which is the second death."

[9]One of the seven angels who had the seven bowls, full of the seven last plagues came, and he spoke with me, saying, "Come here. I will show you the bride, the wife of the Lamb." [10]He carried me away in the Spirit to a great and high mountain, and showed me the holy city, Jerusalem, coming down out of heaven from God, [11]having the glory of God. Her light was like a most precious stone, as if it was a jasper stone, clear as crystal; [12]having a great and high wall; having twelve gates, and at the gates twelve angels; and names written on them, which are the names of the twelve tribes of the children of Israel. [13]On the east were three gates; and on the north three gates; and on the south three gates; and on the west three gates. [14]The wall of the city had twelve foundations, and on them twelve names of the twelve apostles of the Lamb. [15]He who spoke with me had for a measure, a golden reed, to measure the city, its gates, and its wall. [16]The city lies foursquare, and its length is as great as its breadth. He measured the city with the reed, one thousand three hundred eighty miles[k]. Its length, breadth, and height are equal. [17]Its wall is one hundred forty-four cubits,[l] by human measurement, that is, of an angel. [18]The construction of its wall was jasper. The city was pure gold, like pure glass. [19]The foundations of the city's wall were adorned with all kinds of precious stones. The first foundation was jasper; the second, sapphire[m]; the third, chalcedony; the fourth, emerald; [20]the fifth, sardonyx; the sixth, sardius; the seventh, chrysolite; the eighth, beryl; the ninth, topaz; the tenth, chrysoprasus; the eleventh, jacinth; and the twelfth, amethyst. [21]The twelve gates were twelve pearls. Each

---

a   20:12 Some Mss read "God"
b   20:13 Gk. Hades, Heb. Sheol
c   21:2 Some Mss add "John"
d   21:3 Some Mss read "out of heaven"
e   21:3 Some Mss read "peoples"
f   21:3 Some Mss lack "*and be* their God"
g   21:4 Some Mss lack "for"
h   21:5 Some Mss add "to me"
i   21:8 Some Mss add "sinners"
j   21:16 Some Mss add "twelve." Twelve thousand stadia are about 1400 miles
l   21:17 About 248 feet, or 75.6 meters, using the Hebrew royal cubit of 52.5 centimeters
m   21:19 Or, "lapis lazuli"

one of the gates was made of one pearl. The street of the city was pure gold, like transparent glass. ²²I saw no temple in it, for the Lord God of hosts[a] and the Lamb are its temple. ²³The city has no need for the sun, neither of the moon, to shine, for the very glory of God illuminated it, and its lamp is the Lamb. ²⁴The nations will walk[b] in its light. The kings of the earth bring their splendor[c] into it. ²⁵Its gates will in no way be shut by day (for there will be no night there), ²⁶and they will bring the glory and the honor of the nations into it.[d] ²⁷There will in no way enter into it anything profane, or one who causes an abomination or a lie, but only those who are written in the Lamb's book of life.

22 He showed me a[e] river of water of life, clear as crystal, proceeding out of the throne of God[f] and of the Lamb,[g] ²in the middle of its street. On this side of the river and on that was the tree of life, bearing twelve kinds of fruits, yielding its fruit every month.[h] The leaves of the tree were for the healing of the nations. ³There will be no curse any more. The throne of God and of the Lamb will be in it, and his servants serve him. ⁴They will see his face, and his name will be on their foreheads. ⁵There will no longer be any night, and they need no lamp light; for the Lord God will illuminate them. They will reign forever and ever.[i]

⁶He said to me, "These words are faithful and true. The Lord God of the spirits of the prophets sent his angel to show to his servants the things which must happen soon."

⁷"Look, I am coming quickly. Blessed is he who keeps the words of the prophecy of this book."

⁸Now I, John, am the one who heard and saw these things. When I heard and saw, I fell down to worship before the feet of the angel who had shown me these things. ⁹He said to me, "See you do not do it. I am a fellow servant with you and with your brothers, the prophets, and with those who keep the words of this book. Worship God."

¹⁰He said to me, "Do not seal up the words of the prophecy of this book, for the time is near. ¹¹He who acts unjustly, let him act unjustly still. He who is filthy, let him be filthy still. He who is righteous, let him do righteousness still. He who is holy, let him be holy still."

¹²"Look, I am coming quickly. My reward is with me, to repay to each person according to his work.[j] ¹³I am the Alpha and the Omega, the First and the Last, the Beginning and the End.[k] ¹⁴Blessed are they who wash their robes,[l] that they may have the right to the tree of life, and may enter in by the gates into the city. ¹⁵Outside are the dogs, the sorcerers, the sexually immoral, the murderers, the idolaters, and everyone who loves and practices falsehood. ¹⁶I, Jesus, have sent my angel to testify these things to you for the churches. I am the root[m] and the offspring[n] of David; the bright morning star.[o]"

¹⁷The Spirit and the bride say, "Come." He who hears, let him say, "Come." He who is thirsty, let him come. He who desires, let him take the water of life freely. ¹⁸I testify to everyone who hears the words of the prophecy of this book, if anyone adds to them, God will add to him the plagues which are written in this book. ¹⁹If anyone takes away from the words of the book of this prophecy, God will[p] take away his part from the tree of life,[a] and out of the holy

---

a 21:22 Or, "Lord God Almighty." Gk. kurios o theos o pantokrator is used in Hosea, Amos and Nahum LXX for "Lᴏʀᴅ God of hosts"
b 21:24 Some Mss read "nations of the saved will walk"
c 21:24 Some Mss read "splendor and honor into it." Other Mss read "the splendor and honor of the nations"
d 21:26 Some Mss add "so that they may enter"
e 22:1 Some Mss add "pure"
f 22:1 Ezekiel 47:1; Zechariah 14:8
g 22:1 Daniel 7:13,14; Matthew 26:64; John 1:36; Revelation 5:12,13 etc.
h 22:2 Ezekiel 47:12
i 22:5 Daniel 7:27
j 22:12 Isaiah 40:10, 62:11; Romans 2:6, 14:12
k 22:13 Isaiah 41:4
l 22:14 Some Mss read "who do his commandments"
m 22:16 Isaiah 11:1, 10; Revelation 5:5
n 22:16 Matthew 1:1; Romans 1:3
o 22:16 Numbers 24:17
p 22:19 Some Mss read "may God take away"

city, which are written in this book. [20]He who testifies these things says, "Yes, I come quickly."

    Amen. Come, Lord Jesus.

[21]The grace of the Lord Jesus[b] be with all.[c]

---

a   22:19 Some Mss read "book of life"
b   22:21 Most Mss add "Christ"
c   22:21 Some Mss add "the saints. Amen"

Would you like to receive a free PDF version of this Bible or be notified when future editions of the NHEB are available?

Visit: www.TheBiblePeople.com/resources/nheb

CPSIA information can be obtained
at www.ICGtesting.com
Printed in the USA
LVHW081356220120
644426LV00013B/717

9 781947 935068